M000247912

SAFETY SYMBOLS

SAFETY SYMBOLS	HAZARD	PRECAUTION	REMEDY
Disposal	Special disposal required	Dispose of wastes as directed by your teacher.	Ask your teacher how to dispose of laboratory materials.
Biological	Organisms that can harm humans	Avoid breathing in or skin contact with organisms. Wear dust mask or gloves. Wash hands thoroughly.	Notify your teacher if you suspect contact.
Extreme Temperature	Objects that can burn skin by being too cold or too hot	Use proper protection when handling.	Go to your teacher for first aid.
Sharp Object	Use of tools or glassware that can easily puncture or slice skin	Practice common sense behavior and follow guidelines for use of the tool.	Go to your teacher for first aid.
Fumes	Potential danger from smelling fumes	Must have good ventilation and never smell fumes directly.	Leave foul area and notify your teacher immediately.
Electrical	Possible danger from electrical shock or burn	Double-check setup with instructor. Check condition of wires and apparatus.	Do not attempt to fix electrical problems. Notify your teacher immediately.
Irritant	Substances that can irritate your skin or mucous membranes	Wear dust mask or gloves. Practice extra care when handling these materials.	Go to your teacher for first aid.
Chemical	Substances (acids and bases) that can react with and destroy tissue and other materials	Wear goggles and an apron.	Immediately flush with water and notify your teacher.
Toxic	Poisonous substance	Follow your teacher's instructions. Always wash hands thoroughly after use.	Go to your teacher for first aid.
Fire	Flammable and combustible materials may burn if exposed to an open flame or spark	Avoid flames and heat sources. Be aware of locations of fire safety equipment.	Notify your teacher immediately. Use fire safety equipment if necessary.

Eye Safety
This symbol appears when a danger to eyes exists.

Clothing Protection
This symbol appears when substances could stain or burn clothing.

Animal Safety
This symbol appears whenever live animals are studied and the safety of the animals and students must be ensured.

California Edition

GLENCOE
SCIENCE VOYAGES
PHYSICAL SCIENCE

NATIONAL
GEOGRAPHIC
SOCIETY

 **Glencoe McGraw-Hill**

New York, New York   Columbus, Ohio   Woodland Hills, California   Peoria, Illinois

A Glencoe Program

California Edition

Glencoe Science Voyages

California Student Edition
California Teacher Wraparound Edition
Assessment
  Chapter Review
  California Science Content Standards Practice
    Questions
  Performance Assessment
  Assessment—Chapter and Unit Tests
  ExamView Test Bank Software
  Performance Assessment in the Science
    Classroom
  Alternate Assessment in the Science Classroom
Study Guide for Content Mastery, SE and TE
Chapter Overview Study Guide, SE and TE
Reinforcement
Enrichment
Critical Thinking/Problem Solving
Multicultural Connections

Activity Worksheets
Laboratory Manual, SE and TE
Science Inquiry Activities, SE and TE
California Home Involvement
Teaching Transparencies
Section Focus Transparencies
Science Integration Transparencies
Spanish Resources
California Lesson Plans
Lab and Safety Skills in the Science Classroom
Cooperative Learning in the Science Classroom
Exploring Environmental Issues
MindJogger Videoquizzes and Teacher Guide
English/Spanish Audiocassettes
Interactive Lesson Planner CD-ROM
Interactive CD-ROM
Internet Site
Using the Internet in the Science Classroom

THE
PRINCETON
REVIEW

The "Test-Taking Tip" and "Test Practice" features in this book were written by The Princeton Review, the nation's leader in test preparation. Through its association with McGraw-Hill, The Princeton Review offers the best way to help students excel on standardized assessments.

The Princeton Review is not affiliated with Princeton University or Educational Testing Service.

Glencoe/McGraw-Hill

A Division of The McGraw-Hill Companies

Copyright © 2001 by the McGraw-Hill Companies, Inc. All rights reserved. Except as permitted under the United States Copyright Act, no part of this publication may be reproduced or distributed in any form or by any means, or stored in a database or retrieval system, without prior written permission of the publisher.

The "Science Connection" features found in each chapter and the unit opening pages of this textbook were designed and developed by the National Geographic Society's Education Division, copyright © 2001 National Geographic Society. The name "National Geographic Society" and the yellow border rectangle are trademarks of the Society, and their use, without prior written permission, is strictly prohibited.

Send all inquiries to:
Glencoe/McGraw-Hill
8787 Orion Place
Columbus, OH 43240

ISBN 0-07-823991-5
Printed in the United States of America.
4 5 6 7 8 9 10 071/043 10 09 08 07 06

Series Authors

Alton Biggs
Biology Instructor
Allen High School
Allen, Texas

John Eric Burns
Science Teacher
Ramona Jr. High School
Chino, California

Lucy Daniel, Ph.D.
Teacher, Consultant
Rutherford County Schools
Rutherfordton, North Carolina

Cathy Ezrailson
Science Department Head
Oak Ridge High School
Conroe, Texas

Ralph Feather, Jr., Ph.D.
Science Department Chair
Derry Area School District
Derry, Pennsylvania

Patricia Horton
Math and Science Teacher
Summit Intermediate School
Etiwanda, California

Thomas McCarthy, Ph.D.
Science Department Chair
St. Edwards School
Vero Beach, Florida

Ed Ortleb
Science Consultant
St. Louis Public Schools
St. Louis, Missouri

Susan Leach Snyder
Science Department Chair
Jones Middle School
Upper Arlington, Ohio

Eric Werwa, Ph.D.
Department of Physics and Astronomy
Otterbein College
Westerville, Ohio

National Geographic Society
Educational Division
Washington D.C.

Contributing Authors

Al Janulaw
Science Teacher
Creekside Middle School
Rohnert Park, California

Penny Parsekian
Science Writer for
The National Geographic Society
New London, Connecticut

Gerry Madrazo, Ph.D.
Mathematics and Science Education
  Network
University of North Carolina, Chapel Hill
Chapel Hill, North Carolina

Series Consultants

Chemistry

Douglas Martin, Ph.D.
Chemistry Department
Sonoma State University
Rohnert Park, California

Cheryl Wistrom, Ph.D.
Associate Professor of Chemistry
Saint Joseph's College
Rensselaer, Indiana

Earth Science

Maureen Allen
Science Resource Specialist
Irvine Unified School District
Laguna Hills, California

Tomasz K. Baumiller, Ph.D.
Museum of Paleontology
University of Michigan
Ann Arbor, Michigan

Connie Sutton, Ph.D.
Department of Geoscience
Indiana University
Indiana, Pennsylvania

Physics

Thomas Barrett, Ph.D.
Department of Physics
The Ohio State University
Columbus, Ohio

David Haase, Ph.D.
Professor of Physics
North Carolina State University
Raleigh, North Carolina

Life Science

William Ausich, Ph.D.
Department of Geological Sciences
The Ohio State University
Columbus, Ohio

Dennis Stockdale
Asheville High School
Asheville, North Carolina

Daniel Zeigler, Ph.D.
Director
Bacillus Genetic Stock Center
The Ohio State University
Columbus, Ohio

Reading

Nancy Farnan, Ph.D.
School of Teacher Education
San Diego State University
San Diego, California

Gary Kroesch
Mount Carmel High School
San Diego, California

Safety

Mark Vinciguerra
Lab Safety Instructor
Department of Physics
The Ohio State University
Columbus, Ohio

Curriculum

Tom Custer, Ph.D.
Maryland State Department of
    Education
Challenge/Reconstructed Schools
Baltimore, Maryland

Series Reviewers

Jhina Alvarado
Potrero Hill Middle School
    for the Arts
San Francisco, California

Richard Cheeseman
Bert Lynn Middle School
Torrance, California

Linda Cook
Rider High School
Wichita Falls, Texas

John B. Davis
Niagara-Wheatfield
    Central School
Sanborn, New York

Shirley Ann DeFilippo
Timothy Edwards
Middle School
South Windsor, Connecticut

Janet Doughty
H J McDonald Middle School
New Bern, North Carolina

Jason Druten
Jefferson Middle School
Torrance, California

Lin Harp
Magellan Middle School
Raleigh, North Carolina

Doris Holland
West Cary Middle School
Raleigh, North Carolina

Deborah Huffine
Noblesville Intermediate School
Noblesville, Indiana

Paul Osborne
DeValls Bluff High School
DeValls Bluff, Arkansas

Erik Resnick
Robert E. Peary Middle School
Gardena, California

Robert Sirbu
Lowell Junior High School
Oakland, California

Michael Tally
Wake County Public Schools
Raleigh, North Carolina

Cindy Williamson
Whiteville City Schools
Whiteville, North Carolina

Maurice Yaggi
Middlebrook School
Wilton, Connecticut

Donna York
Anchorage School District
Anchorage, Alaska

Activity Testers

Clayton Millage
Science Teacher
Lynden Middle School
Lynden, Washington

Science Kit and Boreal Laboratories
Tonawanda, New York

Contents in Brief

GRADE EIGHT: FOCUS ON PHYSICAL SCIENCE

What are science content standards and why does California have them? Standards are guidelines for schools, students, and parents that describe the essential science concepts and skills for understanding the world in which we live. In 1999, The California State Board of Education established science content standards, and these standards will be the basis for state assessments that measure student achievement in science.

ADDITIONAL CONTENT STANDARDS FOR GRADE 8

- California Science Standards and Case Studies, found at the back of the book
- California Science Content Standards Assessment Practice booklets
- Chapter Assessments at the end of each chapter
- Science Voyages Website at www.glencoe.com/sec/science/ca

Motion

1. The velocity of an object is the rate of change of its position. As a basis for understanding this concept, students know:

   a. position is defined relative to some choice of standard reference point and a set of reference directions.
   Sections 11-1, 17-2, 20-4, page 478

   b. average speed is the total distance traveled divided by the total time elapsed. The speed of an object along the path traveled can vary.
   Sections 11-1, 17-1, 19-1, 19-2, page 478

   c. how to solve problems involving distance, time, and average speed.
   Sections 11-1, 19-1, 19-2, page 479

   d. to describe the velocity of an object, one must specify both direction and speed.
   Section 11-1, page 479

   e. changes in velocity can be changes in speed, direction, or both.
   Sections 11-1, 11-2, page 480

   f. how to interpret graphs of position versus time and speed versus time for motion in a single direction.
   Section 11-1, page 480

Forces

2. Unbalanced forces cause changes in velocity. As a basis for understanding this concept, students know:

   a. a force has both direction and magnitude.
   Sections 5-1, 12-1, 12-2, 12-3, 12-4, 17-2, page 482

   b. when an object is subject to two or more forces at once, the effect is the cumulative effect of all the forces.
   Sections 5-2, 12-1, 12-2, 24-4, 25-3, page 482

   c. when the forces on an object are balanced, the motion of the object does not change.
   Sections 12-1, 12-4, 24-4, pages 482–483

   d. how to identify separately two or more forces acting on a single static object, including gravity, elastic forces due to tension or compression in matter, and friction.
   Sections 12-1, 25-3, page 483

   e. when the forces on an object are unbalanced, the object will change its motion (that is, it will speed up, slow down, or change direction).
   Sections 7-1, 12-1, 12-2, 12-3, 12-4, 17-2, 24-3, 25-3, page 483

   f. the greater the mass of an object, the more force is needed to achieve the same change in motion.
   Sections 11-2, 12-2, 12-3, 19-2, page 484

   g. the role of gravity in forming and maintaining planets, stars, and the solar system.
   Sections 17-2, 17-3, 18-2, 19-1, 19-2, 19-3, 19-4, 20-3, 20-4, page 484

Structure of Matter

3. Elements have distinct properties and atomic structure. All matter is comprised of one or more of over 100 elements. As a basis for understanding this concept, students know:

   a. the structure of the atom and how it is composed of protons, neutrons, and electrons.
   Sections 5-1, 5-2, 7-1, 7-2, 9-2, 10-1, page 487

   b. compounds are formed by combining two or more different elements. Compounds have properties that are different from the constituent elements.
   Sections 4-1, 4-2, 5-1, 7-2, 8-1, 9-

   1, 9-2, 10-1, 10-2, 10-3, page 487

   c. atoms and molecules form solids by building up repeating patterns such as the crystal structure of NaCl or long chain polymers.
   Sections 4-1, 7-2, 10-3, pages 487–488

   d. the states (solid, liquid, gas) of matter depend on molecular motion.
   Sections 4-1, 4-2, 4-3, pages 262–263

   e. in solids the atoms are closely locked in position and can only vibrate, in liquids the atoms and molecules are more loosely connected and can collide with and move past one another, while in gases the atoms or molecules are free to move independently, colliding frequently.
   Sections 4-1, 4-2, 4-3, 9-1, pages 262–263

   f. how to use the Periodic Table to identify elements in simple compounds.
   Sections 6-1, 6-2, 6-3, 7-1, 7-1, pages 488–489

Earth in the Solar System (Earth Science)

4. The structure and composition of the universe can be learned from the study of stars and galaxies, and their evolution. As a basis for understanding this concept, students know:

   a. galaxies are clusters of billions of stars, and may have different shapes.
   Section 20-4, page 490

   b. the sun is one of many stars in our own Milky Way galaxy. Stars may differ in size, temperature, and color.
   Sections 19-1, 19-3, 20-1, 20-2, 20-3, 20-4, page 490

c. how to use astronomical units and light years as measures of distance between the sun, stars, and Earth.
Sections 19-2, 19-3, 20-1, 20-4, page 490

d. stars are the source of light for all bright objects in outer space. The moon and planets shine by reflected sunlight, not by their own light.
Sections 17-1, 18-2, 18-3, 19-1, 19-2, 20-3, pages 490–491

e. the appearance, general composition, relative position and size, and motion of objects in the solar system, including planets, planetary satellites, comets, and asteroids.
Sections 17-2, 17-3, 18-1, 18-2, 18-3, 19-1, 19-2, 19-3, 19-4, page 491

Reactions

5. Chemical reactions are processes in which atoms are rearranged into different combinations of molecules. As a basis for understanding this concept, students know:

a. reactant atoms and molecules interact to form products with different chemical properties.
Sections 8-1, 8-2, 9-3, 10-1, 10-2, 10-3, 22-2, 23-1, page 494

b. the idea of atoms explains the conservation of matter: in chemical reactions the number of atoms stays the same no matter how they are arranged, so their total mass stays the same.
Section 8-1, page 494

c. chemical reactions usually liberate heat or absorb heat.
Sections 8-1, 9-2, 26-2, page 494

d. physical processes include freezing and boiling, in which a material changes form with no chemical reaction.
Sections 4-1, 4-2, 8-1, 9-1, 9-2, page 495

e. how to determine whether a solution is acidic, basic or neutral.
Sections 9-3, 22-2, 27-1, page 496

Chemistry of Living Systems (Life Science)

6. Principles of chemistry underlie the functioning of biological systems. As a basis for understanding this concept, students know:

a. carbon, because of its ability to combine in many ways with itself and other elements, has a central role in the chemistry of living organisms.

Sections 6-2, 10-1, 10-2, 10-3, 21-1, 21-2, 22-2, 23-1, 26-2, page 498

b. living organisms are made of molecules largely consisting of carbon, hydrogen, nitrogen, oxygen, phosphorus and sulfur.
Sections 10-1, 10-2, 10-3, 21-2, 23-1, pages 498–499

c. living organisms have many different kinds of molecules including small ones such as water and salt, and very large ones such as carbohydrates, fats, proteins and DNA.
Sections 9-3, 10-1, 10-3, 23-1, 23-3, 24-4, pages 498–499

Periodic Table

7. The organization of the Periodic Table is based on the properties of the elements and reflects the structure of atoms. As a basis for understanding this concept, students know:

a. how to identify regions corresponding to metals, nonmetals and inert gases.
Sections 6-1, 6-2, 6-3, 7-2, page 501

b. elements are defined by the number of protons in the nucleus, which is called the atomic number. Different isotopes of an element have a different number of neutrons in the nucleus.
Sections 5-2, 6-1, page 501

c. substances can be classified by their properties, including melting temperature, density, hardness, heat, and electrical conductivity.
Sections 6-1, 6-2, 6-3, 7-1, page 502

Density and Buoyancy

8. All objects experience a buoyant force when immersed in a fluid. As a basis for understanding this concept, students know:

a. density is mass per unit volume.
Sections 1-2, 4-3, 18-1, pages 504–505

b. how to calculate the density of substances (regular and irregular solids, and liquids) from measurements of mass and volume.
Sections 1-2, 4-3, pages 504–506

c. the buoyant force on an object in a fluid is an upward force equal to the weight of the fluid it has displaced.
Sections 4-3, 25-1, pages 504–505

d. how to predict whether an object will float or sink.
Sections 1-2, 4-3, pages 504–505

Investigation and Experimentation

9. Scientific progress is made by asking meaningful questions and conducting careful investigations. As a basis for understanding this concept, and to address the content of the other three strands, students
should develop their own questions and perform investigations. Students will:

a. plan and conduct a scientific investigation to test a hypothesis.
Sections 1-1, 1-2, 4-2, 4-3, 5-1, 5-2, 6-2, 6-3, 7-1, 7-2, 8-1, 8-2, 9-2, 10-3, 11-1, 20-4, 21-1, 24-3, 25-4, 27-1, pages 127, 482, 483, 484, 486, 487, 489, 494, 495, 496, 507

b. evaluate the accuracy and reproducibility of data.
Sections 1-1, 5-1, 5-2, 6-3, 7-1, 8-1, 17-2, 21-1, 24-3, 25-4, pages 481, 483, 493, 495, 503

c. distinguish between variable and controlled parameters in a test.
Sections 1-1, 1-2, 6-3, 8-1, 8-2, 9-2, 11-2, 12-2, 18-1, 21-1, 21-2, 24-3, 25-4, 27-1, pages 481, 482, 483, 488, 494, 495, 497, 500, 503, 555

d. recognize the slope of the linear graph as the constant in the relationship y=kx and apply this to interpret graphs constructed from data.
Sections 11-1, 26-1, pages 479, 480, 498, 953–954, 978

e. construct appropriate graphs from data and develop quantitative statements about the relationships between variables.
Sections 1-1, 1-2, 4-1, 4-2, 5-2, 6-1, 9-2, 10-1, 25-1, 25-4, 26-1, pages 121, 149, 233, 479, 480, 498, 502, 978

f. apply simple mathematical relationships to determine one quantity given the other two (including speed = distance/time, density = mass/volume, force = pressure x area, volume = area x height).
Sections 1-1, 1-2, 4-1, 4-2, 4-3, 5-2, 7-1, 8-2, 9-2, 10-1, 10-3, 11-1, 11-2, 11-3, 12-4, 17-1, 17-2, 19-2, 21-2, 23-3, 26-1, 27-1, pages 324, 357, 479, 499, 505

g. distinguish between linear and non-linear relationships on a graph of data.
Sections 1-1, 4-1, 4-2, 5-2, 10-1, 11-1, pages 325, 480, 491, 502, 953–954, 978

Contents

Contents

Contents

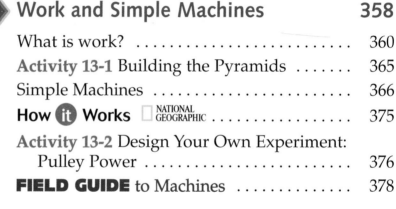

Contents

Contents

Science Connections

NATIONAL GEOGRAPHIC

Activities

Mini Lab

Try at Home Mini Lab

Explore Activities

Problem Solving

Skill Builders

Skill Activities

The
Nature
of Matter

NATIONAL GEOGRAPHIC

What's Happening Here?

As wondrous as this winter scene in Yellowstone National Park (left) appears, beneath the scenic variety there is a sameness. The hanging icicles and sculpted snow, the plunging cascade, the mist hovering above the stream are solid, liquid, and gaseous forms of water. Regardless of these outer forms, the molecules of water are all identical. Beads of mercury (below) create a shimmering galaxy—but, within the element mercury, each atom is the same. Yet, how dynamic is the hidden world of the atom! The molecules of water locked into blocks of ice, the atoms within the shiny mercury, and even the particles that make up this page of your science book are in constant motion. Why are some substances solids, while other are liquids or gases? These are some of the questions explored in this unit.

interNET CONNECTION

Explore the Glencoe Science Web Site at **www.glencoe.com/sec/ science/ca** to find out more about topics found in this unit.

The Nature of Science

Chapter Preview

Skills Preview

Skill Builders
- Sequence
- Interpret Data

Activities
- Design an Experiment
- Use Scientific Methods

MiniLabs
- Measure
- Infer

Reading Check ✓

Before you begin this chapter, write its headings and sub-headings in an outline form to see how the chapter is organized.

Explore Activity

How can a ship that weighs several thousand tons float on water while a coin would sink right next to the ship? Why will the ship sink if the hull of a ship is damaged and water pours in? Around the world, there are many ships at the bottom of the ocean. How can they be floating one minute and sinking the next?

Observe Water Displacement

1. Fill a small bucket with two liters of water.
2. Use a balance to find the mass of an empty soda-pop can and a quarter.
3. Record the mass of each object.
4. Predict which object will float. Place the can on its side in the water. Observe what happens.
5. Place the quarter in the water. Observe what happens.

Science Journal

In your Science Journal, record whether your prediction was correct. Compare and contrast the empty can and the quarter to try to explain what you observed.

Scientific Problem Solving

What You'll Learn

▶ What science is
▶ How to use a scientific method in problem solving

Vocabulary

science
scientific method
hypothesis
theory
law
control
independent variable
dependent variable
constant
graph

Why It's Important

▶ You can use scientific methods to search for new knowledge and to solve everyday problems.

What Science Is

It was Current Events Day in Mr. Hayes's science class. Every other Wednesday, each student presented an article from a newspaper or magazine on a topic that related to science. Mr. Hayes wanted his students to be aware of the latest scientific advances. He also wanted them to understand that science wasn't a subject that disappeared when they closed their science books. "Science affects you every day," he often reminded them.

Several students presented their articles. Then, Deon stood to present. "This article describes how scientists found a shipwreck that was sunk in more than 2400 meters of water. They were able to find hundreds of articles used by the passengers, such as dishes and clothing. They even—"

Brianna waved her hand impatiently. "Excuse me," she interrupted, "but this is science class, not social studies or a movie review. Check your schedule, Dee!"

Several students laughed.

Mr. Hayes spoke. "Why do you think this article doesn't apply to science, Brianna?"

Figure 1-1 What are some ways science affects you and your classmates every day?

Brianna replied, "Because people who look at shipwrecks aren't scientists, they're explorers. They're just looking for something, not inventing something or testing some theory. They're not using scientific methods. They should be discussed in history class."

Mr. Hayes looked at Deon. "Deon, can you respond to what Brianna said? How is your article related to science?"

Deon looked embarrassed. "Well, I'm not sure either. This article says scientists looked for the shipwreck. And, the article was interesting, so I cut it out of the newspaper."

"Why don't you finish your report, Deon," said Mr. Hayes. "Then, we'll continue to debate whether or not it relates to science."

Deon described more of the objects from the ship that were found. He told the class that sonar was used to help find the wreck. Sonar stands for **SO**und **NA**vigation **R**anging. Sound waves are sent through the water and bounce back when they hit something, such as the ocean floor or part of a ship. Scientists can calculate how deep that spot is by the amount of time it takes the sound waves to reach the object and bounce back. A remotely operated vehicle, or ROV, was used to help recover the sunken objects. ROVs are unpiloted, and a person operates them at a distance. They can go places that are too deep or too dangerous for people to go.

LIFE SCIENCE
INTEGRATION

Robot Researcher
Dolphins, bats, and barn owls were all models for a new robot named "Rodolph." These animals depend heavily on sound to help them navigate or find prey. The robot emits sound and "listens" for the echoes to detect objects underwater. Rodolph is so sensitive that it can even tell heads from tails on a dime. Infer how this robot can be used underwater to help scientists explore.

Figure 1-2 The submarine Atlantis helps scientists explore the water off the big island of Hawaii.

Using Math

The speed of a sound wave traveling in ocean water at 20°C is 1522 meters per second. Suppose that a sound wave takes 20 seconds to reach the bottom and return. How deep is the water at that location?

When Deon had finished, Mr. Hayes looked around at the class. "Let's get back to the point Brianna raised. **Science** is a process used to investigate the world around you, providing you with some possible answers. Does anyone see a connection between looking for shipwrecks and science?"

Scientists as Explorers

Enrique raised his hand. "I think the article does relate to science. People use science to find the answers to questions. The people who explored that shipwreck had questions. They were curious. Scientists are curious about the unknown. There are all sorts of scientists, you know. Explorers are scientists because they are curious about the unknown. I guess, in a way, all scientists are explorers. Hey! When I'm curious about something and I try to search for the answer, maybe that makes me an explorer, too."

Mr. Hayes replied, "I think you're on the right track, Enrique. Scientific exploration and discovery has never been limited to one race, sex, culture, or time period. As in the past, people all over the world make discoveries. These people are not only professional scientists. Often, discoveries are made by people pursuing a hobby. In fact, some important discoveries might be made by one of your classmates. Now, let's go back to your other point, Enrique. Are you saying that scientists and explorers only have curiosity in common? What did the explorers mentioned in the article do?"

Enrique thought a moment. "Well, I guess they would have had to use some kind of organized method. They had to pay attention to things like the position of the stars to know where they were headed and cloud formations to predict the weather."

Mr. Hayes asked, "Would the people who found the shipwreck in Deon's article have used some organized or scientific methods?"

Enrique looked confused. "I suppose. But Brianna's right. They didn't do any experiments. They just looked for things."

Sunghee raised her hand. "I think I see how Deon's article relates to science. It's because of the technology they used. I mean, the little robot and stuff. Technology is using science, right? But I have to agree with Brianna and Enrique. Doesn't a scientist always have to do an experiment?"

Mr. Hayes asked, "Well class, does anyone have an answer for Sunghee?"

The class was silent.

Mr. Hayes had an idea he thought might help the class answer his question. He walked to the chalkboard, paused, and began writing. "I have an assignment for you, due next Wednesday. I'd like you to find information that you think shows how scientists are like explorers and how technology helps them. You may look in magazines and books, or use the Internet. Then, list the skills you think the scientists used.

Figure 1-3 This scientist uses technology, such as scientific equipment and instruments, to help her explore.

THE EFFECTS OF CARBON DIOXIDE AND PLANTS ON GLOBAL WARMING

Figure 1-4 Students can be scientists, too. **In what ways have you been a scientific explorer?**

Figure 1-5 What are some things scientists do while searching for new information and solving problems?

Recognize the Problem

Form a Hypothesis

Test your Hypothesis

✔ Plan – Design an Experiment

✔ Do – Observe and Record

Analyze your Data

Draw Conclusions

Also list the steps they took in searching for new knowledge. Finally, compare the two and come up with your answer to the question, 'Does a scientist always need to use an organized approach to solving problems?'"

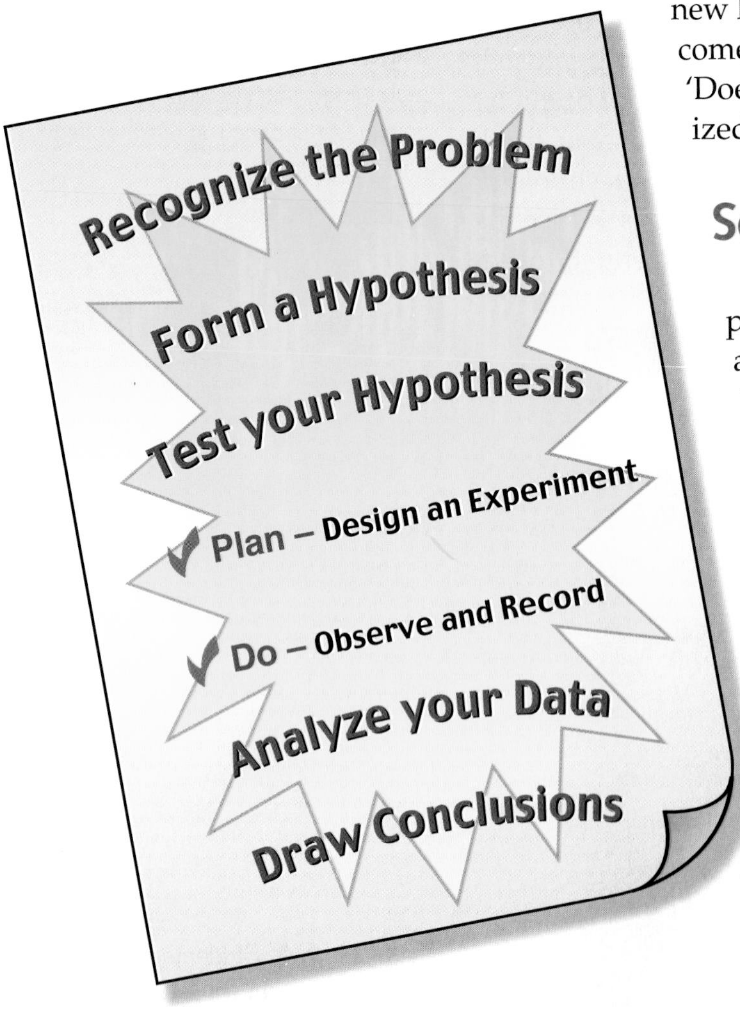

Scientific Methods

Scientists use a variety of ways to solve problems. A **scientific method** is an approach taken to try to solve a problem. The steps, as listed in **Figure 1-6,** form a model to solve problems. But, these steps serve only as a guide. Sometimes, several of the steps are used while others are not needed when solving a particular problem. Or, the steps might be performed in a different order. Let's take a look at a possible method that a person might use.

Figure 1-6 This poster shows one possible way to solve problems.

Recognize the Problem

The problem-solving process generally begins when you recognize a problem or ask a question. Once you know what you want to study, you then choose the methods that will help you find the answers. Kashanna, shown in **Figure 1-7,** liked to listen to hard rock music as she studied. She and her parents argued about it.

"Kashanna, you can't possibly concentrate with that type of music," her mother would say.

"My grades are okay," Kashanna would argue.

"But I think your grades would be higher if you listened to quiet music, like classical," her mother would reply. "I know that soothing music helps me to think more clearly," she explained.

Kashanna decided to use a scientific method to see whether her mother was right. She asked her friend Hiromi to help.

"You're off to a great start. You've definitely got a problem you want to solve," Hiromi laughed.

Preparing to solve a problem or ask a question often involves making observations and doing research. For example, scientists who develop ways to improve crop yields find out the growth needs of the plant. They learn what has worked and not worked. Many times, scientists identify a real problem only after collecting lots of information from their observations.

interNET CONNECTION

Visit the Glencoe Science Web Site at **www.glencoe.com/ sec/science/ca** for more information about the effects of music on concentration. In your Science Journal, compare and contrast the results from different studies.

Figure 1-7 Under what conditions do you study the best?

Form a Hypothesis

Often, the next step in solving a problem is to form a hypothesis. A **hypothesis** (hi PAHTH uh sus) is a prediction about a problem that can be tested. A hypothesis may be based upon a variety of things. It can come about from observations, from personal experiences, or from new information gathered during other experiments. Hypotheses are often written as if-and-then statements. For example, a scientist observes that plants, such as those in **Figure 1-8,** that are fertilized grow taller than plants that are not. A scientist may form the following hypothesis: If plants are fertilized more, then they will grow taller. This hypothesis can be tested by an experiment. Scientists are able to form theories from well-tested hypotheses.

A **theory** is an explanation backed by results obtained from repeated tests or experiments. Not all results lead to the formation of a theory. Actually, there are only a few theories and even fewer laws.

A scientific **law** is a well-tested description of how something in nature works. Generally, laws predict or describe a given situation but don't explain why. An example of a law is Newton's first law of motion. According to this law, an object continues in motion, or stays at rest, until it's acted upon by an outside force. Some other laws include the law of conservation of mass, the law of conservation of energy, and the laws of reflection.

Kashanna wrote in her Science Journal, "My hypothesis is that if I perform a task while listening to different types of music, then my ability to concentrate will not be affected."

Once a hypothesis is formed, a scientist will find ways to test it. Kashanna must now decide how to test the effects of listening to different types of music on her concentration. Two ways to test a hypothesis are by conducting controlled experiments and by making observational studies.

Figure 1-8 One scientist might hypothesize that one plant grew taller than the other because it was fertilized more. **What other hypothesis could you make about the plants?**

In order to form conclusions that make sense from your results, you often need a **control**—a standard with which to compare the results. In Kashanna's experiment, she wants to compare the effects of different kinds of music on concentration. The standard that the results will be compared to is her level of concentration when no music is playing. Kashanna's control is to have no music playing during an activity that requires concentration.

Controlled Experiments

A controlled experiment is made up of a series of steps that test a hypothesis in which a control is used. The basic idea of a controlled experiment is to change only one factor, or variable. The variable that is changed or controlled is the **independent variable.** The **dependent variable** is the factor being observed or measured. Scientists observe or measure the effect on the dependent variable when they control the independent variable. Kashanna determined that the independent variable is the type of music listened to while performing a task. She chose to test the effects of hard rock, soft rock, classical music, and no music. The dependent variable is how well Kashanna performs the task, which is related to her concentration while the music is playing.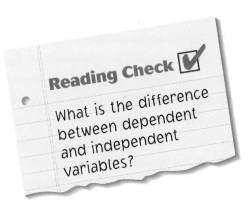

Reading Check ☑

What is the difference between dependent and independent variables?

Plan the Experiment

"How will you know the effect each type of music has on your ability to concentrate?" Hiromi asked. "You need to be able to measure the effect. I don't think you'll convince your parents if you say you felt you concentrated the same with any kind of music."

Kashanna and Hiromi decided to have Kashanna copy various passages out of their science textbook as she listened to each kind of music. Hiromi tried to select passages from the book that wouldn't be any more or less difficult to copy than any of the other passages. Kashanna couldn't copy the same page over and over or she might memorize it, which would affect the results. The number of words written down during a given time period would be the dependent variable.

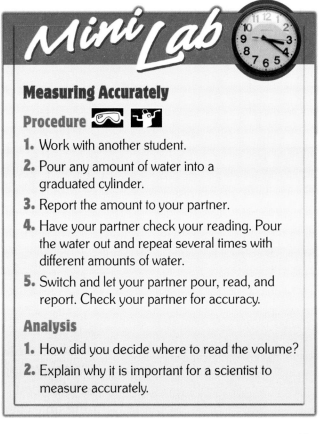

Mini Lab

Measuring Accurately

Procedure 🥽 👕

1. Work with another student.
2. Pour any amount of water into a graduated cylinder.
3. Report the amount to your partner.
4. Have your partner check your reading. Pour the water out and repeat several times with different amounts of water.
5. Switch and let your partner pour, read, and report. Check your partner for accuracy.

Analysis

1. How did you decide where to read the volume?
2. Explain why it is important for a scientist to measure accurately.

Figure 1-9 What else does Kashanna need to do her experiment?

As they wrote their plan, Kashanna and Hiromi tried to think of other variables that might affect the dependent variable. They knew that these variables should be kept the same while changing only the independent variable. That way, any effect on the dependent variable would be caused only by the independent variable. A variable in an experiment that stays the same is a **constant.** Constants that Kashanna and Hiromi identified were the similar passages in the book to be copied, the amount of time given to copy each passage, the volume of the music, the lighting in the room, and interruptions from people entering the room. They also were careful to select three pieces of music that could each be played uninterrupted for five minutes.

Kashanna thought of something else. "What if I speed up, without even realizing it, when I listen to hard rock to try to prove that hard rock is not harmful to my concentration? I would be influencing the results."

To avoid this problem, they asked their friend Mario to participate in the experiment. They did not tell Mario the hypothesis. An experiment in which some or all information is withheld from a subject (Mario) or the investigator (Kashanna) is called a blind experiment.

Kashanna gathered the materials, shown in **Figure 1-9,** she would need before Mario arrived. An important part of planning an experiment is determining the materials needed. You do not want to be in the middle of conducting an experiment and find you do not have everything you need to complete the experiment.

Do the Experiment

When Mario arrived, Kashanna told him only that he would be listening to music and trying to copy as much of the passage as he could until she told him to stop. She took away his watch and any clocks in the room. She did not want Mario to try to "beat the clock." Mario did not know why Kashanna was doing this experiment. That way, he would not try to make the results come out a particular way. This is why the experiment was a blind experiment.

Look at **Figure 1-10.** Kashanna kept the lighting in the room and the volume of the music the same throughout the experiment. She put headphones on Mario to minimize other noises. When Kashanna said "Go!", Mario copied the science textbook page for five minutes. He copied down a different passage from the textbook each time he listened to each of three types of music and also when no music was played.

Part of doing an experiment is observing and recording data. Observations can include measurements and descriptions that can be written in your Science Journal. Each time five minutes was over, Kashanna observed the number of words Mario wrote. She counted and recorded them in her Science Journal. When the experiment was over, she analyzed the data. Mario had copied the fewest words while listening to hard rock.

"These aren't the results I was looking for!" Kashanna exclaimed.

Figure 1-10 There are many variables to consider before doing an experiment. **What variables might be out of Kashanna's control?**

Hiromi suggested that Kashanna repeat the experiment a few more times. Conducting an experiment once is called a trial. Repeating an experiment several times is making multiple trials. A subject in an experiment will perform slightly differently each time. The scientist takes an average of the results. A multiple trial helps strengthen the support or lack of support for the hypothesis. In Kashanna's experiment, each time a different trial was done, the order of the types of music was changed to help reduce the effect that the tiring of Mario's brain or hand muscles would have on the results.

Kashanna set up a data table to record the results of each trial. Data tables help you organize your observations and test results. **Table 1-1** shows Kashanna's data table.

Table 1-1

Number of Words Copied					
Type of Music	Trial 1	Trial 2	Trial 3	Trial 4	Average
No music	56	60	64	60	
Classical	54	62	60	56	
Soft rock	36	42	38	32	
Hard rock	26	36	42	24	

Problem Solving

Flex Your Brain

Solving problems requires a plan. This plan may be a simple thing that you do in your head, or it may be something more complicated that you actually write down. To the right is a process called *Flex Your Brain*, which is one way to help you organize a plan for solving a problem. Skills that you might find helpful in solving problems can be found in the **Skill Handbook** at the back of your textbook.

Sonar uses sound waves to determine ocean depths and to find unseen objects. Use the *Flex Your Brain* chart to help you explore the other possible uses of sound waves.

Think Critically: How can you use technology to help you find the answer to the problem? Why does *Flex Your Brain* ask you to share what you've learned?

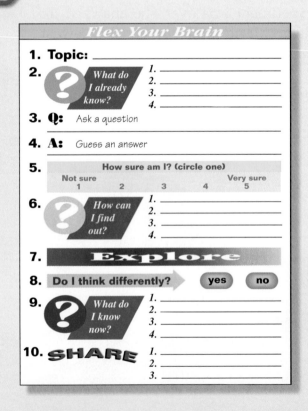

Observational Study

Using scientific methods does not always involve doing a controlled experiment. In an observational study, a scientist does not change or control the variables that are already present in a situation or an environment. The scientist observes and records his or her observations, as in **Figure 1-11.** Suppose scientists wanted to learn more about a particular planet. They might observe the planet with powerful telescopes. They might send a probe, a device to gather information. Suppose scientists wanted to learn more about a particular animal. They might want to know how the animal lives in its natural environment. The scientists would observe the animal without changing its living conditions. Or, suppose scientists wanted to find out more about what causes heart disease. They might observe the rate of heart disease in a group of people and note differences between people who develop heart disease and those who do not.

In each of these three cases, a controlled experiment would not help the scientists obtain the information they seek. This is not to say that observational studies never have variables. Suppose a scientist observes the rate of cancer in people who have a low-fat diet compared to those who have a high-fat diet. The scientist classifies people as belonging in one of the two groups. The independent variable is the amount of fat a person eats. The dependent variable is the rate of cancer.

Figure 1-11 Each of these three scientists must decide, or at times guess, which types of experiments will provide the best information.

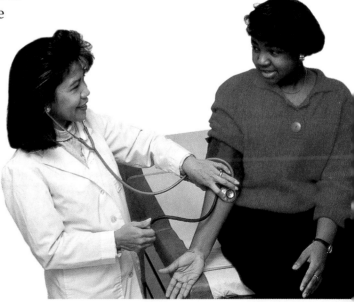

Once a set of data has been collected and organized, it can be analyzed to see if it supports the hypothesis. Data can be analyzed in a number of ways, including performing calculations and making different types of graphs. A **graph** is a diagram that shows the relationship of one variable to another. A graph makes interpretation and analysis of data easier. Look at Kashanna's graph in **Figure 1-12.** Do the results support her hypothesis?

VISUALIZING
Line Graphs

Figure 1-12

C Label each axis with an appropriate scale.

B Always put the dependent variable on the vertical axis, the *y*-axis.

A Always put the independent variable on the horizontal axis, called the *x*-axis.

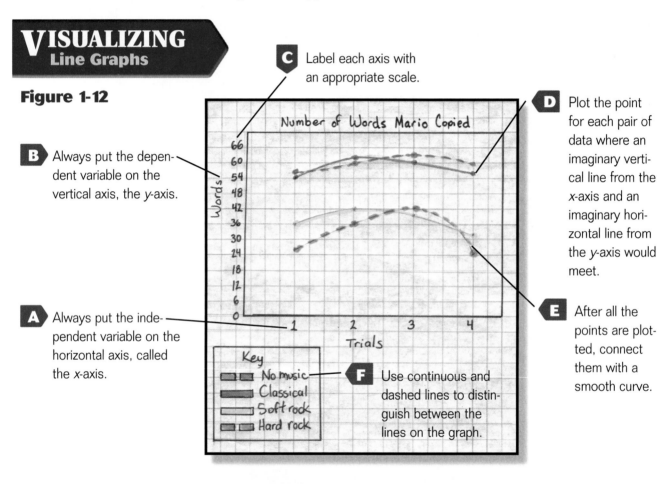

D Plot the point for each pair of data where an imaginary vertical line from the *x*-axis and an imaginary horizontal line from the *y*-axis would meet.

E After all the points are plotted, connect them with a smooth curve.

F Use continuous and dashed lines to distinguish between the lines on the graph.

Draw Conclusions

A conclusion is a statement based on the results of the experiment. It might or might not support the hypothesis. Kashanna's hypothesis was not supported. She concluded that the type of music did have an effect on the ability to concentrate. Keep in mind that a hypothesis is not necessarily wrong just because the results do not support it. An experiment might not be designed correctly. A scientist might make errors in observing, measuring, or recording data. An unidentified variable might affect the dependent variable.

As Kashanna and Hiromi reviewed their results, they identified problems in the design. They concluded that more than one variable could have affected Mario's performance. What if some passages contained a greater number of long or difficult words? Or, what if he became bored during the experiment? What if these results could be applied only to Mario? Was his experience typical of everyone's experience? Kashanna and Hiromi decided to conduct more experiments with other classmates.

Scientists who conduct observational studies also draw conclusions from analyzing data. A scientist who observes a higher rate of skin cancer in people who sunbathe often might conclude that frequent sun exposure is a factor in causing skin cancer.

Scientists, like the astronaut in **Figure 1-13**, often must do many experiments and look at problems in different ways to find answers. Scientists have not failed if they do not get answers the first time, or the second, or even the hundredth. They learn a little more each time. Often, results from scientific experiments and observations raise more questions. An important part of doing science is persistence.

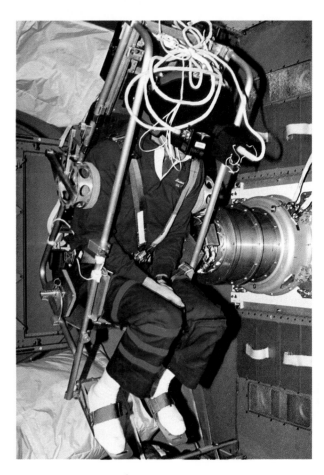

Figure 1-13 This astronaut is using a specially designed chair and helmet to test the effects of space flight on humans.

Section Assessment

1. What are five possible approaches one might take in solving a problem?
2. What is a constant?
3. Why is conducting multiple trials a good idea?
4. **Think Critically:** What else could Kashanna have used as the independent variable in her experiment?
5. **Skill Builder**
   Sequencing Complex tasks are often accomplished by following a series of steps in order. Do the **Chapter 1 Skill Activity** on page 554 to plan a mission to Mars by arranging the steps in the proper sequence.

Using Math

Use the data in **Table 1-1** to find the average number of words copied for each trial. Make a bar graph to show the results of your calculations. Under which conditions would Mario study best?

Follow the Bouncing Ball

Possible Materials

- Balls, such as a baseball, table-tennis ball, golf ball, tennis ball, racquetball, and high-bounce rubber ball
- Meterstick
- Poster paper
- Markers
- Floor materials, such as carpet, foam, hard tile, and wood

Science might be the last thing you are thinking about as you watch a commercial on TV. But, many manufacturers rely on scientists to design and test their products. Suppose you are the owner of a sports store. You want to advertise how high a particular ball bounces. Conduct an experiment to find the surface material on which your ball bounces the highest.

Recognize the Problem

How does the surface of a material affect how high a ball bounces?

Form a Hypothesis

Before a ball is dropped, it has potential energy. Potential energy is energy that is stored. As the ball falls, the potential energy is converted into kinetic energy, which is energy of motion. Some energy is transferred as a ball deforms when it hits the surface. Use this knowledge of potential and kinetic energy to **make a hypothesis** about how the kind of surface material helps determine the bounce of a ball.

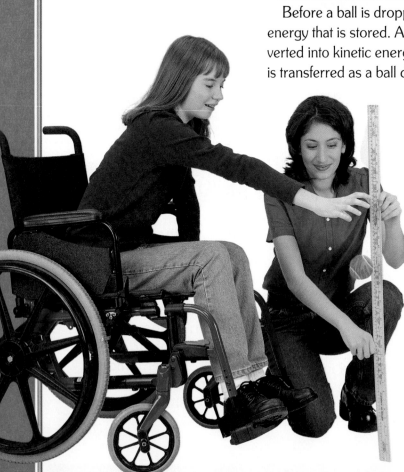

Goals

- **Design an experiment** to find out how high a ball bounces on different surface materials.
- **Separate and control** variables.
- **Measure and record** observations.

Safety Precautions

Do not throw the balls in the classroom.

Test Your Hypothesis

Plan

1. **Decide** how your group will test your hypothesis.

2. **List** the steps that you need to take to test your hypothesis. **Include** in your plan (a) the materials you will use, (b) the dependent variable and how you will **determine** the effect of the independent variable, (c) how you will keep the constants the same, d) the independent variable and how you will **adjust** it, and (e) how many trials you will conduct.

3. **Prepare** a data table in your Science Journal so that it is ready to use as your group collects data. Will the data be summarized in graphs? **Decide** which type of graph to use.

Do

1. Make sure your teacher approves your plan and your data table before you proceed.

2. **Perform** the experiment as planned.

3. **Record** your observations and **complete** the data table in your Science Journal.

Analyze Your Data

1. **Construct** a graph to compare results.

2. **List** the materials in the order that provided the highest bounce to those that provided the lowest bounce. Which surface material provided the highest bounce?

3. **Identify** any other variables that could affect the height of the bounce.

Draw Conclusions

1. **Infer** which surface materials absorb the most energy from the ball.

2. **Explain** why the surface material and the material of the ball are important in how sports, such as tennis and basketball, are played.

3. **Apply** what you learned. Write an advertisement that tells customers how to get the most bounce from the ball.

1·2 Using Science to Explore

What You'll Learn

► How remotely operated vehicles help humans to explore
► How scientists use science skills in different ways

Vocabulary
technology
sequence
inference

Why It's Important

► Using science skills and technology helps you gather information about places that you cannot observe directly.

Figure 1-14 This manned submersible, MIR I, is used to study and explore to a depth of 6000 m.

Using Technology

A week had passed since Mr. Hayes's assignment. The students were eager to share what they had found out.

Mr. Hayes opened the discussion. "Before we begin, who can tell us the difference between science and technology?"

Gabriella raised her hand. "Science is the process of trying to understand the world around you. **Technology** is the application of what has been learned through science."

"Excellent," Mr. Hayes said. "Why don't you go first, Gabriella?"

Gabriella stood. "The ocean is a frontier just waiting to be explored like the American West used to be. There's a difference, though. There are few places people may go underwater. It's too deep and the pressure is too great. That's what is known as a hostile environment—an environment in which the conditions are hazardous to people. People need technology to help them."

She continued, "Remotely operated vehicles, or ROVs, can withstand the pressure at several thousand feet. They have cameras and other instruments that gather data about things such as salinity (salt content) and currents. They have manipulators, or arms, that take samples."

"Volcanoes are another frontier on Earth," Jared volunteered. "I read about a spiderlike, walking robot that was designed to explore the inside of an active volcano."

Hiromi spoke next. "Space is another hostile environment," he said. "I read about a robot that NASA developed that's able to travel over rough terrain. They tested it in a desert that resembled the surface of the moon. Once on the moon, scientists would operate it from Earth. But, one thing that makes this robot different is that it has its own navigation system. Suppose it were going toward a cliff. It would take 2.5 seconds for the scientists to signal the robot on the moon, and by that time, the robot might have fallen off. But, this robot can determine what is safe and what is dangerous. It might even ignore the operator's commands if it detects a hazard."

"That's the kind of technology I read about," said Kashanna. "Scientists are making robots to explore hostile environments that don't need someone giving them commands all the time. One robot is called STAR—that's the Spiral Track Autonomous Robot. It travels on two giant screws—that's the 'spiral' part—so it can turn around in tight spaces and climb steep terrain that other robots can't. It has an onboard computer system that allows it to make decisions—that's the 'autonomous' part."

Figure 1-15 The terrain of Mars was photographed and explored by this rover.

Figure 1-16 Technology, such as STAR, is developed to solve specific problems and explore unique environments.

Several students described other uses for technology in hostile environments such as mining and cleaning up nuclear or chemical spills.

Mr. Hayes pointed out that ROVs and robots help people "see" places they cannot visit directly. "Keep in mind," he said, "that people are seeing the data that are sent back, not the environments themselves. Even the camera images aren't the same as directly seeing something."

Using Science to Develop Technology

The class then discussed the science skills they thought would have been used to explore hostile environments. As they talked, Mr. Hayes wrote the science skills on the board. They agreed that the scientists who built the technology used various skills as they followed some scientific method. The scientists recognized a problem for which they wanted to design an ROV or robot. They compared and contrasted different designs and recorded their findings in their Science Journals, as shown in **Figure 1-17.** Comparing is looking for similarities in objects or events. Contrasting is looking for differences in objects or events. They also used math skills to design a model. For example, they might have calculated the energy needed for the machine to function or have drawn a scale model. ☑

Reading Check ☑

What is the difference between comparing and contrasting?

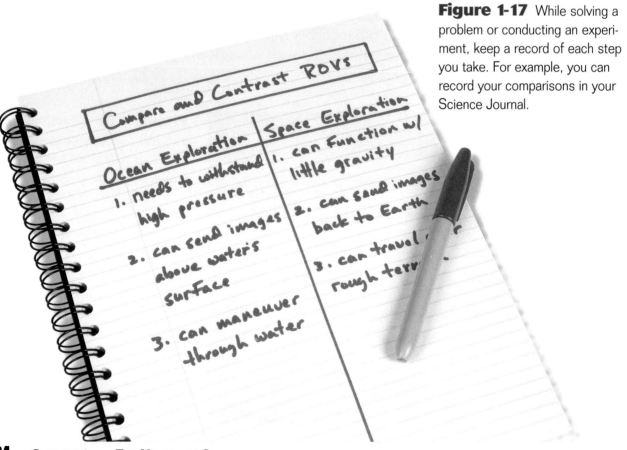

Figure 1-17 While solving a problem or conducting an experiment, keep a record of each step you take. For example, you can record your comparisons in your Science Journal.

Compare and Contrast ROVs

Ocean Exploration	Space Exploration
1. needs to withstand high pressure	1. can function w/ little gravity
2. can send images above water's surface	2. can send images back to Earth
3. can maneuver through water	3. can travel ... rough terr...

After forming a hypothesis that their design would work, the scientists tested the hypothesis. They planned and conducted a controlled experiment. They used sequencing to test the model. A **sequence** is an arrangement of things or events in a certain order. For example, they might test the ROV's ability to grasp and hold an object, then test how much mass the robot's arm can support before dropping an object. They identified and controlled variables. Only one independent variable was changed at a time so that the scientists could pinpoint the cause of any malfunctions. They carefully observed the model's performance to record accurate data.

As they worked, the scientists constantly made inferences. An **inference** is an attempt at an explanation based on observations. This helped them know how to modify the design. As they worked, they made careful measurements. They might have measured the speed of the model or the size of objects it could lift.

Gravity acts on every particle in an object. The center of mass of an object is the point where an object will balance without tipping over. The position of the center of gravity affects an object's stability. When designing a robot, scientists must make sure the robot remains stable as it moves forward, stops, turns, and moves up or down an incline. If a robot is too heavy near the top, it may tip over easily.

Stability can be increased by lowering the center of gravity and by widening the base. Think of football players. They are harder to knock down if their knees are bent, which lowers their center of gravity, and when their feet are spread apart, which widens their base.

Finally, the scientists organized their data into tables and graphs so they could analyze the results and draw conclusions. Scientists use any number of graphs (line, bar, and circle) to help them interpret data. Communicating was an important skill throughout the process. The scientists worked as a team so they needed to share what they were doing and seeing.

interNET CONNECTION

Visit the Glencoe Science Web Site at **www.glencoe.com/ sec/science/ca** for information about ROVs that have been developed recently. In your Science Journal, compare and contrast the designs and functions of several ROVs.

PHYSICS
◄ **INTEGRATION**

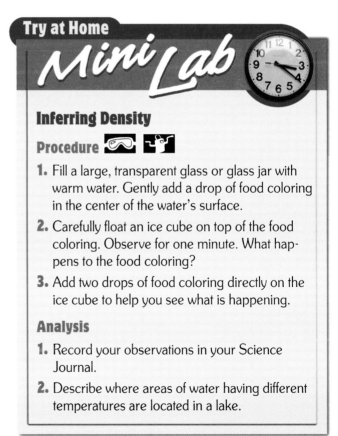

Try at Home

Mini Lab

Inferring Density

Procedure

1. Fill a large, transparent glass or glass jar with warm water. Gently add a drop of food coloring in the center of the water's surface.

2. Carefully float an ice cube on top of the food coloring. Observe for one minute. What happens to the food coloring?

3. Add two drops of food coloring directly on the ice cube to help you see what is happening.

Analysis

1. Record your observations in your Science Journal.

2. Describe where areas of water having different temperatures are located in a lake.

Figure 1-18 When searching and exploring hostile environments, there are no right or wrong methods. Using your imagination and creativity, the world—and beyond—is yours to explore. **What might the researchers on this ocean-research vessel be studying in the Chukchi Sea (between Alaska and Russia)?**

Using Science Skills to Explore

From their assignment, the class decided that the scientists who explore hostile environments using technology do not necessarily follow step-by-step scientific methods. For example, scientists who explore the ocean, as in **Figure 1-18,** might not have a formal hypothesis. The question might be "What's down there?" But, the scientists still use a variety of science skills while following their particular method.

These skills might include observing (looking at the pictures transmitted), inferring (explaining what the pictures are), measuring (determining how much cable to use to lower the ROV in the water), interpreting (using meteorological data to forecast the weather at sea), and communicating (sharing information to position the ROV correctly).

Safe Science

Mr. Hayes emphasized that safety is an important reason for using technology to explore hostile environments. Having equipment become damaged is far less critical than risking a person's life. The class discussed safety rules to follow when conducting science activities or experiments. They designed a poster called SAFE TIPS.

Start a lab activity only with your teacher's permission.
Ask your teacher if you do not understand a procedure.
Follow all safety symbols. Wear goggles during labs.
Engage in responsible behavior.

Tell your teacher immediately of accidents or injuries.
Identify the location of emergency equipment.
Put away chemicals and supplies properly.
Slant test tubes away from you and others when heating.

The students also created the slogan NO TIDE. TIDE stands for **T**asting chemicals, **I**nhaling chemicals, **D**rinking, or **E**ating. This helps them to remember that they should never eat or drink anything in a laboratory. It also reminds them to be cautious around fumes or vapors that could be harmful.

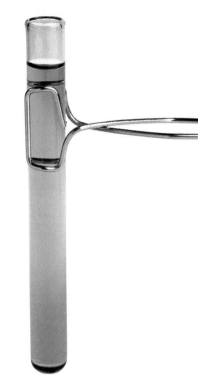

Figure 1-19 Lab equipment, like the test tube shown, must be handled properly.

Section Assessment

1. What are some ways technology is used to explore hostile environments?

2. What are some science skills scientists use to form a hypothesis about the design of an ROV or robot?

3. **Think Critically:** You have read about ways that scientists are like explorers. How are modern scientists different from explorers of the past?

4. **Skill Builder**
   Interpreting Data Suppose you have three plants that are supposed to bloom but are not blooming. You give one plant only water, another plant water and one type of plant fertilizer, and the third plant water and a different type of plant fertilizer. None of the plants bloom. How would you interpret your observations? If you need help, refer to Interpreting Data in the **Skill Handbook** on page 536.

Using Computers

Word Processing
Think of a problem faced by your community such as water pollution. Using a word processor, write a report describing how you would design a robot or an ROV to help solve the problem. If you need help, refer to page 544.

Materials

- Graduated cylinder (100 mL)
- Balance and masses
- Water
- Cooking oil
- Table salt
- Paper cups
- Plastic spoons or stirrers
- Plastic beverage containers (to dispose of oil)

What You'll Investigate

How do the densities of liquids compare?

Goals

- **Infer** why objects float in some liquids but not in others.
- **Measure** liquids to determine their density.
- **Graph** the densities of the liquids.

Safety Precautions

Never taste anything during a lab activity. Wipe up any spills on the floor immediately.

Procedure

1. **Copy** the data table below for recording your measurements.

Comparing Densities

Density is a physical property of a substance. It relates to how much material is contained within an object. In general, an object will float if its density is less than the density of the liquid. For example, ice floats in water because ice is less dense than water. How do the densities of various liquids compare?

2. **Measure** the mass of a paper cup and record.

3. **Measure** 100 mL of water and pour it into the cup. Record the mass.

4. **Make** salt water by dissolving 3.5 g of table salt into 100 mL of tap water. Using a fresh paper cup each time, repeat steps 2 and 3 for the salt water and oil.

5. **Subtract** the mass of the cup to find the mass of the liquid. **Calculate** the density of each liquid using the formula, *density = mass/volume.* The unit used to express density is g/cm^3. One cubic centimeter occupies the same volume as one milliliter.

6. **Graph** your data using a bar graph. How does a graph help you analyze your results?

Conclude and Apply

1. Would a ship be able to carry more cargo in freshwater or salt water? Why?

2. Why might it be harder for aquatic birds to swim in an oil spill than in water?

Liquid's Measurement Data

Liquid	Mass of paper cup (g)	Mass of liquid in cup (g)	Mass of liquid only (g)	Volume of liquid (mL)	Density (g/cm³)
Tap water					
Salt water					
Oil					

The Circle of Life
From: *Nature's Numbers* by Ian Stewart

"We live in a universe of patterns. (See sample patterns at left.) Every night the stars move in circles across the sky. The seasons cycle at yearly intervals. No two snowflakes are ever exactly the same, but they all have sixfold symmetry. Tigers and zebras are covered in patterns of stripes, leopards and hyenas are covered in patterns of spots. Intricate trains of waves march across the oceans; very similar trains of sand dunes march across the desert. Colored arcs of light adorn the sky in the form of rainbows, and a bright circular halo sometimes surrounds the moon on winter nights. Spherical drops of water fall from clouds."

Throughout history, people of various cultures have tried to organize and explain the world around them. Long ago, an elder in the Sioux Nation observed the rings within tree trunks, the structure of birds' nests, the shape of raindrops, and other circular patterns around him. He believed that all of nature is like a circle.

In this Native American view of the world, all of the unique communities in nature interact as part of a whole. An elder and teacher of the Chippewa Nation taught that all living creatures are related because they have the same mother (Earth) and share her gifts. For example, plants take in carbon dioxide and release oxygen for organisms to breathe.

Many cultures that have lived close to nature share the world view that nature is based on circular patterns. In recent times, scientists have provided circular models of the solar system and the atom. Thus, we are finding that some native peoples' view of nature corresponds well with the findings of modern science.

Science JOURNAL ▶

Expository Writing: Observe and describe some other examples of circular or cyclic patterns in nature. What other repeating patterns are you familiar with? What responsibility do humans have in "the circle of life"?

Think Critically

Look through your textbook for additional examples of cyclic patterns. Write down these examples and the pages on which they are located in your Science Journal.

For a **preview** of this chapter, study this Reviewing Main Ideas before you read the chapter. After you have studied this chapter, you can use the Reviewing Main Ideas to **review** the chapter.

GLENCOE TECHNOLOGY

The Glencoe MindJogger, Audiocassettes, and CD-ROM provide additional opportunities for review.

Section 1-1 SCIENTIFIC PROBLEM SOLVING

A **scientific method** consists of steps taken to try to solve a problem. One step is to recognize a problem. A second step is to form a **hypothesis**—a prediction about a problem that can be tested. In another step, scientists test hypotheses by conducting controlled experiments or observational studies. In a controlled experiment, scientists change the **independent variable** and measure its effect on the **dependent variable.** Scientists who conduct observational studies do not change or control variables. They observe the relationships among variables. Another important step is to analyze data. Scientists organize data into tables or **graphs.** Often, the final step in a scientific method is to draw conclusions. A conclusion may or may not support the hypothesis. This does not necessarily mean the hypothesis is wrong. Sometimes, experiments are not designed correctly or unknown variables produce effects on the dependent variable. Scientists often must do many experiments and look at problems in different ways to find answers. *Why should only one variable at a time be changed in a controlled experiment?*

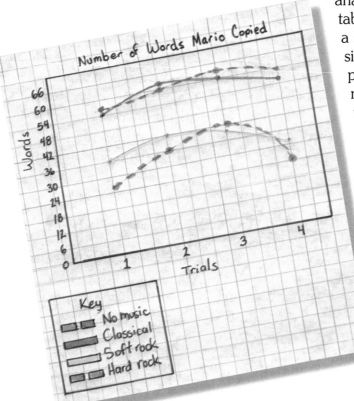

Reading Check ✔

- Variables, controls, and trials are used in scientific experiments. Compare the meaning of each word in this context with its meaning in a nonscientific context.

Section
1-2 **USING SCIENCE TO EXPLORE**

A hostile environment is an environment in which the conditions are hazardous to people. Many places on Earth and in outer space cannot be explored directly by humans. Scientists have constructed robots and remotely operated vehicles, or ROVs, to go to sites of nuclear accidents, deep in the ocean, into volcanoes, into outer space, and into mines. People have increased their knowledge of hostile environments by analyzing data gathered through **technology.** Scientists who design technology to explore hostile environments use various approaches when forming a **scientific method** that will help them solve a particular problem. They design and conduct experiments to test models. Scientists who use technology to explore hostile environments use science skills. In both cases, scientists use science skills to solve a problem or to answer a question. *Does a scientist always have to follow certain steps in a scientific method? Why or why not?*

Career CONNECTION

John Swallow, Forest Technician

John Swallow works in South Dakota's Black Hills National Forest. He is an Oglala Sioux and a forest technician. John determines which trees in the forest can be safely cut down and which trees must be saved. Much of the cutting of trees is done for thinning—to reduce competition between trees for light and nutrients—thus promoting quicker growth. John also works to conserve sensitive or endangered plants in logging areas. *How can science help our understanding of the impact of logging on a forest?*

Chapter 1 Assessment

Using Vocabulary

a. constant	**h.** law
b. control	**i.** science
c. dependent variable	**j.** scientific method
d. graph	**k.** sequence
e. hypothesis	**l.** technology
f. independent variable	**m.** theory
g. inference	

Each of the following sentences is false. Make the sentence true by replacing the italicized word with a word from the list above.

1. A *control* is an approach taken to try to solve a problem.
2. An *inference* is a prediction about a problem that can be tested.
3. *Technology* is the process of trying to understand the world around you.
4. A *constant* is a standard to compare with.
5. The *independent variable* is the factor being measured in a controlled experiment.

Checking Concepts

Choose the word or phrase that best answers the question.

6. How is a hypothesis tested?
   A) experiment   C) graph
   B) infer   D) conclude

7. What will a scientist never do in an observational study?
   A) use technology   C) control variables
   B) record data   D) observe variables

8. What does a scientist use to reduce the effect of errors?
   A) observations   C) hypotheses
   B) constants   D) multiple trials

9. You decide to find out which of three cat foods your cat likes the best. What is the cat food that you try each time called?
   A) control   C) independent variable
   B) dependent variable   D) trial

10. How does a blind experiment differ from other experiments?
    A) Data are collected and interpreted.
    B) A hypothesis is formed after observations are made.
    C) Variables are changed to test the hypothesis.
    D) Some or all of the information is withheld from the subject.

11. What does it mean if an experiment does **NOT** support the hypothesis?
    A) The scientist has failed.
    B) The scientist has learned more.
    C) The scientist is not creative.
    D) The scientist did something wrong.

12. Why are ROVs and robots so useful?
    A) They gather information from hostile environments.
    B) They must follow commands from a person.
    C) They allow people to see hostile environments directly.
    D) They make all decisions on their own.

13. How do scientists who build ROVs use scientific methods?
    A) They test the effects of gravity.
    B) They work according to a sequence.
    C) They keep their data secret.
    D) They use every approach in the model.

14. What is a graph **NOT** used for?
    A) conducting an experiment
    B) interpreting data
    C) communicating information
    D) drawing conclusions

15. What is an explanation backed by experimental results?
    A) a control   C) a law
    B) a theory   D) a hypothesis

Thinking Critically

16. You use the skill of sequencing when you get ready for school. What might happen if you changed the order of your actions?

17. A scientist wants to test a new drug that might relieve symptoms for a particular illness. Why is it important to use a control?

18. Give an example of an observational study you can do at home.

19. Why is it important to follow safety rules in the lab?

20. Why do scientists often do research before forming a hypothesis?

Developing Skills

If you need help, refer to the Skill Handbook.

21. Concept Mapping: Complete the events chain that shows the order in which science skills might be used in observational studies. Use these phrases: *analyze data, ask a question, draw conclusions, observe,* and *record data.*

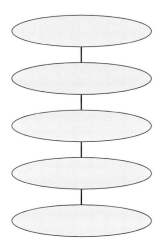

THE
PRINCETON
REVIEW

Test-Taking Tip

Beat the Clock and Then Go Back As you take a test, pace yourself to finish a few minutes early so you can go back and check over your work. You'll usually find a mistake or two. Don't worry. It's better to make corrections than to hand in a test with wrong answers.

Test Practice

Use these questions to test your Science Proficiency.

1. Michaela set up an experiment to find out if running would help her basketball game. Her basketball game did not improve. What can Michaela conclude from her results?
A) Her hypothesis was wrong.
B) Her results did not support the hypothesis.
C) Running does not help a person do well in sports.
D) A person who plays basketball should not run.

2. Alex eagerly arrived to science class early to begin his experiment. He set up the materials, popped a piece of gum into his mouth, and got right to work by himself, even though he wasn't quite sure of the procedure. What is the safety precaution that he ignored **FIRST**?
A) He didn't put on goggles.
B) He didn't ask questions about the correct procedure.
C) He didn't get the teacher's permission to start the lab activity.
D) He was eating during a lab activity.

CHAPTER
2 Matter

Chapter Preview

Section 2-1
Structure of Matter

Section 2-2
Elements

Section 2-3
Compounds and Mixtures

Skills Preview

Skill Builders
- Interpret Data
- Compare and Contrast

Activities
- Make and Use a Table
- Form a Hypothesis

MiniLabs
- Make a Model
- Observe and Infer

Reading Check ✓

Use the headings and sub-headings to make an outline as you read this chapter. Write a few important points under each subheading.

Explore Activity

You've just finished playing basketball. You're hot and thirsty. You reach for your bottle of water and, leaning back, squeeze out a long, thirst-quenching drink. Releasing your grip, you notice that the bottle is nearly empty. But, is the bottle really almost empty? According to the dictionary, empty means containing nothing. When you have finished all the water in the bottle, will it be empty? And, if it's full, what is it full of?

Observe Matter

1. Wad up a small piece of a dry paper towel or tissue paper and tape it to the bottom of the inside of a plastic drinking cup. When you turn the cup upside down, the towel or paper should remain inside the cup.

2. Fill a bowl or sink almost to the top with water. Hold the cup upside down over the water's surface. Slowly push the cup straight into the water as far as you can.

3. Slowly raise the cup straight out of the water. Remove the paper towel and examine it.

In your Science Journal, describe your experiment. Include a description of the paper after you removed it from the cup. Explain what you think happened. Was anything in the cup besides the paper? If so, what was it?

2·1 Structure of Matter

What is matter?

Did you decide that the bottle of water and the plastic cup in the Explore Activity were filled with air? Have you wondered what makes up the air around you? It's mostly nitrogen and oxygen. Nitrogen and oxygen are kinds of matter. Scientists define **matter** as anything that has mass and takes up space. So even if you can't see it or catch hold of it, air is matter.

What about the things you *can* see, taste, smell, and touch when you eat lunch in the cafeteria or walk around your neighborhood? These things are also made of matter. What about your own body? Yes, it's matter too. Through science, you will explore the many amazing kinds of matter that make up the universe—things as common as a flower or as spectacular as a supernova, both shown in **Figure 2-1.**

What isn't matter?

You can see the words on this page because of light. Does light have mass or take up space? What about the warmth from the sun or the heater in your classroom? Neither light nor heat take up any space. They don't have any mass either, so they are not forms of matter. Emotions, thoughts, and ideas also are not matter.

What You'll Learn

▶ What matter is
▶ What makes up matter
▶ The parts of an atom
▶ The models that are used for atoms

Vocabulary

matter
atom
law of conservation
  of matter
electron
nucleus
proton
neutron

Why It's Important

▶ Matter makes up your body, your environment, and the universe.

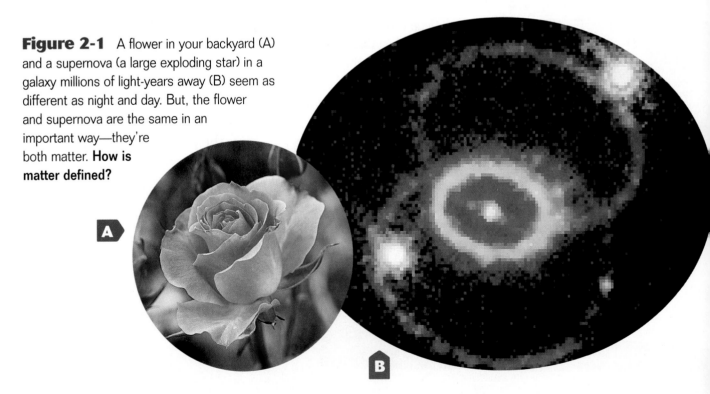

Figure 2-1 A flower in your backyard (A) and a supernova (a large exploding star) in a galaxy millions of light-years away (B) seem as different as night and day. But, the flower and supernova are the same in an important way—they're both matter. **How is matter defined?**

A

B

What makes up matter?

Suppose you cut a sheet of notebook paper into smaller and smaller pieces, as shown in **Figure 2-2.** Do the pieces seem to be made of the same matter as the large sheet you started with? If you could cut a small enough piece, would it still have the same properties as the large sheet of paper? Or, would it no longer be paper at all? People have asked questions like these—and wondered about what matter is made of—for centuries.

An Early Idea

Democritus, who lived from 460 to 370 B.C., was a Greek philosopher who thought the universe was made of empty space and tiny bits of stuff. He believed that the bits of stuff were so small they could no longer be divided into smaller pieces. He called these tiny pieces of stuff atoms. In fact, the term *atom* comes from a Greek word that means "cannot be divided." In science today, an **atom** is defined as a small particle that makes up most types of matter. Democritus thought that different types of atoms exist for every type of matter. His idea proved to be a small step in understanding the structure of matter that continues today.

Lavoisier's Contribution

Antoine Lavoisier (la VWAH see ay), a French chemist who lived about 2000 years after Democritus, was also curious about matter—especially when it changed from one form to another. Before Lavoisier, people thought matter could appear and disappear during changes such as burning and rusting. You might have thought the same thing—that matter can disappear—if you've ever watched wood burn to embers, then ashes in a fireplace. But, Lavoisier showed that wood and the oxygen it combines with during burning have the same mass as the ash, water, and

Figure 2-2 Paper is made up of carbon, hydrogen, and oxygen. So, if you could cut paper into small enough pieces, it wouldn't be paper at all. **What common type of matter is made up of only hydrogen and oxygen?**

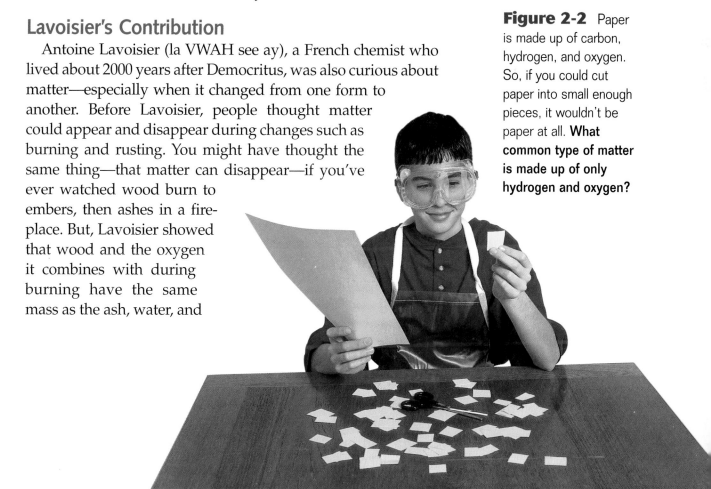

Oxygen

+

Water vapor
and
carbon dioxide

+

Figure 2-3 When wood burns, matter is not lost. The total mass of the wood and the oxygen it combines with equals the total mass of the water vapor, carbon dioxide, and ashes produced. **When you burn wood in a fireplace, what is the source of the oxygen?**

carbon dioxide (KAR bun di AHK side) produced, as shown in **Figure 2-3.** In the same way, iron and oxygen have the same mass as the rust they form. From Lavoisier's work came the **law of conservation of matter.** This law states that matter is neither created nor destroyed, only changed in form.

Models of the Atom

Scientists often use models for things that are too small to be seen and observed easily, as well as things that are too complicated or too large to be understood easily. Throughout history, scientists have created and used models to help find out what atoms are made of and how they act.

One way to make a model is to make a small version of something larger. For example, if you wanted to design a new kind of sailboat, would you just come up with a design, build a full-sized boat, and hope it would float? It would be smarter—and safer—to first build and test a small model of your design. Then, if it doesn't float, you can change your design and build another model. You can keep trying until the model works. As with the model sailboat, scientists' models are changed as new information is gained.

Dalton's Atomic Model

In the early 1800s, an English schoolteacher and chemist named John Dalton studied the experiments of Lavoisier and many others. Dalton thought that an atomic model could explain the results of these experiments. He named his model *the atomic theory of matter.* Dalton's atomic model, like many scientific models, was a set of ideas—not an object. Dalton believed that matter was made of atoms that were too small to be seen by the human eye. He also thought that each type of matter was made of only one kind of atom. For example, gold atoms make up a gold nugget and give a gold ring its shininess, as well as its other properties.

Sizes of Atoms

Atoms are so small it would take about 1 million of them lined up in a row to equal the thickness of a human hair. To give you a better idea of how small atoms are, look at **Figure 2-4.** Imagine you are holding an orange in your hand. If you wanted to use only your eyes to see the individual atoms on the surface of the orange, the size of the orange would need to increase to the size of Earth. Then, imagine it is covered with billions and billions of marbles. Each marble would represent one of the atoms that make up the skin of the orange.

Figure 2-4 Imagining this orange is the size of Earth can help you visualize the size of an atom.

Figure 2-5 In this experiment, the magnet caused the cathode rays inside the tube to bend. **What do you think would happen to the cathode rays if the magnet were removed?**

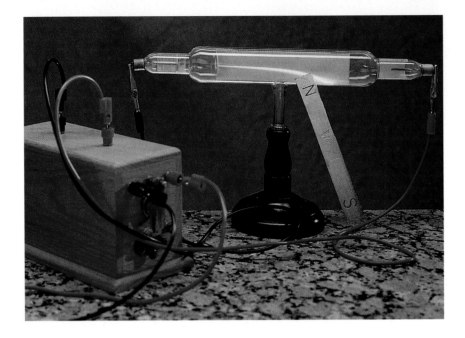

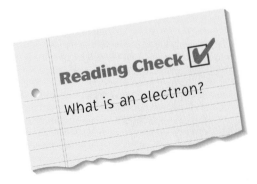

Mini Lab

Making a Model

Procedure

1. Your teacher will give you a sealed shoe box that contains one or more items.
2. Try to find out how many and what kinds of items are inside the box. You cannot look inside the box. The only observations you may make are by handling the box.

Analysis

1. How many items do you infer are in the box? Sketch the apparent shapes of the items and identify them if you can.
2. Compare your procedure with how scientists perform experiments and make models to find out more about the atom.

Reading Check ☑

What is an electron?

Discovering the Electron

One of the many pioneers in the development of today's atomic model was J.J. Thomson, an Englishman. He conducted experiments using a vacuum tube, which is a glass tube that has all the air pumped out of it and then is sealed at both ends. Thomson's tube had metal plates at both ends. The plates were connected to a high-voltage electrical source that gave one of the plates, the *anode,* a positive charge and the other, the *cathode,* a negative charge. During his experiments, Thomson observed rays that traveled from the cathode to the anode. Because the rays came from the cathode, Thomson called them cathode rays. The rays were bent by a magnet, as seen in **Figure 2-5,** showing that the rays were made up of particles that had mass. The rays were bent by charged plates, also. Thomson knew that unlike charges attract each other and like charges repel each other. When he saw that the rays bent toward a positively charged plate, he concluded that the cathode rays were made up of negative particles. These invisible, negatively charged particles, which came from the metal atoms that made up the cathode, are called **electrons.** ☑

Imagine Thomson's excitement at this discovery. He had shown that atoms are not too tiny to divide after all. Rather, they are made up of even smaller subatomic particles. Other scientists soon built on Thomson's results and found that the electron had a small mass—in fact, 1/1837 the mass of the lightest atom, the hydrogen atom. In 1906, Thomson received the Nobel Prize in Physics for his discovery of the electron.

Matter that has equal numbers of positive and negative charges, and therefore has no *net* charge, is said to be neutral. Because most matter is neutral, Thomson knew that atoms had to contain both positive and negative charges. He pictured the atom as being made up of electrons embedded in a ball of positive charge. You might compare his model, shown in **Figure 2-6,** to something like tiny chocolate chips spread around in a ball of cookie dough. But, Thomson's model did not provide all the answers to the questions that puzzled scientists about atoms.

Rutherford—The Nucleus

If electrons are the negatively charged particles in atoms, what are the positively charged particles that also must be present? Also, how are the parts of the atom arranged? In 1909, a team of scientists led by Ernest Rutherford in England began to work on the mystery of atomic structure. They bombarded materials with alpha particles. Alpha particles are high-energy, positively charged particles. When the scientists beamed alpha particles at an extremely thin piece of gold foil, they were amazed at the results. Most of the particles passed straight through the foil as if it were not there at all. Other particles changed direction or even bounced back. Rutherford thought the result so remarkable that he later said, "It was almost as incredible as if you had fired a 15-inch shell at a piece of tissue paper, and it came back and hit you."

Rutherford and his team soon concluded that because so many of the alpha particles passed straight through the gold foil, its atoms must be mostly empty space.

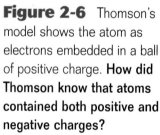

*inter***NET**
CONNECTION

Visit the Glencoe Science Web Site at **www. glencoe.com/sec/ science/ca** for more information about electron energy levels in atoms.

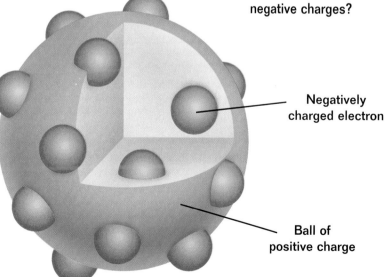

Figure 2-6 Thomson's model shows the atom as electrons embedded in a ball of positive charge. **How did Thomson know that atoms contained both positive and negative charges?**

Negatively charged electron

Ball of positive charge

Figure 2-7 Rutherford concluded that the atom must be mostly empty space in which electrons are scattered. He also thought the nucleus of the atom must be small and positively charged. **Where is most of the mass of the atom concentrated?**

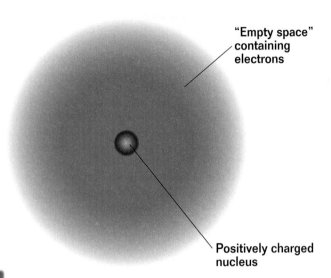

"Empty space" containing electrons

Positively charged nucleus

Try at Home

Mini Lab

Inferring Atomic Structure

Procedure

1. Blow up a rubber balloon just enough to inflate it completely. Tie a knot in the balloon's opening to seal in the air.

2. Rub the balloon vigorously against a wool sweater or coat. Hold the balloon against a wall and then let go of it.

3. Take the balloon from the wall and tie a 30-cm length of string to the balloon's neck. Again, rub the balloon vigorously against a wool sweater or coat.

4. Have someone hold the string suspending the balloon. Run a rubber comb through your hair several times. Bring the comb close to the balloon.

Analysis

1. What did the balloon do when you held it against the wall and let go? Electrically charged objects are able to attract things around them that have either an opposite charge or are neutral. What happened to the balloon when it was rubbed against wool?

2. What happened when you brought the comb near the balloon? A rubber comb acquires a negative charge when rubbed through hair. What does that tell you about the charge acquired by the balloon when rubbed against wool?

However, because some of the alpha particles bounced off something that they hit, the gold atoms must contain small, massive, positively charged objects. Rutherford called the positively charged, central part of the atom the **nucleus** (NEW klee us). He named the positively charged particles in the nucleus **protons.** He also suggested that electrons were scattered in the mostly empty space around the nucleus, as shown in **Figure 2-7.**

Discovering the Neutron

Rutherford had been puzzled by one part of his experiments with alpha particles. Alpha particles seemed to be heavier than they should be. What could possibly cause the extra mass? James Chadwick, a student of Rutherford's, answered the question. Chadwick experimented with particles given off by atoms that had been bombarded with alpha particles. He found that, unlike electrons, the paths of these new particles were not affected by an electric field. To explain his observations, he said that these particles came from the nucleus and had no charge. Chadwick called these uncharged particles **neutrons.** His proton-neutron model of the atomic nucleus is still accepted today.

Today's Model of the Atom

Scientists in the early part of the twentieth century uncovered evidence that electrons in atoms were arranged in energy levels. The lowest energy level is closest to the nucleus and can hold only two electrons. Higher energy levels are farther from the nucleus and can contain more electrons. To explain these energy levels, some scientists thought that the electrons might orbit an atom's nucleus—something like how Earth and the other planets of our solar system orbit the sun.

The Electron Cloud Model

As a result of research that continues today, scientists now realize that because electrons are so small and move so fast, their energy levels are not neat, planetlike orbits around the nucleus. Rather, it seems most likely that the electrons move in what is called the atom's *electron cloud,* as shown in **Figure 2-8.** The electron cloud model helps explain what atoms do and what they don't do.

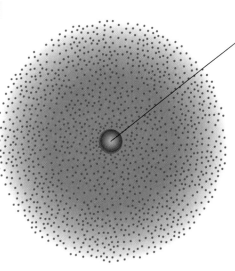

Nucleus

Figure 2-8 One model of the atom pictures the electrons moving around the nucleus in a region called an electron cloud. Dots represent places where electrons might be found. **What does the greater number of dots near the nucleus suggest?**

Section Assessment

1. List five things that are matter and five things that are not matter. Explain your answers.

2. Describe Dalton's contribution to today's understanding of matter.

3. Think of a rule that would help a fourth grader decide which things are matter and which things are not matter.

4. **Think Critically:** What made alpha particles heavier than Rutherford thought they should be?

5.  **Skill Builder**
   Observing and Inferring Scientists inferred the structure of the atom based on their observations. Do the **Chapter 2 Skill Activity** on page 555 and practice observing and inferring.

Science Journal Write a summary of what you learned about atoms. Include all of the vocabulary words listed in the Chapter Assessment in your summary.

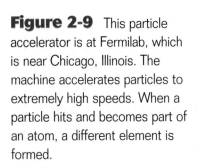

2•2 Elements

Organizing the Elements

Have you watched television today? TV sets are common, yet each one is a complex device. The outer case is made mostly of plastic, and the screen is made of glass. Many of the parts that conduct electricity are metals or combinations of metals called alloys. Other parts in the interior of the set contain materials that barely conduct electricity. These different materials have one thing in common. Each is made up of even simpler materials. In fact, if you had the proper equipment, you could separate the plastics, glass, and metals into these simpler materials.

Eventually, though, you would reach a point where you couldn't separate the materials any further. What you would have is a collection of elements. An **element** is a material that cannot be broken down to simpler materials by ordinary means. At this time, 112 elements are known and 90 of them occur naturally on Earth. These elements make up gases in the air, minerals in rocks, and liquids such as water. Examples include oxygen and nitrogen in the air you breathe and the metals gold, silver, aluminum, and iron. The other 22 are known as synthetic elements. Synthetic elements have important uses in medical testing and in smoke detectors and heart pacemaker batteries. These elements, which may be found in stars, have been made in laboratories by machines like the one shown in **Figure 2-9.**

What You'll Learn

▶ What an element is
▶ The meaning of atomic mass and atomic number
▶ What an isotope is
▶ What metals, metalloids, and nonmetals are

Vocabulary
element
atomic number
atomic mass
isotope
mass number
metal
nonmetal
metalloid

Why It's Important

▶ Everything on Earth is made of the elements found on the periodic table.

Figure 2-9 This particle accelerator is at Fermilab, which is near Chicago, Illinois. The machine accelerates particles to extremely high speeds. When a particle hits and becomes part of an atom, a different element is formed.

Figure 2-10 When you look for a certain book in the library, a system of organization called the Dewey Decimal System helps you find the book quickly and efficiently. **Describe a system of organization that can help you find a pair of matching, black socks quickly in the morning.**

EARTH SCIENCE
INTEGRATION

Elements in Minerals
The mineral fluorite contains fluoride, a form of the element fluorine. Fluorite is added to water and is used in making toothpastes. It makes tooth enamel harder and helps fight tooth decay.

Suppose that you go to a library to look up information for a school assignment. Or, maybe you want to find a book that a friend told you about. When you go to the library, do you look on shelves at random as you walk up and down the rows? Probably not, unless you have lots of time or are just browsing. More likely, you depend on the library's system of organization to find the book you want quickly and efficiently, as shown in **Figure 2-10.**

The Periodic Table

When scientists need to look up information about an element or select one to use in the laboratory, they want to be quick and efficient, too. Chemists have created a chart called the periodic table of the elements to help them organize and display the elements. When you walk into a laboratory or science classroom, you often see this chart on the wall. Each element is represented by a chemical symbol that contains one to three letters. The symbols are a form of chemical shorthand that chemists use to save time and space—both on the periodic table and in written formulas. The symbols are an important part of an international system that is understood by scientists everywhere.

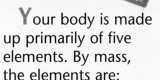

Using Math

Your body is made up primarily of five elements. By mass, the elements are:

oxygen	65%
carbon	18%
hydrogen	10%
nitrogen	3%
calcium	2%
other	2%

Make a circle graph that represents the elements in your body.

Figure 2-11 The periodic table block for chlorine shows its symbol, atomic number, and atomic mass. **Are chlorine atoms more or less massive than carbon atoms?**

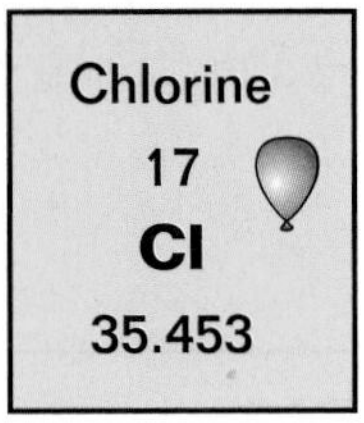

Chlorine
17
Cl
35.453

Atomic Number and Atomic Mass

Look up the element chlorine on the periodic table found inside the back cover of your textbook. Cl is the symbol for chlorine, as shown in **Figure 2-11,** but what are the two numbers? The top number, called the element's atomic number, is always a whole number. The **atomic number** tells you the number of protons in the nucleus of each atom of that element. Every atom of chlorine, for example, has 17 protons in its nucleus.

The number beneath the element's symbol is its atomic mass. An element's **atomic mass** tells you how heavy its atoms are compared with atoms of other elements. The unit scientists use for atomic mass is called the atomic mass unit, which is given the symbol u.

Isotopes and Mass Number

All the atoms of an element don't have to have the same mass. Some atoms of an element can have different numbers of neutrons in their nuclei than other atoms. Every chlorine atom contains 17 protons in its nucleus; however, some chlorine nuclei have 18 neutrons and others have 20. These two naturally occurring types of chlorine atoms are called isotopes. **Isotopes** (I suh tohps) are atoms of the same element that have different numbers of neutrons. You can tell someone exactly what type of chlorine atom you are referring to by using its mass number. An atom's **mass number** is the sum of its protons and neutrons [Mass number = number of protons + number of neutrons].

The atoms of chlorine that contain 17 protons and 18 neutrons have a mass number of 35 and are called chlorine-35. Those atoms that contain 17 protons and 20 neutrons are called chlorine-37. These two isotopes of chlorine are shown in **Figure 2-12.**

Figure 2-12 Chlorine is found naturally as two isotopes, chlorine-37 and chlorine-35. Chlorine-37 atoms are heavier than chlorine-35 atoms. The average mass of all chlorine atoms found naturally is 35.453 u. **Which type of chlorine atom is more numerous in nature?**

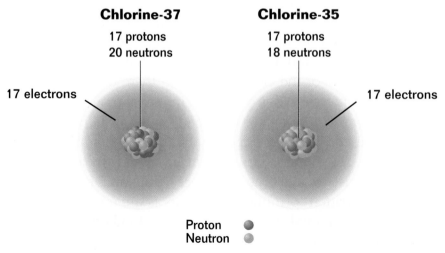

Chlorine-37
17 protons
20 neutrons
17 electrons

Chlorine-35
17 protons
18 neutrons
17 electrons

Proton ●
Neutron ●

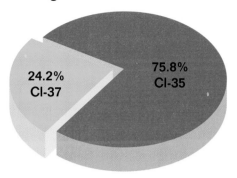

Average Atomic Mass = 35.453 u

24.2%
Cl-37

75.8%
Cl-35

Figure 2-13 Chlorine-35 atoms make up 75.8 percent of chlorine. The remaining 24.2 percent of chlorine atoms are chlorine-37. If you have 1000 atoms of chlorine, 758 of the atoms are chlorine-35. The remaining 242 atoms are chlorine-37. The total mass of the 1000 atoms is 35 453 u, so the average mass of one chlorine atom is 35.453 u. **If an element has only one isotope, how does the mass of the isotope compare with the atomic mass of the element?**

Look at the periodic table block for chlorine, **Figure 2-11.** The element's atomic mass of 35.453 u can be misleading because not one chlorine atom has that mass. About 75 percent of chlorine atoms are chlorine-35 and 25 percent are chlorine-37, as shown in **Figure 2-13.** Therefore, 35.453 u is simply the average mass of chlorine atoms.

Classification of Elements

Elements fall into three general groups: metals, metalloids (MET ul oydz), and nonmetals. You use metals every day because they have many useful physical properties.

Metals generally have a shiny or metallic luster. Metals are good conductors of heat and electricity. For example, copper is often used in electrical circuits and cookware because it conducts heat and electricity well. All metals except mercury are solids at room temperature. Metals are malleable (MAL yuh bul), which means they can be bent and pounded into various shapes. Metals are also ductile, which means they can be drawn into wires without breaking, like the ones shown in **Figure 2-14.** If you look at the periodic table in the back of this textbook, you can see that most of the elements are metals.

Figure 2-14 Metals can be drawn into wires, a property called ductility. A wire's gauge is related to its thickness. A small number means that the wire is thicker.

Figure 2-15 Chlorine, bromine, and iodine are often used as disinfectants. **What nonmetals make up most of the air you breathe?**

Nonmetals are elements that are usually dull. They are poor conductors of heat and electricity. Many are gases at room temperature, as shown in **Figure 2-15.** The solid nonmetals are generally brittle, meaning they cannot change shape easily without breaking. You can see that, except for hydrogen, the nonmetals are found on the right side of the periodic table.

Metalloids are elements such as silicon and germanium, which have characteristics of both metals and nonmetals. Some are shiny and many are conductors, but they are not as good at conducting heat and electricity as metals. All metalloids are solids at room temperature. Metalloids are found between the metals and nonmetals on the periodic table. ☑

Reading Check ☑
What is a metalloid?

Section Assessment

1. What are isotopes?

2. Explain some of the uses of metals.

3. **Think Critically:** Hector is new to your class today. He missed the lesson on how to use the periodic table to find information about the elements. Describe how you would help Hector find the atomic number for the element oxygen. Explain what this information tells him about oxygen.

4. **Skill Builder**
   Interpreting Data Look up the atomic mass of the element boron in the periodic table inside the back cover of this book. The naturally occurring isotopes of boron are boron-10 and boron-11. Which of the two isotopes is more abundant? Explain your reasoning. If you need help, refer to Interpreting Data in the **Skill Handbook** on page 536.

Using Math

An atom of niobium has a mass number of 91. How many neutrons are in the nucleus of the atom?

An isotope of phosphorus has 15 protons and 15 neutrons in the nucleus of each of its atoms. What is the mass number of the isotope?

Elements and the Periodic Table

Materials

- Large index cards
- Merck Index
- Encyclopedia
  * other reference materials
- Large bulletin board
- Paper (8½ × 14)
- Thumbtacks
  * pushpins

  * Alternate Materials

The periodic table organizes the elements. But, what do these elements look like, and what are they used for? In this activity, you'll examine some elements and share your findings with your classmates.

What You'll Investigate

What are some of the characteristics of the chemical elements, and what are they used for?

Goals

- **Classify** the chemical elements.
- **Make** your own periodic table that shows the classification of the elements.

Procedure

1. From the list provided by your teacher, select the number of elements you are assigned.

2. **Design** an index card for each of your selected elements. On each element's card, mark its atomic number in the upper left-hand corner and write its symbol and name in the upper right-hand corner.

3. Research each of the elements and write several sentences on the card about its appearance, its other properties, and its uses.

4. Based upon its properties, **decide** if each of your elements is likely a metal, a metalloid, or a nonmetal. Use the color of magic marker chosen by your teacher to write the appropriate word—*metal, metalloid,* or *nonmetal*—on each of your cards.

5. Work with your classmates to **make** a large periodic table. Use thumbtacks to attach your cards on a bulletin board in their proper positions on the table.

6. Draw your own periodic table on an 8½ × 14 sheet of paper. Put the elements' symbols and atomic numbers in the proper places on the table.

Conclude and Apply

1. **Interpret** the class data and **classify** the elements into the categories: metals, metalloids, and nonmetals. Highlight each of the three categories in a different color on your periodic table.

2. **Predict** the properties of a yet-undiscovered element located directly under francium on the periodic table.

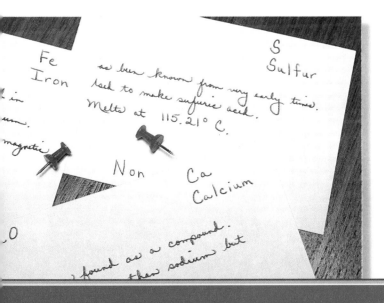

Development of the Periodic Table

Elements such as gold, silver, tin, copper, lead, and mercury have been known since ancient times. As more elements were discovered, people began to recognize patterns in their properties. Later, scientists used the patterns to develop ways of classifying the elements. For example, in 1817, Johann Döbereiner noticed that the atomic mass of strontium was halfway between the masses of calcium and barium, elements with similar chemical properties.

In the Cards

In the mid-nineteenth century, Dmitri Mendeleev published the first periodic table. Mendeleev recognized patterns in the properties and atomic masses of certain elements. In trying to extend the patterns, he created a card for each of the more than 60 elements known at the time. Each card contained the element's symbol, its atomic mass, and its characteristic chemical and physical properties. Mendeleev then arranged the cards on a table in order of increasing atomic mass, grouping elements of similar properties together. The resulting periodic table showed vertical, horizontal, and diagonal relationships. Mendeleev left blank spaces in his table for as-yet-undiscovered elements, and he predicted in detail what the chemical and physical properties of the missing elements would be when they were found.

New Discoveries

With the discovery of the atomic nucleus and isotopes in the early twentieth century, it became apparent that the properties of the elements vary periodically with their atomic numbers. Therefore, modern periodic tables arrange the elements according to atomic number rather than atomic mass. In the mid-1900s, the last major changes to the periodic table resulted from the work of Glenn Seaborg and his coworkers with the discovery of the transuranium elements from atomic number 94 to 102. Locate the element seaborgium on the periodic table. Scientists today continue to discover new elements.

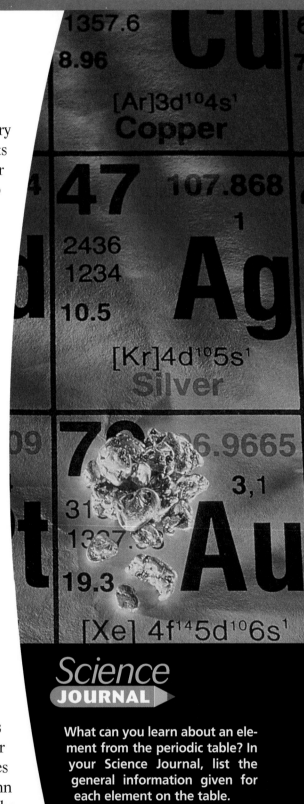

Science JOURNAL

What can you learn about an element from the periodic table? In your Science Journal, list the general information given for each element on the table.

Compounds and Mixtures

Substances

Scientists classify matter in several ways. For example, a sample of matter that has the same composition and properties throughout is called a **substance.** The chemical elements you learned about in Section 2-2 are pure substances. When elements combine with each other, different kinds of matter are formed.

Compounds

What do you call the colorless liquid that flows when you turn on the kitchen faucet? You probably call it water, but maybe you've seen it written H_2O and wondered what that meant. Hydrogen and oxygen occur both naturally as colorless gases, but H_2O tells you that these two elements can combine, as shown in **Figure 2-16,** to form a new, pure substance called a compound. A **compound** is a pure substance whose smallest unit is made up of atoms of more than one element. Millions of compounds can be made from combinations of elements, and the compounds almost always have properties that are different from the elements that make them up. Have you ever used hydrogen peroxide to disinfect a cut? Hydrogen peroxide is another compound made from the elements hydrogen and oxygen.

What You'll Learn

▶ What a compound is
▶ The difference between types of mixtures

Vocabulary
substance
compound
law of definite proportions
mixture

Why It's Important

▶ Compounds and mixtures are part of your everyday life.

Figure 2-16 A space shuttle is powered by the reaction between liquid hydrogen and liquid oxygen. The reaction produces a large amount of energy and a single compound, water. **Why would a car that burns hydrogen rather than gasoline be friendly to the environment?**

Compounds Need Formulas

What's the difference between water and hydrogen peroxide? H_2O is the chemical formula for water, and it tells you more than what elements make up the compound. Look at **Figure 2-17.** Water is made up of two atoms of hydrogen for every one atom of oxygen. H_2O_2 is the formula for hydrogen peroxide. The subscripts, numbers written below and to the right of the elements' symbols, mean that there are two atoms of hydrogen for every two atoms of oxygen in hydrogen peroxide. Carbon dioxide, CO_2, is another common compound. Carbon dioxide is made up of one atom of carbon for every two atoms of oxygen. Carbon and oxygen also can form the compound carbon monoxide, CO, a gas that is poisonous to all warm-blooded animals. As you can see, no subscript is used when one atom is present. The **law of definite proportions** states that a given compound is always made of the same elements in the same proportion by mass. For example, water always has two hydrogen atoms for every oxygen atom. ✔

Reading Check ✔

Propane has three atoms of carbon for every eight atoms of hydrogen. What is propane's chemical formula?

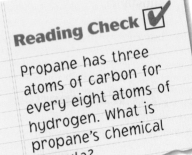

Figure 2-17 The elements hydrogen and oxygen can combine to form two compounds, water and hydrogen peroxide. Although both compounds are made up of the same elements, the ratios of hydrogen and oxygen atoms are different.

A H_2O_2, the formula for hydrogen peroxide, shows that it contains two hydrogen atoms for every two oxygen atoms.

B H_2O, the formula for water, shows that it contains two hydrogen atoms for each oxygen atom. **What is the ratio of hydrogen atoms to carbon atoms in methane, which has the formula CH_4?**

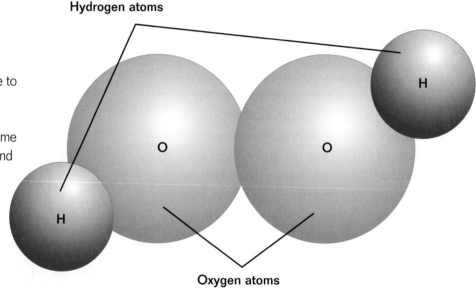

Hydrogen atoms

Oxygen atoms

Mixtures

When two or more substances (elements or compounds) come together but don't combine to make a new, pure substance, a **mixture** results. Unlike compounds, the proportions of the substances in a mixture can be changed. For example, if you put some sand into a bucket of water, you have a mixture of sand and water. If you add more sand or more water, it's still a mixture of sand and water. The makeup of air, a mixture of nitrogen, oxygen, and other gases, can vary somewhat from place to place and time to time. Look around your classroom, home, or neighborhood. What other mixtures do you see? Did you know that your blood is a mixture made up of elements and compounds? It contains white blood cells, red blood cells, water, and a number of dissolved elements. The blood parts can be separated easily and used by different parts of your body.

You can often use a liquid to separate the parts of a mixture of solids. For example, you could add water to a mixture of sugar and sand. Only the sugar would dissolve in the water. The sand could then be separated from the sugar and water by pouring the mixture through a filter. Then, heating would dry off the water, leaving the sugar behind.

Visit the Glencoe Science Web Site at **www. glencoe.com/sec/ science/ca** for more information about mixtures.

LIFE SCIENCE
◄ INTEGRATION

Problem Solving

Drinking Water from Salt Water

Suppose you are on a ship or live in a place that is near an ocean but does not have much freshwater for people to drink.

Can you use change in physical state to create a method for removing salt from ocean water? Distillation is the process of heating a mixture to separate its parts. Parts of the mixture boil at different temperatures. A more nearly pure substance results when the vapor from each part is cooled and condensed.

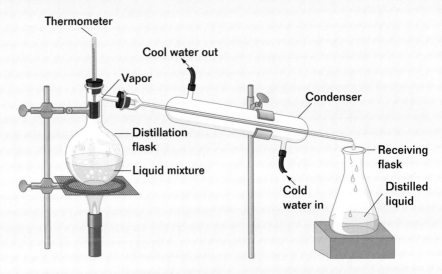

A liquid mixture placed in the flask on the left is heated to boiling. As the vapor passes through the tube in the condenser in the middle, it is surrounded by cold water and condenses to a liquid. The liquid drips into the flask on the right.

Think Critically: Examine the distillation system in the photo. How could you use such a system to produce freshwater from ocean water?

Figure 2-18 Many commom materials are uniform mixtures.

A Sterling silver dinnerware is 92.5 percent silver and 7.5 percent copper.

B The tea in this glass is a uniform mixture that is mostly water. **Is the mixture of ice and tea a uniform mixture?**

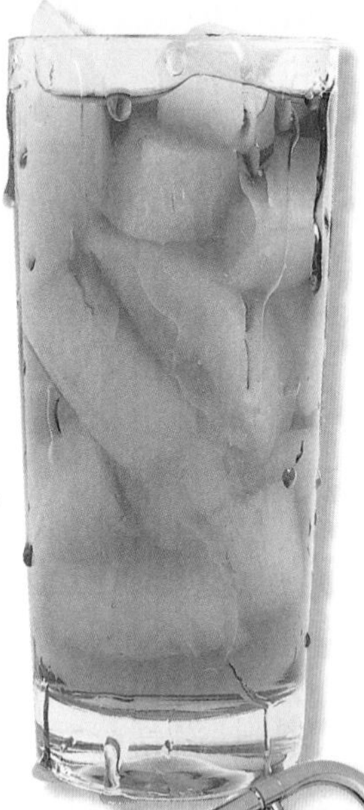

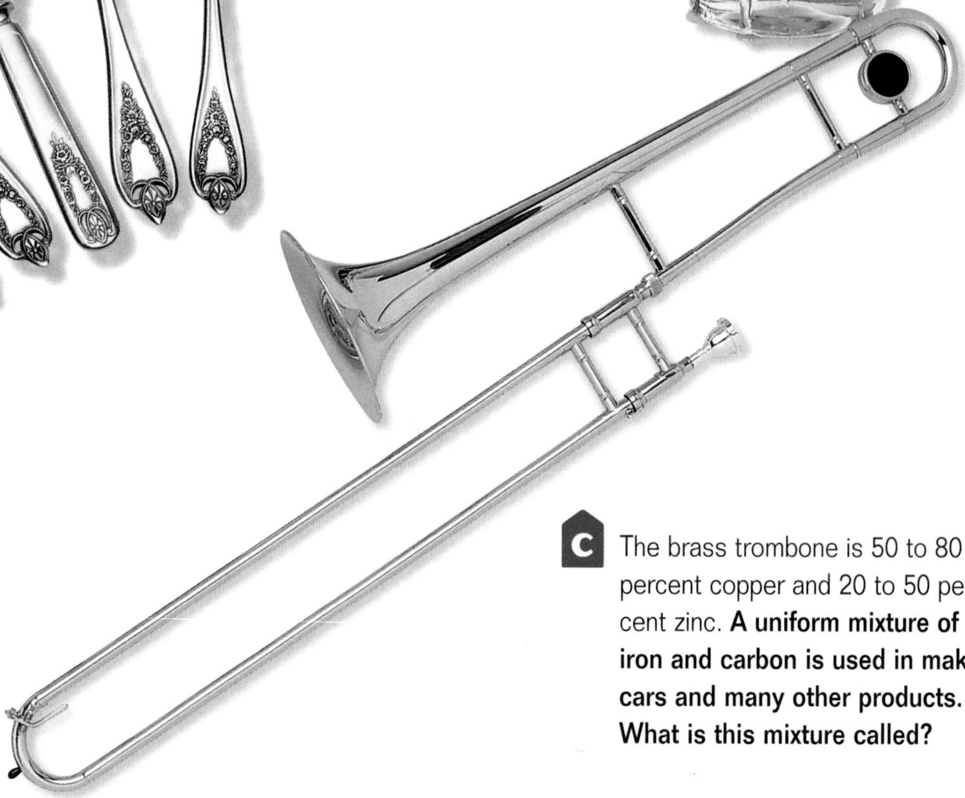

C The brass trombone is 50 to 80 percent copper and 20 to 50 percent zinc. **A uniform mixture of iron and carbon is used in making cars and many other products. What is this mixture called?**

Mixtures can be uniform or nonuniform. Uniform means the same throughout. Several uniform mixtures are shown in **Figure 2-18.** You can't see the different parts in this type of mixture. Air is a uniform mixture of gases. No matter how closely you look, you can't see the individual parts that make up air or the mixture called brass in the trombone shown in **Figure 2-18C.**

In a nonuniform mixture such as sand and water, you can see the different parts. A pepperoni and mushroom pizza is a tasty kind of nonuniform mixture. Other examples of this kind of mixture include tacos, a stew, a toy box full of toys, or your laundry basket at the end of the week. Several nonuniform mixtures are shown in **Figure 2-19.**

Figure 2-19 Nonuniform mixtures are part of your everyday life.

A You can see pieces of solid orange floating in liquid if you look at a glass of orange juice closely.

B Blood is a nonuniform mixture of many materials, including water, proteins, glucose, and fats. Some of these materials can be separated in the laboratory.

C Areas of different color in a rock show that it is made up of crystals of different materials. **A clear fruit drink is made up of many substances. Why is it a uniform mixture?**

Section Assessment

1. List three examples of compounds and three examples of mixtures.

2. The chemical formula for baking soda is $NaHCO_3$. Use the periodic table to write the names of the elements in baking soda. Which element's atoms are most numerous in baking soda?

3. How can you tell that a substance is a compound by looking at its formula?

4. **Think Critically:** Was your breakfast this morning a compound, a uniform mixture, or a nonuniform mixture? Review the definitions for a compound and a uniform mixture. Explain your answer based on these definitions.

5. **Skill Builder**
   Comparing and Contrasting
   Compare and contrast compounds and mixtures. If you need help, refer to Comparing and Contrasting in the **Skill Handbook** on page 532.

Using Computers

Database Use a computerized card catalog to find out about one element from the periodic table. Include information about the mixtures and/or compounds the element is found in. If you need help, refer to page 545.

Mystery Mixture

Materials

- Test tubes (3)
- Cornstarch
- Sugar
- Baking soda
- Mystery mixture
- Small scoops (3)
- Dropper bottles (2)
- Iodine solution
- White vinegar
- Candle
- Test-tube holder
- Small pie pan
- Matches

Cornstarch, baking powder, and powdered sugar are compounds that look alike. To avoid mistaking one for another, you may need to learn how to identify each one. You can learn chemical tests that identify these different compounds. For example, some compounds react with certain liquids to produce gases. Other combinations produce distinctive colors. Some compounds have high melting points. Others have low melting points.

What You'll Investigate

How can the compounds in an unknown mixture be identified by experimentation?

Goals

- **Test** for the presence of certain compounds.
- **Decide** which of these compounds are present in an unknown mixture.

Safety Precautions

Use caution when handling hot objects. Substances could stain or burn clothing. Be sure to point the test tube away from your face and your classmates while heating.

Procedure

1. **Copy** the data table into your Science Journal. **Record** your results for each of the following steps.

2. Place a small scoopful, or the amount indicated by your teacher, of cornstarch on the pie pan. Do the same for sugar and baking soda. Add a drop of vinegar to each. Wash and dry the pan after you have recorded your observations.

3. Place a small scoopful, or the amount indicated by your teacher, of cornstarch, sugar, and baking soda on the pie pan. Add a drop of iodine solution to each.

4. Place a small scoopful, or the amount indicated by your teacher, of each compound in a separate test tube. Hold the test tube with the test-tube holder. Gently heat the bottom of each test tube with the candle.

5. Now, use steps 2 to 4 to **test** your mystery mixture and find out which of these compounds it contains.

Conclude and Apply

1. Use your observations to form a hypothesis as to which compounds are in your mystery mixture. Describe how you arrived at your conclusion.

2. How would you be able to tell if all three compounds were not in your mystery mixture sample?

3. What would you conclude if you tested baking powder from your kitchen and found that it fizzed with vinegar, turned blue with iodine, and did not melt when heated?

Results of Tests			
To be tested	Vinegar fizzes	Iodine turns blue	Compound melts
Cornstarch			
Sugar			
Baking soda			
Mystery mix			

For a **preview** of this chapter, study this Reviewing Main Ideas before you read the chapter. After you have studied this chapter, you can use the Reviewing Main Ideas to **review** the chapter.

 The Glencoe MindJogger, Audiocassettes, and CD-ROM provide additional opportunities for review.

Section

2-1 STRUCTURE OF MATTER

Matter is anything that occupies space and has mass. It includes all the things that you can see, touch, taste, or smell. Matter does not include light, sound, or heat. *Can you think of anything else that is not matter?*

WHAT MAKES UP MATTER?

Matter is made up of atoms. **Atoms** are made of smaller parts called **protons, neutrons, and electrons.** Many models of atoms have been created as scientists try to discover and define the atom's internal structure. *What other models do you know about?*

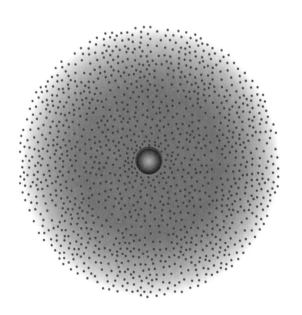

Section
2-2   ELEMENTS

Elements are the basic building blocks of matter. Each element has a unique set of properties and is generally classified as a metal, metalloid, or nonmetal. The chemical symbol for each element is understood by scientists everywhere. An element's **atomic number** tells how many protons its atoms contain, and its **atomic mass** tells how heavy its atoms are. **Isotopes** are two or more atoms of the same element that have different numbers of neutrons. *What element has the symbol Co?*

Chlorine

17

Cl

35.453

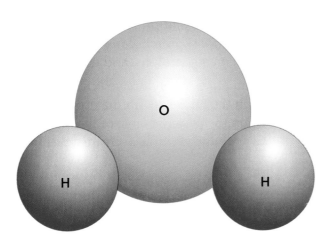

Section
2-3   COMPOUNDS

Compounds are pure substances produced when elements combine. Compounds contain specific proportions of the elements that make them up. A compound's properties are different from those of the elements from which it is formed. *Name five common compounds.*

MIXTURES

Mixtures are combinations of compounds and elements that have not formed new, pure substances. Uniform mixtures contain individual parts that cannot be seen. However, you can see the individual parts of nonuniform mixtures. *What are two mixtures of each type that you know about?*

Chapter 2 Assessment

Using Vocabulary

a. atom
b. atomic mass
c. atomic number
d. compound
e. electron
f. element
g. isotopes
h. law of conservation of matter
i. law of definite proportions
j. mass number
k. matter
l. metals
m. metalloids
n. mixtures
o. neutron
p. nonmetals
q. nucleus
r. proton
s. substance

Using the list above, replace the underlined words with the correct Vocabulary word.

1. The particle in the nucleus of the atom that carries a positive charge is the <u>neutron</u>.

2. The new substance formed when elements join is a <u>mixture</u>.

3. Anything that has mass and takes up space is <u>metal</u>.

4. The particles in the atom that account for most of the mass are protons and <u>electrons</u>.

5. Elements that are shiny, malleable, ductile, and good conductors of heat and electricity are <u>nonmetals</u>.

Checking Concepts

Choose the word or phrase that best answers the question.

6. What is a solution an example of?
   A) element
   B) nonuniform mixture
   C) compound
   D) uniform mixture

7. The nucleus of one atom contains 12 protons and 12 neutrons, while the nucleus of another atom contains 12 protons and 16 neutrons. What are the atoms?
   A) chromium atoms
   B) two different elements
   C) isotopes of magnesium
   D) negatively charged

8. What is a compound?
   A) a mixture of compounds and elements
   B) a combination of two or more elements
   C) anything that has mass and occupies space
   D) the building block of matter

9. What does the atom consist of?
   A) electrons, protons, and alpha particles
   B) neutrons and protons
   C) electrons, protons, and neutrons
   D) elements, protons, and electrons

10. In an atom, where is an electron located?
    A) in the nucleus with the proton
    B) on the periodic table of the elements
    C) with the neutron to create a positive charge
    D) in a cloudlike formation surrounding the nucleus

11. How is matter defined?
    A) the negative charge in an atom
    B) anything that has mass and occupies space
    C) the mass of the nucleus
    D) sound, light, and energy

12. What are two atoms that have the same number of protons?
    A) metals
    B) nonmetals
    C) isotopes
    D) metalloids

13. What are the majority of the elements on the periodic table?
    A) metals
    B) metalloids
    C) nonmetals
    D) compounds

14. Which element is a metalloid?
    A) bromine
    B) silicon
    C) potassium
    D) iron

15. What are nonuniform mixtures?
    A) two kinds of mixtures
    B) the same throughout—the parts cannot be seen
    C) made of several different parts that can be seen
    D) like a soft drink

Thinking Critically

16. A chemical formula is written to indicate the makeup of a compound. What is the ratio of sulfur atoms to oxygen atoms in SO_2?
17. An atom contains seven electrons and seven protons. What element is this atom? Explain your answer.
18. What happens to an element when it becomes part of a compound?
19. Cobalt-60 and cobalt-59 are isotopes. How can they be the same element but have different mass numbers?
20. What did Rutherford's gold foil experiment tell scientists about atomic structure?

Developing Skills

If you need help, refer to the **Skill Handbook.**

21. **Interpreting Scientific Illustrations:** Look at the drawings of the two atoms below. Explain whether or not the atoms are isotopes.

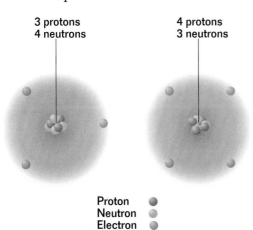

3 protons
4 neutrons

4 protons
3 neutrons

Proton
Neutron
Electron

THE PRINCETON REVIEW

Test-Taking Tip

What Does the Test Expect of Me? Find out what concepts, objectives, or standards are being tested well before the test. Keep these concepts in mind as you solve the questions.

Test Practice

Use these questions to test your Science Proficiency.

1. Which list of terms **BEST** describes the properties of metals?
   A) dull, brittle, nonconducting
   B) malleable, ductile, shiny, good conductors
   C) shiny, brittle, can conduct electricity
   D) gaseous, high density

2. Mixtures are divided into two categories. Which pair of examples **BEST** represents the two types of mixtures?
   A) a pizza and a tossed salad
   B) a baseball card collection and a CD collection
   C) a soft drink and a taco
   D) an iced soft drink and iced tea

3. What particles are found in the nucleus of a carbon-12 atom?
   A) 12 protons
   B) 12 neutrons and 12 protons
   C) 12 neutrons
   D) 6 protons and 6 neutrons

4. Which of these is **NOT** an element?
   A) water
   B) hydrogen
   C) chlorine
   D) oxygen

Chapter Preview

Skills Preview

Skill Builders
- Make and Use a Graph
- Use Numbers

Activities
- Observe and Infer
- Interpret Data

MiniLabs
- Classify
- Compare and Contrast

Reading Check ✓

As you read this chapter about energy, list the cause-and-effect relationships you identify.

Explore Activity

Imagine yourself downhill skiing in the winter. You skillfully change the direction and speed of your skis by changing your body position. A surfboard rider feels the same sense of connection between his body position and the board's motion. So do a cyclist on a bike and a young child on a swing. All are aware of something changing—position, speed, or direction. Energy plays a part in all of these changes. Where else have you seen energy causing change?

Observe Energy

1. Obtain a new, wide rubber band.

2. As you hold the rubber band in both hands, touch it to your lower lip.

3. After moving it away from your face, quickly stretch the rubber band several times.

4. Touch the rubber band to your lip again. What differences do you observe?

5. Obtain additional materials from your teacher to observe more energy changes.

6. Throw away the rubber band after the activity.

Record your observations for each material in your Science Journal. Set up a table to help you compare your results.

Energy Changes

What You'll Learn

► What energy is and the forms it takes

► The difference between potential energy and kinetic energy

Vocabulary
energy
kinetic energy
potential energy
law of conservation of energy

Why It's Important

► The more you know about energy, the more efficiently you will use it.

Energy

Energy is a term you probably use every day. You may say that eating a plate of spaghetti gives you energy or that a gymnast has a lot of energy. But, do you know that a burning fire, a bouncing ball, and a tank of gasoline also have energy? Exactly what is energy?

What is energy?

The ancient Greek word for energy was *energos*, which means "active." Until the 1900s, people thought that energy was stored inside objects. Now we say that **energy** is the ability to cause change. Energy can change the temperature, shape, speed, or direction of an object. Energy can change the shape of modeling clay or the temperature of a cup of water. As you can see in **Figure 3-1,** you can use the energy of your muscles to change the speed of a bicycle by pedaling faster or slower, or by putting on the brakes. The person on a skateboard in **Figure 3-1** uses energy to the change the direction the skateboard takes.

Figure 3-1 The riders of the skateboard and bike use energy to change their speed and direction.

Energy Transformations

If you ask your friends what comes to mind when they think of energy, you will get many different answers. Some may mention the energy in a flame. Others may say energy is needed to run a race. These answers suggest that energy comes in different forms from a variety of sources. Is that true? A flame gives off energy in the form of heat and light. Eating a good breakfast gives your body the energy to move, think, and grow. Your body stores most of its energy in the form of fat. Nuclear power plants use energy from the center of the atom. It seems that energy comes in many forms. What other examples of energy can you think of?

Change Can Cause Change

Push down a bicycle pedal and the gears in the back wheel turn. The chemical energy in your muscles has been changed to mechanical energy. In the natural world, energy often changes from one form to another. Any change of energy from one form to another is called an energy transformation. Energy transformations take place all around you. When a car sits in the sun all day, the energy of light waves changes to a form of energy that warms the inside of the car. The energy in the chemicals used to make the fireworks in **Figure 3-2** changes to light, sound, and motion. In the Explore Activity, the energy you used to stretch and move the rubber band changed into energy that raised the temperature of the band.

During these and other types of energy transformations, the total amount of energy stays the same. No energy is ever lost or gained. Only the form of energy changes.

LIFE SCIENCE
INTEGRATION

Energy in Your Body
You change energy every time you eat. The corn on the cob, tossed salad, and baked potato you eat for dinner contain chemical energy. The energy in those foods originally came from the sunlight that plants trapped in their leaves. Energy contained in food is changed into energy that keeps your body warm and moves your muscles. Your body releases some energy as heat when your muscles contract. Infer why you become warm while running or working hard, even on a cold day.

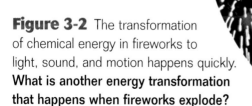

Figure 3-2 The transformation of chemical energy in fireworks to light, sound, and motion happens quickly. **What is another energy transformation that happens when fireworks explode?**

Figure 3-3 Glen Canyon Dam is located on the Colorado River in Arizona. Pipes lead water from the reservoir behind the dam to the hydroelectric generators in the power plant, which is located in front of the dam. The energy of the rushing water spins the generators' turbines, and kinetic energy is transformed into electricity. **What are some benefits of using water as a source of energy?**

Useful Changes

Since the earliest times, humans have experimented with different forms of energy. When early humans learned to make fires, they learned to use the chemical energy in wood to cook, stay warm, and light their way in the dark. Today, electrical energy is changed into thermal energy that warms your home. Also, electrical energy changes to light energy in a lightbulb when you flip on a switch. Chemical energy in fuel changes to the type of energy that runs the engine in the bus you take to school. The water heater in your home transforms energy in natural gas, or in electrical energy, to thermal energy that warms the water for a bath or shower. A hydroelectric plant, as shown in **Figure 3-3,** and a wind power plant transform the energy of moving water and wind into electrical energy.

Kinetic and Potential Energy

You've seen that energy can take many forms, such as light, heat, and motion. Two main types of energy are called kinetic energy and potential energy.

Kinetic Energy

If you were asked if a football thrown downfield has energy, you might say that it does because it is moving. Objects in motion have a type of energy called **kinetic** (kuh NET ihk) **energy.** A football thrown by a quarterback has kinetic energy. A skydiver falling toward Earth also has kinetic energy.

How much kinetic energy does it have?

Not all moving objects have the same amount of kinetic energy. Look at **Figure 3-4.** Which would have more kinetic energy, a train coming down the track or a girl in-line skating? The amount of kinetic energy an object has depends on the mass and speed of the object. If the train and the girl are traveling at the same speed, the train has more kinetic energy than the girl on skates because it has more mass. In this example, even if the train moves slowly and the girl skates as fast as she can, the train still has more kinetic energy because its mass is so much greater than the skater's mass. What would happen if two objects had the same mass? How would the kinetic energies of two trains heading toward the city compare if they had the same mass? The train that is traveling at the higher speed would have more kinetic energy than the slower one.

Figure 3-4 When comparing the kinetic energies of any objects, you must consider both the masses and the speeds of the objects.

A Suppose this train and skater are moving at the same speed. **Which of them has more kinetic energy? Explain.**

B The racehorse and empty luggage cart are about the same mass. The horse is running around the track while the luggage cart is at rest. **Which of them has more kinetic energy? Explain.**

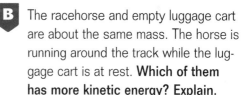

Potential Energy

Suppose the ski lift in **Figure 3-5** takes a skier to the top of a hill and lets her rest there. Do you think the skier still has energy? She does. An object does not have to be moving to have energy. The skier has potential energy. A teacher may say that you have potential—the ability to do more work than you are doing right now. **Potential** (puh TEN chul) **energy** is not energy that comes from motion. It is energy that comes from position or condition. A skier at the top of a hill has potential energy. Even though she is not moving, she has the ability to move.

In general, whenever you raise an object above its original position, you give it the ability to fall. The energy the ski lift uses in taking a skier up a hill is changed. This energy becomes stored as potential energy in the skier. When more energy is used to raise her higher, there is more energy that has been transformed and stored in the skier as potential energy. This idea is similar to pouring water into a bottle and storing it to be used later during a basketball game. You can store potential energy to be used later when you need it. ☑

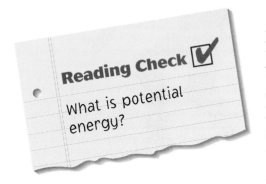

Reading Check ☑

What is potential energy?

Potential Energy and Kinetic Energy Are Related

One of the easiest ways to see the difference between potential and kinetic energy is to work with a pendulum, as in **Figure 3-6**. A pendulum is a weight that swings back and forth from a single point.

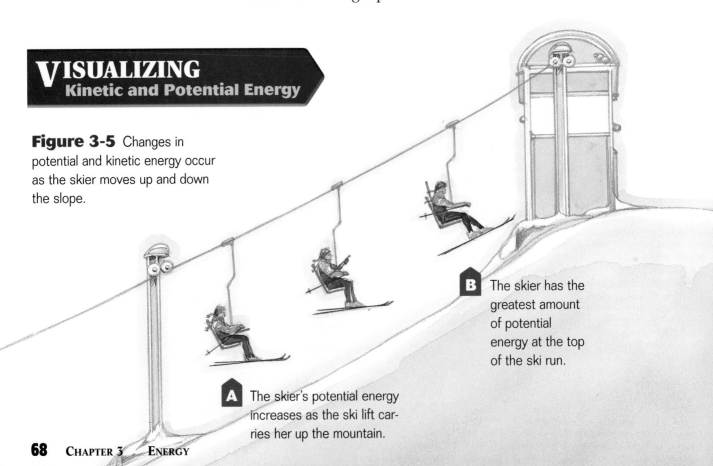

VISUALIZING
Kinetic and Potential Energy

Figure 3-5 Changes in potential and kinetic energy occur as the skier moves up and down the slope.

B The skier has the greatest amount of potential energy at the top of the ski run.

A The skier's potential energy increases as the ski lift carries her up the mountain.

A swing on a backyard swing set is a pendulum. The energy you use to pull back on a swing is changed and stored in the swing as potential energy. Similarly, potential energy can be stored in any pendulum by moving the weighted end to one side. When you let go of a pendulum, any stored potential energy in the pendulum is released. The pendulum swings down in a curved path, called an arc. The instant the pendulum moves, potential energy is transformed into kinetic energy.

There is a direct relationship between the amount of potential energy an object has and the amount of energy that can be transformed into kinetic energy. When a book is placed on a shelf, it has potential energy. That energy becomes kinetic energy if the book falls off the shelf. A book placed on a higher shelf has more potential energy—and more kinetic energy as it falls—than it would have on a lower shelf.

Transfer of Kinetic Energy

Kinetic energy can be transferred from one object to another when those objects collide. Think about the changes and transfer of energy during bowling. Success in bowling depends on the fact that energy can be transferred from one object to another. Even if the bowling ball does not touch all the pins, you can knock them all down with one roll of the ball. A transfer of kinetic energy also takes place when dominoes fall. You only need to give the first domino in the row a bit of kinetic energy by tapping it just enough to make it fall against the next

Figure 3-6 The people on this amusement park ride experience energy changes as the pendulum swings. **At what points would the potential energy be the greatest? The kinetic energy?**

C When the skier begins to ski down the slope, her potential energy starts to transform into kinetic energy.

D As the skier moves further down the mountain, more and more potential energy changes to kinetic energy. She has the least amount of potential energy just before reaching the bottom of the ski run.

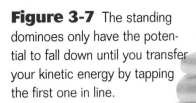

Figure 3-7 The standing dominoes only have the potential to fall down until you transfer your kinetic energy by tapping the first one in line.

Classifying Types of Energy

Procedure

1. Examine the following list of activities.

2. Classify each activity as involving potential or kinetic energy. Hint: Ask yourself if the energy involved is stored (potential), moving (kinetic), or both.

   a. Eat an apple.

   b. Turn on a flashlight.

   c. Push a ball along the floor.

   d. Lift a weight.

   e. Burn a birthday candle.

Analysis

1. Make a table in your Science Journal with two columns.

2. Label the left column "potential" and the right column "kinetic."

3. List the type of activity you examined above in the correct column.

4. Compare your classifications with those of your lab partner.

domino. As the first domino falls into the next one, its kinetic energy is transferred to the second domino. This transfer of kinetic energy continues from domino to domino until the last one falls, as shown in **Figure 3-7.** It is important to know the difference between potential and kinetic energy. It is this difference that sometimes allows you to store energy for later use.

Conserving Energy

Following the trail of energy as it moves from source to source can be a challenge. In 1840, James Joule described the law of conservation of energy. According to the **law of conservation of energy,** energy cannot be created or destroyed. It only can be transformed from one form into another. This means the total amount of energy in the whole universe never changes. The universe doesn't make more energy. Energy doesn't just vanish into thin air either. The only change is the form in which energy may appear. Track the flow of energy in the case of a soccer ball. A soccer player has chemical energy in her muscles from the food she ate. The chemical energy is released as she swings her leg. Her leg now has kinetic energy.

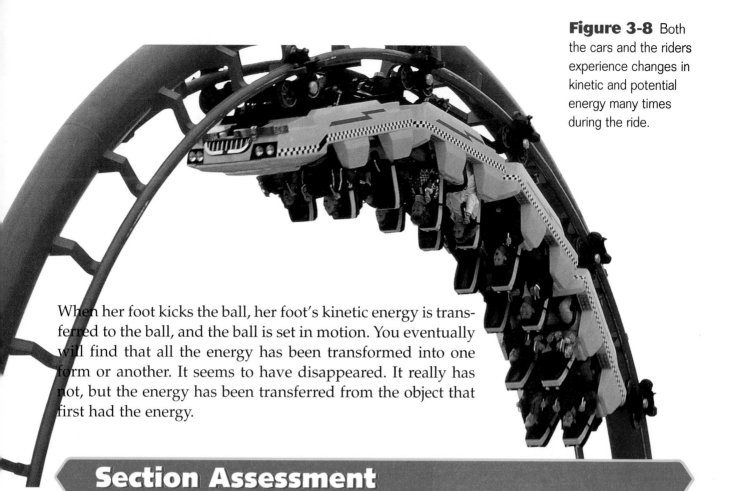

When her foot kicks the ball, her foot's kinetic energy is transferred to the ball, and the ball is set in motion. You eventually will find that all the energy has been transformed into one form or another. It seems to have disappeared. It really has not, but the energy has been transferred from the object that first had the energy.

Section Assessment

1. If you are riding in a roller coaster as in **Figure 3-8,** how do you think your speed is related to your kinetic energy? Your potential energy?

2. As a roller coaster climbs to the top of the steepest hill on its track, when does the first car have the greatest potential energy? When does it have the greatest kinetic energy?

3. State the law of conservation of energy in your own words.

4. **Think Critically:** You get up in the morning, get dressed, eat breakfast, walk to the bus stop, and ride to school. List three different energy transformations that have taken place.

5.  **Skill Builder**
   Making and Using Graphs A pendulum swings seven times per minute. If the string were half as long, the pendulum would swing ten times per minute. If the original length were twice as long, the pendulum would swing five times per minute. Make a bar graph that shows these data. Draw a conclusion from the results. If you need help, refer to Making and Using Graphs in the **Skill Handbook** on page 529.

Science Journal
In your Science Journal, write a short paragraph about what energy transformations took place when last night's dinner was prepared.

Where's the energy?

Did you know that several energy transfers occur during the process of making ice cream? At the beginning of this activity, you will transfer energy to the container of ingredients by rolling it back and forth across the desk. This will help the ingredients mix together. As the ingredients form small crystals, you also will observe another type of energy transfer as you make the ice cream.

What You'll Investigate

What are the various energy transfers that occur during the process of making ice cream?

Materials

- A desk
  table
- Sugar (30 g)
- Whole milk (120 mL)
  half & half (120 mL)
- Small, self-sealing freezer bag (1-quart or less)
- Ice
- Coffee can (large with lid)
- Rock salt (230 g)
- Thermometer
  Alternate Materials

Goals

- **Observe** a transfer of energy.
- **Measure** a temperature change.

Safety Precautions

Do not taste, eat, or drink any materials used in the lab.

Procedure

1. **Put** the milk and sugar into the freezer bag.
2. **Take** the temperature of the mix and record it.
3. **Seal** the bag well and place the freezer bag inside the large coffee can.
4. **Pack** ice around and over the freezer bag.
5. **Pour** rock salt over the ice. Put the lid on the coffee can.
6. **Roll** the can across the desk at least 15 times.
7. **Let** the can stand for 15 minutes.
8. **Check** to see if the ice cream has frozen. If not, repeat steps 6 and 7.
9. **Take** the temperature of the ice cream and record it.

Conclude and Apply

1. What different types of energy can you **conclude** were involved in making the ice cream?
2. **Infer** what type of energy transferred out of the liquid mixture so it could become ice cream. How do you know?

Temperature and Thermal Energy

Temperature

What's today's temperature? If you looked at a thermometer, listened to a weather report on the radio, or saw a weather map on the news similar to the map in **Figure 3-9,** you probably used the air temperature to help you decide what to wear. Some days are so hot you don't need a jacket. Others are so cold you want to bundle up.

Hot and cold are terms that are used in everyday language to indicate temperature. They are not scientific words because they mean different things to different people. A summer day that seems hot to one person may seem just right to another. If you usually live in Florida but go swimming in the ocean off the coast of Maine while on vacation, you might find the water unbearably cold. Have you ever complained that a classroom was too cold when other students insisted that it was too warm?

Temperature Is an Average

What is temperature? Any material or object is made up of particles that are invisible to the naked eye. The particles that make up any object are constantly moving, even if the object appears to be perfectly still. Everything you can think of— your hand, the pencil on your desk, or even the desktop—is made up of moving particles. You learned that moving objects have kinetic energy. Because the particles that make up an object are in constant motion, they have kinetic energy. Faster-moving particles have more kinetic energy.

What You'll Learn

► The differences among temperature, thermal energy, and heat
► Important uses of thermal energy
► How thermal energy moves

Vocabulary
temperature
thermal energy
heat
radiation
conduction
convection

Why It's Important

► The transfer of thermal energy is involved in warming Earth, producing weather, cooking your food, and warming and cooling your home.

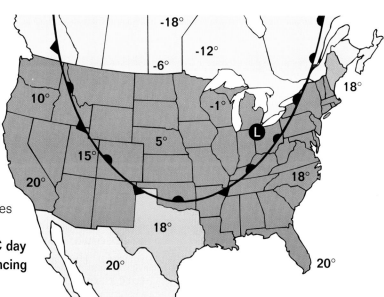

Figure 3-9 Each person senses temperature differently. **Would a person in Texas describe an 18°C day differently from a person experiencing an 18°C day in Maine? Why?**

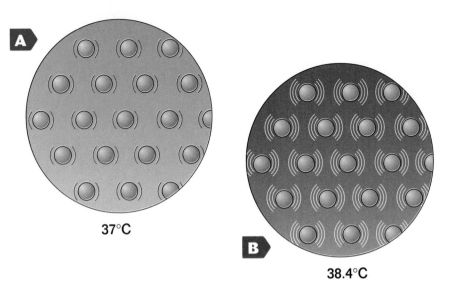

Figure 3-10 The temperature of the particles in B is higher than the temperature of the particles in A. **How does the motion of the particles differ in A and B? Why?**

37°C

38.4°C

If you could measure the kinetic energy of each particle in an object and average them, you would find the average kinetic energy of the particles. **Temperature** is a measure of the average kinetic energy of the particles in any object. The greater the average kinetic energy is, the higher an object's temperature is. For example, **Figure 3-10** shows particles at the normal human body temperature of 37°C. If a person has a body temperature of 38.4°C, the particles in the person's body have more kinetic energy than usual.

Temperature Scales

Because everyone experiences temperature differently, you cannot accurately measure temperature by how it feels to you. Recall that temperature is the average kinetic energy of all the particles. But, there is no easy method to measure the kinetic energy of each particle and then calculate an average. That is because the particles are extremely small. Even scientists using sensitive instruments have a difficult time observing them. Different temperature scales are used to measure the average kinetic energy of particles. These scales divide changes in kinetic energy of the particles into regular intervals. That is, the units are spaced apart evenly.

One scale you may use is the Fahrenheit (FAYR un hit) scale. On the Fahrenheit scale, water freezes at 32°F and boils at 212°F. A second temperature scale you will use in science class is the Celsius (SEL see us) scale. On the Celsius temperature scale, the freezing point of water is 0°C and water's boiling point is 100°C. Scientists often use the Kelvin, or absolute, temperature scale. It has this name because 0 K is the absolute lowest temperature an object can have. One can visualize that all particle motion stops at 0 K. As the temperature rises above 0 K, the particles begin to move with greater kinetic energy.

Thermal Energy

Hot soup will warm you because it has a large amount of thermal energy. **Thermal energy** is the total kinetic energy of the particles in a material. Because temperature is a measure of the average kinetic energy of an object's particles, it is also a measure of thermal energy. The amount of thermal energy in a bowl of soup is determined by the amount of soup in the bowl and the total amount of energy in the particles that make it up. Thermal energy flows from a warmer object to a cooler one. Thermal energy in the bowl of soup will transfer to your body and you will become warmer. ☑

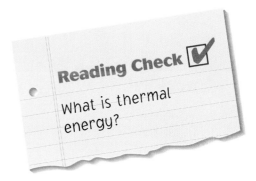

Reading Check ☑
what is thermal energy?

Heat and Thermal Energy

Thermal energy is what you may have been calling heat. It is important to note that heat and thermal energy are not the same. Look at **Figure 3-11.** Suppose you pick up a tall glass of iced tea. If you hold the glass for a long time, the drink warms up. Thermal energy from your hand transfers to the drink. A transfer of thermal energy from one object to another because of a difference in temperature is **heat.** Heat flows from warmer objects to cooler ones. Heat flows out of your hand and into the glass of iced tea. The thermal energy of the drink increases so it's temperature increases.

Heat also flows from warmer to cooler objects in a refrigerator. Your food is kept cold because thermal energy of the food is decreased by the flow of heat to the cold air inside the refrigerator. Refrigerators are designed to remove heat from the space inside where the food is stored.

How much heat?

When the same amount of heat is transferred to different materials, those materials may not experience the same increase in temperature. This difference is based on the chemical makeup and the amount of the material.

For example, water must absorb a large amount of heat before its temperature rises one degree. That is why water often is used as a coolant. The water in a car's radiator carries thermal energy away from the engine. How does the temperature of the water in a swimming pool compare to the air on a hot summer day? How do they compare at night when the air has cooled? The water is slower than its surroundings to change temperature. It takes longer for a large body of water to warm up or cool down

Figure 3-11 Heat flows from your hand to the glass of iced tea, making your hand feel cold. **Why do people wear gloves in cold weather?**

than it takes an equally large area of land or the surrounding air. As a result, air temperatures near a large lake or ocean remain fairly moderate year-round.

How do you feel heat?

Think about getting into a car that has been closed up on a sunny day. Do you prefer a car that has fabric-covered or vinyl-covered seats? Even though the masses of the seats are similar and the temperatures of the surroundings are the same, the vinyl material feels hotter on your skin than the fabric does. Your sense of touch responds to heat not to the actual temperature. Heat flows to your skin more easily from the vinyl than from the fabric. The greater the heat flow, the hotter the object feels to your skin. ☑

Reading Check ☑

Why do some materials feel hotter on your skin than others?

Transfer of Thermal Energy

A transfer of thermal energy into a material may cause a rise in the temperature of the material. The amount of thermal energy absorbed depends on the type of material. It also depends on the amount of material. The greater the amount of material there is, the more thermal energy it absorbs before its temperature rise can be measured. Suppose you transferred enough thermal energy to cause a small pot of water to boil. If you put the same amount of energy into a bathtub full of water, the temperature rise would be small, as shown in **Figure 3-12.** The heat absorbed must be shared by more particles of water in the bathtub. The average increase of thermal energy in each particle is quite small.

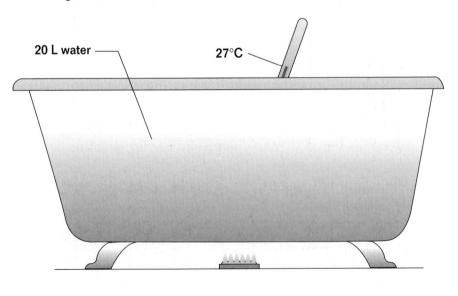

Figure 3-12 Applying an equal amount of thermal energy to the pan of water and the bathtub of water would not increase the water temperature the same number of degrees.

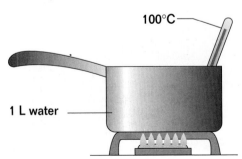

Figure 3-13

A microwave oven uses microwave radiation to transfer thermal energy to a food item. Microwaves increase the motion of the particles of water in the food. As the particles move faster, the food becomes warmer and cooks.

Thermal Energy on the Move

An overall transfer of energy occurs if there is a temperature difference between two areas or objects. Heat flows from warm places to cooler ones. Remember that temperature is a measure of thermal energy in an object. Heat flows from an area having greater thermal energy to an area that has less thermal energy. Thermal energy is transferred three ways: radiation, conduction, and convection. Conduction and convection transfer thermal energy through solids, liquids, or gases. Radiation however transfers thermal energy when little or no matter is present.

Radiation

Radiation is energy that travels by waves in all directions from its source. These waves may be visible light waves or types of energy waves that you cannot see. When these strike an object, their energy can be absorbed and the object's temperature rises. Radiation can travel through air and even through space where there is almost no material. The sun transfers energy to Earth through radiation. If you are out walking on a cool but sunny day, bend down to touch the sidewalk that is exposed to the sunlight. Perhaps you will notice that it feels warm. The pavement absorbs energy transferred from the sun by radiation. You take advantage of radiation when you warm yourself by a fire. The fire transfers its thermal energy to you. You become warmer. You also can use radiation to cook food. The microwave oven in your kitchen, such as the one shown in **Figure 3-13,** cooks food because of a transfer of energy by radiation.

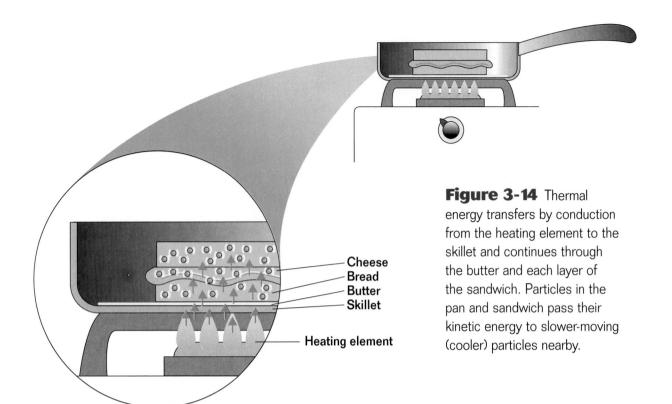

Figure 3-14 Thermal energy transfers by conduction from the heating element to the skillet and continues through the butter and each layer of the sandwich. Particles in the pan and sandwich pass their kinetic energy to slower-moving (cooler) particles nearby.

Cheese
Bread
Butter
Skillet

Heating element

Conduction

Have you ever picked up a silver spoon that was in a pot of boiling water and discovered that the spoon was now hotter than it was when you placed it there? Yeow! Quick! Where is the pot holder? The spoon handle became hot because of conduction. **Conduction** is the transfer of thermal energy from particle to particle through a material when there is a temperature difference. Conduction occurs because of the exchange of kinetic energy between the particles in a material, much the same way kinetic energy is transferred from a bowling ball to the pins. In the example of the spoon, kinetic energy continues to be transferred from the hotter end of the spoon to the cooler end because of the temperature difference.

Look at **Figure 3-14.** When you put a pan on the stove to make a grilled-cheese sandwich, the thermal energy from the stove transfers to the pan, making the particles within the pan move faster. Some of these particles bump into the particles in the bread and butter that are on the surface of the pan. Energy is transferred to the sandwich. This transferred energy causes the bread to toast and the cheese to melt. Even though conduction is a transfer of kinetic energy from particle to particle, the particles involved don't travel from one place to another. They simply move in place, bumping into each other and transferring energy from faster-moving particles to slower-moving ones. ✔

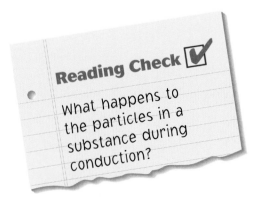

Reading Check ✔

What happens to the particles in a substance during conduction?

Conductors

Sometimes you want thermal energy to transfer rapidly, for example, as when you thaw frozen food. You could put a frozen hamburger on a metal tray to speed up the thawing process. Materials through which it is easy to transfer thermal energy are conductors. Most metals are good conductors of thermal energy. Metals such as gold, silver, and copper are superior conductors. That is why the silver spoon became so hot in the boiling water. Copper is widely available and less expensive than gold or silver. Copper can be attached to another metal, such as steel, to make a cooking pan. Many steel cooking pans have copper bottoms. A copper bottom conducts thermal energy more evenly. It helps spread heat across the bottom surface of the pan to prevent hot spots from forming. This allows food to cook evenly. ☑

Reading Check ☑
What materials make good conductors?

Insulators

Materials that don't allow thermal energy to be conducted easily are insulators. You usually want your pizza to stay warm, so the best pizza places deliver it in an insulated box, as shown in **Figure 3-15.** The material used is one that will not transfer thermal energy. If you put a plastic spoon in boiling water, it's easy to hold it for a long time without burning your fingers because plastic transfers thermal energy poorly. Many cooking pans have plastic handles that won't melt instead of metal ones. These handles remain at a comfortable temperature while the pans are used for cooking. Other examples of insulators include wood and rubber. Ceramic tiles or several layers of cloth often are used as insulators.

Using Math

The yearly copper production average is 8 million metric tons. Most copper ores contain less than two percent copper. How many metric tons of copper ore are mined each year?

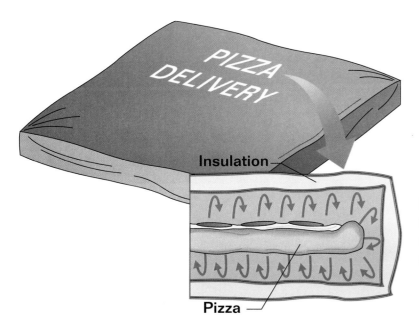

Figure 3-15 The material inside an insulated pizza carrier keeps the thermal energy from transferring out of the box and the carrier so your pizza stays warm.

Comparing Energy Content

Procedure

1. Pour equal amounts of hot, cold, and room-temperature water into each of three transparent, labeled containers.
2. Measure and record the temperature of the water in each container.
3. Use a dropper to gently put a drop of food coloring in the center of each container.
4. After two minutes, observe each container.

Analysis

1. How are kinetic energy and temperature related?
2. In which container do the water particles have the most kinetic energy?
3. Based on the speed at which the food coloring spreads through the water, rank the containers from fastest to slowest. What can you infer about how water temperature affected the movement of the food coloring?

They protect a table surface from the hot bottoms of pans because these materials do not transfer thermal energy easily.

Convection

Some energy transfers involve particles that do not stay in place but move from one place to another. **Convection** transfers thermal energy when particles move from one place to another where there is a difference in temperature. This is most common in gases and liquids. Cool air sinks because it is more dense than warm air. Your home is heated by using the idea of convection. Look at **Figure 3-16.** Air is warmed in the furnace. The warm, less-dense air is then forced up through the air duct by the furnace's fan. The warm air circulates and rises through the room. As the air cools, it becomes more dense. The cool air sinks toward the floor, and it is then pulled through the air duct by the furnace's fan to be warmed again and recirculated. In the case of water, the warmer, less-dense water is forced up as the cooler, more-dense water sinks. Have you ever seen noodles cooking? The noodles are carried upward and downward as the hot water moves to the top, cools at the surface,

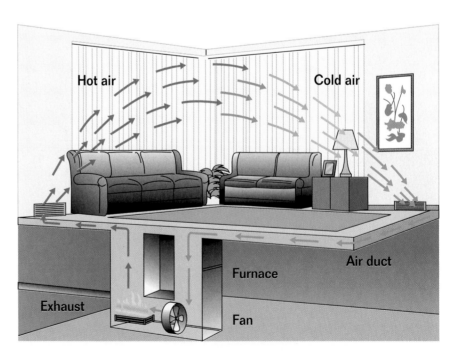

Figure 3-16 The furnace's fan helps circulate thermal energy through your home. Warmer air particles move upward while cooler air particles move downward.

and then sinks. Convection causes warm and cool currents in the atmosphere, which produce Earth's weather.

The effects of warm and cool air currents are especially important to understanding how hurricanes and tornadoes form. Convection currents also are formed in oceans by cold water flowing from the poles and warm water flowing from tropical regions.

Have you ever seen an eagle or a hawk coasting high in the air? Look at the seagull in **Figure 3-17.** A bird can stay in the air without flapping its wings because it is held up by a thermal. A thermal is a column of warm air that is forced up as cold air around it sinks. It is a convection current in the air. A thermal is the same type of current used by people who are hang gliding. It helps keep them in the air as long as possible. You can see that thermal energy and its transfer affect you daily. How many uses of thermal energy can you see around you right now?

Figure 3-17 Moving air caused by convection helps lift this seagull so it does not need to flap its wings constantly.

Section Assessment

1. How is thermal energy transferred? List three ways and give an example for each from nature.

2. Popcorn can be cooked in a hot-air popper, in a microwave oven, or in a pan on the stove. Identify each method as convection, conduction, or radiation.

3. What condition must exist for transfer of thermal energy to occur?

4. **Think Critically:** How are temperature, thermal energy, and heat different?

5. 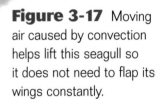 **Skill Builder**
   Using Numbers When selecting an energy source for heating a home, consumers try to think about cost. Do the **Chapter 3 Skill Activity** on page 556 and use proportions to determine the area of the solar collector needed to heat a home.

Using Math

To change a temperature from the Fahrenheit scale to the Celsius scale, you subtract 32 from the Fahrenheit temperature and multiply the difference by 5/9. If the temperature is 77°F, what is the Celsius temperature?

Materials

- Thermometers (−10°C to 110°C) (4)
- Self-sealing freezer bags (2)
- Water (100 mL)
- Ice cubes (2 to 3)
- Pancake syrup (100 mL)
  *corn syrup
- Beakers (4 large)
  *heat-safe glass containers
- Spoon
  *stirring rod
  *Alternate Materials

Can you observe a temperature change?

Different substances absorb thermal energy differently. You will heat two different materials. Then, by comparing the temperature of each material, you will infer which substance can absorb the most thermal energy before rising in temperature.

What You'll Investigate

Which material can absorb more thermal energy?

Goals

- **Measure** a temperature change.
- **Infer** a material's ability to absorb thermal energy.

Safety Precautions

- Use care when handling the heated bags and hot water.
- Do not taste, eat, or drink any materials used in the lab.

Procedure

1. **Design** two data tables in which to record your data of the temperature measurements of the hot- and cold-water beakers. Use the sample table to help you.

2. **Pour** 200 mL of hot tap water (about 90°C) into each of two large beakers.

3. **Pour** 200 mL of cool, tap water into each of two large beakers. Add two or three ice cubes and stir until the ice melts.

4. **Pour** 100 mL of room-temperature water into one bag and 100 mL of syrup into the other bag. Tightly seal both bags.

5. **Record** the starting water temperature of each hot beaker.

Place each bag into its own beaker of hot water.

6. **Record** the water temperature in each of the hot-water beakers every two minutes until the temperature does not change.

7. **Record** the starting water temperature of each cold beaker. If any ice cubes remain, **remove** them from the cold water.

8. Carefully **remove** the bags from the hot water and **put** each into its own beaker of cold water.

9. **Record** the water temperature in each of the cold-water beakers every two minutes until there is no change in temperature.

Water Temperatures—Hot Beaker			
Water–filled bag		**Syrup–filled bag**	
Time (min)	**Temperature (°C)**	**Time (min)**	**Temperature (°C)**
0		0	
2		2	
4		4	
6		6	
8		8	

Conclude and Apply

1. **Look** at your data. Which beaker of hot water reached a lower temperature—the beaker with the water-filled or syrup-filled bag?

2. In which beaker of cold water did you observe the greater temperature change after adding the bags?

3. Which material absorbed more heat? Which released more heat?

4. **Infer** which material conducts thermal energy better. Would either material make a good insulator? Explain.

3·3 Chemical Energy

What You'll Learn

► Where chemical energy is found

► How reaction rates are changed

Vocabulary
chemical energy

Why It's Important

► Chemical energy makes it possible for your body to move, grow, and stay warm.

Observing Chemical Energy

At dusk on a hot summer day, you may have seen fireflies glowing. Did you ever wonder how they make their eerie light? If you have seen light sticks at Halloween that glow for a short period of time, you have observed the same principle as behind the fireflies' glow. Energy in the form of light is released when a chemical reaction takes place inside the light stick. A campfire or a fire in an outdoor grill, such as the one in **Figure 3-18,** releases thermal energy and light energy because of a chemical reaction taking place. Whether or not you realize it, you experience and observe chemical energy in many reactions every day.

What is a chemical reaction?

In a chemical reaction, substances are either made or broken down. When particles of substances combine, bonds form between them. These bonds hold the particles together and a new product is formed. When a substance is broken down, the bonds between the particles are broken. This causes the particles to split apart.

Figure 3-18 The chemical energy stored in these charcoal briquettes is released and transformed into thermal energy and light energy.

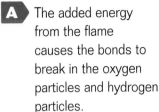

VISUALIZING
Chemical Reactions

Figure 3-19 The oxygen and hydrogen gases will not react unless energy is added.

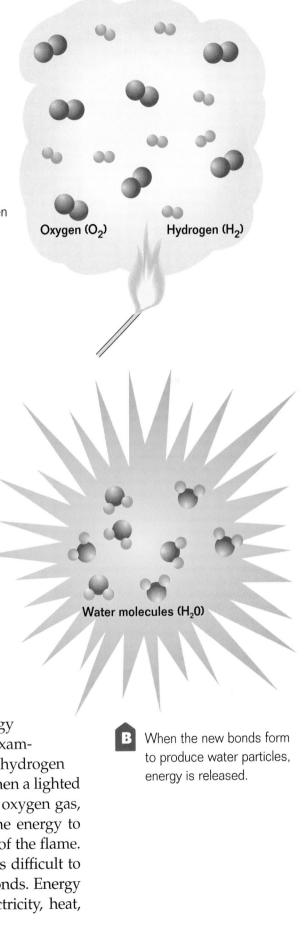

A The added energy from the flame causes the bonds to break in the oxygen particles and hydrogen particles.

Oxygen (O₂)   Hydrogen (H₂)

Energy is stored in the bonds between particles in a substance. This stored (potential) energy within chemical bonds is called **chemical energy.** The potential energy stored in oil, gas, and coal is an important source of chemical energy. Food provides a source of chemical energy for our bodies. The muscles in our bodies transform some of this chemical energy into mechanical energy when they move. A weight lifter stores chemical energy in muscles in order to be able to lift heavier weights. Can you think of other examples of chemical reactions you participated in today?

Energy in Reactions

Changes in energy are a part of every chemical reaction. To break bonds, energy must be added. The reverse is also true. When bonds form, energy is released. Most reactions do not take place on their own. In some reactions, energy must be added before the reaction can begin. For example, energy is needed to start the reaction between hydrogen and oxygen to form water. Look at **Figure 3-19.** When a lighted match is placed in a mixture of hydrogen gas and oxygen gas, the mixture will explode and water will form. The energy to begin the reaction comes from the thermal energy of the flame. Once particles are bound together, as in water, it is difficult to split them apart. It requires energy to break the bonds. Energy to break chemical bonds can be supplied by electricity, heat, light, or motion, depending on the reaction.

Water molecules (H₂0)

B When the new bonds form to produce water particles, energy is released.

Figure 3-20 Many processes take place in the preparation of food. The ingredients in moist, soft cookie dough use energy to change and become crispy, airy cookies.

Energy-Absorbing Reactions

Some chemical reactions need energy to keep going. A reaction that absorbs energy is called an endothermic (en duh THUR mihk) reaction. Endothermic chemical reactions take place in the preparation of food as shown in **Figure 3-20.** Thermal energy is absorbed by the food as it cooks. For example, an endothermic reaction takes place in some kinds of cookie dough. The baking soda absorbs energy and produces a gas that puffs up the cookies.

A process in nature that absorbs a lot of energy is photosynthesis. During photosynthesis, some cells in the leaves of green plants transform the energy from sunlight into chemical energy in the form of sugar. Once the plant is deprived of sunlight, the reaction stops. Photosynthesis is probably the most important endothermic process on Earth. Because of photosynthesis, plants provide us, and almost all other living things, with food and oxygen.

Problem Solving

Chemical Energy in Action

Lashawna twisted her ankle at track practice. To help ease the pain until she could have it checked, her coach suggested that she soak her ankle in a solution of Epsom salts.

Lashawna filled a small tub with lukewarm water. She then added half a box of Epsom salts to the water. As she was stirring the solution with her hand, the water became cool.

Lashawna didn't understand why the temperature of the water changed. Was she imagining things? How can you explain why the water became cold?

Think Critically: What kind of process takes place in the solution of Epsom salts, endothermic or exothermic? Explain.

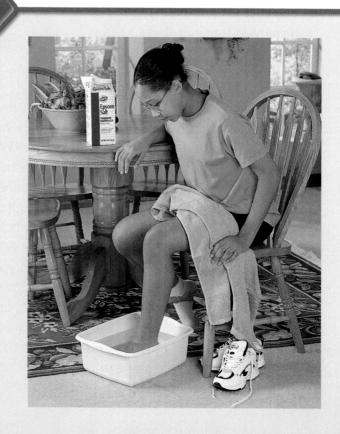

Figure 3-21 Demolition experts use the energy released by the reaction that causes the dynamite explosion to destroy this building in Hartford, Connecticut.

Energy-Releasing Reactions

Some chemical reactions are important because of their products. Other reactions are important because of the energy that is released. Exothermic (ek soh THUR mihk) reactions are reactions that give off energy. If you have used a chemical hand warmer on a cold day, then you felt the thermal energy released by the exothermic reaction taking place inside the hand warmer. The energy released from a dynamite explosion will demolish an old building as in **Figure 3-21.** Charcoal briquettes release a lot of energy as they react with oxygen, causing them to burn at a high temperature. Combustion, the burning of material in the presence of oxygen, is a familiar exothermic reaction. What other exothermic reactions can you think of?

Rate of Reaction

The rate of a chemical reaction can be sped up or slowed down by changing the temperature, stirring the mixture, or adding a catalyst. For example, will a spoonful of sugar dissolve faster in a glass of iced tea or in a cup of hot tea? If you have ever watched closely, you might have noticed that sugar dissolves faster in the hot tea. Dissolving sugar is a process that can be sped up by increasing the temperature.

What if you added sugar to your iced tea only to watch it sink and sit at the bottom of the glass? How would you get the sugar to dissolve? You would probably stir the iced tea to make the sugar dissolve faster. Even though the sugar dissolves on its own at the bottom of the glass, stirring it makes the dissolving process go more quickly.

A catalyst is a substance that changes the rate of a chemical reaction without any change to its own structure. Many cell processes in your body are sped up by the presence of catalysts. Catalysts in your body are substances called enzymes.

LIFESCIENCE
◀ INTEGRATION

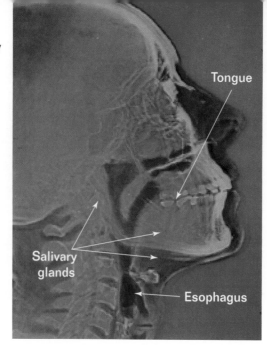

Figure 3-22 Salivary glands release saliva as you chew. The enzyme in saliva speeds up the chemical reaction that breaks down food as it travels to the stomach.

Tongue

Salivary glands

Esophagus

interNET
CONNECTION

Visit the Glencoe Science Web Site at **www. glencoe.com/sec/ science/ca** for more information about enzymes.

For example, when you chew a piece of bread, glands in your mouth, as shown in **Figure 3-22,** produce saliva that contains an enzyme. The enzyme in saliva acts as a catalyst to help break down starches more quickly into smaller molecules.

Many other chemical reactions depend on catalysts to help them work better. For example, the production of vegetable shortening, synthetic rubber, and high-octane gasoline are all chemical processes that succeed with the help of catalysts.

Section Assessment

1. Where is chemical energy found?
2. What happens to bonds when new products are made?
3. Name three ways to speed up a reaction.
4. **Think Critically:** How are exothermic and endothermic reactions different? How are they similar?

5. **Skill Builder**
   Classifying Divide the following list of reactions into two groups by classifying each reaction as endothermic or exothermic: burning wood, striking a match to light it, baking bread, and exploding dynamite. Explain why you placed each reaction into one group. If you need help, refer to Classifying in the **Skill Handbook** on page 525.

Using Computers

Word Processing Write one sentence that states, in your own words, the main idea of each major paragraph in this section about chemical energy. Use a word processor to type your summary of these important concepts. If you need help, refer to page 544.

Hot-Vent Inhabitants

Some Like It Hot

Deep below the ocean surface, where no sunlight can reach, Earth's crust moves apart and forms cracks in the seafloor called hydrothermal vents. Superheated, mineral-rich fluid as hot as 350°C flows out of the vents. In spite of the extreme temperatures, more than 300 species of organisms live in and around hydrothermal vents. Fish and giant tube worms (seen at left), giant clams, mussels, crabs, shrimp, microorganisms such as bacteria, and other life-forms live in this harsh, deep-ocean environment.

Extreme Environments

Microorganisms that live at these high temperatures are called thermophiles. Thermophiles living around hydrothermal vents have remarkable adaptations for surviving in such an environment. For example, some of these microorganisms use sulfur-containing compounds—rather than sunlight—as an energy source. Scientists once thought that life could not exist under extreme environmental conditions. Because life was discovered around hydrothermal vents, however, scientists theorize that microorganisms similar to those in hot-vent communities exist in other places long thought to be lifeless.

Europa, Jupiter's fourth-largest moon, is one place scientists are looking for signs of life. Although Europa's surface is solid ice, there may be a warm layer of liquid water underneath. If water and a geothermal energy source exist on Europa, life-forms also might be there and would give clues to early life-forms on Earth.

Future Uses

Research has shown that thermophilic bacteria have unique enzymes that help them survive brutal heat. Unlike more common enzymes, those of thermophiles do not stop functioning when exposed to high temperatures. Such enzymes may be useful in medicine and industry. For instance, medical researchers are investigating the use of these enzymes as anticancer and anti-AIDS agents.

interNET CONNECTION

Visit the Glencoe Science Web Site at **www.glencoe.com/sec/science/ca** to find more information about deep-sea vents.

For a **preview** of this chapter, study this Reviewing Main Ideas before you read the chapter. After you have studied this chapter, you can use the Reviewing Main Ideas to **review** the chapter.

The Glencoe MindJogger, Audiocassettes, and CD-ROM provide additional opportunities for review.

Section 3-1 ENERGY CHANGES

Energy has the ability to cause change. It can change the temperature, shape, speed, or direction of an object. Some common types of energy forms are mechanical, chemical, thermal, light, nuclear, and electrical. *What are some examples of how energy changes form?*

KINETIC AND POTENTIAL ENERGY

Moving objects have **kinetic energy.** An object's mass and speed affect how much kinetic energy it has. Objects at rest can have stored energy in the form of **potential energy.** This energy comes from an object's position or condition—not from motion. *How are potential and kinetic energy related?*

CONSERVING ENERGY

Kinetic energy, as well as other forms of energy, can be transferred from one object to another. When energy is transferred or changes form, the total amount of energy stays the same. Energy cannot be created or destroyed. *After the last domino in the row falls, what happens to all the kinetic energy from the first domino?*

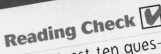

Reading Check ☑️

List at least ten questions that a child might ask about energy and the changes it causes. Choose questions that are answered in the chapter.

^{Section}
3-2   TEMPERATURE

Temperature measures the average kinetic energy of the particles in a material. Particles having more kinetic energy have higher temperatures than particles with less kinetic energy. The Fahrenheit, Celsius, and Kelvin scales are used to measure temperature. *Which would have more kinetic energy—the particles in an ice cube or a glass of water?*

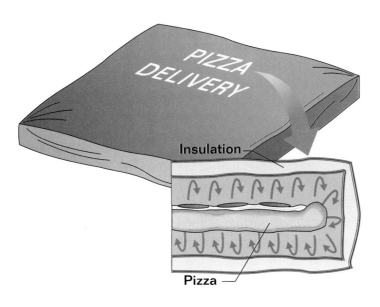

Insulation

Pizza

THERMAL ENERGY

Thermal energy is the total amount of kinetic energy of the particles in a material. The movement of thermal energy from a warmer object to a cooler one is called **heat.** The ability to absorb heat depends on the type of material and its quantity. Thermal energy moving by **radiation** travels by waves in all directions.

Conduction is the transfer of kinetic energy from particle to particle as they bump into each other.

Convection transfers energy by the movement of particles from one place to another. *What kind of energy transfer is involved in cooking a meal in a pan on the stove?*

^{Section}
3-3   CHEMICAL ENERGY

The energy stored in chemical bonds is **chemical energy.** The energy stored in food and oil is an important source of chemical energy. Chemical reactions that release energy are exothermic reactions. Reactions that absorb energy are endothermic reactions. Raising the temperature, stirring, and adding catalysts can speed up chemical reactions. Reactions taking place in your body every day use enzymes as catalysts. Catalysts are used in making a number of commercial products. *How do catalysts affect chemical reactions?*

Chapter 3 Assessment

Using Vocabulary

a. chemical energy
b. conduction
c. convection
d. energy
e. heat
f. kinetic energy
g. law of conservation of energy
h. potential energy
i. radiation
j. temperature
k. thermal energy

Each of the following sentences is false. Make the sentence true by replacing the italicized word with a word from the above list.

1. Transfer of energy by direct contact is *radiation.*
2. Energy of motion is *potential energy.*
3. The movement of thermal energy from warm to cool objects is *temperature.*
4. A measure of the average kinetic energy of the molecules in a substance is called *heat.*
5. *Kinetic energy* is energy that is stored.

Checking Concepts

Choose the word or phrase that best answers each question.

6. Which of the following correctly describes energy?
   A) It can be created.
   B) It can be destroyed.
   C) It cannot change form.
   D) It can cause change.

7. What does a thermometer measure?
   A) heat
   B) total energy
   C) average kinetic energy
   D) chemical energy

8. What happens if two objects at different temperatures are touching?
   A) Thermal energy transfers from the warmer object.
   B) Thermal energy transfers from the cooler object.
   C) Thermal energy transfers to the warmer object.
   D) No thermal energy transfer takes place.

9. During an energy transfer, what happens to the total amount of energy?
   A) It increases.
   B) It decreases.
   C) It stays the same.
   D) It depends on the energy form being transferred.

10. How does the sun's energy reach us?
    A) conduction   C) radiation
    B) convection   D) insulation

11. When would you have the most potential energy?
    A) walking up the hill
    B) sitting at the top of the hill
    C) running up the hill
    D) sitting at the bottom of the hill

12. Which is **NOT** the name of a temperature scale?
    A) Joule   C) Celsius
    B) Kelvin   D) Fahrenheit

13. What is the name given to any material that transfers thermal energy easily?
    A) thermal   C) metal
    B) insulator   D) conductor

14. What also will increase as the speed of an object increases?
    A) kinetic energy   C) weight
    B) mass   D) potential energy

15. What type of energy transfer produces weather?
    A) radiation   C) convection
    B) conduction   D) atmospheric

Thinking Critically

16. Much discussion has focused on the need to drive more efficient cars and use less electricity. If the law of conservation of energy is true, why are people concerned about energy usage?

17. If heat flows in only one direction, how can both hot and cold liquids reach room temperature as they sit on a table?

18. Think about what happens to Jack and Jill in the nursery rhyme. What kinds of energy are used? How was each energy form used?

19. Compare the three temperature scales you learned about. How are they different? How are they similar?

20. Use what you know about the movement of thermal energy to explain why you would place a minor burn on your arm under cool, running water.

Developing Skills

If you need help, refer to the Skill Handbook.

21. **Concept Mapping:** Below is a concept map of the energy changes of a gymnast bouncing on a trampoline. Complete the map by indicating the type of energy—kinetic, potential, or both—the gymnast has at each of the following stages:
a) halfway up, b) the highest point,
c) halfway down, d) the lowest point, just before hitting the trampoline.

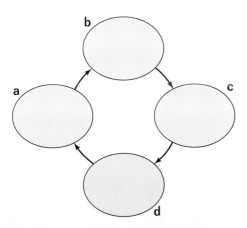

THE PRINCETON REVIEW

Test-Taking Tip

Make Yourself Comfortable When you take a test, try to make yourself as comfortable as possible. You will then be able to focus all your attention on the test.

Test Practice

Use these questions to test your Science Proficiency.

1. The sun is a source of thermal energy. Which description below **BEST** illustrates a change from thermal energy to potential chemical energy when solar energy strikes Earth?
   A) ocean water warms
   B) atmosphere cools
   C) leaves of plants make food
   D) icebergs melt

2. As you ski down a mountain, what type of energy transformation occurs?
   A) Kinetic energy changes to potential energy.
   B) Potential energy changes to kinetic energy.
   C) Chemical energy changes to potential energy.
   D) Mechanical energy changes to potential energy.

3. In an endothermic reaction, what happens to the energy?
   A) Energy is released.
   B) Energy is absorbed.
   C) Energy is made.
   D) There is no energy transfer.

States of Matter

Chapter Preview

Skills Preview

Skill Builders
- Make and Use a Graph
- Compare and Contrast

Activities
- Observe
- Design

MiniLabs
- Predict

Reading Check ✔

Before beginning this chapter,
read the Reviewing Main Ideas
pages at the end of the chapter. They will help you focus
on the most important ideas
in each section.

Explore Activity

Arctic glaciers flow across Greenland's landscape and break off into the sea, creating icebergs. The icebergs slowly melt as they travel across Earth's oceans. As cold water mixes with warm, some of it is drawn into the air as vapor—only to fall again as rain, sleet, or snow. Sometimes the rain falls in torrents driven by furious, hurricane-force winds. What unseen and relentless forces drive this never-ending cycle of water changing from a solid to a liquid to a gas and back again?

Observe a Freezing Liquid

1. Your teacher will bring you a test tube containing an unknown, liquid substance. Place the test tube in a rack, and insert a thermometer into the substance.

2. Starting immediately, read and record the substance's temperature, appearance, and physical state every 30 s.

3. Continue making measurements and observations until your teacher tells you to stop or the substance reaches room temperature.

Science Journal

In your Science Journal, describe your experiment and what you discovered. Were you surprised by anything that happened while you were taking data? Explain why you think the mystery substance behaved as it did.

Solids

Kinetic Theory of Matter

You're familiar with water in the three physical states shown in **Figure 4-1.** The **state of matter** tells you whether a material is a solid, a liquid, or a gas. You know from experience that solids, liquids, and gases behave quite differently from one another. But, do you know why? Learning about matter and the types of particles that make it up will help you understand why.

Matter is anything that takes up space and has mass. Anything you can touch, taste, or smell is matter. For example, Earth, the food you eat, the books you read, and your body are matter. Your thoughts and emotions are not matter because they don't have mass or take up space. Heat and light aren't matter, either.

Atoms

An atom is the smallest particle that makes up a given type of matter. For example, atoms of gold make up a gold ring. Atoms of helium make up the helium gas that fills balloons for a birthday party. When two or more atoms combine, they form a particle called a molecule. Two atoms of hydrogen combine with one atom of oxygen to make a water molecule. Similarly, one atom of carbon combines with two atoms of oxygen to form a carbon dioxide molecule.

Most matter is made up of atoms or molecules. But, you've probably noticed some important differences in the many types of matter that are all around you. Looking around the room, you see many things that are solids. When you wash your hands, you see and feel water, a liquid. The air you

What You'll Learn

▶ Matter is made of particles that are in constant motion
▶ How a solid forms and what happens when it melts

Vocabulary
state of matter
matter
kinetic theory of matter
melting point
heat of fusion
freezing point

Why It's Important

▶ Anything that you can see, touch, taste, or smell is matter. The particles that make up matter are in a state of constant motion.

Figure 4-1 In nature, water can exist in three physical states. **What physical states of water do you see in this photo taken near Juneau, Alaska?**

breathe is a mixture of gases. What makes a solid a solid? A liquid a liquid? A gas a gas? The physical state of a type of matter depends mostly upon how its atoms and molecules are arranged and how they move.

Matter in Motion

While watching a shaft of sunlight stream into a room, you've probably noticed the constant, irregular motion of dust particles in the air. In 1827, a Scottish botanist named Robert Brown saw something similar while observing water samples with a microscope. He noticed that pollen grains suspended in the water moved continuously—and in random patterns. Studying dye particles in water, Brown saw that they moved in the same way. Today, scientists understand that Brown's pollen grains and dye particles moved because of their collisions with moving water molecules, as illustrated in **Figure 4-2.** In Brown's honor, the constant, random motion of tiny particles of matter is called Brownian motion. The idea that the particles of all matter are in constant, random motion is called the **kinetic theory of matter.** The energy of moving particles is called kinetic energy.

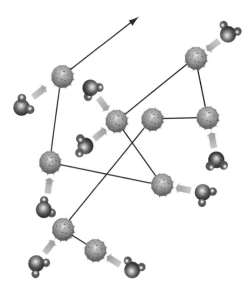

Figure 4-2 Water molecules colliding with a pollen grain in a water droplet push it first in one direction, then another. **What causes the random motion of dust particles in the air?**

Temperature and Heat

Think about the difference between hot tea and iced tea. Although both contain the same kinds of particles, the movements of the particles are different. The temperature of a material is an indirect measure of the average kinetic energy of the particles that make up the material. The higher the temperature, the faster the particles are moving. **Figure 4-3** illustrates particle movement in hot tea and iced tea.

Figure 4-3 The particles in hot tea move faster than those in iced tea. **In which container do the particles have more kinetic energy?**

Figure 4-4 It's a hot day, and this girl is playing in cool water. **How does heat transfer help her keep comfortable?**

As the temperature falls, the particles slow down. Although it's impossible to completely stop particles of matter from moving, scientists have come close. The temperature at which the particles of matter would cease to move is called absolute zero. Absolute zero is –273.15°C.

When matter at a higher temperature touches matter at a lower temperature, faster-moving particles collide with slower ones. The faster particles transfer some of their energy to the slower particles. For example, suppose you walk outside on a cold winter day while wearing a short-sleeved shirt. The slower-moving molecules that make up the air hit the faster-moving molecules that make up your warm skin. The molecules that make up your skin transfer energy to those in the air. Your nervous system senses this, and your brain tells you to go indoors or put on a coat because you're losing too much heat to the cold air. Heat is energy transferred from matter at a higher temperature to matter at a lower temperature. Just as heat transfer can make you shiver on a cold day, it can keep you comfortable on a hot day, as shown in **Figure 4-4.**

Matter in the Solid State

Water molecules attract each other, and the attractions are especially strong when the molecules are close together. For example, imagine an ice cube at a temperature of –250°C. At this low temperature, the water molecules are barely moving and the attractions hold them together easily. Now, imagine slowly heating the ice cube. As the temperature rises, the molecules shake more in all directions, but each molecule remains in its original position. This is how kinetic theory describes a solid—an arrangement of shaking particles.

Crystalline Solids

In some solids, particles of matter are arranged in repeating geometric patterns. Solids that have such arrangements are crystalline solids. As more particles become part of a crystalline solid, the geometric pattern is repeated over and over.

The geometry of a crystal depends on many factors, such as the sizes and numbers of particles that make it up. In the

PHYSICS
INTEGRATION

Kinetic Energy
The kinetic energy of an object is its energy of motion. Kinetic energy depends upon both the mass and the speed of the object. The unit of energy is the joule (J).

Figure 4-5 The particles that make up crystals of table salt shake back and forth, but they don't move out of their positions completely. **What happens to the motion of the particles if a salt crystal is heated?**

magnified view of **Figure 4-5,** you can see that crystals of table salt are shaped like cubes. Diamond, another crystalline solid, is made entirely of carbon atoms that form pyramid-shaped crystals. This shape gives a diamond its great hardness.

The large crystal shown in **Figure 4-6** is unusual. Crystals usually don't grow large. The pull of gravity, the presence of impurities, the rate of cooling, and abnormal growth patterns all limit a crystal's final size. NASA is trying to grow large crystals in space, where the effect of gravity is greatly reduced. These crystals will be used to make more reliable computer chips.

Figure 4-6 Large crystals, such as the blue, copper sulfate crystal shown here, contain more atoms than small crystals. **What location would you choose for growing the largest crystals possible?**

Noncrystalline Solids

Some solids form without creating crystal structures. These solids often consist of large molecules that don't arrange into repeating patterns to form crystals as they cool. The molecules get stuck in a random arrangement. These solids have no definite pattern or form. Glass and many types of plastic are examples of this type of solid.

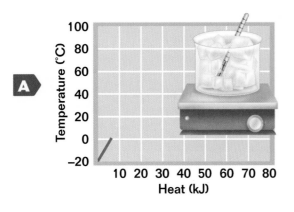

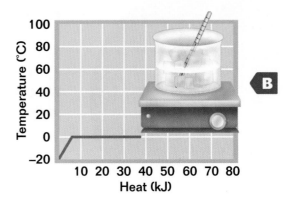

Figure 4-7 As heat is added to ice below its melting point of 0°C (A), its temperature rises. However, as heat is added at the melting point (B), the temperature remains constant until all the ice melts. **What happens to the molecules while the temperature remains constant at 0°C?**

Figure 4-8 At such high temperatures, glass flows so much that it drips off the blowing tube if not turned continually.

How does a solid become liquid?

Think again about the ice cube being heated. As its temperature continues to rise, the water molecules shake faster. But, each molecule is still held captive by the attractive forces from the molecules around it. When the temperature of the ice cube reaches 0°C, the molecules begin to break free. Their movements have become so large that the attractive forces of neighboring molecules can no longer hold them in place. The crystal structure then begins to collapse, and the solid becomes a swarm of freely flowing molecules. The molecules have entered the liquid state. The temperature at which a substance changes from a solid to a liquid is called the substance's **melting point.**

Heat of Fusion

While ice melts, its temperature remains the same, as shown in **Figure 4-7.** This means the molecules aren't moving any faster. The heat that is entering the solid is only breaking down the crystal's structure and freeing the molecules. The heat required to melt 1 kg of a solid at its melting point is called its **heat of fusion.** Water's heat of fusion is 334 kJ/kg. That's how much energy you would use taking the stairs to the top of the 110-story Sears Tower in Chicago.

Solids without crystalline structure don't melt in exactly the same way as crystalline solids. Because they don't have crystal structures to break down, these solids just get softer and softer as heat is added. For example, glass is such a solid at room temperature. As glass is heated, it begins to flow at a temperature of about 1000°C. Above 2000°C, glass is so soft that you can cut it with scissors and blow it up like a balloon. The glass blower shown in **Figure 4-8** continually turns the glass so it won't drip off the blowing tube.

Freezing

The process of melting a crystalline solid can be reversed if the liquid is cooled. As the liquid cools, its particles slow down and come closer together. Attractive forces begin to trap particles here and there, and crystals begin to form. The temperature at which this occurs, called the liquid's **freezing point,** is the same temperature as the solid's melting point. The temperature remains constant while the crystal structure forms and the heat of fusion is released. After all of the liquid has become a solid, the temperature can continue to fall. ☑

Viscosity is a material's resistance to flow. For a material such as glass, the liquid becomes more and more viscous as its temperature decreases. This means it becomes thicker and more resistant to flow, until it finally becomes brittle glass. So, glass has no definite freezing point—it just gradually hardens as it cools. The particles settle into a random arrangement rather than a crystal structure.

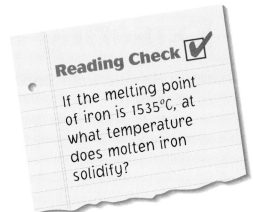

Reading Check ☑

If the melting point of iron is 1535°C, at what temperature does molten iron solidify?

Section Assessment

1. What happens to the particles of a crystalline solid as it is heated at its melting point?

2. What property must a solid have to be considered a crystalline solid?

3. Describe the motion of the particles of a solid as it cools from −250°C to −273.15°C.

4. **Think Critically:** On a cold winter day, you leave the door open when you come in from school. Someone shouts, "Close the door, you're heating the neighborhood!" Explain the meaning of this statement according to the kinetic theory of matter.

5. **Skill Builder**
   Making and Using Graphs Using the data you collected in the Explore Activity, plot a temperature-time graph. Draw a smooth curve through the data points. Describe your graph. At what temperature does the graph level off? What was the liquid doing during this time period? Compare your graph with others in the class. What do you conclude? If you need help, refer to Making and Using Graphs in the **Skill Handbook** on page 529.

Using Math

If it takes 334 kJ of energy to melt 1 kg of ice, how much energy does it take to melt 150 g of ice placed in a glass of warm tea? What is the source of the heat that melts the ice?

Exploring Symmetry

What do salt, gold, and diamonds have in common?*

In the sixteenth century, scientists began to look more closely at crystals and their structure. They discovered that many kinds of crystals are made up of small unit cells that have a characteristic and uniform shape. For instance, table salt is made up of unit cells that are cube shaped (see salt crystals at right). Unit cells can bond together to form larger crystals.

A cube is a three-dimensional figure with six square faces (like the dice below). A square is a four-sided figure with all sides having the same length. An important property of crystals is symmetry. When a figure can be folded in half so that the two parts are identical, the figure is said to have symmetry. A line of symmetry is the line where the fold is made.

Symmetry of a Square

Follow these steps to find how many lines of symmetry a square has:

1. On a sheet of paper, draw and cut out a square with sides that are 10 cm long.

2. Fold the square in half so that you end up with two identical parts, or halves. The paper crease between the two identical halves represents a line of symmetry. Find other ways you can fold the square to form identical halves. Make a crease for each line of symmetry.

3. Count the creases that you have made on your square. Your square should have four lines of symmetry.

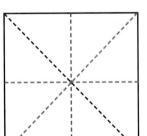

Practice
PROBLEMS

1. Crystalline gold can occur in the shape of an octahedron. An octahedron is a three-dimensional figure with eight triangular faces. Draw and cut out a triangle having all three sides equal in length. Find the number of lines of symmetry for the triangle.

2. Diamond crystals can occur in several shapes. One shape is a dodecahedron. A dodecahedron is a three-dimensional figure with 12 faces that are pentagons. Draw and cut out a pentagon having all five sides equal in length. Find the number of lines of symmetry for the pentagon.

3. Three-dimensional figures can have a plane of symmetry. On a piece of paper, draw a cube and sketch in three planes of symmetry.

*The answer: symmetry

Liquids and Gases

Matter in the Liquid State

The kinetic theory of matter considers atoms and molecules to be like billiard balls that are constantly moving and bouncing into each other. However, unlike billiard balls, there's no friction or noise when atoms and molecules collide. Therefore, they don't lose their energy of motion. As long as the temperature of the particles remains constant, they will continue to collide with the same overall kinetic energy forever.

The particles that make up a liquid move more freely than particles in a solid, as illustrated in **Figure 4-9.** The attractive forces between particles are strong enough to keep them close together but not strong enough to hold them in fixed positions. Because the particles are free to move about, gravity makes them flow, and the liquid takes the shape of its container. For example, when you pour yourself a glass of water, attractive forces hold the molecules together as a liquid while gravity holds them at the bottom of the glass.

What You'll Learn

► How liquids and gases are formed
► The enormous amounts of energy involved in evaporation and condensation

Vocabulary
boiling point
heat of vaporization
evaporation
condensation

Why It's Important

► The kinetic theory explains how your body cools itself on a hot summer day and why you shiver when you get out of the shower.

Figure 4-9 Particles in liquids move in a different way than particles in solids.

Liquid

Solid

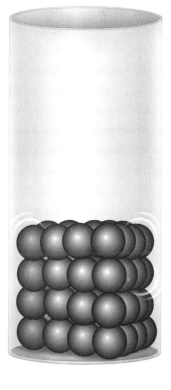

A Liquid particles have enough energy to move around each other but not enough energy to break away from each other completely.

B Solid particles can't move from place to place because they don't have enough energy to overcome their attractions for one another. **What holds liquid and solid particles in the bottom of an open container?**

Figure 4-10 Water's surface tension gives it interesting properties.

A Surface tension gives this glob of water photographed aboard the space shuttle *Columbia* a spherical shape.

B Surface tension is caused by cohesive forces between molecules, as shown in the drawing of a water droplet. Inside the droplet, molecules are pulled equally in all directions by the cohesive forces. However, at the surface of the drop, the water molecules are only pulled inward by the cohesive forces.

Cohesive forces

C This water strider uses the surface tension of water to stand on its surface. **What would happen if a water strider tried to walk on the surface of a liquid that had almost no surface tension?**

Predicting Drops of Water on a Penny

Procedure

1. Predict how many drops of water you can put on a penny before the water spills.
2. Set a penny on the counter or lab table near a sink.
3. Fill a dropper with water and carefully place a drop at the center of the penny.
4. Counting drops, carefully add more drops until the water spills off the penny.

Analysis

1. How many drops were you able to place on the penny and how does the number compare with your prediction?
2. Why were you able to put so many drops on the penny before the water spilled off the edge? Base your explanation on adhesive and cohesive forces.

Forces Between Molecules

You've probably watched astronauts play with, and then drink, floating globs of water while orbiting Earth. The attractive forces between water molecules produce the wiggly sphere of liquid shown in **Figure 4-10A.** On Earth, attractive forces make water molecules pull themselves together and form beads of water on a freshly waxed car.

If you're careful, you can float a needle on water. The water molecules at the surface pull themselves together, resulting in surface tension, as shown in **Figure 4-10B.** Water does not adhere to the metal needle, and water's surface tension is strong enough to support the needle's weight. Surface tension enables water striders to scoot around on the surface of a pond or lake, as in **Figure 4-10C.**

How does a liquid become a gas?

Have you watched a pan of water being heated on the stove? First, you'll notice small bubbles collecting on the sides and bottom of the pan. These bubbles are made of air that was dissolved in the water.

Continuing to heat the water, you start to see a swirling motion. While the warmer, less-dense water moves upward, the colder, heavier water at the surface falls to the bottom.

As the water becomes hotter still, you see trails of bubbles spiraling upward. The swirling motion becomes more active, and large bubbles of steam form at the bottom, as in **Figure 4-11.** At this temperature (100°C for water), called the **boiling point,** some of the water is entering the gaseous state. Boiling also is called vaporization.

Figure 4-11 When water is heated to boiling, large bubbles of steam form and rise to the surface. **Why does water take up more space as steam than it does as liquid water?**

Heat of Vaporization

The temperature remains the same at the boiling point while the added heat continues to vaporize the water, as illustrated in **Figure 4-12.** The amount of energy required to change 1 kg of a liquid to a gas is called the liquid's **heat of vaporization.** Water's heat of vaporization is 2260 kJ/kg, which is almost seven times the amount of heat needed to melt the same amount of ice.

Evaporation

You've seen large puddles on the sidewalk or roadway after a rainstorm. These puddles can quickly disappear if the sun comes out and the weather is warm. Does the water boil away? That seems impossible. Its temperature must be well below 100°C. The kinetic theory of matter can help you understand this mystery behavior.

Figure 4-12 Adding heat energy to liquid water causes the molecules to move faster. The graph (A) shows the steady rise in temperature after the ice melts at 0°C. Adding the heat of vaporization completely overcomes the force of attraction between molecules and changes the water to steam (B). **Why is water's heat of vaporization so much greater than its heat of fusion?**

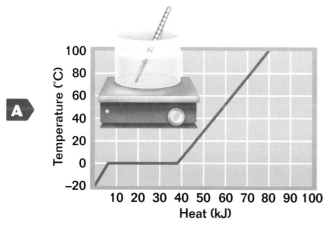

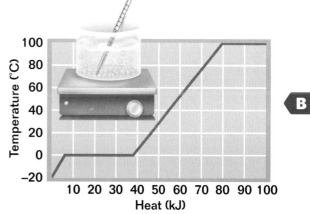

Reading Check ✔

Why does the rate of evaporation of a liquid increase as its temperature is raised?

Using Math

If you step out of a swimming pool and 85 g of water remain on your skin, how much heat does your body lose to evaporate this much water?

Imagine that you could watch individual water molecules in a glass of water. You would notice that the molecules move at different speeds. Although the temperature of the water may be constant, remember that temperature is a measure of the average kinetic energy of the molecules. Some of the fastest-moving molecules actually overcome the attractive forces of other molecules and escape from the surface of the water. The process by which individual particles of a liquid escape from the surface of a liquid that is not boiling and form a gas is called **evaporation.** But, it takes more than speed for water molecules to escape. These faster molecules also must be near the surface, heading in the right direction, and avoid hitting other water molecules as they leave. ✔

Cooling by Evaporation

With the faster molecules evaporating from the surface of a liquid, the molecules that remain are the slower, cooler ones. So, evaporation cools the liquid and anything the liquid touches. You experience this cooling effect whenever perspiration evaporates from your skin. In fact, you sometimes have a chill when you climb out of a swimming pool on a hot day as your body provides the heat to evaporate even more of the water.

Have you noticed that it sometimes cools down outside after a rain storm? The storm's water is absorbing energy from everything around as it evaporates, leaving the air a lot cooler than before the storm. With the sun shining, the air's energy is quickly replaced, sometimes leading to powerful storms, such as the ones seen in **Figure 4-13.**

Figure 4-13 This powerful Texas tornado (A) and hurricane Emilia (B) unleashed some of the sun's energy that had been stored in Earth's atmosphere.

Matter in the Gaseous State

When water evaporates, each molecule escapes completely from the attractions of its neighboring molecules. When water is in the gaseous state, the molecules are much farther apart than they are in the liquid state. This is why it's a lot easier to wave your arms through the air than to wave them through water. There's lots of empty space between the molecules in air.

If you pour only enough of a liquid into a glass to fill the glass halfway, the liquid stays in the bottom half of the glass. But, something different happens with a gas. A gas completely fills any container you put it in. If the container has no lid, the gas particles will keep spreading out until they meet some other barrier, such as the walls of a room.

Condensation

As a gas cools, its particles slow down. When particles move slowly enough for their attractions to bring them together, droplets of liquid form. This process is called **condensation.** As a gas condenses to a liquid, it releases the heat absorbed by the liquid when it became a gas. For this reason, steam can cause severe burns. Steam burns the skin not only because it's hot, but also because it releases even more heat as it condenses to liquid water.

interNET CONNECTION

Visit the Glencoe Science Web Site at **www.glencoe.com/ sec/science/ca** for more information about the powerful forces that drive the melting of the polar ice caps and the development of hurricanes.

Section Assessment

1. Have you noticed water collecting on the outside of a glass containing an ice-cold drink? Where did this water come from, and why did it collect on the glass?

2. A glass of water is placed next to a puddle that contains the same amount of water. Explain why water in the glass evaporates more slowly than water in the puddle.

3. **Think Critically:** Use the kinetic theory to explain why a gas completely fills its container while a liquid or solid may not.

4.  **Skill Builder**
   Making and Using Graphs The melting point of aluminum is 660°C. Draw the heating graph for a sample of aluminum between 500°C and 800°C. If you need help, refer to Making and Using Graphs in the **Skill Handbook** on page 529.

Science Journal

In your Science Journal, explain why you can step out of the shower into a warm bathroom and begin to shiver.

Visit Three States in Science Class

Materials

- Hot plate
- Ice cubes (100 mL)
- Stirring rod
- Celsius thermometer
- Beaker (250 mL)
- Wall clock with a second hand
  - *stopwatch
  - *Alternate Materials

T he cycle of the seasons is marked by major changes in the weather driven by the sun's energy. Because water covers much of Earth, changes in water's physical state greatly affect people's lives.

What You'll Investigate

What energy changes occur as water changes its temperature and physical states?

Goals

- **Measure** the temperature of water as it is heated.
- **Observe** what happens as the water changes state.
- **Graph** a heating curve.

Procedure

1. **Copy** the data table shown.
2. Put about 150 mL of water and 100 mL of ice into the beaker and place the beaker and contents on the hot plate.
3. Put the thermometer into the ice-water mixture. **Do not** stir with the thermometer or allow it to rest on the bottom of the beaker. After 30 s, **measure** and record the temperature in your data table. Be sure to stir the ice and water before making each temperature measurement. Record the physical state(s) in your data table.
4. Plug in the hot plate and turn the temperature knob to the medium setting.
5. Every 30 s, **measure** and record the temperature and **observe** and record the physical state of the ice and/or water in the beaker.
6. Continue until the water has reached boiling and boiled for three minutes.

Conclude and Apply

1. Use your data to **make a Temperature-Time graph.** Draw a smooth curve through the data points. Do not connect the data points with straight lines.
2. On the graph, what was happening to the water during the flat portions of the graph? Write down the temperatures for these portions.
3. How do the flat portions relate to water's heat of fusion and heat of vaporization?

Heating Data and Observations		
Time (min)	Temperature (°C)	Physical State
0.0		
0.5		
1.0		
1.5		
2.0		

Behavior of Liquids and Gases

4•3

Diffusion

Imagine you're walking by a bakery's open door. The wonderful aroma of baking bread fills the air. If the aroma consists of molecules in the gaseous state, how do the molecules reach your nose? According to the kinetic theory, the warm molecules are moving about rapidly, and many of them flow out the door and mix with the cool morning air. Because of their ability to flow, liquids and gases are called fluids.

Because particles of a gas are far apart and move about freely, they easily mix with particles of other gases. For example, **Figure 4-14** shows the gradual mixing of bromine gas with air as liquid bromine evaporates at the bottom of a glass container. This mixing of particles is called **diffusion.** Many times, you don't notice a gas mixing with other gases because you can't see or smell its particles. Although you can smell some of the gases emitted from automobile engines, you can't smell the deadly gas carbon monoxide. Because you can't smell carbon monoxide mixing with the air you breathe, a car with its engine running should always be parked in a well-ventilated area.

What **You'll Learn**

► How pressure is transmitted through fluids
► Why some things float while others sink

Vocabulary
diffusion
pressure
Pascal's principle
density
Archimedes' principle
buoyancy

Why **It's Important**

► Pressure enables you to squeeze toothpaste from a tube and to float in water.

Figure 4-14 As time passes, liquid bromine vaporizes and mixes with the gases that make up air.

Pressure

Suppose you fill a plastic drink bottle completely full of water, put the cap on tightly, and squeeze. Nothing happens because it's nearly impossible to compress solids and liquids. The force applied by your muscles is spread out over the surface area of your hand that is in contact with the bottle. This creates **pressure,** which is the amount of force applied per unit of area. Pressure (P), force (F), and area (A) are related by the following formula.

$$\text{Pressure} = \frac{\text{force}}{\text{area}}$$

$$P = \frac{F}{A}$$

The SI unit of pressure is the pascal (Pa). One *pascal* is the pressure produced by a force of one newton (N) applied per square meter (m^2) of surface area. What pressure is produced when 25.0 N of force are applied to an area of 10.0 m^2? ☑

$$P = \frac{F}{A}$$

$$P = \frac{25.0 \text{ N}}{10.0 \text{ m}^2} = 2.50 \ \frac{\text{N}}{\text{m}^2} = 2.50 \text{ Pa}$$

The pressure produced is 2.50 pascals.

Reading Check ☑

What pressure is created when 5.0 N of force are applied to an area of 2.0 m^2?

Problem Solving

Calculating Pressure

The circus is coming to your town. You're in charge of installing a floor that will withstand the antics of all the animals and performers. Zebras will prance on the floor. Elephants will rear up, standing on two legs. A performer shot from a cannon will land after flying 50 m through the air. Someone wearing spike heels will maneuver animals through their routines. Which is the greater threat to your floor, an elephant standing on two feet or the person wearing spike-heeled shoes? The circus's largest elephant has a weight of 9250 N. The elephant's two feet contact the ground over a surface area of 0.180 m^2. The person wearing spike-heeled shoes has a weight of 485 N and sometimes stands on the heel of one shoe, contacting the ground over an area of 0.000 200 m^2.

Think Critically: Calculate the pressures exerted on the floor by the elephant and the heel of one spike-heeled shoe. Which is greater? How is your result possible?

Figure 4-15
Pascal's principle
explains many
common events.

A Applying pressure
to the bottom of
the bottle makes
water shoot out of
a small hole near
the top.

B Applying pressure to the tube
forces toothpaste out of the
opening. **Why can't the particles that make up the
water and toothpaste be
squeezed closer together?**

Pascal's Principle

What happens if you make a small hole near the top of a
full plastic drink bottle and squeeze it near the bottom? Why
does water shoot out the hole near the top, as shown in
Figure 4-15A? When you squeeze the bottle, molecules
throughout the water press against each other. In this way,
the pressure applied at any point to a confined fluid is transmitted unchanged throughout the fluid. This statement is
known as **Pascal's principle.** Every time you squeeze a tube
of toothpaste, you see Pascal's principle in action, as in
Figure 4-15B.

Gas Pressure

Gases are easy to compress because their particles are so far
apart. When you pump up a bicycle tire or a basketball, as
shown in **Figure 4-16,** you increase the pressure by forcing
more particles into the same amount of space. Gases exert
pressure because their particles collide with each other, the
walls of the container, and anything else that gets in their
way. By increasing the number of gas particles in a given
space, you increase the number of collisions and the pressure.

Figure 4-16 What do you
think would happen to the pressure inside the ball if you took it
outside on a cold day after inflat-
ing it to the correct pressure in a
warm building? Explain your
answer.

VISUALIZING
Air Particles

Figure 4-17 The volume of air in these two cylinders is the same. The unheated air in the left cylinder exerts enough pressure to lift a 1-kg block. The heated air in the right cylinder exerts more pressure—enough to lift a 2-kg block. **Why does the heated air exert more pressure than the unheated air?**

Visit the Glencoe Science Web Site at **www.glencoe.com/ sec/science/ca** for more information about pressure and temperature.

Have you ever noticed that the instructions on some tires caution you to inflate them a bit below the recommended pressure during the summer months? The tires on a car become hot after driving for a while on a hot day, and gas particles move faster at higher temperatures. The particles inside the tires collide more frequently and with greater kinetic energies, increasing the pressure. For this reason, the pressure inside tires can increase to a dangerously high level and cause them to burst on a hot day.

To better understand the relationship between temperature and pressure, examine **Figure 4-17.** A sample of gas is trapped inside a container with a fixed volume. When you heat the gas, its particles move faster and exert more pressure. When you cool the gas, its particles move slower and exert less pressure.

Atmospheric Pressure

Particles in Earth's atmosphere are constantly colliding with the surface of your body. You don't notice the collisions because they're the same on all sides of your body. These collisions exert a pressure of 101.3 kPa at sea level, which is about 100 000 N of force for every square meter. A force of 100 000 N is approximately the weight of a large truck. A pressure of 101.3 kPa is equal to 1 atmosphere (atm).

Your body is very sensitive to changes in air pressure. Why does a trip to the top of a tall building, a drive up a mountain road, or a flight on an airplane make your ears pop?

In the seventeenth century, a French physician named Blaise Pascal measured the pressure of the atmosphere at different altitudes. For one of his experiments, Pascal had his brother-in-law carry a partially filled balloon to the top of the

Puy-de-Dome mountain in France. (Pascal would have performed the experiment himself but his health was so poor that he could not make the climb.) Pascal's experiment is illustrated in **Figure 4-18.** As Pascal had predicted, the balloon expanded as it was carried up the mountain, indicating that air gets "thinner" at higher altitudes. That is, air contains fewer particles per cubic meter at higher altitudes than at lower altitudes. For this reason, you may feel the difference in air pressure when you travel to higher altitudes. Because the air pressure in your ear canals is greater than the air pressure outside your body, some of the air trapped inside your ears is released. This release of air can make your ears pop.

As the atmospheric pressure decreases, the boiling points of liquids also become lower. For example, if you boiled your vegetables in water in an open pot on Mount Everest, they would be served uncooked because water boils there at a temperature of only 76.5°C, whereas at sea level, water boils at 100°C. Boiling occurs when the pressure of the liquid's moving molecules matches the air pressure pushing down on the surface.

Density and Buoyancy

One day, the king of Syracuse asked the mathematician Archimedes (287–212 B.C.) to solve a riddle. The king had asked a jeweler to make him a crown made entirely of gold. When the king received the crown, it looked magnificent. But, when it was placed upon his head, it seemed lighter than he expected. The king told Archimedes to find out if some of the gold had been replaced with a cheaper metal. To make his task more difficult, Archimedes had to do it without damaging the crown.

Puy-de-Dome mountain

Figure 4-18 Why did the balloon become larger as it was carried up the mountain?

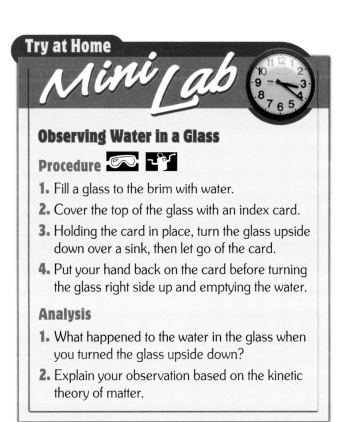

Try at Home

Mini Lab

Observing Water in a Glass

Procedure

1. Fill a glass to the brim with water.
2. Cover the top of the glass with an index card.
3. Holding the card in place, turn the glass upside down over a sink, then let go of the card.
4. Put your hand back on the card before turning the glass right side up and emptying the water.

Analysis

1. What happened to the water in the glass when you turned the glass upside down?
2. Explain your observation based on the kinetic theory of matter.

Density

Archimedes loved to solve problems—and this one was a serious challenge. He could weigh the crown, but that wouldn't reveal the presence of impurities. But, if he also could measure the crown's volume, then he could divide the mass by the volume to get the crown's density. **Density** (D) equals mass (m) divided by volume (V). The equation form follows.

$$\text{Density} = \frac{\text{mass}}{\text{volume}}$$

$$D = \frac{m}{V}$$

For example, the density of a 16.4-g object that has a volume of 4.0 mL is calculated as follows.

$$D = \frac{m}{V}$$

$$D = \frac{16.4 \text{ g}}{4.0 \text{ mL}} = \frac{4.1 \text{ g}}{\text{mL}}$$

The density of the object is 4.1 g/mL.

Gold has a density of 19.3 g/mL. Knowing that any other metal that had been used in place of gold had a lower density, Archimedes put a sample of pure gold that weighed the same as the crown into a tub of water and measured how much water it pushed aside. Then, he did the same thing with the crown. When he saw that the pure gold pushed aside less water than the crown, he knew that the crown could not be pure gold.

Using Math

A woman's ring has a mass of 3.82 g and a volume of 0.294 mL. What is the ring's density? Can the ring be made of pure gold?

Figure 4-19 Why do some people find it difficult to float in a swimming pool?

A When an object is immersed in water, the water pushes upward on the object with a force called the buoyant force. The buoyant force is equal to the weight of the water displaced. Because the buoyant force opposes the force of gravity that pulls the object downward, the apparent weight of the object is less than the actual weight.

B The boy floats because he has displaced an amount of water equal to his weight.

Buoyancy

What Archimedes discovered is called Archimedes' Principle. **Archimedes' principle** states that when an object is placed in a fluid, the object weighs less by an amount equal to the weight of the displaced fluid. The net upward force caused by the displaced fluid is called the buoyant force. You experience **buoyancy,** which is the decrease in weight caused by the buoyant force, when you float in a swimming pool or lake. Archimedes' principle is illustrated and explained in **Figure 4-19.**

You can use Archimedes' principle to explain why some things sink and others float. If an object's density is less than that of a fluid, it floats in the fluid. On the other hand, if an object's density is greater than that of the fluid, it sinks. That's why a beach ball floats in water while an anchor sinks, as illustrated in **Figure 4-20.**

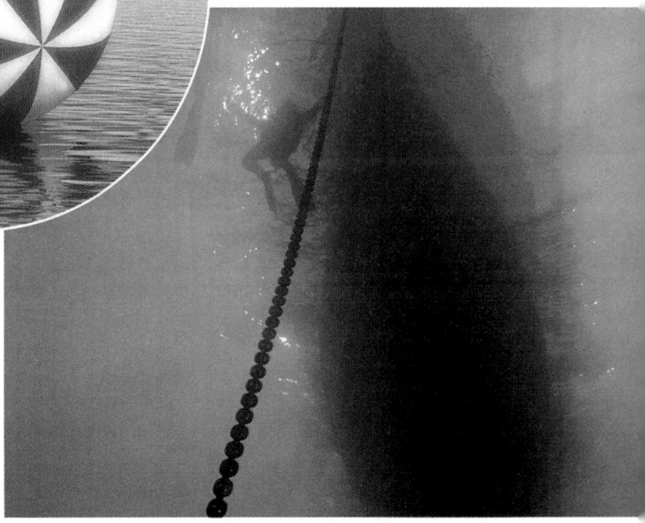

Figure 4-20 Because the anchor attached to the boat's chain is more dense than water, it sinks to the bottom and holds the boat in place.

Section Assessment

1. Use the kinetic theory to explain why a balloon bursts when overinflated.

2. Calculate the density of an object that has a mass of 3.0 g and a volume of 5.0 cm^3. Will the object float or sink when placed in water, which has a density of 1.0 g/cm^3?

3. Why is atmospheric pressure greater at sea level than at the top of a mountain 5000 m above sea level?

4. **Think Critically:** Use Archimedes' principle to explain why a helium balloon rises while a balloon filled with air falls.

5. **Skill Builder**
   Comparing and Contrasting Do the **Chapter 4 Skill Activity** on page 557 to form a hypothesis about what kinds of matter were in the cup.

Using Computers

Word Processing Use word processing software to create a report explaining how water creates the buoyant force that causes an ice cube to float. If you need help, refer to page 544.

Design Your Own Boat

Possible Materials

- Balance
- Small plastic cups (2)
- Graduated cylinder into which the cups will fit
- Metric ruler
- Scissors
- Marbles
- Sink or basin
  - *basin, pan, or bucket
  - *Alternate Materials

Have you ever wondered how a boat designer knows how much cargo a particular boat can carry? If you were given an amount of cargo and asked to design a boat that would just hold the cargo afloat, how would you decide what size to make the boat?

Recognize the Problem

How can you determine the size of boat needed to float a certain mass of cargo?

Form a Hypothesis

Think about Archimedes' principle and how it relates to buoyant force. **Form a hypothesis** about how the volume of water a boat displaces relates to the mass of cargo the boat can float.

Goals

- **Design an experiment** that uses Archimedes' Principle to determine the size of boat needed to carry a given amount of cargo.

Test Your Hypothesis

Plan

1. Your teacher will give you a set of marbles or other cargo that your boat must float. Decide how your group is going to test your hypothesis.

2. List the steps you need to take to test your hypothesis. Include in your plan how you will (a) **measure** the mass of your cargo, (b) **calculate** how much water your boat must displace in order to just float your boat and cargo, (c) **measure** the volume and mass of the displaced water, and (d) **determine** how to trim your cup to the exact size so that it will just float your cargo.

3. **Prepare a data table** in your Science Journal so that it is ready to use as your group collects data.

Do

1. Make sure your teacher approves your plan and your data table before you proceed.

2. Carry out your experiment as planned.

3. While doing the experiment, **record** your observations and **complete** the data table in your Science Journal.

Analyze Your Data

1. **Show** your calculations to determine the volume of displaced water needed to float your boat and cargo.

2. Did your boat (a) just float the cargo, (b) sink, or (c) float with excess freeboard, which is the distance between the waterline and the top of the boat?

Draw Conclusions

1. If your boat sank or had excess freeboard, how would you change your experiment or calculations to correct the problem?

2. What does the density of a ship's cargo have to do with the volume of cargo the ship can carry?

For a **preview** of this chapter, study this Reviewing Main Ideas before you read the chapter. After you have studied this chapter, you can use the Reviewing Main Ideas to **review** the chapter.

The Glencoe MindJogger, Audiocassettes, and CD-ROM provide additional opportunities for review.

Section 4-1 KINETIC THEORY OF MATTER

All **matter** is composed of incredibly small particles. The **kinetic theory of matter** describes the way these particles move about. Temperature is an indirect measure of the average kinetic energy of these particles. *When the particles that make up a material collide with each other, how much energy is lost? Explain your answer.*

SOLIDS

In the solid state, the attractive forces between particles lock them in place. A crystalline solid consists of particles in an orderly arrangement, while a noncrystalline solid consists of particles arranged in a random manner. If enough heat is added to a solid, melting occurs as the attractive forces between particles are overcome and the solid becomes a liquid. *Why does a liquid release heat as it freezes?*

Section 4-2 LIQUIDS

Molecules in the liquid state are free to move about within the liquid. When gravity is present, a liquid takes the shape of its container. At a liquid's **boiling point,** its particles enter the gaseous state in large numbers. *How do cohesive forces explain why water beads up on a waxed surface?*

Reading Check ✓

What would cause water to change its state? What would cause it to change again?

GASES

To enter the gaseous state from the liquid state, particles must absorb the **heat of vaporization.** Particles in the gaseous state are much farther from neighboring particles than in the liquid state. Gaseous particles move about freely and completely fill their containers. *Use the kinetic theory to explain what happens to the particles of a gas when it condenses to a liquid.*

 Section

4-3 PRESSURE

Pressure is force per unit area. Pressure applied to a liquid is transmitted throughout the liquid. This is known as **Pascal's principle.** Gases exert pressure because their moving particles continually collide with each other and the walls of their container. *Why do the boiling points of liquids depend upon the atmospheric pressure?*

BUOYANCY

Archimedes' principle states that when an object is placed in a fluid, the object seems lighter by an amount equal to the weight of the displaced fluid. The displaced fluid's weight creates additional pressure throughout the fluid, resulting in **buoyancy.** *What determines whether an object floats or sinks in a fluid?*

Chapter 4 Assessment

Using Vocabulary

a. Archimedes' principle
b. boiling point
c. buoyancy
d. condensation
e. density
f. diffusion
g. evaporation
h. freezing point
i. heat of fusion
j. heat of vaporization
k. kinetic theory of matter
l. matter
m. melting point
n. Pascal's principle
o. pressure
p. state of matter

Using the list above, replace the underlined words with the correct Vocabulary words.

1. When a liquid freezes, the <u>heat of vaporization</u> is given off.
2. The particles of gas coming together to form a liquid is called <u>evaporation.</u>
3. Mass divided by volume equals <u>pressure.</u>
4. The temperature at which a solid becomes a liquid is called the <u>boiling point.</u>
5. <u>Archimedes' principle</u> states that the pressure exerted on a fluid is transmitted unchanged throughout the fluid.

Checking Concepts

Choose the word or phrase that best answers the question.

6. Which of the following is used to explain whether an object will sink or float?
   A) Archimedes' principle
   B) viscosity
   C) temperature
   D) kinetic theory of matter
7. What holds the molecules of a substance together?
   A) buoyant force   C) attractive forces
   B) pressure   D) temperature
8. What is required to melt a kilogram of a solid at the melting point?
   A) heat of fusion   C) density
   B) boiling   D) heat of vaporization
9. Which of the following is a unit of pressure?
   A) Pa   C) J/m^2
   B) J/kg   D) kg/m^3
10. What is glass an example of?
    A) viscous liquid   C) noncrystalline solid
    B) crystalline solid D) fluid
11. Which of the following is used to explain how temperature affects matter?
    A) density   C) pressure
    B) Pascal's principle D) kinetic theory
12. Which of the following is not a state of matter?
    A) gas   C) density
    B) solid   D) liquid
13. What is greatly affected by atmospheric pressure?
    A) melting point   C) boiling point
    B) freezing point   D) heat of fusion
14. What best explains how you can smell burned toast from another room?
    A) evaporation   C) diffusion
    B) fusion   D) fire
15. What is a characteristic shared by solids and liquids?
    A) incompressibility C) fluidity
    B) low density   D) buoyancy

Thinking Critically

16. Use the kinetic theory to explain why the bathroom mirror becomes fogged after you take a shower.
17. A crown is found to have a volume of 110 cm³ and a mass of 1800 g. The density of gold is 19.3 g/cm³. Is the crown pure gold?

18. When you travel on an airplane, your ears pop and a pen leaks ink in your pocket. Explain why these events occur.

19. After Archimedes discovered his principle on buoyancy, it became clear that a boat could be made out of a metal like iron, even though a piece of iron sinks in water. Explain how this is possible.

20. If you have an automatic ice-cube maker in your freezer, you may have noticed that the older ice cubes at the bottom of the tray are much smaller than the newer cubes at the top. Use the kinetic theory to explain why.

Developing Skills

If you need help, refer to the Skill Handbook.

21. **Forming Operational Definitions:** Write operational definitions that explain the properties of and differences between solids, liquids, and gases.

22. **Making and Using Graphs:** In May of 1997, the Cuban free-diver Francesco Ferraras dove to a new record depth of 150 m without any scuba equipment. Make a Depth-Pressure graph for the pressure he felt as he descended. Estimate the water pressure at a depth of 300 m.

Deep Depth Dive	
Depth (m)	**Pressure (atm)**
0	1.0
25	3.5
50	6.0
75	8.5
100	11.0
125	13.5
150	16.0

THE PRINCETON REVIEW

Test-Taking Tip

All or None When filling in answer ovals, remember to fill in the whole oval. A computer will be scoring your answers. Don't give the right answer for a problem only to lose points on it because the computer couldn't read your oval.

Test Practice

Use these questions to test your Science Proficiency.

1. Pascal was the first to suggest that Earth's atmosphere did not extend out into space forever. Which statement **BEST** describes his reasoning for this?
   A) Hot air expands and gets thinner as it rises.
   B) Part of the atmosphere is water vapor, and it forms clouds that are not high off the ground.
   C) If you walk up a mountain, the air pressure drops.
   D) The sky is blue during the day when the sun shines on the atmosphere, but at night the sky is dark and clear, even when there is a full moon.

2. Which of the following statements explains what happens to a liquid at the freezing point?
   A) The temperature falls rapidly.
   B) The temperature rises.
   C) For most substances, the solid that forms is much less dense than the liquid.
   D) The temperature remains constant until all of the solid has formed.

Inside the Atom

Chapter Preview

Skills Preview

Skill Builders
- Map Concepts
- Make a Table

Activities
- Make a Model
- Design an Experiment

MiniLabs
- Make a Model
- Make and Use a Graph

Reading Check ✓

Before reading this chapter, list the vocabulary terms for each section. As you read, write a definition next to each term.

Explore Activity

By day, they are clear, glass tubes filled with colorless gases. Flip the switch, and they instantly light up the night with their messages. This is advertising magic! Electricity paints pictures that you can't help but notice. What's going on? What are the gases in the tubes? What are they made of, and why do they glow with color at the flick of a switch?

Observe Inside an Atom

1. Your teacher will give you a piece of clay and some pieces of metal. Count the pieces of metal.

2. Bury these pieces in the modeling clay so they can't be seen.

3. Exchange clay balls with another group.

4. With a toothpick, probe the clay to find out how many pieces of metal are in the ball and what shapes they are.

Science Journal

In your Science Journal, sketch the shapes of the metal pieces as you identify them. How does the number of pieces you found compare with the number that were actually in the clay ball? How do their shapes compare?

5·1 The Story of the Atom

What You'll Learn

▶ How scientists discovered subatomic particles
▶ How today's model of the atom developed
▶ The structure of the nuclear atom

Vocabulary
element
electron
proton
neutron
electron cloud

Why It's Important

▶ Atoms make up everything in your world.

An Old Idea

Trying to find out what something looks like when you can't see it is not a new challenge. People began wondering about matter more than 2500 years ago. Some of the Greek philosophers thought that matter was composed of tiny particles. They reasoned that you could take a piece of matter, cut it in half, cut the half-piece in half again, and continue to cut again and again. Eventually, you wouldn't be able to cut any more. You would have only one particle left. They named these particles atoms, a term that means "cannot be divided." Think about matter as being like a string of beads. If you keep dividing the string into pieces, you eventually come to one single bead.

The Greek philosophers didn't try to prove their theories by doing experiments as scientists now do. Today, scientists like the one in **Figure 5-1** will not accept a theory that is not supported by experimental evidence. But even if the Greeks had experimented, they could not have proven the existence of atoms. People had not yet discovered much about what is now called chemistry, the study of matter. The kind of equipment needed to study matter was a long way from being invented. Even 2000 years later, atoms were a mystery.

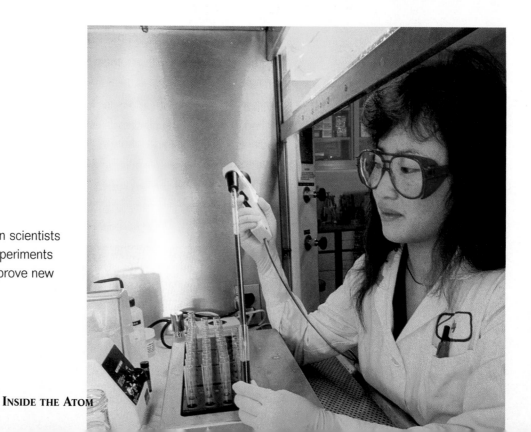

Figure 5-1 Modern scientists design and carry out experiments to either support or disprove new hypotheses.

Figure 5-2 The 1700s were years of great interest in science. Scientists created laboratories like this one to test their theories by doing experiments.

Dalton's Atomic Model

For a long time after the ancient Greeks, people didn't think much about atoms. Finally, during the eighteenth century, scientists in laboratories like the one in **Figure 5-2** again began debating the existence of atoms. Chemists were learning about matter and how it changes. They were putting substances together to form new substances and taking substances apart to find out what they were made of. They found that there was a limit to how far a substance could be broken down. Certain substances couldn't be broken down into simpler substances. Scientists came to realize that all matter is made up of elements. An **element** is a substance that cannot be broken down into simpler substances. John Dalton, an English schoolteacher, combined the idea of elements with the Greek theory of the atom. He proposed that matter is made up of atoms, that atoms cannot be divided into smaller pieces, and that all the atoms of an element are exactly alike, and different elements are made of different kinds of atoms. For example, iron is an element made of iron atoms. Silver, another element, is made of silver atoms. Dalton pictured an atom as a hard sphere that was the same throughout, something like a tiny marble. His model is shown in **Figure 5-3.**

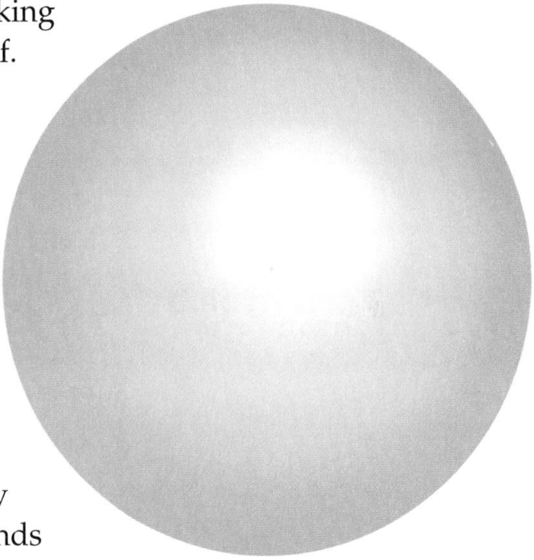

Figure 5-3 Dalton pictured the atom as a hard sphere that was the same throughout.

Where's the proof?

By the second half of the nineteenth century, scientists had equipment to test Dalton's theory of the atom. In 1870, the English scientist William Crookes did experiments with a glass tube that had almost all the air removed from it. The glass tube had two pieces of metal called electrodes sealed in the glass. The electrodes were connected to a battery by wires.

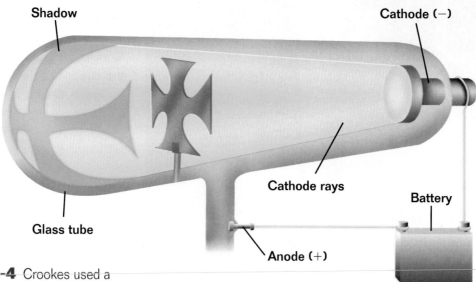

Shadow

Cathode (−)

Glass tube

Cathode rays

Battery

Anode (+)

Figure 5-4 Crookes used a glass tube containing only a small amount of gas. When the glass tube was connected to a battery, something flowed from the negative electrode on the right to the positive electrode. **Was this "something" light or a stream of particles?**

PHYSICS
INTEGRATION ▸

An electrode is a piece of metal that can conduct electric current. One electrode, called the anode, has a positive charge. The other, called the cathode, has a negative charge. In Crookes's tube, the metal cathode was a disk at the right end of the tube. Beyond the anode was an object shaped like a cross, as you can see in **Figure 5-4.** When the battery was connected, the glass tube suddenly lit up with a greenish glow. A shadow of the cross-shaped object appeared at the left end of the tube. The shadow indicated that something was traveling in a straight line from the cathode to the anode, just like the beam of a flashlight. The object was getting in the way of the beam and casting a shadow just like the shadow you would get of your hand if you put it in the beam of a flashlight or movie projector. You can see this in **Figure 5-5.**

Was the greenish glow light? Or, was it a stream of charged particles? This question was answered by placing a magnet beside the tube. In **Figure 5-6,** you can see that the beam is bent by the magnet. Light is not bent by a magnet, so the

Figure 5-5 The shadow cast by the rays in Crookes's tube were just like the shadows cast by light, but it turned out that Crookes's rays were not light.

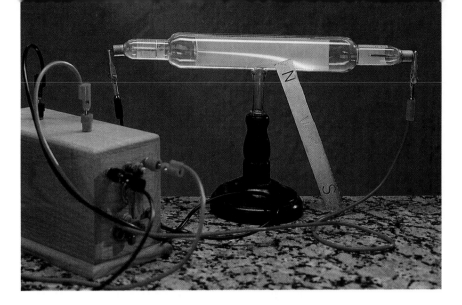

Figure 5-6 When a magnet is placed near a glass tube similar to the one Crookes used, the rays bend. **A magnet cannot bend light, so what must be the "something" that causes the green glow?**

beam is not light. Therefore, the beam must be negatively charged particles of matter that came from the metal of the cathode. How was it posssible to know that the particles were negatively charged? Opposite charges attract each other. These particles were attracted to the positively charged anode, so the particles must be negatively charged. These rays were called cathode rays because they were produced at the cathode. Crookes's tube is known as a cathode-ray tube, or CRT. It's the forerunner of all TV and computer display screens like the one in **Figure 5-7.**

J. J. Thomson's Contribution

You can imagine how excited scientists were when they heard the results of Crookes's work. But, many scientists were not convinced that the cathode rays were streams of particles. In 1897, J.J. Thomson, an English physicist, repeated the CRT experiment using different metals for the cathode and different gases in the tube. But, the same negatively charged particles were produced regardless of the metal used for the cathode or the gas in the tube. Thomson concluded that cathode rays are negatively charged particles of matter. These particles are now called **electrons.** He also inferred that electrons are a part of every kind of atom because they are produced by every kind of cathode material. Thomson's experiments also proved that atoms are not impossible to divide because atoms are made up of even smaller particles.

Figure 5-7 Crookes's tube became known as a cathode-ray tube because the particles he observed started at the cathode and traveled to the anode. There is a cathode-ray tube or CRT in every TV and computer monitor.

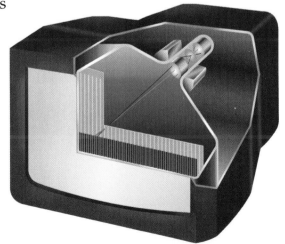

Thomson's Atomic Model

Thomson's experiments answered some of the questions scientists had about atoms. But, they led to another scientific puzzle. If atoms contain one or more negatively charged particles, then matter, which is made of the atoms, also should be negatively charged. But, it isn't. How can this be explained? Could it be that atoms also contain one or more positively charged particles? The negatively charged electrons and the unknown positively charged particles would then neutralize each other in the atom. Thomson continued his experiments and found evidence for the existence of a particle that has the same mass and charge as a positively charged hydrogen atom. However, it took until 1920 for scientists to identify this particle as a proton. A **proton** is a positively charged particle that is present in all atoms. A proton is almost 2000 times heavier than an electron. ✔

Using his new findings, Thomson revised Dalton's model of the atom. Instead of a solid ball that was the same throughout, Thomson pictured a sphere that contained all the positive charge. The negatively charged electrons were spread evenly throughout the sphere. You can compare Thomson's idea of the atom to the ball of raisin-cookie dough shown in **Figure 5-8.** The cookie dough represents the protons, which are most of the mass of the atom. The raisins represent the electrons. They are scattered throughout the dough and make the atom electrically neutral.

Reading Check ✔

What particle has the same mass and charge as a positively charged hydrogen atom?

Figure 5-8 Well-mixed cookie dough is a model for the J.J. Thomson atom.

A The dough contains all the positive charge of the atom. The raisins, which represent the negatively charged electrons, are mixed evenly in the dough.

B Thomson pictured the negatively charged electrons as evenly spaced throughout the atom. The negative charges of the electrons and the positive charges of the protons balanced each other.

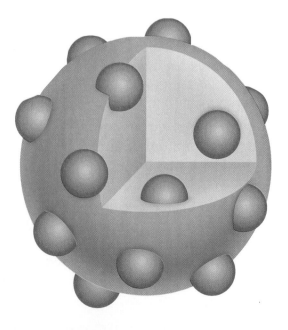

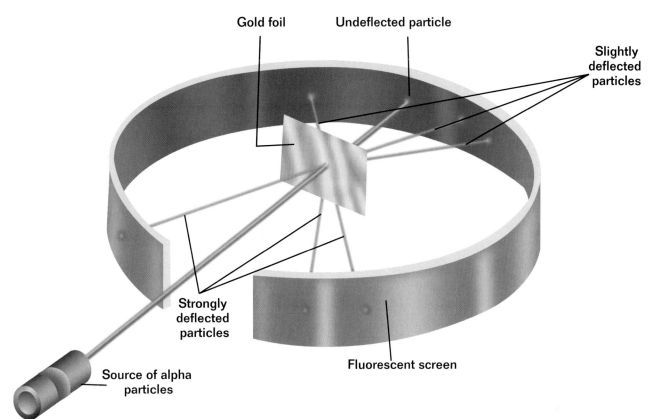

Gold foil   Undeflected particle

Slightly deflected particles

Strongly deflected particles

Source of alpha particles

Fluorescent screen

Rutherford's Atom

Was Thomson's model of the atom correct? In 1906, Ernest Rutherford and his coworkers began an experiment to find out. They wanted to see what would happen when they bombarded a thin film of a metal such as gold with fast-moving bits of matter called alpha particles. Alpha particles come from unstable atoms. Because they are positively charged, alpha particles are repelled by particles of matter with a positive charge.

Figure 5-9 shows how the experiment was set up. A source of alpha particles was aimed at the sheet of thin gold foil. The foil was surrounded by a fluorescent (fluh RES unt) screen that gave a flash of light when it was hit by a charged particle.

Rutherford thought he knew what the results of this experiment would be. He expected that most of the speeding alpha particles would crash right through the foil and hit the screen on the other side, just like a bullet fired through a glass pane. Rutherford reasoned that in the thin gold film, there wasn't enough matter to stop the speeding alpha particle or to change its path. There also wasn't enough charge in any one place in the cookie-dough atom to strongly repel the alpha particle. He thought that the positive charges on the protons in the gold atoms might cause a few minor deflections if an alpha particle happened to come close to a proton. However, he assumed that there would be only a few of these occasions.

Figure 5-9 In Rutherford's experiment, alpha particles bombarded the gold foil. Most particles passed right through the foil or veered slightly from a straight-line path, but some particles bounced right back. The path of a particle is shown by a flash of light when it hits the fluorescent screen.

Figure 5-10 Rutherford had some explaining to do when he realized how amazing the results of his experiment were. A 15-inch shell just doesn't bounce off a piece of tissue paper!

That was a reasonable assumption to make because in the cookie-dough model, the positive charges of the protons are essentially neutralized by nearby electrons. Rutherford was so sure of what the results would be that he turned the work over to a graduate student.

Surprising Results

Imagine Rutherford's surprise when his student rushed in to tell him that some alpha particles were veering off at large angles. You can see this in **Figure 5-9.** Rutherford expressed his amazement by saying, "It was about as believable as if you had fired a 15-inch shell at a piece of tissue paper, and it came back and hit you." How could an event like the cartoon in **Figure 5-10** be explained? The positively charged alpha particles were moving with such high speed that it would take a large positive charge to cause them to bounce back. But, in the cookie-dough model of the atom, the mass and charges of the electrons and protons are all uniformly mixed.

The Nuclear Atom

Picture in your mind Rutherford and his team wrestling to make sense of this experiment. They might have drawn diagrams like those in **Figure 5-11.** Diagram A, using the cookie-dough model, shows what Rutherford expected. Now and then, an alpha particle might be slightly affected by a positive charge in the atom and turn a bit off course. However, no large changes in direction would be expected. The actual results did not fit this model, so Rutherford proposed a new one. He hypothesized that almost all the mass of the atom and all of its positive charge are crammed into an incredibly small region of space at the center of the atom called the nucleus. The rest of the atom is empty space occupied by the atom's almost-massless electrons. ✓

Diagram B, in **Figure 5-11,** shows Rutherford's new model of the atom and how it fits the experimental data. You could

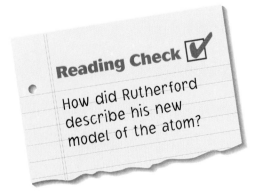

Reading Check ✓

How did Rutherford describe his new model of the atom?

Figure 5-11 Rutherford had to relate his findings to the structure of the atom.

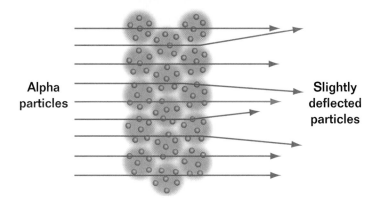

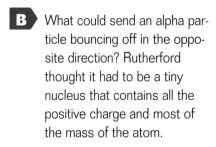
Alpha particles

Slightly deflected particles

A He thought that if the atom could be described by Thomson's cookie-dough model, then only minor bends in the paths of the particles would have occurred. However, some particles bounced back off the foil.

B What could send an alpha particle bouncing off in the opposite direction? Rutherford thought it had to be a tiny nucleus that contains all the positive charge and most of the mass of the atom.

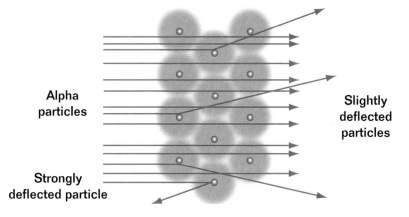

Alpha particles

Strongly deflected particle

Slightly deflected particles

predict that if an alpha particle made a direct hit on the nucleus of a gold atom, which has 79 protons, the alpha particle would be strongly repelled and bounce back. But, most alpha particles could move through the foil with little or no interference because most of the atom is empty space.

The Neutron

Other scientists reviewed Rutherford's nuclear model of the atom with great interest and enthusiasm. However, some data didn't fit. For instance, recall that an atom's electrons have almost no mass. That means that the mass of an atom should be approximately equal to the mass of its protons. But, it isn't. The mass of most atoms is at least twice as great as the mass of its protons. Where does the extra mass come from?

Try at Home

Modeling the Nuclear Atom

Procedure

1. On a sheet of paper, draw a circle with a diameter equal to the width of the paper.
2. Small dots of paper in two colors will represent protons and neutrons. Using a dab of glue on each paper dot, make a model of the nucleus of the oxygen atom in the center of your circle. Oxygen has eight protons and eight neutrons.

Analysis

1. What particle is missing from your model of the oxygen atom?
2. How many of the missing particles should there be, and where should they be placed?

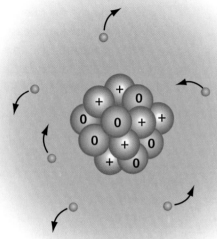

Figure 5-12 This atom of carbon has six protons and six neutrons in its nucleus. **How many electrons are in the "empty" space surrounding the nucleus?**

Rutherford reasoned that there must be another particle in the nucleus. The particle, which was later called the **neutron** (NEW trahn), would have the same mass as a proton and be electrically neutral. Proving the existence of neutrons was difficult, however, because a neutron has no charge, so it doesn't respond to magnets or cause fluorescent screens to light up. It took another 20 years before scientists were able to show by experiments that atoms contain neutrons.

The model of the atom was revised again to include neutrons in the nucleus. The nuclear atom, shown in **Figure 5-12,** has a tiny nucleus tightly packed with positively charged protons and neutral neutrons. Electrons occupy the space surrounding the nucleus. The number of electrons in an atom equals the number of protons in the atom.

Comparing Atom and Nucleus

When you look at drawings of atoms such as **Figure 5-12,** be aware that the nuclei are always drawn much larger than they actually are compared to the size of the atom. Picture the nucleus as being the size of a ping-pong ball. Then, the atom would have a diameter of more than 2.4 km. Another way to compare the size of a nucleus with the size of the atom is shown in **Figure 5-13.** You can see that it isn't surprising that in Rutherford's experiment, most of the alpha particles went directly through the gold foil without any interference from the gold atoms. An atom is mostly empty space.

Figure 5-13 If the nucleus of an atom were the size of one poppyseed on your bagel, the atom would have the diameter of this stadium.

What about the electrons?

In the early 1900s, physicists were trying to figure out how the electrons are arranged in an atom. It was natural to think that the negatively charged electrons are attracted to the positive nucleus in the same way Earth's moon is attracted to Earth. Then, electrons would travel in orbits around the nucleus. But, scientists soon learned that electrons are in constant, unpredictable motion and can't be pinned down. It's impossible to know precisely where an electron is at any moment. Instead, scientists talk about where the atom's electrons probably are. Electrons are probably in a region surrounding the nucleus, which is called the **electron cloud.** The model for the electron cloud, shown in **Figure 5-14,** is shaped like a sphere with the nucleus at its center. The electrons are more likely to be close to the nucleus rather than farther away because they are attracted to the positive charges of the protons. Notice the fuzzy outline of the cloud. There is no firm boundary because the electrons could be anywhere.

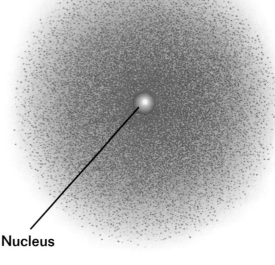

Figure 5-14 The electrons are more likely to be close to the nucleus rather than farther away, but they could be anywhere.

Nucleus

Section Assessment

1. Describe the three kinds of particles found in atoms. Where are they located in the atom and what are their charges?

2. If an atom has 49 protons, how many electrons does it have?

3. How does the nuclear atom differ from the uniform sphere model of the atom?

4. **Think Critically:** In Rutherford's experiment, why wouldn't the electrons in the atoms of the gold foil affect the paths of the alpha particles?

5. **Skill Builder**
   Concept Mapping Make a concept map using all the words in the Vocabulary list for this section. Add any other terms or words that will help create a complete diagram of the section. If you need help, refer to Concept Mapping in the **Skill Handbook** on page 526.

Using Math

The mass of an electron is $9.11 \times 12-28$ g. The proton is 1836 times heavier. What is the mass of the proton in grams and in kilograms?

Materials

- Sealed box
- Paper and pencil

Making a Model of the Invisible

How do scientists make models of things they can't see? First, they do experiments and gather as much information as possible. Then, they try to fit the information together into some kind of pattern and make inferences. From the data and inferences, they create a model that fits all their data.

What You'll Investigate

How can you determine the inside structure of a box?

Goals

- **Observe** the motion of a marble inside a closed box.
- **Infer** the structure inside the box.

Procedure

1. **Record** the number of the box your teacher gives you. Don't take the lid off the box or look inside.

2. **Lift** the box. **Tilt** the box. Gently **shake** it. In your Science Journal, record all your observations. Make a sketch of the way you think the marble in the box is rolling.

3. Use your observations to **infer** what the inside of the box looks like.

4. **Compare** your inferences with those of students who have the same box as you do. Then, you may want to make more observations or revise your inferences.

5. When you have gathered all the information you can, **sketch** your model in your Science Journal.

6. **Open** your box and **compare** your model with the actual inside structure of the box.

Conclude and Apply

1. How did your model of the inside of the box compare with the actual inside?

2. Is there any other test you could have used to gather more information?

3. How is an observation different from an inference?

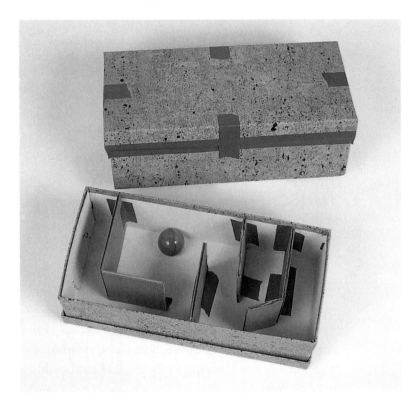

The Nucleus

What's in the nucleus?

The modern idea of the atom pictures all of the protons and neutrons packed into a tiny nucleus that is surrounded by electrons. How does the nucleus in an atom of one element differ from the nucleus of an atom of another element? The atoms of different elements contain different numbers of protons. The **atomic number** of an element is the number of protons in the nucleus of an atom of that element. The smallest of the atoms, the hydrogen atom, has one proton in its nucleus, so hydrogen's atomic number is 1. Chlorine has 17 protons, so chlorine's atomic number is 17. Uranium, the heaviest naturally occurring element, has 92 protons. Its atomic number is 92. Atoms of the same element always have the same number of protons.

Isotopes

The atomic number tells the number of protons, but what about the number of neutrons in an atom's nucleus? Atoms can have the same number of neutrons as protons, or they can have more or fewer neutrons than protons. Most atoms of carbon have six protons and six neutrons. But, some carbon atoms have seven neutrons and some have eight, as you can see in **Figure 5-15.** They are all carbon atoms because they all have six protons. These three kinds of carbon atoms are called isotopes. **Isotopes** (I suh tohps) are atoms of the same element that have different numbers of neutrons. The isotopes of carbon are called carbon-12, carbon-13, and carbon-14. The numbers 12, 13, and 14 are the mass numbers of the isotopes.

What You'll Learn

► The process of radioactive decay
► What is meant by half-life
► How radioactive isotopes are used

Vocabulary
atomic number
isotope
mass number
radioactive decay
half-life

Why It's Important

► Radioactive elements are both beneficial and dangerous.

Figure 5-15 The three isotopes of carbon differ only in the number of neutrons in each nucleus.

VISUALIZING
Isotopes

Carbon-12

Carbon-13

Carbon-14

Table 5-1

Isotopes of Carbon			
	Carbon-12	Carbon-13	Carbon-14
Mass Number	12	13	14
Number of Protons	6	6	6
Number of Neutrons	6	7	8
Number of Electrons	6	6	6
Atomic Number	6	6	6

Using Math

The atomic number of thorium-234 is 90. The atomic number of uranium-234 is 92. How many neutrons does each isotope have?

*inter*NET
CONNECTION

Visit the Glencoe Science Web Site at **www.glencoe.com/ sec/science/ca** for more information about radioactive decay.

The **mass number** of an isotope is the number of neutrons plus protons in the nucleus. **Table 5-1** shows the particles that make up each of the carbon isotopes. You can find the number of neutrons in an isotope by subtracting the atomic number (the number of protons) from the mass number. For example, carbon-14 has $14 - 6 = 8$ neutrons.

Nuclear Glue

When you need to hold something together, what do you use? Rubber bands? String? Glue? What do you suppose holds the protons and neutrons together in the nucleus of an atom? Because protons are positively charged, they repel each other just as the north ends of two magnets tend to push each other apart. The uncharged neutrons neither attract nor repel the protons, but they help keep the protons apart and reduce the repelling electric force. So, what force holds the nucleus together? That force is called the strong nuclear force. The strong nuclear force can hold the protons together only if they are nearly touching, as they are in the nucleus of the atom.

Radioactive Decay

Many atomic nuclei are stable when they have about the same number of protons and neutrons. Carbon-12 is the most stable isotope of carbon. It has six protons and six neutrons. Some nuclei are unstable because they have too many or too few neutrons. This is especially true for heavier elements such as uranium and plutonium. In these nuclei, repulsion builds up. The nucleus must release a particle to become stable. When particles are released, energy is given off. The release of nuclear particles and energy is called **radioactive decay.** When particles are ejected from a nucleus, the atomic number of the nucleus can change. One element is changed into another. The changing of one element into another through radioactive decay is called transmutation.

Figure 5-16 This life-saving smoke detector makes use of the radioactive isotope americium-241. The isotope is located inside the slotted chamber. When smoke particles enter the chamber, the alarm goes off.

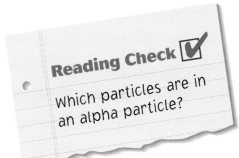

Some Isotopes Release Alpha Particles

Each year, thousands of homes are saved from fires by smoke detectors like the one in **Figure 5-16.** This device makes use of americium-241, which undergoes transmutation by ejecting an alpha particle. An alpha particle consists of two protons and two neutrons. Energy is released with the alpha particle. Together, the energy and particles are called nuclear radiation. In the smoke detector, the fast-moving alpha particles cause air to conduct an electric current. As long as the electric current is flowing, the smoke detector is silent. When smoke enters the detector, the flow of electric current is interrupted and the alarm is triggered. ☑

The atomic number of americium (a muh RIH shee um) is 95, so americium has 95 protons. When americium expels an alpha particle, it loses two protons and two neutrons. It's no longer americium. It has become the element that has 93 protons, neptunium. In **Figure 5-17,** notice that the mass and atomic numbers of neptunium and the alpha particle add up to the mass and atomic number of americium. All the nuclear particles of americium still exist after the transmutation, but a good deal of energy has been released.

Reading Check ☑
Which particles are in an alpha particle?

Figure 5-17 Americium expels an alpha particle, which is made up of two protons and two neutrons, so americium is changed into the element neptunium which has two fewer protons than americium.

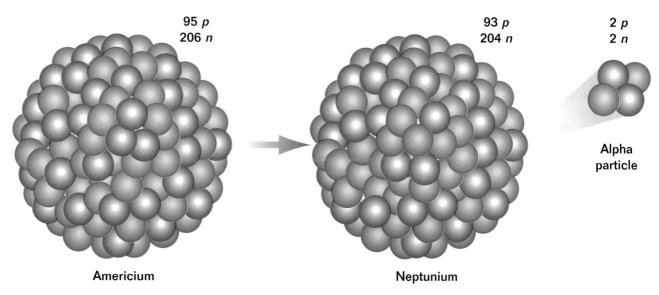

95 *p*
206 *n*

93 *p*
204 *n*

2 *p*
2 *n*

Alpha particle

Americium

Neptunium

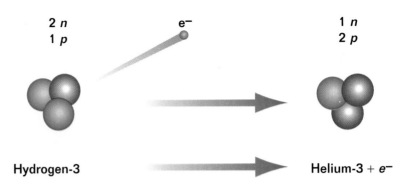

Figure 5-18 The hydrogen-3 isotope converts a neutron into a proton and an electron and tosses out the electron. **What is the element with two protons that remains?**

2 n
1 p

e⁻

1 n
2 p

Hydrogen-3

Helium-3 + e⁻

Using Math

The atomic number of polonium-218 is 84. Its mass number is 218. When this isotope decays by releasing an alpha particle, what is the atomic number of the resulting isotope? What is its mass number?

Some Isotopes Release Beta Particles

Some elements undergo transmutations through a different process. Their nuclei emit an electron called a beta particle. A beta particle is a high-energy electron that comes from the nucleus, not from the electron cloud. But, the nucleus only contains protons and neutrons. How can it give off or emit an electron? During this kind of transmutation, a neutron becomes unstable and splits into an electron and a proton. The electron or beta particle is released with a large amount of energy.

Because a neutron has been changed into a proton, the nucleus of the element has an additional proton. The atomic number of the element that results is greater by one. **Figure 5-18** shows the beta decay of the hydrogen-3 isotope. With two neutrons in its nucleus, hydrogen-3 is unstable. One neutron is converted to a proton by beta decay, and an isotope of helium is produced. The mass of the element stays almost the same because the mass of an electron is so small.

Half-Life

How can you tell when a nucleus in a sample will decay? You can't. Radioactive decay is random. It's like watching popcorn begin to pop. You can't predict which kernel will explode or when. But, if you're an experienced popcorn maker, you might be able to predict how long it will take for half the kernels to pop. A convenient way to measure the rate of decay of a nucleus is by half-life. The **half-life** of a radioactive isotope is the amount of time required for half of a sample of the element to decay. For example, iodine-131 has a half-life of eight days. If you start with a sample of 4 g of iodine-131, after eight days you would have only 2 g of iodine-131 remaining. After 16 days, or two half-lives, half of the 2 g would have decayed and you would have only 1 g. After yet another half-life, only 0.5 g would remain. **Figure 5-19** is a diagram of the process.

Figure 5-19 Half-life is the amount of time in which one half of a sample decays. **What happens to the mass of the remaining isotope at the end of each eight days?**

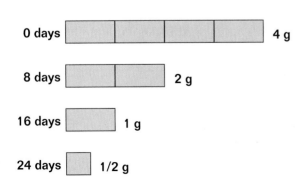

0 days   4 g

8 days   2 g

16 days   1 g

24 days   1/2 g

The radioactive decay of unstable atoms goes on at a steady pace, unaffected by conditions such as weather, pressure, magnetic or electric fields, and even chemical reactions. Half-lives, which are different for each isotope, range in length from fractions of a second to billions of years.

Carbon Dating

Carbon-14 is used to determine the age of dead animals, plants, and humans. The half-life of carbon-14 is 5730 years. In a living organism, the amount of carbon-14 remains in constant balance with the levels of the isotope in the atmosphere or ocean. This balance occurs because living organisms both take in and release carbon. For example, animals take in carbon from food such as plants, and release carbon as carbon dioxide. While life processes go on, any carbon-14 nucleus that decays is replaced by another from the environment. When the plant or animal dies, the decaying nuclei can no longer be replaced. When archaeologists find an ancient item, such as the one in **Figure 5-20,** they can find out how much carbon-14 it has and compare it with the amount of carbon-14 there would have been in the organism when it was alive. Knowing the half-life of carbon-14, they can then calculate when the organism lived.

Mini Lab

Graphing Half-Life
Procedure

1. Make a table with three columns. Label the first column *Number of Half-Lives.* Label the second column *Days Passed* and the third column *Mass of Thorium Remaining.*

2. Thorium-234 has a half-life of 24 days. Fill the first column with the number of half-lives: zero, one, two, and so on up to the number of half-lives that equals 144 days.

3. Fill the second column with the number of days that have passed since the start of the experiment: zero days, 24 days, 48 days, 72 days, and so on up to 144 days.

4. Assume that you have a sample of 64 kg of thorium. Calculate the mass of thorium remaining after each half-life and fill in the third column.

5. Plot the data in the first and third columns on a graph with half-life on the *x*-axis and mass of thorium on the *y*-axis.

Analysis

1. During which 24-day period does the most thorium-234 decay?

2. How much thorium-234 was left in your sample on the 144th day?

3. Compare the mass of thorium-234 after each half-life to the previous mass. How are they related?

Figure 5-20 Using carbon-14 dating techniques, archaeologists can find out when the biological materials in this artifact were living.

Nuclear Waste Products

Waste products from nuclear power plants are a problem because nuclear fuels produce leftover isotopes that still release much radiation. This radioactive waste must be permanently isolated from people and the environment because it continues to produce harmful radiation. Special disposal sites that can contain the radiation must be found. One such site is in Carlsbad, New Mexico, where nuclear waste is buried 655 m below the surface of Earth.

New Elements by Transmutation

Scientists now create elements by smashing atomic particles into a target element. Alpha and beta particles, for example, are accelerated in particle accelerators like the one in **Figure 5-21** to speeds high enough that they can smash into a large nucleus and be absorbed on impact. The absorbed particle converts the target element into another element with a higher atomic number. These artificial transmutations have created new elements that do not exist in nature. Elements with atomic numbers 93 to 112 have been made in this way.

Tracer Elements

The process of artificial transmutation has been adapted so that radioactive isotopes of normally stable elements can be made in hospitals and clinics using specially designed equipment. These isotopes, called tracer elements, are used to diagnose disease and to study environmental conditions. The radioactive isotope is introduced into a living system and then followed as it decays by a device that detects radiation. These devices often present the results as a visual display or photograph. The isotopes chosen for medical purposes have short

Radiation Therapy

When a person has cancer, cells reproduce rapidly, causing a tumor. When radiation is focused directly on the tumor, it can slow or stop the cell division while leaving healthy surrounding tissue largely unaffected. Find out more about radiation therapy and summarize your findings in your Science Journal.

Figure 5-21 Giant particle accelerators, such as HERA in Hamburg, Germany, are needed to speed up particles to the speeds necessary to cause an atomic transmutation.

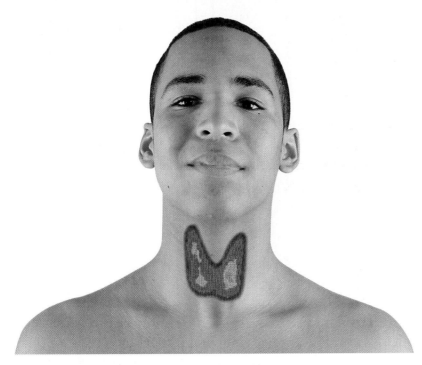

Figure 5-22 Most of the iodine in your diet goes to your thyroid. This image of a healthy thyroid was made by injecting a solution of iodine-131 into the bloodstream. The colors in the image indicate amounts of iodine-131 absorbed at various locations inside the thyroid. **How could this image be used to help diagnose thyroid disease?**

half-lives, which allow them to be used without the risk of exposing living organisms to prolonged radiation.

The isotope iodine-131 has been used to diagnose problems with the thyroid, a gland located at the base of the neck. The radioactive iodine, which is absorbed by the thyroid, creates an image of the thyroid like the one in **Figure 5-22.** Other radioactive isotopes are used to detect cancer, digestion problems, and circulation difficulties.

Problem Solving

Designing a Safe Container

You have been hired to design a container to transport radioactive waste. A whole raw egg will represent the waste. You must consider problems such as accidents, leaks, and ease of transportation. Your design will need to withstand the following tests.

Drop Test: Your teacher will drop your container of radioactive waste from the top of a ladder or a high structure (7 m − 10 m) onto a hard surface.

Side Impact Test: A 1-L plastic bottle filled with sand will be suspended from a door frame. When it is released at a 45 degree angle, it will strike your radioactive waste container.

After each test, open your container to examine the egg. Did it leak? Break apart? Stay in one piece?

Solve the Problem

1. In your Science Journal, write a hypothesis about how you can keep your waste from breaking or spilling.
2. Build your radioactive waste container.
3. Test your hypothesis using the Drop Test and Side Impact Test.
4. Was your hypothesis supported?

Think Critically

1. What could be improved in your design?
2. What other test would you propose?
3. What safety measures must be considered when transporting and storing radioactive waste? Why are these safety measures important?

Figure 5-23 Using fertilizer containing a small amount of a radioactive isotope, scientists can see how the fertilizer is absorbed by the plant.

interNET
CONNECTION

Visit the Glencoe Science Web Site at **www.glencoe.com/ sec/science/ca** for more information about the use of isotopes in medicine and agriculture.

In the environment, tracers such as sulfur-35 can be placed in pesticides and followed to see what impact the pesticide has as it moves through an ecosystem. As you can see in **Figure 5-23,** fertilizers containing small amounts of radioactive isotopes are used to see how well plants absorb fertilizers.

Section Assessment

1. What are isotopes?

2. How are radioactive isotopes used to detect health problems?

3. Explain what is meant by radioactive decay. How is the rate of radioactive decay measured?

4. **Think Critically:** Suppose you had two samples of the same radioactive isotope. One sample was 25 g. The other was 50 g. Would the same number of particles be ejected from each sample in the first hour? Explain.

5. **Skill Builder**
   Making Models You have learned how scientists used marbles, cookie dough, and a cloud to model the structure of the atom. The poppy seed and the stadium in this chapter modeled the difference in size between the nucleus and atom. Do the **Chapter 5 Skill Activity** on page 558 to make paper-and-pencil models of the electrons, protons, and neutrons in the atoms of different isotopes.

Using Computers

Word Processing Use a word processing program to make a table of the three particles found in atoms. Include columns labeled *Particle, Charge,* and *Mass.* For the masses of the three particles, refer to Using Math in the Section 5-1 Section Assessment. Protons and neutrons have approximately the same mass. If you need help, refer to page 544.

Preserving Food by Irradiation

Eating food contaminated with harmful bacteria, parasites, or fungi can be a serious health risk. According to the Centers for Disease Control and Prevention in Atlanta, Georgia, every year millions of people in the United States become ill from eating contaminated food, and some 9000 Americans die as a result of food-borne illnesses. Worldwide, many more people die of malnutrition and starvation because they don't have enough fresh, high-quality food to eat.

For centuries, people have been preserving food—and in so doing preventing the growth of harmful bacteria and other organisms—by canning, pickling, drying, smoking, freezing, and freeze-drying it. However, all of these methods change the flavor, texture, and consistency of the preserved food in some way. Food irradiation, on the other hand, is a food preservation process that is growing in popularity because it destroys potentially harmful organisms in food without changing the food's quality.

What is irradiation?

In the irradiation process, food is exposed to low-level radiation but never comes into direct contact with the radiation source. Irradiation kills bacteria, prevents cell division in other kinds of organisms, helps prevent spoilage, and slows ripening in fresh vegetables and fruits, such as the papayas at left.

Foods that are commonly irradiated are ground wheat and other cereal grain products, spices, fresh fruits and vegetables, frozen seafood, poultry, and pork.

Are irradiated foods safe?

Many people fear radiation and any nuclear-related technology. Consumers need to understand that food does not become radioactive as a result of exposure to low-level radiation and that the nutritional quality of the food does not change. Based on decades of research, the Food and Drug Administration (FDA) has approved a variety of specific applications of food irradiation. FDA regulations require that irradiated food be labeled as such.

interNET CONNECTION

Visit the Glencoe Science Web Site at **www.glencoe.com/sec/science/ca** to find more information about the debate on food irradiation.

Activity 5•2

Half-Life

T he decay rates of most radioactive isotopes range from milli-seconds to billions of years. If you know the half-life of an isotope and the size of a sample of the isotope, can you predict how much will remain after a certain amount of time? Is it possible to predict when a specific atom will decay?

Possible Materials

• Pennies
• Graph paper

Recognize the Problem

How can you use pennies to create a model that will show how half-life can predict the amount of a radioactive isotope remaining after specific periods of time?

Form a Hypothesis

Based on the definition of *half-life*, write a hypothesis that shows how half-life can be used to predict how much of a radioactive iso-tope will remain after a certain amount of time.

Goals

• **Model** isotopes in a radio-active sample. For each half-life, determine the amount of change in the objects that represent the isotopes in the model.

• **Design an experiment** to test the usefulness of half-life in predicting how much radioactive material still remains after a specific length of time.

Test Your Hypothesis

Plan

1. With your group, **write** the hypothesis statement.

2. **Write** down the steps of the procedure you will use to test your hypothesis. Assume that each penny represents an atom in a radioactive sample. Each coin that lands heads up after flipping has decayed.

3. **List** the materials you will need.

4. In your Science Journal, **make a data table** with two columns. Label one *Half-Life* and the other *Atoms Remaining*.

5. Decide how you can use the pennies to represent the radioactive decay of an isotope.

6. **Determine** (a) what will represent one half-life in your model, and (b) how many half-lives you will investigate.

7. **Decide** (a) what variables there will be in your model, and (b) which variable will be represented on the *y*-axis of your graph and which will be represented on the *x*-axis.

Do

1. Make sure your teacher approves your plan and your data table before you proceed.

2. Carry out your plan.

Analyze Your Data

1. The relationship among the starting number of pennies, the number of pennies remaining (*Y*), and the number of half-lives (*X*) is the following:

$$Y = \frac{\text{(starting number of pennies)}}{2^X}$$

Graph this equation using a graphing calculator. Use your graph to find the number of pennies remaining after 2.5 half-lives.

2. **Compare** your results with those of other groups in your class.

Draw Conclusions

1. Is it possible to use your model to predict which individual atoms will decay during one half-life? Why or why not?

2. Can you predict the total number of atoms that will decay in one half-life? **Explain.**

3. How many half-lives are necessary for the transmutation of the entire sample?

For a **preview** of this
chapter, study this
Reviewing Main Ideas
before you read the chapter.
After you have studied this
chapter, you can use the
Reviewing Main Ideas to
review the chapter.

GLENCOE TECHNOLOGY

The Glencoe
MindJogger,
Audiocassettes,
and CD-ROM
provide additional
opportunities for review.

Section 5-1 EARLY MODELS OF THE ATOM

The idea that matter is composed of indivisible atoms was first introduced in ancient Greece. In the eighteenth and nineteenth centuries, scientists performed experiments to determine the properties of an atom. John Dalton proposed that an atom is a sphere of matter that is the same through-out. Then, J.J. Thomson discovered that all atoms contain **electrons,** which are tiny, negatively charged particles. Thomson proposed that an atom is a sphere containing all the **protons** with their positive charges. The electrons are mixed uniformly in the sphere like raisins in a ball of cookie dough. *How does the number of protons compare with the number of electrons?*

THE NUCLEAR ATOM

Ernest Rutherford tested Thomson's model by bombarding thin gold foil with speeding, positively charged **alpha particles.** Rutherford expected the alpha particles to pass through the foil because Dalton's model pre-dicted there would be no large concentration of mass or charge to change the paths of the alpha particles. Because some of the alpha particles were deflected from their paths, Rutherford revised the model of the atom again. He hypothesized that almost all the mass and all the positive charge of an atom is concentrated in an extremely tiny nucleus at the center of the atom. *Where are the electrons in this model of the atom?*

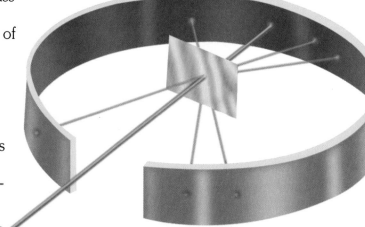

Reading Check ✓

Should the early models of atom structure be labeled as fact or opinion? Explain your answer.

Section 5-2 RADIOACTIVITY

An atom's nucleus contains protons and neutrons held together by the strong nuclear force. If the numbers of neutrons and protons are not approximately equal, the nucleus can become unstable and undergo radioactive decay. Some nuclei decay by emitting an alpha particle. Other nuclei decay by ejecting a **beta particle.** Transmutation is a process in which one element is changed into another through radioactive decay. Some radioactive **isotopes** are made in this way by smashing speeding atomic particles into a target element. These isotopes may be used in medicine and for the study of the environment. *What particles are released from the nucleus in alpha emission and in beta emission?*

HALF-LIFE

Half-life is a measure of the decay rate of a nucleus. It is the time needed for one-half of the mass of a sample of a radioactive isotope to decay. Half-lives vary from fractions of a second to billions of years. *If an isotope has a half-life of 4 s, how many grams remain of a 100-g sample after 8 s have passed?*

Using Vocabulary

a. atomic number   **f.** isotope
b. electron   **g.** mass number
c. electron cloud   **h.** neutron
d. element   **i.** proton
e. half-life   **j.** radioactive decay

Explain the difference between terms in each of the following sets.

1. alpha particle, beta particle
2. electron, proton
3. mass number, atomic number
4. element, isotope
5. half-life, radioactive decay

Checking Concepts

Choose the word or phrase that best answers the question.

6. What is the atomic number of an element equal to?
   A) the number of energy levels in an atom
   B) the number of protons in an atom's nucleus
   C) the number of neutrons in an atom's nucleus
   D) the total number of protons and neutrons in an atom's nucleus

7. The atomic number of boron is 5, so boron-11 contains which particles?
   A) 11 electrons
   B) five neutrons
   C) five protons and six neutrons
   D) six protons and five neutrons

8. What are atoms of the same element that have different numbers of neutrons?
   A) protons   C) ions
   B) electrons   D) isotopes

9. In beta decay, a neutron in the nucleus of an isotope is converted to which of the following?
   A) a proton and an electron
   B) a nucleus
   C) an alpha particle
   D) a beta particle

10. What is the process by which an atom of one element changes into an atom of another element?
    A) half-life
    B) a chemical reaction
    C) a chain reaction
    D) transmutation

11. How did William Crookes know that the glow in the cathode-ray tube resulted from a stream of charged particles?
    A) It was green.
    B) It caused a shadow of the anode.
    C) It was deflected by a magnet.
    D) It occurred only when the battery was connected.

12. Why did Rutherford infer that most of the mass and all of the positive charge in an atom is in a tiny nucleus?
    A) All of the alpha particles went straight through the gold foil.
    B) None of the alpha particles went straight through the gold foil.
    C) The positive and negative charges were uniform throughout the atom.
    D) Only a concentrated charge could deflect energetic alpha particles.

13. What did J.J. Thomson's experiment show?
    A) The atom is like a uniform sphere.
    B) Cathode rays are made up of electrons.
    C) All atoms undergo radioactive decay.
    D) Isotopes undergo radioactive decay.

14. A radioactive isotope has a half-life of two years. At the end of four years, how much of the original isotope remains?
A) one half
C) one third
B) one fourth
D) none

15. How can the model of the nuclear atom be described?
A) a nucleus that can decay
B) a ball of raisin cookie dough
C) an electron cloud
D) a nucleus in an electron cloud

Thinking Critically

16. How is it possible for atoms of an element to have different masses?

17. Matter can neither be created nor destroyed, but would it be possible for the amounts of some elements in Earth's crust to decrease? Increase?

18. Why must a neutral atom have the same number of protons and electrons?

Developing Skills

If you need help, refer to the **Skill Handbook.**

19. Predicting: If radium-226 releases an alpha particle, what is the mass number of the isotope formed?

20. Using Graphs: The radioactive decay of an isotope is plotted in the graph. What is the half-life of the isotope? How many grams of the isotope remain after three half-lives?

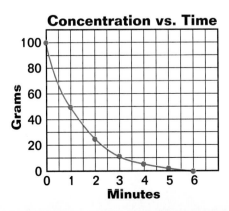

Concentration vs. Time

Grams / Minutes

THE PRINCETON REVIEW

Test-Taking Tip

Use Process of Elimination On any multiple-choice test, you can use a process of elimination to exclude any answers that you know are wrong. Find the ones you know are wrong, eliminate them, and you'll have fewer choices from which to select your answer.

Test Practice

Use these questions to test your Science Proficiency.

1. What did Rutherford's alpha particle experiment show?
A) Electrons have a negative charge.
B) Most of the mass and all of the positive charge of an atom is found in a tiny nucleus.
C) A proton is a hydrogen atom without its electron.
D) Electrons circle the nucleus of an atom in orbits.

2. What is the difference between chlorine-35 and chlorine-37?
A) Chlorine-37 has two more electrons than chlorine-35.
B) Chlorine-37 has two more protons than chlorine-35.
C) Chlorine-37 has two more neutrons than chlorine-35.
D) Chlorine-37 has one more proton and one more neutron than chlorine-35.

The Periodic Table

Chapter Preview

Skills Preview

Skill Builders
- Compare and Contrast
- Observe and Infer

Activities
- Observe
- Compare

MiniLabs
- Design
- Infer

Reading Check ✔

As you read this chapter, list and define the forms of these words that you encounter: *metal, period, element,* and *atom.* Then find more variations of each word in a dictionary and define them.

Explore Activity

Every 29.5 days, the full moon rises over Louisville, Kentucky, and begins to cycle through its phases from full moon to new moon and back again to full moon. This monthly cycle was one of the earliest patterns recognized and recorded by humans. Events that follow a predictable pattern are called periodic events. Modern calendars are based on a different periodic event—Earth's yearly journey around the sun. The opening of school in the fall and the celebration of your birthday are periodic events. What other periodic events can you think of?

Model a Periodic Pattern

1. On a blank sheet of paper, make a grid with four squares across and four squares down. The grid should fill the sheet of paper.

2. Your teacher will give you 16 pieces of paper with different shapes and colors. Identify properties you can use to distinguish one piece of paper from another.

3. Place a piece of paper in each square on your grid. Arrange the pieces on the grid so that each column contains pieces that are similar.

4. Within each column, arrange the pieces to show a gradual change in their appearance.

In your Science Journal, describe the patterns you created. Explain how the properties change in the rows across the grid and in the columns down the grid.

6·1 Introduction to the Periodic Table

What You'll Learn

▶ The history of the periodic table
▶ How to interpret an element key
▶ How the periodic table is organized

Vocabulary

period   nonmetal
group   metalloid
metal

Why It's Important

▶ The periodic table organizes a lot of information about the elements and makes it easier for you to learn.

Development of the Periodic Table

Early civilizations were familiar with a few of the substances scientists now call elements. They made coins and jewelry from gold and silver. Warriors at the Battle of Troy wore armor and carried shields made from bronze, a mixture of copper and tin. The Assyrians built an empire using steel weapons made by combining iron with carbon. In the nineteenth century, chemists began to search for new elements. By 1830, they had isolated and named 55 different elements. As the list of elements grew, chemists wondered how many elements were left to be discovered.

Mendeleev's Contribution

In 1860, the First International Chemical Congress met in Germany. One of the 140 delegates who attended was the Russian chemist Dmitri Mendeleev (men duh LAY uhf). When he returned to Russia, he used what he had learned at the congress to build a table of the elements. When Mendeleev arranged the elements in order of increasing atomic mass, as shown in **Figure 6-1,** he began to see a pattern. Elements with similar properties fell into groups on the table.

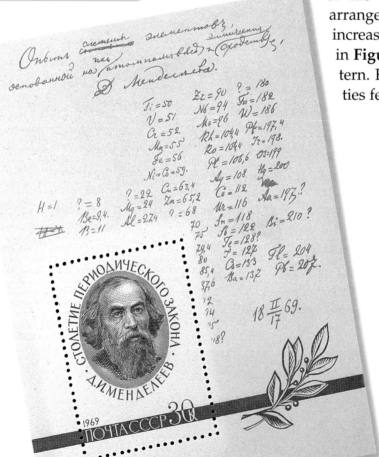

Figure 6-1 Mendeleev continued to work on this table. Notice where he put question marks. He predicted that elements would be discovered to fill these places on the table.

Mendeleev published the first version of his periodic table in the *Journal of the Russian Chemical Society* in 1869. At that time, not all the elements were known. To make his table work, Mendeleev had to leave gaps for undiscovered elements. Based on the groupings in his table, he predicted the properties for six of the unknown elements. Mendeleev's predictions spurred other chemists to look for the missing elements. Within 15 years, three of the missing elements—gallium, scandium, and germanium—were discovered. In **Table 6-1,** you can see that Mendeleev's predictions about germanium were close.

Moseley's Improvement

Although Mendeleev's table correctly organized most of the elements, a few elements seemed out of place. In the early twentieth century, the English physicist Henry Moseley realized that Mendeleev's table could be improved by arranging the elements according to atomic number rather than atomic mass. The atomic number of an element is the number of protons in the nucleus of its atoms. Each element in the table has one more proton than the previous element, so the atomic numbers of missing elements could be filled in by comparing the number of protons in each known element. With Moseley's table, it was clear how many elements were still undiscovered.

The Modern Periodic Table

In the table on the following pages, the elements are organized by increasing atomic number into rows or periods labeled 6-7. A **period** is a row of elements in the periodic table whose properties change gradually and predictably. The first period has only two elements. The second and third periods each have eight elements. Periods 4 and 5 have 18 elements. Period 6 has 32. New elements are still being added to period 7.

Table 6-1

Properties of Germanium		
Property	Predicted (1869)	Actual (1886)
Atomic mass	72	72.6
Melting point	very high	937°C
Density	5.5 g/cm^3	5.32 g/cm^3
Color	dark gray	gray-white

Try at Home

MiniLab

Designing a Periodic Table

Procedure

1. Collect pens and pencils from everyone in your class.

2. Decide which properties of the pens and pencils you will use to organize them into a periodic table. Consider properties such as color, mass, or length. Then, create your table.

Analysis

1. Explain how your periodic table is similar to the periodic table of the elements.

2. If your classmates brought different pens or pencils to class tomorrow, how would you decide where to place them on the table?

PERIODIC TABLE OF THE ELEMENTS

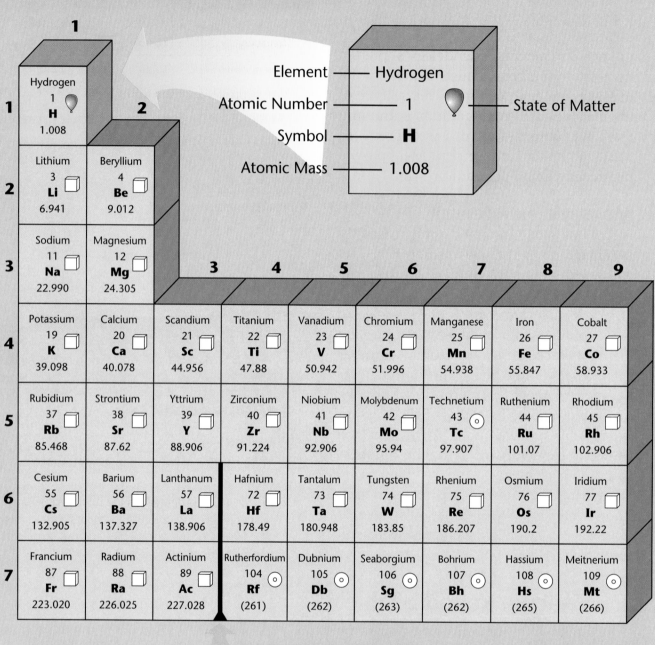

1								
Hydrogen 1 **H** 1.008	**2**							
Lithium 3 **Li** 6.941	Beryllium 4 **Be** 9.012							
Sodium 11 **Na** 22.990	Magnesium 12 **Mg** 24.305	**3**	**4**	**5**	**6**	**7**	**8**	**9**
Potassium 19 **K** 39.098	Calcium 20 **Ca** 40.078	Scandium 21 **Sc** 44.956	Titanium 22 **Ti** 47.88	Vanadium 23 **V** 50.942	Chromium 24 **Cr** 51.996	Manganese 25 **Mn** 54.938	Iron 26 **Fe** 55.847	Cobalt 27 **Co** 58.933
Rubidium 37 **Rb** 85.468	Strontium 38 **Sr** 87.62	Yttrium 39 **Y** 88.906	Zirconium 40 **Zr** 91.224	Niobium 41 **Nb** 92.906	Molybdenum 42 **Mo** 95.94	Technetium 43 **Tc** 97.907	Ruthenium 44 **Ru** 101.07	Rhodium 45 **Rh** 102.906
Cesium 55 **Cs** 132.905	Barium 56 **Ba** 137.327	Lanthanum 57 **La** 138.906	Hafnium 72 **Hf** 178.49	Tantalum 73 **Ta** 180.948	Tungsten 74 **W** 183.85	Rhenium 75 **Re** 186.207	Osmium 76 **Os** 190.2	Iridium 77 **Ir** 192.22
Francium 87 **Fr** 223.020	Radium 88 **Ra** 226.025	Actinium 89 **Ac** 227.028	Rutherfordium 104 **Rf** (261)	Dubnium 105 **Db** (262)	Seaborgium 106 **Sg** (263)	Bohrium 107 **Bh** (262)	Hassium 108 **Hs** (265)	Meitnerium 109 **Mt** (266)

Element —— Hydrogen
Atomic Number —— 1 —— State of Matter
Symbol —— **H**
Atomic Mass —— 1.008

Lanthanide Series

Cerium 58 **Ce** 140.115	Praseodymium 59 **Pr** 140.908	Neodymium 60 **Nd** 144.24	Promethium 61 **Pm** 144.913	Samarium 62 **Sm** 150.36	Europium 63 **Eu** 151.965

Actinide Series

Thorium 90 **Th** 232.038	Protactinium 91 **Pa** 231.036	Uranium 92 **U** 238.029	Neptunium 93 **Np** 237.048	Plutonium 94 **Pu** 244.064	Americium 95 **Am** 243.061

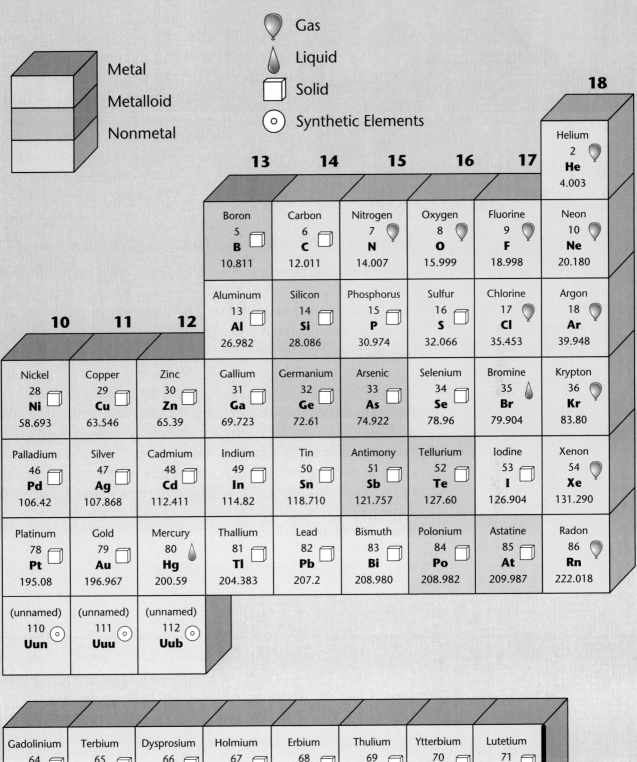

The periodic table has 18 columns of elements. Each column contains a group, or family, of elements. A **group** contains elements that have similar physical or chemical properties. The human family in **Figure 6-2** has similarities such as facial features, hair color, and build, but the similarities among a family of elements may not always be clear from appearance alone. For example, Group 17 contains a greenish-yellow gas called chlorine, a red-brown liquid called bromine, and a shiny black solid called iodine. Despite these differences, the elements in Group 17 behave in similar ways.

Figure 6-2 Groups of elements can be compared to human families. The members of this family have noticeable family traits. **What traits do they share? How are they different?**

Sections of the Periodic Table

The periodic table can be divided into two sections. One section consists of the first two groups, Groups 1 and 2, plus the elements in Groups 13-18. These eight groups are called the representative elements. They include metals, metalloids, and nonmetals. The elements in Groups 5-12 are called transition elements. They are all metals. Some transition elements, called the inner transition elements, are placed below the main table. These elements are called the lanthanide and actinide series because one series follows the element lanthanum, element 57, and the other series follows actinium, element 89. The lanthanides and actinides are placed below the table so that the table will take up less space. **Figure 6-3** shows what the periodic table would look like with the inner transition elements included.

Figure 6-3 This table shows you how the inner transition elements fit into the periodic table.

	1	2	3												
1	H														
2	Li	Be													
3	Na	Mg													
4	K	Ca	Sc												
5	Rb	Sr	Y												
6	Cs	Ba	La	Ce	Pr	Nd	Pm	Sm	Eu	Gd	Tb	Dy	Ho	Er	Tm	Yb
7	Fr	Ra	Ac	Th	Pa	U	Np	Pu	Am	Cm	Bk	Cf	Es	Fm	Md	No

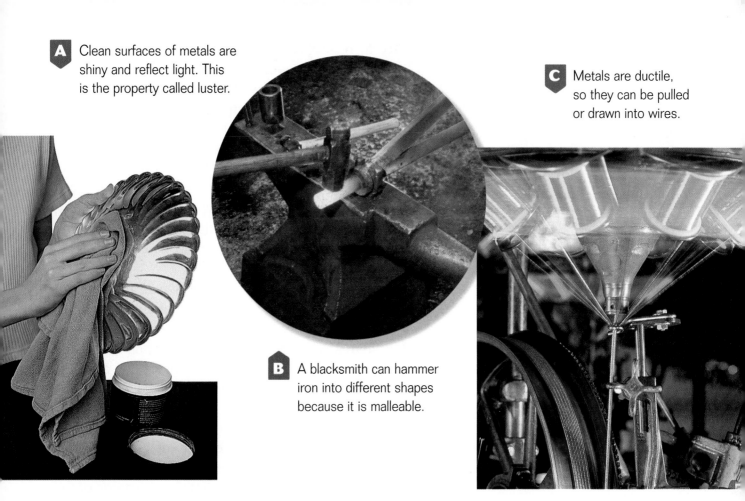

A Clean surfaces of metals are shiny and reflect light. This is the property called luster.

B A blacksmith can hammer iron into different shapes because it is malleable.

C Metals are ductile, so they can be pulled or drawn into wires.

Metals, Nonmetals, and Metalloids

Look again at the periodic table. The table is color coded to show which elements are metals, which are nonmetals, and which are metalloids. With the exception of mercury, all the metals are solids, most with high melting points. A **metal** is an element that has luster and is a good conductor of heat and electricity. Other properties of metals are illustrated in **Figure 6-4**.

Figure 6-4 Metals can be distinguished from nonmetals and metalloids by their physical properties—luster, malleability, and ductility.

												13	14	15	16	17	18
																	He
												B	C	N	O	F	Ne
	4	5	6	7	8	9	10	11	12			Al	Si	P	S	Cl	Ar
	Ti	V	Cr	Mn	Fe	Co	Ni	Cu	Zn			Ga	Ge	As	Se	Br	Kr
	Zr	Nb	Mo	Tc	Ru	Rh	Pd	Ag	Cd			In	Sn	Sb	Te	I	Xe
Lu	Hf	Ta	W	Re	Os	Ir	Pt	Au	Hg			Tl	Pb	Bi	Po	At	Rn
Lr	Rf	Db	Sg	Bh	Hs	Mt	Uun	Uuu	Uub								

Using Math

One kilogram of high-quality coal can produce enough energy to extract 55 g of aluminum from its bauxite ore. Recycling aluminum requires only five percent of the energy used to extract aluminum from bauxite. How many grams of aluminum can be recycled using 1 kg of high-quality coal?

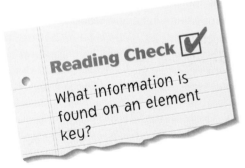

Reading Check

What information is found on an element key?

The ability to reflect light is a property of metals called luster. When a metal is polished or cut to expose a fresh surface, it reflects light. Many metals can be pressed or pounded into thin sheets or shaped into objects because they are malleable (MAL yuh bul). Metals are also ductile (DUK tul), which means that they can be drawn out into wires.

Nonmetals are usually gases or brittle solids at room temperature and poor conductors of heat and electricity. Although there are only 16 nonmetals, they include many elements that are essential for life: carbon, sulfur, nitrogen, oxygen, phosphorus, and iodine.

The elements that form a bridge between metals and nonmetals on the periodic table are called metalloids (MET ul oydz). As you might expect from the name, a **metalloid** is an element that shares some properties with metals and some with nonmetals. For example, boron has luster like a metal, but, like a nonmetal, it is a poor conductor of electricity.

The Element Keys

Each element is represented on the periodic table by a box called the element key. An enlarged key for hydrogen is shown in **Figure 6-5.** An element key contains the name of the element, its atomic number, its symbol, and its average atomic mass. Elements that do not occur naturally on Earth are marked with a bull's-eye logo. These are synthetic elements. Element keys for elements that occur naturally on Earth include a logo that tells you whether the element is a solid, a liquid, or a gas at room temperature. All the gases except hydrogen are located on the right side of the table. They are marked by a balloon logo. Most of the other elements are solids at room temperature and are marked by a cube. Locate the two elements on the periodic table that are liquids at room temperature. Their logo is a drop.

Figure 6-5 As you begin to use the periodic table, the element keys on the periodic table will provide you with useful information.

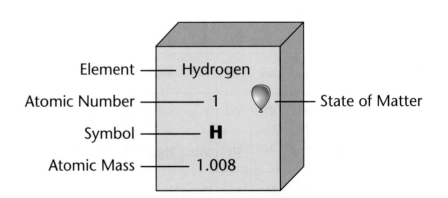

Symbols for the Elements

The symbols for the elements are either one- or two-letter abbreviations, often based on the element name. For example, V is the symbol for vanadium, and Sc is the symbol for scandium. Sometimes, the symbols don't match the names, for example, Ag for silver and Na for sodium. In those cases, the symbol may come from Greek or Latin names for the elements. Some elements are named for scientists such as Lise Meitner (meitnerium, Mt). Some are named for geographic locations such as France (francium, Fr). The symbols Uun, Uuu, and Uub are temporary symbols for unnamed elements. **Table 6-2** shows the origin of some element names and symbols.

Table 6-2

Chemical Symbols and Their Origins		
Name	**Symbol**	**Origin**
Mendelevium	Md	For Dmitri Mendeleev
Lead	Pb	The Latin name for lead is *plumbum*.
Thorium	Th	The Norse god of thunder is Thor.
Polonium	Po	For Poland, where Marie Curie was born
Hydrogen	H	From Greek words meaning "water former"
Mercury	Hg	Hydrargyrum means "liquid silver" in Greek.
Gold	Au	*Aurum* means "shining dawn" in Latin

Section Assessment

1. Use the elements in period 4 to show how the physical state of the elements changes as the atomic number increases across a period.

2. What are the two sections of the periodic table?

3. Where are the metals located in the periodic table? The nonmetals? The metalloids?

4. **Think Critically:** How would the modern periodic table be different if elements were still arranged by average atomic mass instead of atomic number? Give two specific examples.

5. **Skill Builder**
   Classifying Every day, you compare, contrast, and classify objects in the world around you. Then, you classify what you have learned. Do the **Chapter 6 Skill Activity** on page 559 to classify some of the elements.

Using Math

Prepare a circle graph of the most abundant elements by weight in Earth's crust. What percent by weight of the crust is from metals? Metalloids? Nonmetals?
Data: oxygen, 46.6%; silicon, 27.7%; aluminum, 8.1%; iron, 5.0%; calcium, 3.6%; sodium, 2.8%; potassium, 2.6%; magnesium, 2.1%; other, 1.5%

6•2 Representative Elements

What You'll Learn

▶ Properties of the representative elements
▶ Uses for the representative elements

Vocabulary
alloy
semiconductor

Why It's Important

▶ Many representative elements play key roles in your body, your environment, and in the the things you use every day.

Groups 1 and 2

You probably have friends who like to interact with other people and do so easily and often. They're like the elements in Groups 1 and 2. These two groups of elements are always found in nature combined with other elements. They're called active metals because of their readiness to form new substances with other elements. They are all metals except hydrogen, the first element in Group 1. Although hydrogen is placed in Group 1, it shares properties with the elements in both Group 1 and Group 17.

The Alkali Metals

The Group 1 elements—lithium, sodium, potassium, rubidium, cesium, and francium—have a special family name. They are called the alkali metals. All the alkali metals are silvery solids with low densities and low melting points as shown in **Figure 6-6.** From lithium at the top of the group to francium at the bottom, the elements become more and more ready to combine with other substances to form new substances. Some other properties and uses of the alkali metals are shown in **Figure 6-7.**

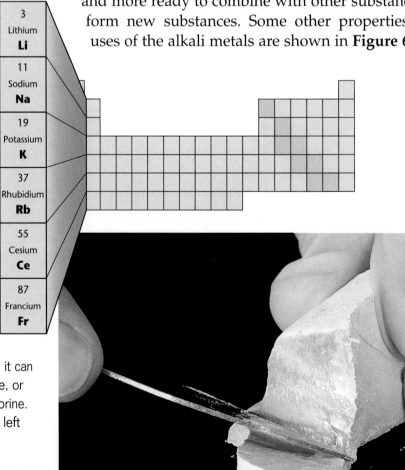

| 1 |
| 3 Lithium **Li** |
| 11 Sodium **Na** |
| 19 Potassium **K** |
| 37 Rhubidium **Rb** |
| 55 Cesium **Ce** |
| 87 Francium **Fr** |

Figure 6-6 Sodium is so soft, it can be cut with a knife. Sodium chloride, or table salt, contains sodium and chlorine. Sodium chloride is one of the salts left behind when seawater evaporates.

Figure 6-7 The activity of the alkali metals makes them useful elements.

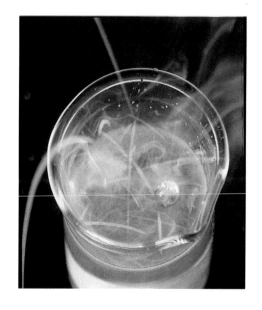

A Potassium is more active than lithium and sodium. Look at what happens when a small piece of potassium is dropped into water. Heat and hydrogen gas are generated. Enough heat is released to cause the hydrogen gas to burst into flames.

B When sodium is added to water, the same kind of reaction occurs. After the reaction, the water contains a substance known as sodium hydroxide or lye. Lye can eat away at grease in clogged drains or digest wood pulp during the manufacture of paper.

C In your body, sodium and potassium have the important job of transmitting nerve impulses. Potassium and sodium are lost from the body in sweat and urine. Most diets contain more than enough sodium. It's more difficult to make sure that you get enough potassium. Bananas and potatoes are good sources of potassium.

The Alkaline Earth Metals

Next door to the alkali metals' family are their Group 2 neighbors, the alkaline earth metals—beryllium, magnesium, calcium, strontium, barium, and radium. The two families have much in common, but some differences. Each alkaline earth metal is denser and harder and has a higher melting point than the alkali metal in the same period. Alkaline earth metals are active, but not as active as the alkali metals.

Magnesium and calcium are the most common elements in Group 2. When magnesium combines with water, a substance called magnesium hydroxide is formed. Magnesium hydroxide is used as the medicine milk of magnesia to soothe an upset stomach. Chlorophyll, the green pigment found in the leaves of trees and plants, contains magnesium atoms. Magnesium is often combined with aluminum to form alloys that resist corrosion. Corrosion can occur when a metal combines with oxygen in the air. An **alloy** (AL oy) is a mixture of two or more elements, one of which is a metal. Some uses of the alkaline earth elements are shown in **Figure 6-8.**

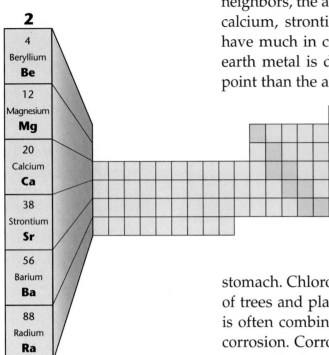

Figure 6-8 Alkaline earth metals are a big part of your life.

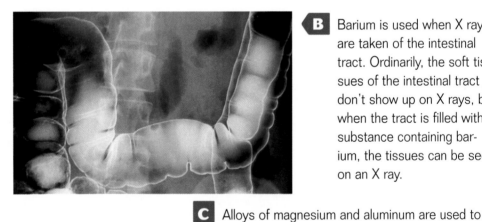

A You have probably been advised to drink milk so that you get the calcium you need for strong bones and teeth. Calcium is also important in controlling your heartbeat and preventing blood clots.

B Barium is used when X rays are taken of the intestinal tract. Ordinarily, the soft tissues of the intestinal tract don't show up on X rays, but when the tract is filled with a substance containing barium, the tissues can be seen on an X ray.

C Alloys of magnesium and aluminum are used to make frames for racing bikes and tennis rackets, and parts for automobile and aircraft engines. An alloy of magnesium and aluminum is not only strong and durable, but lightweight.

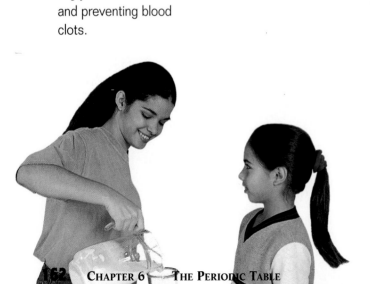

From Metals to Nonmetals

The next group of representative elements is Group 13, located on the other side of the transition elements. Notice that the elements in Groups 13-18 are not all solid metals like the elements of Groups 1 and 2. A single group may contain metals, nonmetals, and metalloids, and have members that are solids, liquids, and gases.

Boron's Family

The elements in Group 13—boron, aluminum, gallium, indium, and thallium—are all metals except boron, which is a brittle, black metalloid. **Figure 6-9** tells you more about this family.

13

5 Boron **B**
13 Aluminum **Al**
31 Gallium **Ga**
49 Indium **In**
81 Thallium **Tl**

Figure 6-9 Here are some of the many uses and properties of the elements of Group 13.

A Cookware made with boron can be moved directly from the refrigerator into the oven without cracking.

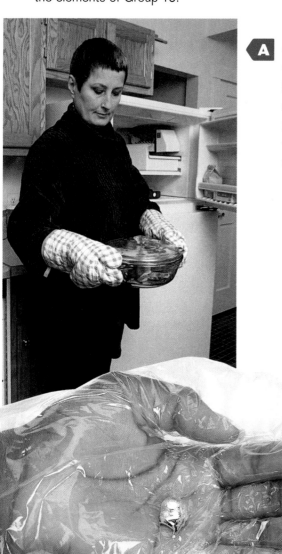

B Aluminum is the most common metal in Earth's crust. **What property of metals makes it possible to shape aluminum into soft-drink cans, cookware, aluminum siding, and baseball bats?**

C Gallium follows aluminum in Group 13. Gallium is a solid metal, but its melting point is low enough that it will melt in your hand.

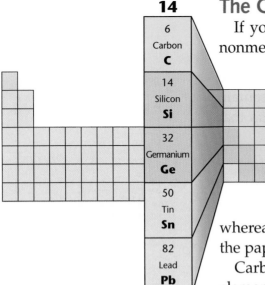

The Carbon Group

If you look down Group 14, you can see that carbon is a nonmetal, silicon and germanium are metalloids, and tin and lead are metals. The nonmetal carbon exists in several forms. You're familiar with two of them—diamond and graphite. A diamond is an array of carbon atoms arranged in an interlocking pattern. Graphite's atoms have a different arrangement, and so graphite and diamond have different properties. Diamond is one of the hardest materials on Earth, whereas graphite is soft. It is soft graphite that rubs off on the paper as you write.

Carbon is followed by the metalloid silicon, an abundant element contained in sand. Sand is ground-up particles of minerals such as quartz, which is composed of silicon and oxygen. Glass is an important product made from sand. ☑

Both silicon and its Group 14 neighbor, germanium, are metalloids. They are used in electronics as semiconductors. A **semiconductor** is an element that doesn't conduct electricity as well as a metal but does conduct electricity better than a nonmetal. Through a process called *doping*, traces of elements such as boron or arsenic are added to silicon to increase its electrical conductivity. One use for doped silicon is shown in **Figure 6-10.**

Tin and lead are the two heaviest elements in Group 14. When you think of the element tin, the tin cans filled with canned fruit and vegetables at the grocery store may come to mind. These cans are actually made of steel coated with tin to protect them from corrosion.

As you can see in **Figure 6-11,** lead is no longer used in gasoline because it is poisonous. Today, the most important use for lead is in car batteries.

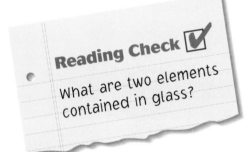

Reading Check ☑

What are two elements contained in glass?

Figure 6-10 Doped silicon is used in computer chips and in solar cells, like these that convert sunlight to electricity.

Figure 6-11
Gasoline is unleaded to avoid the health risk of lead in the environment.

Nitrogen's Group

At the top of Group 15 are the two nonmetals nitrogen and phosphorus. Next come two metalloids, arsenic and antimony, and one metal, bismuth. Nitrogen and phosphorus are required by living beings. These elements are parts of the biological materials that store genetic information and energy in living organisms. Although almost 80 percent of the air you breathe is nitrogen, you can't get the nitrogen your body needs by breathing nitrogen gas. Bacteria in the soil must first change nitrogen gas into substances that can be absorbed through the roots of plants. Then, by eating the plants, nitrogen becomes available to your body.

Ammonia is a gas containing nitrogen and hydrogen. When ammonia is dissolved in water, it can be used as a cleaner and disinfectant. You can smell the sharp fumes of ammonia gas when you open a bottle of ammonia cleaning solution. In **Figure 6-12A,** liquid ammonia is being applied directly to soil as a fertilizer. Ammonia also can be converted into solid fertilizers. Ammonia also is used in the making of many products, such as the nylon of the parachute in **Figure 6-12B.**

The element phosphorus comes in two forms—white and red. White phosphorus is so active it can't be exposed to oxygen in the air or it will burst into flames. The heads of matches contain the less active red phosphorus, which ignites from the heat produced by friction when the match is struck. **Figure 6-12C** shows both forms of phosphorus. Phosphorus is an essential ingredient of healthy teeth and bones. Plants also need phosphorus, so phosphorus is one of the nutrients in most fertilizers.

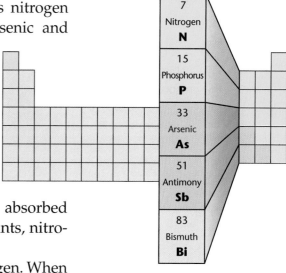

Figure 6-12 Nitrogen and phosphorus are necessary for your body and useful in your daily life.

A Ammonia is a nitrogen-containing substance that can be injected into the soil and used directly by plants.

C Both white and red phosphorus are active. **Why is white phosphorus submerged in a liquid in this photo?**

B Nylon is a tough, light fiber capable of replacing silk in many applications, such as in parachutes.

Figure 6-13 Other members of Group 15 have everyday uses.

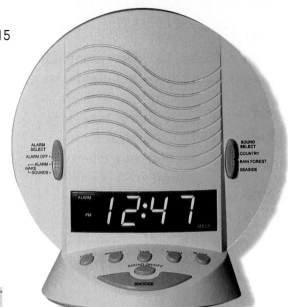

A A substance containing gallium and arsenic is responsible for the lighted time display on digital clocks.

B Overhead sprinkler heads use the low melting point of bismuth as a trigger.

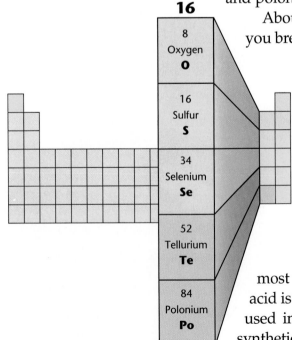

The metalloid arsenic and the metal gallium combine to form a substance used to create the lighted display on digital clocks, radios, and VCRs, as you can see in **Figure 6-13A**. Bismuth is used in the sprinkler heads of fire-fighting systems like the one in **Figure 6-13B**. The system turns on automatically when a fire starts because bismuth has a low enough melting point that the heat from a fire causes it to melt. The melting triggers a signal that opens the water valves.

Oxygen's Family

The first two members of Group 16, oxygen and sulfur, are essential for life. Selenium is also necessary for health, but in trace amounts. The heavier members of the group, tellurium and polonium, are both metalloids.

About 20 percent of Earth's atmosphere is the oxygen you breathe. Your body needs oxygen to release the energy from the foods you eat. Ozone, a less common form of oxygen, is formed in the upper atmosphere through the action of electricity during thunderstorms. The presence of ozone is important because it shields living beings from some harmful radiation from the sun. Oxygen is abundant in Earth's rocks and minerals because it readily combines with other elements.

Sulfur is a solid, yellow nonmetal, as you can see in **Figure 6-14**. Large amounts of sulfur are used to manufacture sulfuric acid, one of the most commonly used chemicals in the world. Sulfuric acid is a combination of sulfur, hydrogen, and oxygen. It is used in the manufacture of paints, fertilizers, detergents, synthetic fibers, and rubber.

Figure 6-14 These piles of sulfur will be used to make sulfuric acid, one of the most important chemicals for making a wide variety of products you use every day.

Selenium conducts electricity when exposed to light, so it is used in solar cells and in light meters. Its most important use is as the light-sensitive component in photocopy machines. You'll find a small amount of selenium in some multivitamin preparations because selenium is one of the trace elements your body needs. Large amounts of selenium, however, can be poisonous.

LIFE SCIENCE
INTEGRATION

A Strand of Evidence
Arsenic disrupts the normal function of an organism by combining with sulfur, which is an essential element. Because arsenic builds up in hair, forensic scientists can test hair samples to confirm or disprove a case of arsenic poisoning. Tests of Napoleon's hair suggest that he was poisoned. Use reference books to find out who Napoleon was and why someone might have wanted to poison him.

Problem Solving

Predicting Periodicity

Comets are large masses of frozen water in which pieces of rock are embedded. Seen through a telescope, a comet has a glowing head and a long, bright tail. Comets orbit the sun just as Earth and the sun's other planets do. To *orbit* means "to follow a path usually shaped like an ellipse." Some comets orbit the sun every few years. Some take thousands of years to complete one trip. The time it takes for a comet to make one trip around the sun is called its period.

People have been watching comets since they first noticed them in the night sky. Early astronomers kept records of unusual events such as eclipses, meteor showers, and the appearance of comets. The famous Comet Halley is named for the eighteenth-century English astronomer Edmund Halley. While researching the records of earlier astronomers, Halley noticed descriptions of bright comets that appeared in 1531, 1607, and 1682. Halley thought these comets might

all be a single comet and that the dates of the three observations were evidence of the comet's periodic motion. He correctly predicted the return of Halley's comet.

Think Critically: What year did Halley predict the comet would return? Approximately how long is the period of Halley's comet—the time it takes to orbit the sun? When was it last seen from Earth? When will it be seen again?

The Halogens

17
9 Fluorine **F**
17 Chlorine **Cl**
35 Bromine **Br**
53 Iodine **I**
85 Astatine **At**

All the elements in Group 17 are nonmetals except for astatine, which is a radioactive metalloid. These elements—fluorine, chlorine, bromine, iodine, and astatine—are called halogens, which means "salt-former." Table salt, sodium chloride, is a substance made from sodium and chlorine. All of the halogens form similar salts with sodium and with the other alkali metals. Fluorine and chlorine are gases. Bromine is a reddish-brown liquid. Iodine is a shiny black solid.

The halogen fluorine is the most active of the halogens in combining with other elements. Chlorine is less active than fluorine, and the trend continues down the family to iodine, which is the least active of the four. **Figure 6-15** shows some of the uses of the halogens.

Figure 6-15 Because they are active, you'll find that the halogens are useful in many ways.

A The halogens are used to fight bacteria. For example, chlorine is at work in this swimming pool.

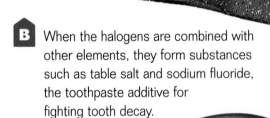

B When the halogens are combined with other elements, they form substances such as table salt and sodium fluoride, the toothpaste additive for fighting tooth decay.

C Some pots and pans are easier to clean up than others because they have a nonstick surface made from a substance containing fluorine.

Mini Lab

Inferring the Presence of Chlorine

Procedure

1. Place 2 mL of salt water, 2 mL of distilled water, and 2 mL of tap water into separate test tubes.
2. Carefully add 5 drops of silver nitrate solution to each test tube and stir. **CAUTION:** *Silver nitrate solution can stain skin and clothing.*

Analysis

1. What happened when you added silver nitrate to the salt water?
2. What happened in the test tube with distilled water?
3. Does your tap water contain chlorine? Explain.

The Noble Gases

Why are the Group 18 elements called the noble gases? The answer is because they rarely combine with other elements. Like the nobility, they stand apart from the crowd. All the Group 18 elements—helium, neon, argon, krypton, xenon (ZEE nawn), and radon—are colorless gases.

Helium is a lighter-than-air gas, so it's great for all kinds of balloons, from party balloons to blimps that carry television cameras high above sporting events. Helium balloons, such as the one in **Figure 6-16A,** lift instruments into the upper atmosphere to measure atmospheric conditions. Even though hydrogen is lighter than helium, helium is preferred for these purposes because helium will not burn.

The "neon" lights you see in advertising signs, like the one in **Figure 6-16B,** may actually contain any of the noble gases, not just neon. In the glass tubes that make up the sign, electricity is passed through the noble gas and the electricity causes the gas to glow. Each noble gas produces its own color. Helium glows pink, neon glows red-orange, and argon produces a purple color.

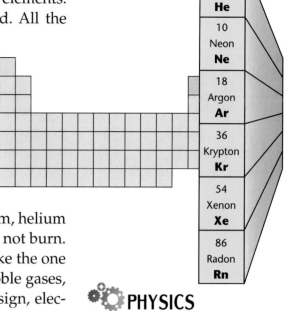

18

| 2 Helium **He** |
| 10 Neon **Ne** |
| 18 Argon **Ar** |
| 36 Krypton **Kr** |
| 54 Xenon **Xe** |
| 86 Radon **Rn** |

PHYSICS
◀ **INTEGRATION**

Figure 6-16 Scientists used to call the noble gases inert gases because they were never found combined with other elements.

A Instruments carried by weather balloons contain helium that gathers information about the conditions in the upper atmosphere around the world. **How might this information be helpful to you?**

B Each color in this advertising sign is caused by a different noble gas.

Argon, the most abundant of the noble gases on Earth, was first found in 1894. Krypton is used with nitrogen in ordinary lightbulbs because these gases keep the glowing filament from burning out. When a mixture of argon, krypton, and xenon is used, a bulb can have a life ten times longer than bulbs available today. Krypton lights are used to illuminate landing strips at airports, and xenon is used in strobe lights and photographic flash cubes.

At the bottom of the group is radon, a radioactive gas produced naturally as uranium in rocks and soil decays. If radon seeps into a home, the gas can be harmful because it continues to emit radiation. When people breathe the gas over a period of time, it can cause lung cancer. People in regions where granite and shale are abundant are encouraged to have their homes tested for radon.

Chemists originally thought that it was impossible for any of the noble gases to combine with other elements. However, in 1962, a new substance was formed that contained xenon, platinum, and fluorine. Since then, chemists have succeeded in making combinations of xenon and krypton with fluorine.

interNET CONNECTION

Visit the Glencoe Science Web Site at **www.glencoe.com/sec/science/ca** for more information about representative elements.

Section Assessment

1. What do the elements in Group 1 have in common with the elements in Group 17? How are Group 1 elements different from the elements in Group 18?

2. Explain how silicon's role as a semiconductor confirms that silicon is a metalloid.

3. List the five most important elements for life and tell what groups on the periodic table they are in.

4. **Think Critically:** Francium is a rare radioactive alkali metal at the bottom of Group 1. Its properties have not been studied carefully. Would you predict that francium would combine with water more or less readily than cesium?

5. **Skill Builder**
   Predicting Predict how readily astatine would form a salt compared to the other elements in Group 17. If you need help, refer to Predicting in the **Skill Handbook** on page 542.

Using Computers

Using a Database
Search an on-line database for recent articles on the environment. Pick one area of concern such as water quality, air quality, or global warming. Then track the impact of one representative element. If you need help, refer to page 545.

Activity
6•1

Preparing an Alloy

Many of the most important materials in the world are mixtures of elements called alloys. Bronze is an alloy of copper and tin. Brass is an alloy of copper and zinc. Many types of steel are produced by adding carbon and other metals to iron.

What You'll Investigate

How can two metals be combined to form an alloy?

Goals

- **Observe** the changes that occur during the preparation of an alloy.
- **Compare** the plating of a metal to the formation of an alloy.

Safety Precautions

CAUTION: *Nitric acid and sodium hydroxide can cause burns. If you spill nitric acid or sodium hydroxide on your skin, notify your teacher immediately. Rinse the affected area with large amounts of tap water.*

Procedure

1. Carefully **pour** dilute nitric acid into one evaporating dish until the dish is half full. Using tongs, **hold** the penny in the nitric acid for about 20 s.

2. Still using the tongs, **remove** the penny from the acid and rinse it in the beaker of cold water.

3. **Place** one teaspoonful of 30-mesh zinc in the second evaporating dish.

4. Slowly **pour** dilute sodium hydroxide into the dish to a depth of about 2 cm above the zinc.

5. Using tongs, gently **place** the penny on top of the zinc. Rinse the tongs in cold water.

6. Gently **heat** the contents of the evaporating dish on a hot plate until the penny turns a silver color.

Materials

- Copper penny
  *copper wire
- Zinc, 30-mesh
- Hot plate
- Nitric acid, dilute
- Sodium hydroxide, dilute
- Evaporating dishes
  *beakers (2)
- Tongs
- Beaker of cold tap water
  *Alternate Materials

7. Set the control on the hot plate to medium high. Using tongs, **remove** the penny from the dish and rinse it in the cold tap water.

8. Dry the penny and **place** it directly on the hot plate until the penny turns a golden color.

9. Your teacher will dispose of the contents of the two evaporating dishes.

Conclude and Apply

1. What caused the change in the appearance of the penny when it was placed in the nitric acid?

2. When one metal is coated with a layer of a second metal, the process is called plating. At which point in this activity did plating occur?

3. What alloy formed when the penny was heated on the hot plate?

4. **Infer** why heat is necessary for the alloy to form.

Transition Elements

What **You'll Learn**

▶ Properties of some transition elements
▶ How to distinguish lanthanides from actinides

Why **It's Important**

▶ Without transition elements, your electrical appliances wouldn't work, there would be no magnets on your refrigerator, and the world would be a less colorful place.

The Metals in the Middle

What about that large block of elements sandwiched between Group 2 and Group 13? Groups 5-12 are called the transition elements. All transition elements are metals. Across any period from Group 3 through Group 12, the properties of the elements change less noticeably than they do across a period of representative elements. Most transition elements are found combined with oxygen, sulfur, or other elements in ores such as malachite shown in **Figure 6-17**. A few transition elements such as gold, silver, and copper are sometimes found as pure elements in Earth's crust.

Figure 6-17 Many substances that contain transition elements are colored.

The Iron Triad

Three elements in period 4—iron, cobalt, and nickel—have such similar properties that they are known as the iron triad. A triad is a group of three. The elements in the iron triad have magnetic properties. Industrial magnets are made from an alloy of nickel, cobalt, and aluminum. Nickel is used in batteries along with cadmium. Iron is a necessary part of hemoglobin, the substance that transports oxygen in the blood.

Iron is the most important of the transition elements. Usually, iron is mixed with other metals and with carbon to create a variety of steels with different properties. Structures such as bridges and skyscrapers like the one shown in **Figure 6-18** depend upon steel for their strength. But, structures made from steel can be eaten away by rust, which results when iron and steel are

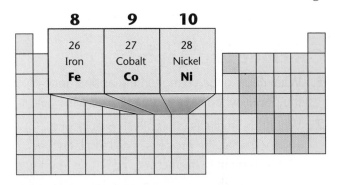

	8	9	10	
	26 Iron **Fe**	27 Cobalt **Co**	28 Nickel **Ni**	

Figure 6-18 The strength of a tall building is in its skeleton, which is made from steel.
What qualities of steel are important in its use in buildings and bridges?

exposed to oxygen in the air. Iron or steel can be painted to protect the metal from rusting. Iron structures also can be coated with zinc for protection from corrosion.

The Coinage Metals

Ancient civilizations made coins from copper, silver, and gold, so these three elements came to be called the coinage metals. They are often found uncombined in nature because they don't readily combine with other elements. **Figure 6-19** illustrates some uses for the coinage metals.

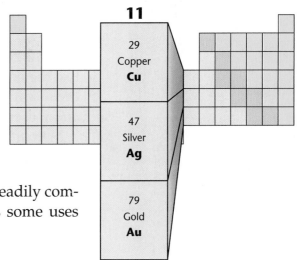

Figure 6-19 Today, copper, silver, and gold are no longer used for coins, but they have many other uses.

A From earliest times, silver and gold were used for jewelry and precious objects of art.

B Photographic film is coated with a thin layer of gelatin that contains a substance composed of silver and bromine or silver and iodine. These substances release silver when they are exposed to light. The amount of silver released depends upon the intensity of the light and the length of exposure. The silver atoms form a pattern that emerges when the film is developed.

C Copper is a good conductor of both electricity and heat. Copper wires carry electricity, and copper-bottomed pans distribute heat evenly. Copper resists corrosion so it used to be the preferred choice for plumbing pipes. Now copper is getting scarcer and more expensive. Plastic piping is being used instead.

Other Transition Metals

Most of the transition metals have higher melting points than the representative elements. The filaments of lightbulbs like the one in **Figure 6-20** are made of tungsten, element 74, because it has the highest melting point of any metal (3410°C) and will not melt with the heat of the bulb.

Mercury, which has the lowest melting point of any metal (–39°C), is used in thermometers and in barometers. Mercury is the only liquid metal at ordinary temperatures. Like many of the heavy metals, mercury is poisonous to living beings.

Chromium's name comes from the Greek word for color, *chroma,* and the element lives up to its name. Two substances containing chromium are shown in **Figure 6-21.** Many other transition elements combine to form substances with equally brilliant colors.

Ruthenium, rhodium, palladium, osmium, iridium, and platinum are sometimes called the platinum group because they have similar properties. They do not combine easily with other elements, so they can be used for electrodes and as catalysts. A catalyst is a substance that can cause changes to occur faster but is not changed itself. The catalytic converters in automobiles, like the one in **Figure 6-22,** help change pollutants into harmless substances before they are exhausted from the tailpipe into the air.

Figure 6-20 You can see that the tungsten filament can be heated to a high temperature but it doesn't melt. **What happens to the filament after long use?**

Figure 6-21 These two substances containing chromium are typical of many substances containing transition elements. They are used to make brightly colored paints.

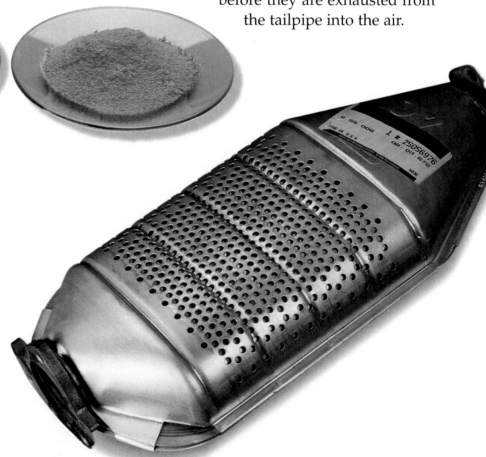

Figure 6-22 The presence of catalytic converters in all recently manufactured cars has improved the quality of the air you breathe.

Inner Transition Elements

Do any of the elements in the two rows located below the table seem familiar to you? Except for uranium, which you may have heard about, they are not the metals that you find in most of the things you use every day. But, some inner transition elements have important uses, particularly when combined with other metals.

There are two series of inner transition elements. The first series, from cerium to lutetium, is called the lanthanides. The lanthanides also are called the rare earths because at one time they were thought to be scarce. The word *earth* is an old-fashioned word that refers to a substance formed when a metal combines with oxygen. The lanthanides are usually found combined with oxygen in Earth's crust. The second series of elements, from thorium to lawrencium, are called the actinides.

Using Math

Gold jewelry that is 100 percent pure gold is called 24-carat gold. How much gold is in 18-carat gold? In 12-carat gold?

58 Ce	59 Pr	60 Nd	61 Pm	62 Sm	63 Eu	64 Gd	65 Tb	66 Dy	67 Ho	68 Er	69 Tm	70 Yb	71 Lu
90 Th	91 Pa	92 U	93 Np	94 Pu	95 Am	96 Cm	97 Bk	98 Cf	99 Es	100 Fm	101 Md	102 No	103 Lr

The Lanthanides

The lanthanides are soft metals that can be cut with a knife. The elements are so similar that they are hard to separate when they occur in the same ore, which they often do. The element dysprosium gets its name from the Greek word meaning "hard to get at." Three of the lanthanides are named for a town in Sweden, Ytterby, where their ores are mined—erbium (Er), ytterbium (Yb), and terbium (Tb).

Despite the name *rare earth*, the lanthanides are not as rare as originally thought. Earth's crust contains three times as much cerium as lead. Cerium makes up 50 percent of an alloy called misch metal. The other ingredients are lanthanum, neodymium, and iron. Flints in lighters, like the one in **Figure 6-23**, are made from misch metal.

Reading Check

Why is dysprosium hard to get at?

Figure 6-23 The flint in this lighter is made of an alloy called misch metal, whose principal ingredient is the lanthanide cerium.

Neodymium and praseodymium are added to the glass used in welders' masks to absorb high-energy radiation that could damage eyes. The glass used in television screens and computer monitors contains yttrium and europium, both combined with oxygen. When these substances are struck by a beam of electrons, they produce a bright red color. Compounds of lanthanides are also used in high-intensity searchlights, lasers, and movie projectors. Some lanthanides are used in the control rods of nuclear reactors to absorb excess neutrons.

The Actinides

All the actinides are radioactive. The nuclei of atoms of radioactive elements are unstable and decay to form other elements. Thorium, protactinium, and uranium are the only actinides that are now found naturally on Earth. All the others are synthetic elements. They may have existed on Earth at one time, but because most decay within a few days, none can be found today. Uranium is still found in Earth's crust because its half-life is long—4.5 billion years. The synthetic elements have many uses. Plutonium is used as a fuel in nuclear power plants. Americium is used in some home smoke detectors. Some actinide isotopes have medical uses. For example, californium-232 is used to kill cancer cells.

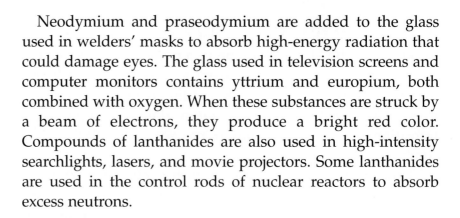

interNET
CONNECTION

Visit the Glencoe Science Web Site at www.glencoe.com/sec/science/ca for more information about transition elements.

Section Assessment

1. What is the major difference between the lanthanides and actinides? Would you expect neodymium and uranium to have similar properties? Explain.

2. How do the elements in the iron triad differ from other transition metals?

3. What is one drawback to using steel for structures such as skyscrapers, and how can that drawback be overcome?

4. **Think Critically:** Of the elements iridium and cadmium, predict which is likely to be toxic and which could act as a catalyst. Explain.

5.  **Skill Builder**
   Observing and Inferring How does the appearance of a burned-out lightbulb compare to a new bulb? What could explain the difference? If you need help, refer to Observing and Inferring in the **Skill Handbook** on page 532.

Science Journal In your Science Journal, discuss the term *valuable* as it relates to elements. How do relative abundance, number of uses, and durability contribute to value?

Dentistry and the Elements

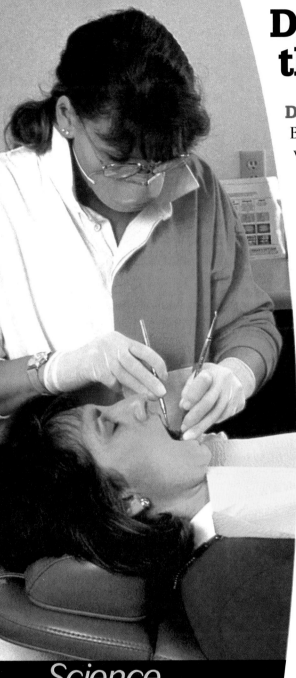

Dental Materials

Before dentistry became a science, a person's decayed tooth would eventually fall out or have to be pulled. Since the 1930s, dentists, like the one at left, have successfully used elements found in the periodic table to repair and replace decayed teeth. The elements mercury and silver traditionally have been used to fill cavities. Mercury is a poisonous liquid metal, but mixing it with silver, copper, and zinc forms a hard substance that has been considered safe to put in people's mouths. Today, other materials also are used for fillings.

A combination of gold, silver, and copper is used to make gold coverings, called crowns, for damaged or weakened teeth. If a tooth is broken off at the root and needs single-tooth replacement, the element titanium is used as a post to support a replacement tooth made from plastic.

The framework for dentures—replacements for teeth that have fallen out—is made from the elements chromium and cobalt. When mixed together, these metals are flexible, strong, and rust resistant.

Elements and the Orthodontist

Orthodontists, dentists who are specialists in the positioning of teeth, use braces (see below) or retainers to reposition crowded or misplaced teeth. Braces are often made of stainless steel, a combination of iron, nickel, and carbon. The stainless steel is mixed with chromium to keep the braces from rusting.

With all these materials available for fixing teeth, dentists still emphasize prevention: regular brushing, flossing, and checkups.

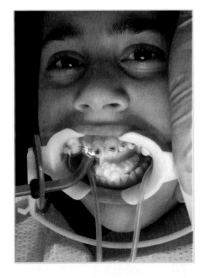

Science JOURNAL

In your Science Journal, write a paragraph summarizing some of the advantages of modern materials in dentistry. Base your summary on library or online research.

Health Risks from Heavy Metals

Whether it's lip balm that blocks UV rays from the sun or cream cheese with lower fat, society benefits from using chemicals in many products. But, chemicals, such as heavy metals, can be dangerous if they are used incorrectly or leak into the environment where they are not meant to be.

Recognize the Problem

Do heavy metals and other chemicals pose a threat to the health of humans? One way to reduce any threat is to know as much as possible about the chemical, its source, and its environmental impact.

Form a Hypothesis

Could health problems be caused by exposure to heavy metals, such as lead, or a radioactive chemical element, such as radon? Is the incidence of these problems higher in one area than another? Form a hypothesis as to the potential health risk of a chemical in your area.

Goals

- **Organize and synthesize** information on a chemical or heavy metal thought to cause health problems in your area.
- **Communicate** your findings with others in your class.

Data Sources

Go to the Glencoe Science Web Site at **www.glencoe. com/sec/science/ca** to obtain information, hints, and data from other students.

Health Risk Data Table

Location	Chemical or Heavy Metal	How People Come in Contact with Chemical	Potential Health Problem	Who is affected

Test Your Hypothesis

Plan

1. **Read** general information concerning heavy metals and other potentially hazardous chemicals.

2. Use the sites listed on the Glencoe Science Web Site to **research** possible health problems in your area caused by exposure to chemicals or heavy metals.

3. Check the Glencoe Science Web Site to see what others have learned.

Do

1. Make sure your teacher approves your plan before you proceed.

2. **Search** for resources that can help you find out about health risks in your area.

3. **Organize** your information in a data table like the one shown.

4. **Write** a report in your Science Journal about the results of your research.

5. **Post your data** in the table provided on the Glencoe Science Web Site.

Analyze Your Data

1. Did all your sources agree on the health risk of the chemical or heavy metal?

2. Analyze all your sources for possible bias. Are some sources more reliable than others?

3. How did the health risk differ for adults and children?

Draw Conclusions

1. Were the same substances found to be health risks in other parts of the country? From the data on the Glencoe Science Web Site try to predict what chemicals or heavy metals are health risks in different parts of the country.

2. From your report, what information do you think is the most important for the public to be aware of?

3. What could be done to decrease the risk of the health problems you identified?

For a **preview** of this chapter, study this Reviewing Main Ideas before you read the chapter. After you have studied this chapter, you can use the Reviewing Main Ideas to **review** the chapter.

The Glencoe MindJogger, Audiocassettes, and CD-ROM provide additional opportunities for review.

6-1 PERIODICITY

When organized according to atomic number in a table, elements with similar properties occupy the same column, called a **group** or family. The properties of the elements change gradually across a horizontal row called a **period. Metals** are usually shiny, malleable, and ductile. They are good conductors of heat and electricity. Many **nonmetals** are gases. Solid nonmetals are often brittle and poor conductors of heat and electricity. **Metalloids** have properties between those of metals and nonmetals. The periodic table can be divided into representative elements and transition elements. *What do families on the periodic table have in common with human families?*

6-2 ALKALI AND ALKALINE EARTH METALS

Atoms of elements in Groups 1 and 2 readily combine with atoms of other elements. The ease with which the atoms of the elements combine with other atoms increases down the two groups. Each element in Group 2 combines less readily than its neighbor in Group 1. Each alkaline earth metal is denser and has a higher melting point than the alkali metal in its period. Sodium, potassium, magnesium, and calcium have important biological roles. *What element is magnesium mixed with to form strong, lightweight alloys?*

Reading Check ✓

Construct a chart that shows what each symbol in an element key represents. What other feature could be indicated with a symbol?

ELEMENTS IN GROUPS 13–18

Aluminum, the most common metal in Earth's crust, has many uses. Carbon is found in two common forms—diamond and graphite. Nitrogen, oxygen, sulfur, and phosphorus are essential for life. Ammonia and sulfuric acid are important chemicals in manufacturing. Silicon is a metalloid used as a semiconductor in electronics. The halogens combine with other elements to form a variety of substances such as table salt and sodium fluoride. The noble gases have many uses that depend upon the fact that they do not combine with other elements. *What are the two groups of elements that together form common salts?*

6-3 TRANSITION ELEMENTS

Iron is the most important transition element because of its strength and durabilty, but it must be protected from corrosion. Magnets contain elements from the iron triad. The coinage metals are fairly unreactive, malleable elements. The uses of copper depend upon its superior ability to conduct heat and electricity. Substances containing silver are in the coating on photographic film. Platinum is used as electrodes and as a catalyst. The lanthanides are naturally occurring elements with similar properties. The actinides are radioactive elements. All actinides except thorium, proactinium, and uranium are synthetic. *Why is it dangerous to handle the mercury that is spilled when a thermometer or barometer breaks?*

Chapter 6 Assessment

Using Vocabulary

a. alloy
b. group
c. metal
d. metalloid
e. nonmetal
f. period
g. semiconductor

Answer the following questions about the Vocabulary words.

1. What is the difference between a group and a period?
2. What is the connection between a metalloid and a semiconductor?
3. How are a metal and an alloy alike?
4. Arrange the terms *nonmetal, metal,* and *metalloid* according to increasing electrical conductivity.
5. How is a metalloid like a metal? How is it different?

Checking Concepts

Choose the word or phrase that best answers the question.

6. Which of the following groups combines most readily with other elements?
   A) coinage metals
   B) alkaline earth metals
   C) alkali metals
   D) iron triad

7. Which element is located in Group 6, period 4?
   A) tungsten   C) titanium
   B) chromium   D) hafnium

8. Which element is **NOT** found uncombined in nature?
   A) gold   C) silver
   B) calcium   D) copper

9. Which group contains only nonmetals?
   A) Group 1   C) Group 2
   B) Group 12   D) Group 18

10. Which of the following elements is likely to be contained in a substance with a brilliant yellow color?
    A) chromium   C) iron
    B) carbon   D) tin

11. Which halogen is radioactive?
    A) astatine   C) bromine
    B) chlorine   D) iodine

12. Which of the following is unlikely to happen to zinc?
    A) It is rolled into sheets.
    B) It is used to coat a steel hull.
    C) It is used in a battery.
    D) It is used as an insulator.

13. Which of the following describes the element tellurium?
    A) alkali metal   C) metalloid
    B) transition metal D) lanthanide

14. Which element has the highest melting point?
    A) bromine   C) mercury
    B) iodine   D) tungsten

15. Which of these elements is **NOT** essential for living organisms?
    A) strontium   C) sodium
    B) sulfur   D) selenium

Thinking Critically

16. Why is it important that mercury be kept out of streams and waterways?

17. If you were going to try to get the noble gas argon to combine with another element, would fluorine be a good choice for the other element? Explain.

18. Hydrogen, which is lighter than helium, used to be used in blimps that carried passengers. Why is helium a better choice?

19. Why is water **NOT** used for putting out some chemical fires?

20. It's possible that some of the actinides beyond uranium were once present in Earth's crust. If that is true, how would their half-lives compare with the half-life of uranium, which is 4.5 billion years?

Developing Skills

If you need help, refer to the Skill Handbook.

21. Recognizing Cause and Effect: Why do photographers work in low light when they develop film?

22. Predicting: How would life on Earth be different if the atmosphere were 80 percent oxygen and 20 percent nitrogen instead of the other way around?

23. Making and Using Graphs: Make a bar graph of the representative elements that shows how many of the elements are solids, liquids, and gases at room temperature.

24. Concept Mapping: Draw a concept map of the periodic table. Make the first division between representative elements and transition elements.

25. Making and Using Tables: The periodic table below shows the locations of a few elements. For each element shown, give the element's period and group number; whether the element is a metal or a nonmetal; and whether it is a solid, liquid, or gas at room temperature.

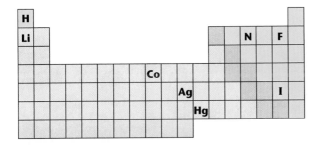

Test-Taking Tip

When Eliminating, Cross It Out List the answer choice letters on the scratch paper. Use your pencil to cross out choices you've eliminated. You'll stop yourself from choosing an answer you've mentally eliminated.

Test Practice

Use these questions to test your Science Proficiency.

1. Diamond is one of the hardest substances on Earth. Graphite is soft. Which is the best explanation for the difference in hardness?
   A) Graphite and diamond are made from different elements.
   B) Graphite is a mixture of elements.
   C) The atoms in diamond and graphite are arranged in different patterns.
   D) Diamond is made from carbon-14 atoms. Graphite contains mainly carbon-12 atoms.

2. Which is the best description of sulfur?
   A) period 2, Group 16, transition element, important industrial element
   B) period 3, oxygen family, representative element, biologically important
   C) period 5, oxygen family, representative element, poisonous
   D) period 6, inner transition element, radioactive, metal

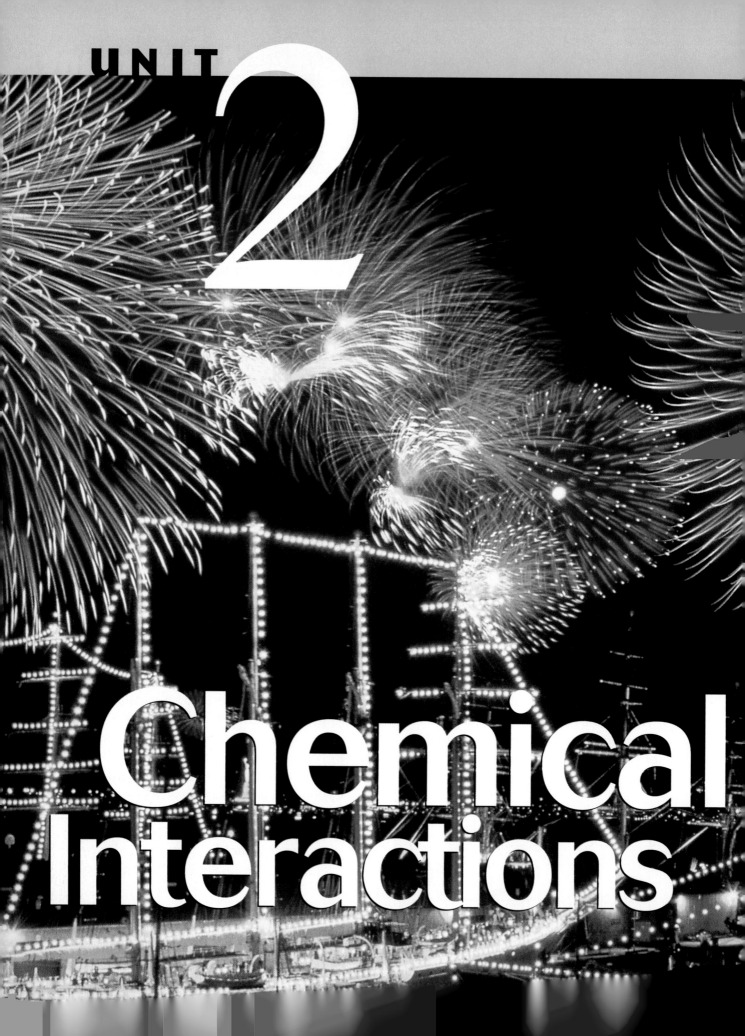

UNIT 2

Chemical Interactions

What's Happening Here?

Have you ever seen a firecracker before it exploded? It doesn't look anything like this spectacle of glowing colors illuminating the night sky over New York City's East River (left). How does the firecracker change from a cardboard tube to this magical fireworks display? By a chemical reaction. The chemical bonds that hold atoms together break, and new combinations of atoms are formed, releasing energy in the form of light and heat. But, fireworks displays are only one example of the wonders of chemistry. The salt water you find in the ocean (below) is another. Though you can taste the salt, you cannot see it, even with the aid of a microscope. Why? Where is the salt hiding? In this unit, you will learn how the interplay of atoms explains some of these seeming mysteries.

interNET CONNECTION

Explore the Glencoe Science Web Site at **www.glencoe.com/sec/science/ca** to find out more about topics found in this unit.

Chemical Bonds

Chapter Preview

Skills Preview

Skill Builders
- Classify
- Map Concepts

Activities
- Hypothesize
- Design an Experiment

MiniLabs
- Make and Use a Table
- Make a Model

Reading Check ✓

Before you read this chapter—and all the other ones—read the What You'll Learn feature at the beginning of each section. Explain why each section includes this feature.

Explore Activity

It's time to clean out the garage and attic and get rid of stuff. Look at it all—stuff made out of wood, glass, plastic, metal, cloth, and even paper. Where do all the different materials that make up everyday things come from? There are fewer than 100 different kinds of naturally occurring atoms on Earth. They combine with each other in countless ways to make countless different substances. Why is this so? What makes elements combine with other elements? The answer is in their electrons.

Model the Energy of Electrons

1. Pick up a paper clip with a magnet. Touch the paper clip to another paper clip and pick it up.

2. Continue to pick up paper clips until you have a strand of them and no more will attach.

3. One by one, gently pull off the paper clips.

Science **Journal**

In your Science Journal, write down which paper clip was easiest to remove and which was hardest. Think of the magnet as if it were the nucleus of an atom. How do you suppose the magnet and the paper clips are a model for the nucleus and the electrons in an atom?

Why do atoms combine?

What You'll Learn

▶ How the electrons are arranged in an atom
▶ The energy of electrons in atoms
▶ How the arrangement of electrons in an atom is related to the periodic table

Vocabulary
electron dot diagram
chemical bond

Why It's Important

▶ When you know about an atom's electrons, you can predict how the atom will behave.

Atomic Structure

At the center of an atom is a tiny nucleus containing the atom's protons and neutrons. The rest of the space in the atom is empty, except for the atom's electrons. The electrons are in constant motion around the nucleus. Scientists know that they cannot say exactly where the electrons are at any time. They use a model, the electron cloud model, which tells where the electrons are most likely to be. They are most likely to be clustered around the nucleus because their negative charges are attracted to the positively charged nucleus. But, the electrons could be anywhere. That's why the model for an electron cloud in **Figure 7-1** has a fuzzy outline.

How many electrons are in the electron cloud of an atom, and how are they arranged? Each element has a different number of protons and electrons, so each has a different atomic structure. For example, lithium has three protons in its nucleus, and three electrons move around lithium's nucleus.

The Periodic Table

When the elements are arranged in order of increasing atomic number, they fall into groups in which the members share common properties. Could those common properties depend upon similarities in the way electrons are arranged in the atoms?

Electron Arrangements and Energy

All the electrons in an atom are in the electron cloud, but within the cloud, some electrons are closer to the nucleus than others. How do scientists know this? Think about the Explore Activity. It took more energy on your part to pull off the paper clip closest to the magnet than it took to remove the one farthest away. That's because the closer a paper clip is to the magnet, the stronger

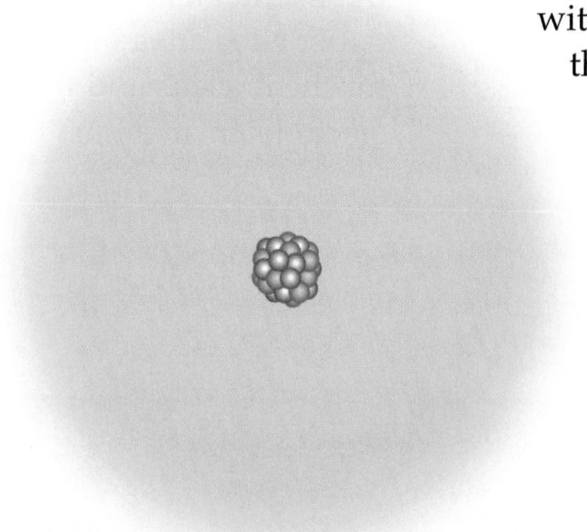

Figure 7-1 In the electron cloud model, the electrons are more likely to be in the heavily shaded area than in the lightly shaded area, but they could be anywhere. **Why is there no definite boundary for an atom?**

the magnet's attractive force on the clip. Scientists have found that the closer an electron is to the nucleus, the stronger the attractive force between the positively charged nucleus and the negatively charged electrons. So, removing electrons that are close to the nucleus takes more energy than removing those farther away from the nucleus. A diagram of how the electrons might be arranged in energy levels around the nucleus of an atom is shown in **Figure 7-2.** Notice that the electrons are arranged in spheres at different distances from the nucleus. That means that each sphere must represent a different energy.

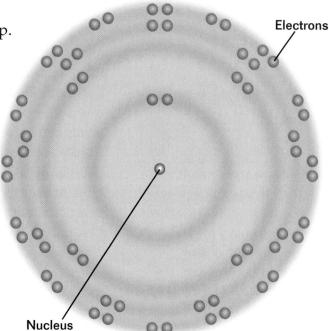

Electrons

Nucleus

Figure 7-2 The energy of an electron is different depending upon which energy level it occupies.

An Energy Stairway

The stairway, shown in **Figure 7-3,** is a model for picturing the energy differences among electrons in the electron cloud. Think of the nucleus as being at floor level. The difference in heights of the steps represents the difference in energy between electrons on different steps. Electrons in the sphere closest to the nucleus are in the lowest energy level. They are on the first energy step. These electrons are held most tightly to the nucleus because they occupy the space closest to the nucleus. Electrons in the next sphere are on the second energy step. They are at a higher energy level because they are farther from the nucleus. Electrons in the outermost sphere have even higher energy because they are still farther from the attractive force of the positively charged nucleus.

VISUALIZING
Energy Levels

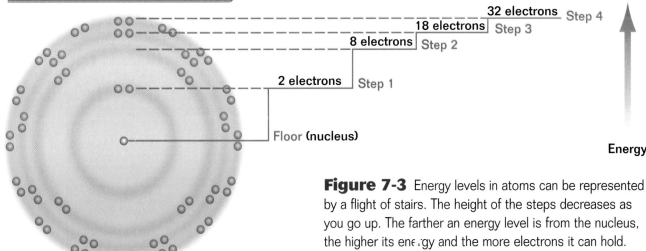

32 electrons Step 4
18 electrons Step 3
8 electrons Step 2
2 electrons Step 1
Floor (nucleus)

Energy

Figure 7-3 Energy levels in atoms can be represented by a flight of stairs. The height of the steps decreases as you go up. The farther an energy level is from the nucleus, the higher its energy and the more electrons it can hold.

Using Math

You can calculate the number of electrons in each electron energy level by using the formula $2n^2$. n is the number of the level and can have the values of the integers 1, 2, 3, 4, 5, and so on. Calculate the number of electrons in the first five energy levels.

interNET CONNECTION

Visit the Glencoe Science Web Site at **www.glencoe.com/ sec/science/ca** for more information about electrons in atoms.

Figure 7-4 Lithium and carbon have their outermost electrons in the second energy level. **In what level do sodium and chlorine have theirs?**

How many electrons?

You can see in **Figure 7-3** that the farther an energy level is from the nucleus, the bigger its sphere. The bigger the sphere, the more electrons it can hold. **Figure 7-3** shows the maximum number of electrons that each of the first four energy levels can hold. The first energy level can hold only two electrons. Notice in the periodic table in **Figure 7-6** that there are two elements in the first period. The periods of the periodic table are the horizontal rows. Period 1 contains only hydrogen and helium. These elements have electrons only in the first energy level. Hydrogen has one electron. Helium has a completed outer energy level with two electrons. The second energy level holds eight electrons. In **Figure 7-4,** you can see that eight elements are in the second period. These elements have two electrons in the first energy level, plus different numbers of electrons in the second energy level. Starting with lithium, each element in the second period has one more electron in the second energy level than the element that comes before it. The final element in this period, neon, has a completed outer energy level with eight electrons.

Electron Arrangement and Groups

The elements in the same column of the periodic table are called a group or a family of elements. Fluorine, chlorine, and bromine are three members of Group 17, the halogen family. Just as people in a family may have similar smiles, noses, or eating habits, elements in the same family have similar properties. This is because they all have the same number of electrons in their outer energy levels. **Figure 7-5** shows the electron arrangements of sodium, Group 1, and chlorine, Group 17. Notice that sodium has one electron in its outer energy level and chlorine has seven. Compare the diagrams of these elements in **Figure 7-5** with the diagrams of lithium and fluorine in **Figure 7-4.** You can see that the Group 1 elements, lithium and sodium, have one electron in their outer energy levels. Fluorine and chlorine both have seven electrons in their outer energy levels. You know that bromine is in the same family as fluorine and chlorine, so

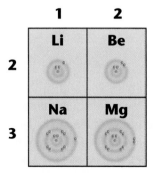

	1	2		13	14	15	16	17	18
2	Li	Be		B	C	N	O	F	Ne
3	Na	Mg		Al	Si	P	S	Cl	Ar

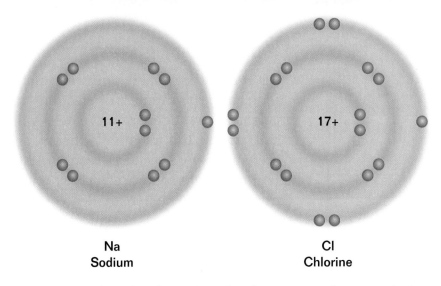

Na
Sodium

Cl
Chlorine

Figure 7-5 Compare the electron arrangements of sodium and chlorine with the electron arrangements of lithium and fluorine in Figure 7-4. **What can you conclude about elements that are in the same families?**

you can predict that bromine also has seven electrons in its outer energy level. The number of electrons in an atom's outer energy level determines how the element will combine with other elements. ☑

Look at the elements in Group 18 of the periodic table in **Figure 7-6.** The number of electrons in the outer energy level of each group is shown at the top of the column. The members of Group 18, the noble gases, have eight electrons in their outer energy levels. They do not combine easily with other elements. The noble gases are stable, which means that they resist change. The reason for their stability is that their outer energy levels are filled.

Reading Check ☑

How many electrons are in the outer energy level of bromine?

Using Math

An atom of copper has an effective volume of 1.18×12^{-23} cm^3. The volume of a penny is 0.314 cm^3. Calculate the number of copper atoms in a pure copper penny.

1e⁻ 1							8e⁻ 18
1 Hydrogen **H** 1	2e⁻ 2	3e⁻ 13	4e⁻ 14	5e⁻ 15	6e⁻ 16	7e⁻ 17	Helium **He** 2
2 Lithium **Li** 3	Beryllium **Be** 4	Boron **B** 5	Carbon **C** 6	Nitrogen **N** 7	Oxygen **O** 8	Fluorine **F** 9	Neon **Ne** 10
3 Sodium **Na** 11	Magnesium **Mg** 12	Aluminum **Al** 13	Silicon **Si** 14	Phosphorus **P** 15	Sulfur **S** 16	Chlorine **Cl** 17	Argon **Ar** 18
4 Potassium **K** 19	Calcium **Ca** 20	Gallium **Ga** 31	Germanium **Ge** 32	Arsenic **As** 33	Selenium **Se** 34	Bromine **Br** 35	Krypton **Kr** 36
5 Rubidium **Rb** 37	Strontium **Sr** 38	Indium **In** 49	Tin **Sn** 50	Antimony **Sb** 51	Tellurium **Te** 52	Iodine **I** 53	Xenon **Xe** 54
6 Cesium **Cs** 55	Barium **Ba** 56	Thallium **Tl** 81	Lead **Pb** 82	Bismuth **Bi** 83	Polonium **Po** 84	Astatine **At** 85	Radon **Rn** 86
7 Francium **Fr** 87	Radium **Ra** 88						

Figure 7-6 You can see that the number of electrons (e^-) in the outer energy levels increases from one to eight across a period of these groups.

Drawing Electron Dot Diagrams

Procedure

1. Draw a periodic table that includes the first 18 elements. These are the elements from hydrogen through argon. Make each block a 3-cm square.

2. Fill in each block with the electron dot diagram of the element.

Analysis

1. What do you observe about the electron dot diagram of the elements in the same family?

2. Describe any changes you observe in the electron dot diagrams across a period.

Electron Dot Diagrams

As you're probably beginning to understand, the number of electrons in an element's outer energy level tells you a lot about the element's behavior. Different atomic structures result in different physical properties such as color; hardness; and whether an element is a solid, liquid, or gas. Atomic structure also determines the chemical properties of an element, such as how the element behaves with other elements. If you want to predict how atoms of one element will behave in the presence of atoms of another element, it would help to have an easy way to represent the atoms and show how many electrons are in their outer energy levels. You can do this with electron dot diagrams. An **electron dot diagram** is the chemical symbol for the element surrounded by as many dots as there are electrons in its outer energy level.

Writing Dot Diagrams

How do you know how many dots to make? For Groups 1, 2, and 13–18, you can use a periodic table. Group 1 has one outer electron. Group 2 has two. Group 13 has three, Group 14, four, and so on to Group 18, which has eight. Helium is an exception. It has only two electrons in its single energy level. How many electrons are in the outer energy level of the oxygen family? These elements are in Group 16, so the answer is six.

How would you write a dot diagram for the element phosphorus? First, write the symbol for the element phosphorus—P. Then, find phosphorus in the periodic table. Next, ask what group it is in. It's in Group 15. This means that it has five electrons in its outer energy level. The completed dot diagram with the five electrons is shown in **Figure 7-7.**

What happens when atoms form chemical bonds with each other? A **chemical bond** is a force that holds two atoms together. Chemical bonds form when atoms combine in ways that give them eight electrons in their outer energy levels. When this happens, the atoms have outer energy levels that are filled, just like the noble gases. Each atom then has greater stability than before it interacted. A chemical

Figure 7-7 The electron dot diagram shows the symbol for phosphorus and the five electrons in its outer energy level.

Phosphorus

Figure 7-8 Chemical bonds hold atoms together like friends linking arms. **Why do atoms form chemical bonds?**

bond is like friends linking arms as in **Figure 7-8.** In the next section, you'll learn how gaining, losing, or sharing electrons provides the link that holds atoms together.

Section Assessment

1. How many electrons does nitrogen have in its outer energy level? How many does bromine have?

2. How many electrons does oxygen have in its first energy level? Second energy level?

3. Which electrons in oxygen have the higher energy, those in the first energy level or those in the second?

4. **Think Critically:** Atoms in a group of elements increase in size as you move down in the periodic table. Explain why this is so.

5. **Skill Builder**
   Classifying Use the periodic table to organize the following elements into families: K, C, Sn, Li, F, Na, Pb, and I. Then, write the electron dot diagram for each element and compare the diagrams in each family. What can you conclude? If you need help, refer to Classifying in the **Skill Handbook** on page 525

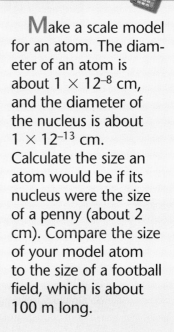

Using Math

Make a scale model for an atom. The diameter of an atom is about 1×12^{-8} cm, and the diameter of the nucleus is about 1×12^{-13} cm. Calculate the size an atom would be if its nucleus were the size of a penny (about 2 cm). Compare the size of your model atom to the size of a football field, which is about 100 m long.

Atomic Structure

As more information has become known about the structure of the atom, scientists have developed new models of the atom. Making your own model and studying the models of others will help you learn how protons, neutrons, and electrons are arranged in an atom.

Possible Materials

- Magnetic board
- Rubber magnetic strips
- Paper
- Marker
- Half-inch squares of paper
- Grapes
- Candy-coated peanuts
- Coins

Recognize the Problem

Can an element be identified based on a model that shows the arrangement of the protons, neutrons, and electrons of an atom?

Form a Hypothesis

Write a hypothesis that explains how your group will construct a model of an element that others will be able to identify.

Goals

- **Design an experiment** to create a model of a chosen element.

- **Observe** the models made by others in the class and identify the elements they represent.

Safety Precautions

Never eat any food used in a laboratory experiment. Dispose of all food after your experiment.

Test Your Hypothesis

Plan

1. **Choose** an element from periods 2 or 3 of the periodic table. How can you find out the number of protons, neutrons, and electrons in an atom?

2. What materials will you use to represent the electrons of the atom? How will you represent the nucleus? How can you show the difference between protons and neutrons?

3. How will you model the arrangement of electrons in the atom? Will the atom have a charge? Is it possible to identify an atom by the number of protons it has?

Do

1. Make sure your teacher approves your plan before you proceed.

2. **Construct** your model, then **record** your observations in your Science Journal and include a sketch.

3. **Construct** a model of another element.

4. **Observe** the models made by your classmates. **Identify** the elements they represent.

Analyze Your Data

1. What elements did you identify using your hypothesis?

2. In a neutral atom, **identify** which particles are always present in equal numbers.

3. **Predict** what would happen to the charge on an atom if one of the electrons were removed. What happens to an atom if one proton and one electron are removed?

4. **Compare and contrast** your model with the electron cloud model of the atom.

Draw Conclusions

1. What is the minimum amount of information you need to know to identify a neutral atom of an element?

2. If you made models of the isotopes boron-10 and boron-11, how would these models be different?

WhatYou'll Learn

► How to describe ionic and covalent bonds
► The difference between polar and nonpolar covalent bonds
► Chemical shorthand

Vocabulary
ion
ionic bond
compound
covalent bond
molecule
formula

WhyIt's Important

► Everything in the world is held together by bonds.

Ionic Bonds—Loss and Gain

Some metal atoms can obtain the stable atomic structure of a noble gas by losing an electron. This is easy for elements in Group 1. Think about sodium as an example. Sodium has one electron in its outer energy level. If a sodium atom loses that electron, the energy level occupied by the electron becomes empty as you can see in **Figure 7-9**. The energy level below that is filled. By losing one electron, sodium's atomic structure becomes the same as the stable noble gas neon.

Other nonmetal atoms can acquire the stable structure of a noble gas by gaining an electron. Elements in Group 17, such as chlorine and fluorine, have seven electrons in their outer energy levels. These elements readily gain an electron. In doing so, they fill their outer energy levels. For example, if an atom of chlorine gains an electron, its atomic structure becomes the same as the noble gas argon. The diagram in **Figure 7-9** shows the chlorine atom as it gains an electron.

Positive and Negative Ions

When a sodium atom loses an electron, the atom becomes positively charged because there is one electron less in the atom than there are protons in the nucleus. Similarly, when a chlorine atom gains an electron, it becomes negatively charged because there is one more electron in the atom than there are protons in the nucleus. An atom that is no longer neutral because it has lost or gained an electron is called an **ion** (I ahn). A sodium ion is represented by the symbol Na^+. A chlorine ion

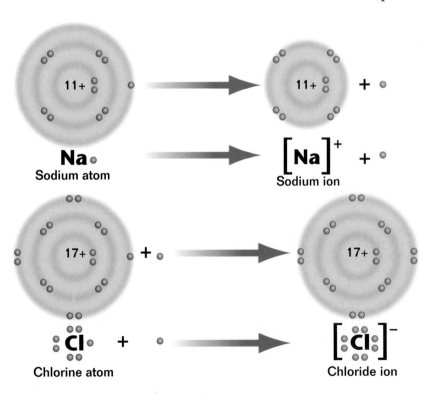

Na Sodium atom → **[Na]$^+$** Sodium ion + ·

Cl Chlorine atom + · → **[Cl]$^-$** Chloride ion

Figure 7-9 When sodium loses an electron and chlorine gains an electron, their outer energy levels become full.

Figure 7-10 The symbols in brackets represent the sodium ion and the chloride ion. These ions form when sodium loses an electron and chlorine gains one. When sodium loses an electron and chlorine gains it, ordinary table salt, sodium chloride, is the result.

Na · ⟶ [Na]⁺ + ·

:Cl·̈ + · ⟶ [:C̈l:]⁻

Na · + :C̈l· ⟶ [Na]⁺[:C̈l:]⁻

Sodium   Chlorine   Sodium chloride

is represented by the symbol Cl⁻. **Figure 7-10** shows dot diagrams for the formation of the two ions.

The positive sodium ion and the negative chlorine ion are attracted to each other. This attraction, which holds the ions close together, is a chemical bond called an **ionic bond.** In **Figure 7-10,** you can see that when sodium and chlorine ions form an ionic bond, the compound sodium chloride, ordinary table salt, is formed. A **compound** is a pure substance that contains two or more elements.

Ionic Salts

Sodium chloride, the stuff that comes out of your salt shaker, is an example of an ionic salt. An ionic salt is a hard, crystalline (KRIH stuh lihn) compound in which positive ions of metal atoms and negative ions of nonmetal atoms are lined up in a regular pattern as shown in **Figure 7-11.** When ionic salts are dissolved in water, the ions separate. A solution of an ionic salt will conduct an electric current because the charged particles can move through the solution. Pure water is a poor conductor of electric current.

Sodium ion, Na⁺

Chloride ion, Cl⁻

Figure 7-11 In ionic compounds such as sodium chloride, the positive and negative ions line up in regular fashion. Each positive ion is surrounded by negative ions, and each negative ion is surrounded by positive ions.

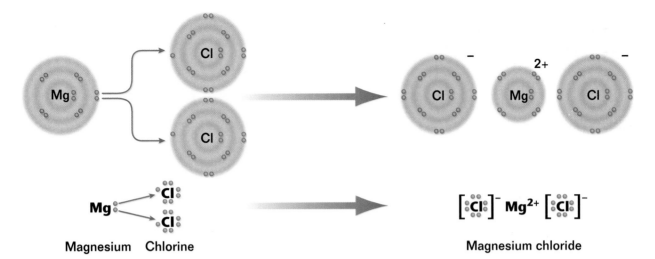

Magnesium   Chlorine

Magnesium chloride

$$\left[\ddot{\underset{..}{Cl}}\right]^{-} \quad Mg^{2+} \quad \left[\ddot{\underset{..}{Cl}}\right]^{-}$$

Figure 7-12 Magnesium divides up its two electrons between two chlorines to form $MgCl_2$, but it also could give two electrons to one atom, as it does in MgO.

Using the periodic table, you can predict that ionic salts similar to sodium chloride would form between all the elements of the alkali metals family and all of the halogens. Some examples are sodium fluoride, the anticavity ingredient in some toothpastes, and potassium iodide, which is frequently added to table salt to prevent iodine deficiency.

More Gains and Losses

You have seen what happens when elements gain or lose one electron. Now see what happens when elements gain or lose more than one. The element magnesium, Mg, in Group 2 has two electrons in its outer energy level. Magnesium can lose these two electrons and have the same structure as a stable neon atom. The two electrons can be gained by two chlorine atoms. As you can see in **Figure 7-12,** a single magnesium ion represented by the symbol Mg^{2+} and two chlorine ions are produced. The two negatively charged chlorine ions are attracted to the positively charged magnesium ion. The compound magnesium chloride is produced.

The two electrons released by magnesium could be gained by a single atom such as oxygen. When oxygen gains two electrons to form the ion O^{2-}, it can combine in a one-to-one ratio with a positive ion in Group 2. If the positive ion is Mg^{2+}, magnesium oxide (MgO) is formed.

Covalent Bonds—A Matter of Sharing

Some atoms of nonmetals are unlikely to lose or gain electrons. For example, carbon has six protons and six electrons. Four of the six electrons are in its outer energy level. To obtain a noble gas structure, carbon would either have to gain four electrons or lose four electrons. If carbon gained four electrons, that would mean that the carbon nucleus, with its charge of 6+, would have to hold its own six electrons plus four more—a total of ten negatively charged

EARTH SCIENCE
INTEGRATION

Mineral Structure
Some minerals are made up of a single element, but most are compounds of different elements. The properties and appearance of a mineral occur because of how the atoms of its elements are arranged. Use an Earth science textbook or other source to find out the elements that make up the most common minerals.

electrons. That would take too much energy. Too much energy also would be needed to remove four electrons. Each time an electron is removed, the nucleus holds the remaining electrons even more tightly. So, how do atoms of an element like carbon form bonds with other atoms?

The Covalent Bond

Atoms that do not gain or lose electrons become more stable by sharing electrons. The chemical bond that forms between atoms when they share electrons is called a **covalent** (koh VAY luhnt) **bond.** Shared electrons are attracted to the nuclei of two atoms at the same time. They move between the outer energy levels of each atom in the covalent bond so that each atom has a full outer energy level some of the time. The atoms in a covalent bond form a neutral particle, which means that the particle contains the same numbers of positive and negative charges. The neutral particle formed when atoms share electrons is called a **molecule** (MAH luh kyewl). You can see a model of electron sharing and molecule formation in **Figure 7-13.** Notice that no charged particles are involved because no electrons are gained or lost.

Try at Home
MiniLab

Constructing a Model for Methane

Procedure

1. Using circles of different colored paper to represent protons, neutrons, and electrons, build paper models of one carbon atom and four hydrogen atoms.

2. Use your models of atoms to construct a molecule of methane by forming covalent bonds. The methane molecule has four hydrogen atoms chemically bonded to one carbon atom.

Analysis

1. In the methane molecule, do the carbon and hydrogen atoms have the same arrangement of electrons as two noble gas elements? Explain.

2. Is the methane molecule charged?

Figure 7-13 The sharing of electrons allows each atom to have a filled outer energy level. **Which noble gas is hydrogen similar to? Which is chlorine similar to?**

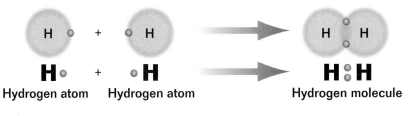

H + H → H H

H∘ + ∘H → H∘∘H

Hydrogen atom   Hydrogen atom   Hydrogen molecule

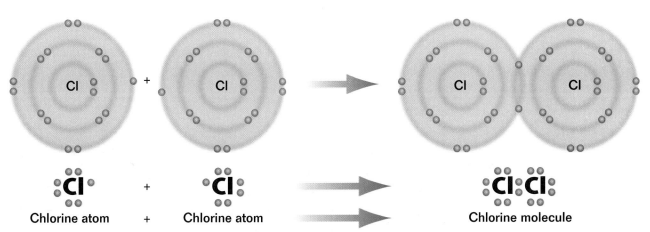

Cl + Cl → Cl Cl

Chlorine atom + Chlorine atom → Chlorine molecule

Figure 7-14 Convince yourself, by counting the electrons, that all of carbon's four electrons and all of the two oxygens' 12 electrons are present in the electron dot diagram of CO_2. **Does each atom in the two covalent compounds have eight electrons around it?**

Carbon atom   Oxygen atoms   Carbon dioxide molecule

Nitrogen atoms   Nitrogen molecule

Sometimes an atom shares more than one electron with another atom. In the molecule carbon dioxide, shown in **Figure 7-14,** each of the oxygen atoms shares two electrons with the carbon atom. When two pairs of electrons are involved in a covalent bond, the bond is called a double bond. **Figure 7-14** also shows the sharing of three pairs of electrons between two nitrogen atoms in the nitrogen molecule. When three pairs of electrons are shared by two atoms, the bond is called a triple bond. Nitrogen molecules make up about 80 percent of the air in the atmosphere. ☑

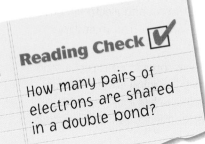

Reading Check ☑

How many pairs of electrons are shared in a double bond?

Problem Solving

Beyond Diamond and Graphite

Is there no end to the variety of nature? Bursting onto the scene in 1985 came a new form of carbon. If you could see this new kind of carbon, you might say that it looks like a soccer ball. In fact, it's called a buckyball, which is a nickname for buckminsterfullerene. Buckminster Fuller is the architect who designed the first geodesic dome. The dome at right is located at EPCOT near Orlando, Florida. Buckminsterfullerene looks a lot like the dome created by its namesake. This amazing form of carbon is a molecule containing 60 carbon atoms bonded together in a hollow sphere.

In early 1990, *Science* magazine named buckminsterfullerene the "Molecule of the Year" because it held so much yet-to-be-developed promise. Medical applications were proposed in which disease-attacking agents would be attached to the outside of the molecule or radioactive isotopes would be carried inside the molecule. The molecule could then be injected into a patient. Another application concerned the separation of mixtures. How might that work?

Solve the Problem

1. Fill a tall, glass cylinder with glass marbles. The marbles will represent the spherical buckyballs. The mixture to be separated could be sand or salt mixed with barley or rice. These substances represent two different chemical compounds.

2. Pour the sand and barley mixture over the marbles and observe.

Think Critically

1. Did the mixture change as a result of being poured over the marbles? How do you think the packing of the marbles helped with the separation?

2. How might buckyballs be used to separate a mixture of chemical compounds?

3. Can you think of any other uses for buckyballs?

Figure 7-15 The balloon became electrically charged by rubbing it on someone's hair. Now, it attracts a stream of water. The two pairs of electrons in the two bonds between oxygen and hydrogen spend more time near the oxygen than near the hydrogen. This makes oxygen slightly negative and hydrogen slightly positive.

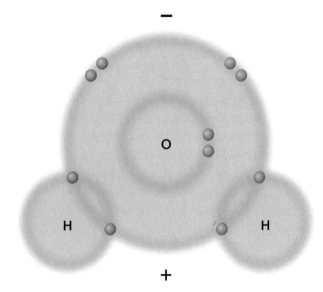

Polar and Nonpolar Molecules

You have seen that atoms often share electrons to become more stable. Do the atoms always share electrons equally? The answer is no. Some atoms have a greater attraction for electrons than others do. Oxygen, for example, attracts electrons more strongly than hydrogen does. When a covalent bond forms between hydrogen and oxygen, the shared pair of electrons tends to spend more time near the oxygen atom than the hydrogen atom.

The Polar Water Molecule

Water molecules are formed when hydrogen and oxygen share electrons. **Figure 7-15** shows evidence of the unequal sharing of electrons by hydrogen and oxygen in water. Because the oxygen atom has a greater share in the electron pair, the oxygen end of a water molecule has a slight negative charge, and the hydrogen end has a slight positive charge. This type of bond is a polar bond. *Polar* means having two opposite ends or poles. Often, one or more polar bonds result in a polar molecule such as the water molecule. Molecules that do not have these unbalanced charges are called nonpolar molecules. Because all atoms have different atomic structures, they all have different attractions for electrons, so the only truly nonpolar bonds are bonds between the same two atoms. The nitrogen molecule, which has two nitrogen atoms joined in a covalent bond, is an example of a nonpolar bond.

*inter*NET
CONNECTION

Visit the Glencoe Science Web Site at **www.glencoe.com/ sec/science/ca** for more information about polar molecules.

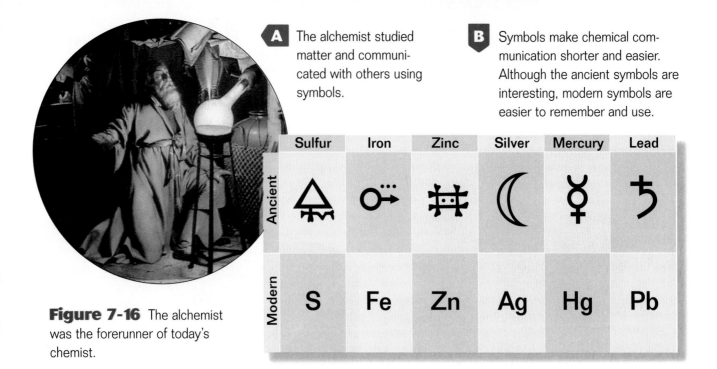

A The alchemist studied matter and communicated with others using symbols.

B Symbols make chemical communication shorter and easier. Although the ancient symbols are interesting, modern symbols are easier to remember and use.

	Sulfur	Iron	Zinc	Silver	Mercury	Lead
Ancient						
Modern	S	Fe	Zn	Ag	Hg	Pb

Figure 7-16 The alchemist was the forerunner of today's chemist.

Chemical Shorthand

The medieval alchemist (AL kuh mist) in **Figure 7-16A** looks quite different from a modern chemist, but like the ancient alchemists, today's chemist investigates matter, records results to share with others, and uses symbols to represent the elements. Some of the symbols used by alchemists are shown in **Figure 7-16B.** The modern chemist knows that the black tarnish that forms on silver is a compound made up of the elements silver and sulfur. She uses symbols to represent the compound: Ag_2S. If the alchemist knew the composition of tarnish, how might he have used his symbols to represent it? Modern symbols make it easy to write down chemical information and have other people understand it.

Formulas for Molecules

When you write Ag_2S, chemists everywhere know exactly what you mean. Chemical formulas allow scientists to communicate and share research. **Figure 7-17** shows a model of the way a hydrogen molecule is formed. Two hydrogen atoms join together in a covalent bond. The resulting molecule is represented by the chemical formula H_2. The small 2 after the H in the formula is called a subscript. *Sub-* means "below" and *script* means "write," so a subscript is a number that is written below. The subscript 2 means that two atoms of hydrogen are in the molecule.

Figure 7-17 Two hydrogen atoms make up one hydrogen molecule. The formula for the hydrogen molecule makes that clear by placing the subscript 2 after the H.

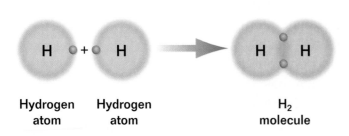

Hydrogen atom   Hydrogen atom H_2 molecule

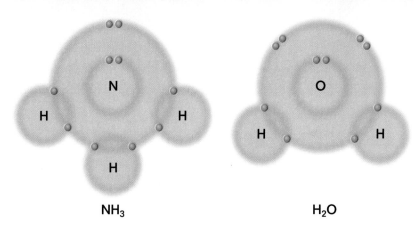

NH₃   H₂O

Figure 7-18 Ammonia has
three hydrogen atoms and one
nitrogen atom, so its formula is
NH₃. The water molecule, H₂0,
has two hydrogen atoms and one
oxygen atom.

A chemical **formula** is a combination of chemical symbols of
the elements that tells what elements are present in a molecule
and how many atoms of each element are present. Similarly,
the formula for the molecule containing two chlorine atoms
is Cl_2. When there is no subscript, the number of atoms is
understood to be one.

Covalently bonded molecules also can be compounds like
ammonia and water shown in **Figure 7-18.** These molecules
have more than one kind of atom joined together in covalent
bonds. Ammonia has the formula NH_3, and the formula for
water is H_2O. The formula for silver tarnish, Ag_2S, tells you
that silver tarnish is a compound that contains two silver
atoms and one sulfur atom.

Using Math

A container holds
a gas made up of
molecules that con-
tain carbon and
hydrogen. Of the
atoms in the con-
tainer, 20 percent are
carbon. Determine
the chemical formula
of the gas molecules.

Section Assessment

1. Use the periodic table to decide whether lithium
   would form a positive or a negative ion. Would
   fluorine form a positive or a negative ion? Write
   the formula for the compound the two elements
   would form.

2. What is the difference between a polar and a
   nonpolar bond?

3. What does a chemical formula tell you?

4. **Think Critically:** Most laundry detergents are
   long molecules with one end that is soluble in grease
   and the other end soluble in water. What is the most
   probable type of molecule in detergents? Explain.

5. **Skill Builder**
   Predicting Scientists use what they have
   learned to predict what they think will happen. Do
   the **Chapter 7 Skill Activity** on page 560 to
   predict the type of bond that will form between
   elements.

Using Computers

Spreadsheet Design a
table using spreadsheet
software to compare
and contrast ionic, polar
covalent, and nonpolar
covalent bonds. If you
need help, refer to page
550.

Ionic Compounds

Materials

- Paper (8 different colors)
- Tacks (2 different colors)
- Corrugated cardboard
- Scissors

Metals in Groups 1 and 2 often lose electrons and form positive ions. Nonmetals in Groups 15, 16, and 17 often gain electrons and become negative ions. What are the possibilities for the formation of compounds between these five groups of elements?

What You'll Investigate

How do different atoms combine with each other to form compounds?

Goals

- **Construct** models of electron gain and loss.
- **Write** formulas for the ions that form when electrons are gained or lost.
- **Determine** the formulas of compounds formed between positive and negative ions.

Procedure

1. **Cut** three paper disks to represent each of these elements: Li, S, Mg, O, Ca, N, Al, and I. The disks should be about 7 cm in diameter. Use a different color of paper for each element.

2. On each disk, **write** the symbol of the element it represents.

3. Lay circles that represent an atom of lithium and an atom of sulfur side by side on a piece of corrugated cardboard.

4. **Choose** a color of thumbtack to represent the outer electron of lithium. Choose another color of thumbtack to represent the outer electrons of sulfur. **Place** one tack for each electron around the outside of each disk. Space the tacks evenly.

5. **Move** one or more electrons from the metallic atom to the nonmetallic atom so that both elements achieve a noble gas arrangement of electrons. If necessary, add more atoms of one or the other element.

6. Write the formulas for each of the ions in the ionic compound.

7. Repeat steps 3 through 6 for the remaining combinations of atoms: Mg and O, Ca and N, Al and I.

Conclude and Apply

1. **Draw** electron dot diagrams for all of the ions produced.

2. **Identify** the noble gas elements that have the same electron arrangements as the ions you produced.

3. How many lithium atoms combine with one sulfur atom?

4. Why did you have to use more than one atom in some cases? Why couldn't you just take more electrons from one metal atom or add extra ones to a nonmetal atom?

Metallic Bonding

Knowing the type of bonding in a substance can help you predict many of its physical properties. An ionic compound may form a solid with a high melting point that conducts electricity in the liquid state or when it is dissolved in water. Many covalent compounds are gases, liquids, or soft solids at room temperature. They do not conduct electricity or easily dissolve in water.

Bonding in metals is not due to the formation of compounds. Metallic bonding is the sharing of electrons between all the atoms in the metal. This type of bonding explains why some metals have the strength to support a high-rise office building (left), why other metals can be formed into the thin wire filaments within lightbulbs, and why still other metals can be rolled or shaped into soft drink cans or hammered into horseshoes.

IN METALLIC BONDING

1 The outer electrons of each atom in the metal are not held tightly to the nucleus. Instead, they are free to move from one nucleus to another.

2 The metal atoms are bonded together in a large network. A sea of electrons surrounds each positively charged nucleus.

3 The bonding in metals is not rigid. Each nucleus can slide through the sea of electrons to new positions and stay connected to the other nuclei. As a result, metals can be hammered into thin sheets or pulled into long, thin wires.

4 The electrons can easily flow through the metal to conduct electricity.

Thinking Critically

1. How does metallic bonding differ from ionic bonding? From covalent bonding?

2. Explain why a metal with three outer electrons would be a better conductor than a metal with one outer electron.

Career **CONNECTION**

Use the library to research the difference between a metallurgist and a metalsmith.

Chapter 7 Reviewing Main Ideas

For a **preview** of this chapter, study this Reviewing Main Ideas before you read the chapter. After you have studied this chapter, you can use the Reviewing Main Ideas to **review** the chapter.

The Glencoe MindJogger, Audiocassettes, and CD-ROM provide additional opportunities for review.

Section 7-1 ELECTRON ARRANGEMENT

The electrons in the electron cloud of an atom are arranged in energy levels. Each energy level contains a definite number of electrons. The number of electrons in the outer energy level of the atom increases across any period of the periodic table. The noble gas elements are stable because they have filled outer energy levels. *How many electrons are in the outer energy level of fluorine?*

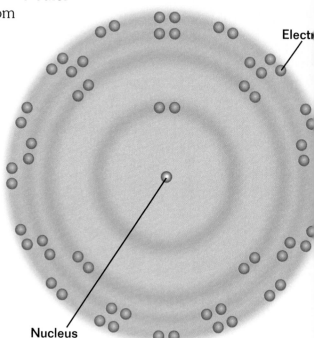

Electr

Nucleus

Sodium ion, Na⁺

Chloride ion, Cl⁻

Section 7-2 IONIC AND COVALENT BONDS

Atoms can become more stable if they gain, lose, or share electrons until their outer energy level is filled with electrons. **Ionic bonds** are created when a metal atom loses one or more electrons and a nonmetal atom gains one or more electrons. **Covalent bonds** are created when nonmetal atoms share one or more electrons. The unequal sharing of electrons results in a polar covalent bond. *How does the number of electrons in the outer energy level determine the type of bond that will be formed?*

CHEMICAL SYMBOLS AND FORMULAS

In order to communicate clearly about elements and combinations of elements, chemists created chemical symbols and **formulas.** This chemical language tells what elements are in **molecules** and **compounds,** and how many atoms of each element are present. The formula for silver sulfide, Ag_2S, shows there are two silver atoms and one sulfur atom in every molecule of silver sulfide. *How many hydrogen atoms and how many nitrogen atoms are in one molecule of ammonia, NH_3?*

> **Reading Check** ✓
> Locate words that are not on the vocabulary list but were unfamiliar to you before you read this chapter. Define these words in your Science Journal.

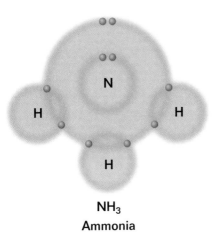

NH_3
Ammonia

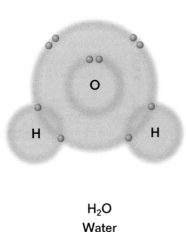

H_2O
Water

Career CONNECTION

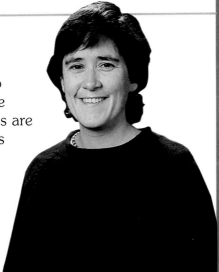

Dr. Brenna Flaugher, Particle Physicist

As a particle physicist, Brenna Flaugher uses a supercollider to study the particles that make up protons and neutrons, and the forces that bind these particles together. Though these particles are small, they can help understand big things, like why matter has mass, why gravity works, and how the universe was formed. Brenna chose a career in particle physics because it represents an exciting scientific frontier. *How does studying atoms help us understand chemical interactions?*

Using Vocabulary

a. chemical bond
b. compound
c. covalent bond
d. electron dot diagram
e. formula
f. ion
g. ionic bond
h. molecule

Distinguish between the terms in each of the following pairs.

1. ion, molecule
2. molecule, compound
3. electron dot diagram, formula
4. formula, molecule
5. ionic bond, covalent bond

Checking Concepts

Choose the word or phrase that best answers the question.

6. Which term is used to represent a molecule?
   A) equation
   B) formula
   C) chemical symbol
   D) number

7. Which of the following is a covalently bonded molecule?
   A) Cl_2
   B) air
   C) Ne
   D) salt

8. Which of the following is represented by the symbol Cl^-?
   A) an ionic compound
   B) a polar molecule
   C) a negative ion
   D) a positive ion

9. Which phrase describes what happens to electrons when a polar covalent bond forms?
   A) They are lost.
   B) They are gained.
   C) They are shared equally.
   D) They are shared unequally.

10. Which of the following compounds is unlikely to contain ionic bonds?
    A) NaF
    B) CO
    C) LiCl
    D) $MgBr_2$

11. Which term describes the units that make up compounds with covalent bonds?
    A) ions
    B) molecules
    C) salts
    D) acids

12. In the chemical formula CO_2, the subscript 2 shows which of the following?
    A) There are two oxygen ions.
    B) There are two oxygen atoms.
    C) There are two CO_2 molecules.
    D) There are two CO_2 compounds.

13. Which term describes the units that make up substances formed by ionic bonding?
    A) ions
    B) molecules
    C) acids
    D) atoms

14. Which is **NOT** true about the molecule H_2O?
    A) It contains two hydrogen atoms.
    B) It contains one oxygen atom.
    C) It is a polar covalent compound.
    D) It is an ionic compound.

15. What is the number of the group in which the elements have a filled outer energy level and are stable?
    A) 1
    B) 13
    C) 16
    D) 18

Thinking Critically

16. Groups 1 and 2 form many compounds with Groups 16 and 17. Explain.

17. What would you need to know about the atoms in a covalent bond in order to decide if the bond is polar?

18. When salt is dropped into a glass of water, the salt dissolves in the water and the sodium and chlorine ions are separated. Explain why this might occur.

19. Cesium in period 6 is more reactive than lithium in period 2. Both elements are in the alkali metals family. Explain the difference in reactivity on the basis of the outer energy levels of the two atoms.

20. Use the fact that water is a polar molecule to explain why water has a much higher boiling point than other molecules of the same size.

Developing Skills

If you need help, refer to the **Skill Handbook.**

21. **Predicting:** Suppose that equal masses of CuCl and CuCl$_2$ are decomposed into their component elements, copper and chlorine. Predict which compound will yield more copper. Explain your answer.

22. **Concept Mapping:** Draw a concept map starting with the term *chemical bond* and use all the vocabulary words.

23. **Recognizing Cause and Effect:** A helium atom has only two electrons. Why does helium behave as a noble gas?

24. **Observing and Inferring:** Suppose you have a sample of an element. You identify it as iron. List observations that you made that allowed you to infer that it is iron.

25. **Making and Using a Table:** Fill in the second column of the table with the number of metal atoms in one unit of the compound. Fill in the third column with the number of atoms of the nonmetal in one unit.

Formulas of Compounds		
Compound	Number of Metal Atoms	Number of Nonmetal Atoms
Cu$_2$O		
Al$_2$S$_2$		
NaF		
PbCl$_4$		

THE PRINCETON REVIEW

Test-Taking Tip

Your Answers Are Better Than the Test's When you know the answer, answer the question in your own words before looking at the answer choices. Often, more than one answer choice will look good, so arm yourself with yours before looking.

Test Practice

Use these questions to test your Science Proficiency.

1. Which of the following statements is true?
   A) A molecule also can be a compound.
   B) A compound can contain only two different kinds of atoms.
   C) A compound can contain only one kind of atom.
   D) A molecule can contain only one kind of atom.

2. Which statement below **BEST** explains why atoms react chemically with each other?
   A) When atoms react, they lose all of their electrons and become more stable.
   B) When atoms react, they lose, gain, or share electrons to reach a full outer energy level and are then more stable.
   C) When atoms react, they gain protons and are then more stable.
   D) When atoms react, they lose, gain, or share electrons and are then less stable.

Chemical Reactions

Skills Preview

Skill Builders
- Predict
- Interpret Data

Activities
- Design an Experiment
- Make a Model

MiniLabs
- Observe and Infer
- Compare and Contrast

Reading Check ✔

As you read, use context clues to figure out unfamiliar terms. For example, what clues help you understand the term *jostling* in the caption for Figure 8-12A? *Proteases* in the caption for Figure 8-13?

Explore Activity

An unfortunate accident caused this awful scene. Dramatic changes are going on as chemical reactions rage. When the action stops, the matter that existed before the chemical reactions will not be the same as before. It may look different, smell different, have a different physical state, or have different chemical properties. A chemical reaction is a change in matter, sometimes complex, as in this photo, and sometimes simple, as you will see in this Explore Activity.

Observe a Chemical Reaction

1. Pour 50 mL of vinegar into the bottom of a small plastic bag with a zipper closing. Have your partner hold the bag open so that you can pour the vinegar without getting any on the sides of the bag.

2. Cinch the bag together in the middle and tie it off with a twist tie.

3. Put one teaspoonful of baking soda into the top of the bag. Force out as much air as possible and zip the bag.

4. Untie the tie and shake the baking soda down into the vinegar. Observe.

Science Journal

In your Science Journal, draw a sketch of what happened after you mixed the vinegar and baking soda. Write a paragraph explaining your picture.

8·1 Describing a Chemical Reaction

What You'll Learn

► Ways to tell whether or not a chemical reaction is occurring
► How to read and understand a balanced chemical equation
► That some reactions release energy and others absorb energy

Vocabulary
chemical reaction
reactant
product
endothermic reaction
exothermic reaction

Why It's Important

► Almost every important process in your life is a chemical reaction.

Evidence of Chemical Reactions

You can smell a rotten egg and the smoke from a campfire. These are signs of chemical reactions. It's easy to tell when these chemical reactions occur. They give off smoke or smell bad. Other reactions are less obvious, but you can usually tell they have occurred.

Physical and Chemical Changes

Matter undergoes two kinds of changes—physical changes and chemical changes. Physical changes in a substance are those that affect its physical properties, such as its size and shape or its state (solid, liquid, or gas). For example, when water is frozen into ice, its physical state changes from liquid to solid, but it's still water. Chemical changes in a substance result in the formation of new substances that have properties different from those of the original substance. For example, a chemical change has occurred when a spot of rust appears on the steel body of a car, when an egg is fried, or when the leaves turn red in the fall. A process in which chemical changes occur is called a **chemical reaction.**

The same substance can undergo both physical and chemical changes. Look at the newspaper shown in **Figure 8-1.** If you take a piece of newspaper in your hands and crumple it

Figure 8-1 How do physical and chemical changes differ?

A Tearing or crumpling a piece of newspaper doesn't really change its substance. It's still newspaper, so only a physical change has occurred.

B The energy of the sun causes changes in the color of the newspaper. A chemical change has occurred.

Figure 8-2 Look for evidence of chemical change. It's all around you.

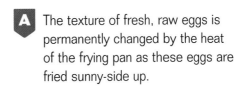

A The texture of fresh, raw eggs is permanently changed by the heat of the frying pan as these eggs are fried sunny-side up.

B Bubbles stream from an antacid tablet when it dissolves in water. Bubbles also formed in the chemical reaction of vinegar and baking soda.

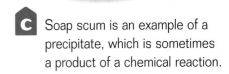

C Soap scum is an example of a precipitate, which is sometimes a product of a chemical reaction.

D Smoke and ash are left after a newspaper burns as kindling for these logs. Heat is also evidence that a chemical reaction is occurring.

up, you change its size and shape, but you still have a piece of newspaper. Crushing the paper is a physical change. If you leave that piece of newspaper in sunlight for a long time, it will turn yellow. If you use it as kindling in a campfire and touch a match to it, it will burst into flames. These processes are chemical reactions. The final substances are chemically different from the starting substances. How can you tell that a chemical reaction has occurred? Sometimes it is obvious, sometimes not. **Figure 8-2** shows several clues to look for to determine whether or not a change is chemical.

Mini Lab

Observing a Chemical Change

Procedure

1. Place about ¼ teaspoon of baking soda in an evaporating dish. Add 2 mL of white vinegar.
2. Allow the mixture to dry.
3. Examine the result and compare it with baking soda. Do they look the same?
4. To further investigate the residue, add 2 mL of vinegar and observe.

Analysis

1. Did a chemical reaction occur in step 1? In step 4? Explain.
2. Are the chemical properties of the residue the same as those of baking soda? Explain.

*inter*NET
CONNECTION

Visit the Glencoe Science Web Site at **www.glencoe.com/ sec/science/ca** for more information about chemical reactions.

Chemical Equations

In order to describe a chemical reaction, you must know what substances react. The substances that react, called the **reactants** (ree AK tunts), are substances that exist before the reaction begins. The substances that are formed by the reaction are called the **products.**

When you mix baking soda and vinegar, a vigorous chemical reaction occurs. Bubbles form. The reaction mixture foams up inside the container. Baking soda and vinegar are the common names for the reactants in this reaction. They also have chemical names. Baking soda is the compound sodium hydrogen carbonate, and vinegar is acetic (uh SEE tihk) acid in a water solution. These are the reactants. What are the products? You saw bubbles form when the reaction occurred, but is that enough of a description? There are many kinds of bubbles. Are bubbles the only product, or do some atoms from the vinegar and baking soda end up forming something else? What goes on in the chemical reaction may be more than what you can see with your eyes. Chemists try to find out everything that happens in a chemical reaction. Then, they record it in a shorthand known as a chemical equation.

Word Equations

One way to describe a chemical reaction is with an equation that uses words to describe the reactants and products. The reactants are listed on the left side of an arrow, separated from each other by plus signs. The products are placed on the right side of the arrow. They also are separated by plus signs. The arrow between the reactants and products represents the changes that occur during the chemical reaction. When reading the equation, the arrow is read *produces.* How would you write a word equation for the reactants and products in the chemical reaction between baking soda and vinegar, shown in **Figure 8-3?**

Chemical names rather than common names are used in word equations. In the baking soda and vinegar reaction, you already know the chemical names of the reactants—sodium hydrogen carbonate and acetic acid. The names of the products are sodium acetate, water, and carbon dioxide gas. The word equation for the reaction is as follows.

acetic acid + sodium hydrogen carbonate → sodium acetate + water + carbon dioxide

Equations with Formulas

The word equation for the reaction of baking soda and vinegar is long. That's why chemists use chemical formulas to represent the chemical names of pure substances in the equation. You can convert a word equation into a chemical equation by substituting chemical formulas for the chemical names. For example, the chemical equation for the reaction between baking soda and vinegar can be written as follows.

$$HC_2H_3O_2 + NaHCO_3 \rightarrow NaC_2H_3O_2 + H_2O + CO_2$$

| acetic acid (vinegar) | sodium hydrogen carbonate (baking soda) | sodium acetate | water | carbon dioxide |

Figure 8-3 Observing a reaction is the first step toward writing a chemical equation to describe it.

Remember that in these formulas, the subscripts tell you the number of atoms of a particular element in that molecule. The subscript 2 in CO_2 means that each molecule of carbon dioxide has two oxygen atoms. If an atom has no subscript, it means that there is only one atom of that element in the molecule.

Conservation of Mass

What happens to the atoms in the reactants when the reactants are converted into products? Do they disappear? No, they don't. According to the *law of conservation of mass*, the mass of the products of a chemical reaction is always the same as the mass of the reactants in that reaction.

In your math class, you have seen equations with equal signs. In these math equations, the right side of the equation is numerically equal to the left side. But, in a chemical equation, it is the number and kind of atoms that are equal on the two sides. Every atom that appears on the reactant side of the equation also appears on the product side.

HCCHHHOO NaHCOOO   NaCCHHHOO HHO COO

$$HC_2H_3O_2 + NaHCO_3 \longrightarrow NaC_2H_3O_2 + H_2O + CO_2$$

Figure 8-4 Count all the carbon atoms, all the hydrogen atoms, all the oxygen atoms, and all the sodium atoms on each side of the balance. **Are there equal numbers of each kind of atom on each side?**

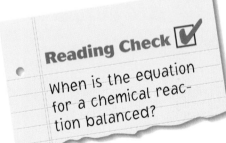

Reading Check ✔

When is the equation for a chemical reaction balanced?

Atoms are not lost or created in a chemical reaction. They just change partners, as old chemical bonds in the reactants break and new chemical bonds form in the products.

Balancing Chemical Equations

When you write the chemical equation for a reaction, you must observe the law of conservation of mass. Sometimes, this is easy, as in the vinegar and baking soda reaction. All that you needed to do was write down the chemical formulas for the reactants and products. Look at **Figure 8-4.** It shows that when you count the number of carbon, hydrogen, oxygen, and sodium atoms on each side of the arrow in the equation, you find that the numbers of each kind of atom are equal, or balanced. ✔

Not all chemical equations are balanced so easily. For example, here is the equation for the reaction that occurs when silver tarnishes.

$$Ag + H_2S \rightarrow Ag_2S + H_2$$

silver hydrogen silver hydrogen
       sulfide sulfide

Count the number of atoms of each type in the reactants and in the products. Two hydrogen atoms are on the reactant side, and two hydrogen atoms are on the product side. One sulfur atom is on the reactant side and one sulfur atom is on the product side. Notice that one silver atom is on the reactant side and two silver atoms are on the product side. The law of conservation of mass says this cannot be true. A chemical reaction cannot create a silver atom, so the equation as it is written does not represent the reaction correctly. The equation must show that two atoms of silver react. Check to see that the equation is balanced when it is written as follows with a 2 in front of the reactant Ag.

$$2Ag + H_2S \rightarrow Ag_2S + H_2$$

Energy in Chemical Reactions

Recall that atoms form chemical bonds because they become more stable by gaining, losing, or sharing electrons. When atoms become more stable, they have a lower total energy. This means that when atoms form bonds, energy is released. The reverse is also true. When bonds break, energy must be added. This energy is taken up by the atoms that form the products of such a reaction.

In a chemical reaction, some bonds in the reactant molecules break while new bonds in the products form, so changes in energy are a part of every chemical reaction. Noticeable amounts of energy often are released or absorbed during a chemical reaction, as you can see in the example of an energy-releasing reaction shown in **Figure 8-5.**

Energy Is Absorbed

In some chemical reactions, the energy needed to break the old bonds in the reactants is greater than the energy released when the new bonds form in the products. Energy must be absorbed if these reactions are to occur. A reaction in which energy is absorbed is called an **endothermic reaction.** In the equation for an endothermic (en duh THUR mihk) reaction, the word *energy* is sometimes written along with the reactants in the chemical equation. Think of energy as a necessary reactant in the reaction. An example of an endothermic reaction is the reaction that breaks down water into hydrogen and oxygen.

$$2H_2O + energy \rightarrow 2H_2 + O_2$$
$$\text{water} \qquad \text{hydrogen} \quad \text{oxygen}$$

*inter***NET**
CONNECTION

Visit the Glencoe Science Web Site at **www.glencoe.com/ sec/science/ca** for more information about energy in chemical equations.

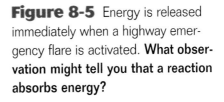

EARTH SCIENCE
INTEGRATION

The Sun's Energy
Without energy from the sun, life on Earth, as we know it, could not exist. Infer whether the reactions that occur inside the sun are exothermic or endothermic.

Figure 8-5 Energy is released immediately when a highway emergency flare is activated. **What observation might tell you that a reaction absorbs energy?**

Energy Is Released

If the energy needed to break the old bonds in the reactants is less than the energy released when the new bonds form in the products, then the reaction will release energy. A reaction in which energy is released is called an **exothermic reaction.** Some examples of reactions in which energy is being released or absorbed are shown in **Figure 8-6.** Can you identify each of them as exothermic or endothermic?

When writing a chemical equation for a reaction that releases energy, the word *energy* is sometimes written along with the products. An example of an exothermic (ek soh THUR mihk) reaction is the reaction that occurs when you burn propane in a gas grill.

$$C_3H_8 + 5O_2 \rightarrow 3CO_2 + 4H_2O + \text{energy}$$

propane   oxygen   carbon   water
dioxide

But, it's not always necessary to include energy in a chemical equation. Usually, it's included only when it's important to know whether a reaction absorbs or releases energy. A fuel like propane, for example, is burned for the purpose of

Figure 8-6 Some reactions require energy or they won't happen. Others release energy as they take place.

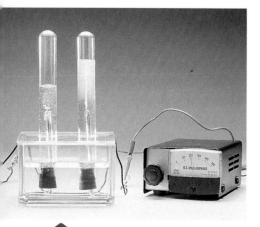

A Electrical energy is being used to break apart water molecules. The two gases, hydrogen and oxygen, are being collected in separate test tubes.

C You can infer that the release of energy occurred because of the motion created by this explosion. Sound and heat also were produced.

B The chemical process that takes place when a cold compress is activated requires energy. **Where does the energy come from?**

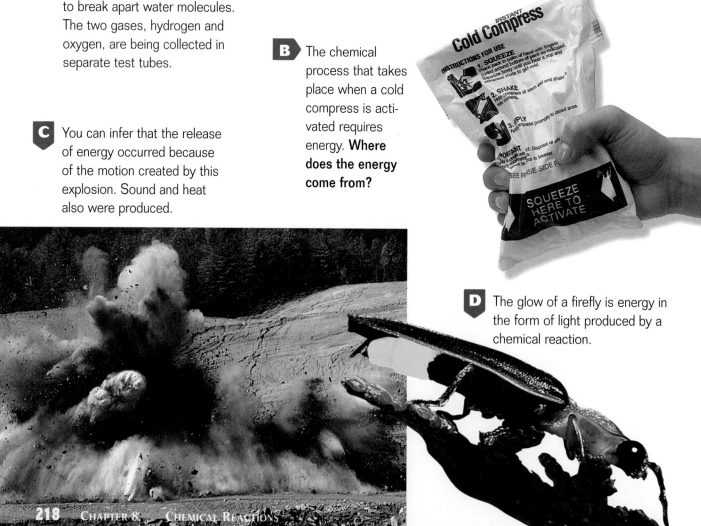

D The glow of a firefly is energy in the form of light produced by a chemical reaction.

obtaining energy to cook food, as shown in **Figure 8-7.** Therefore, energy is included in the equation. For the breakdown of water, energy is included so that you know the reaction will not occur unless energy is provided. In a reaction such as the tarnishing of silver, energy may be released or absorbed, but because this is not the most useful thing to know about this reaction, energy is not included in the equation at this time.

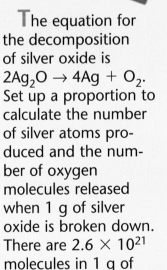

Figure 8-7 Burning propane is an exothermic reaction. **What other fuels can you list that are important because they provide energy?**

Section Assessment

1. Are the following chemical equations balanced? Why or why not?

   a. $Ca + Cl_2 \rightarrow CaCl_2$

   b. $Zn + Ag_2S \rightarrow ZnS + Ag$

   c. $Cl_2 + NaBr \rightarrow NaCl + Br_2$

2. What evidence might tell you that a chemical reaction has occurred?

3. What is the difference between an exothermic and an endothermic reaction?

4. **Think Critically:** After a forest fire, the ashes left over have less mass and take up less space than the trees that lived there before the fire. How can this be explained in terms of the law of conservation of mass?

5. **Skill Builder**
   Comparing and Contrasting
   The energy released when hydrogen and oxygen combine to form water can supply the energy that takes the space shuttle into orbit. The reaction is $2H_2 + O_2 \rightarrow 2H_2O +$ energy. When water is broken down into the elements H_2 and O_2, the reaction is $2H_2O +$ energy $\rightarrow 2H_2 + O_2$. Compare the energy released in the first equation with the energy absorbed in the second equation. If you need help, refer to Comparing and Contrasting in the **Skill Handbook** on page 532.

Using Math

The equation for the decomposition of silver oxide is $2Ag_2O \rightarrow 4Ag + O_2$. Set up a proportion to calculate the number of silver atoms produced and the number of oxygen molecules released when 1 g of silver oxide is broken down. There are 2.6×10^{21} molecules in 1 g of silver oxide.

Exothermic or Endothermic?

Possible Materials

- Test tubes (8)
- Test-tube rack
- Hydrogen peroxide solution (3%)
- Raw liver
- Raw potato
- Thermometer
- Stopwatch
  * *clock with second hand*
- Graduated cylinder (25-mL)
  * *Alternate Materials*

Energy is always a part of a chemical reaction. Some reactions must have energy supplied to them from the environment or they won't happen. An example is the cold packs you may have used when you were injured in sports. The endothermic reaction inside the cold pack cools you by taking energy away from you. Other reactions release energy into the environment.

Recognize the Problem

Does a reaction give off heat if it is exothermic or endothermic? What evidence can you find to show that a reaction between hydrogen peroxide and liver or potato is exothermic?

Form a Hypothesis

Think about the difference between endothermic and exothermic reactions. Consider the goals of the experiment and **make a hypothesis** that describes how you can use the reactions between hydrogen peroxide and liver or potato to determine if a reaction is exothermic or endothermic.

Goals

- **Design an experiment** to test whether a reaction is exothermic or endothermic.
- **Measure** the energy released in a chemical reaction.

Safety Precautions

Wear a lab apron and goggles at all times. Be careful when handling glass thermometers. Test tubes containing hydrogen peroxide should be placed and kept in racks. Dispose of materials as directed by your teacher. Wash your hands when you complete this activity. **CAUTION:** *Hydrogen peroxide can irritate skin and eyes and damage clothing.*

Test Your Hypothesis

Plan

1. As a group, look at the list of materials. **Decide** (a) what procedure you will use to test your hypothesis, and (b) what measurements you will make.

2. **Decide** how you will measure the heat released to the environment while a reaction is going on. **Determine** how many measurements you will need to make during a reaction.

3. You will get more accurate data if you repeat each experiment several times. Each repeated experiment is called a trial. Use the average of all the trials as your data for supporting your hypothesis.

4. Copy the data table in your Science Journal before you begin your experiment.

Do

1. Make sure your teacher approves your plan and your data table before you proceed.

2. Carry out your plan.

3. **Record** your measurements immediately in your data table.

Analyze Your Data

1. Can you **infer** that a chemical reaction took place? If so, what evidence did you observe?

2. **Identify** the variables in this experiment.

Draw Conclusions

1. Do your observations allow you to distinguish between an exothermic reaction and an endothermic reaction? Use your data to **explain** your answer.

2. Where did the energy in this experiment come from?

3. Suppose you had used smaller pieces of liver and potato. **Predict** what changes you would have observed.

Temperature After Adding Liver/Potato				
Trial	Temperature after adding liver (°C)		Temperature after adding potato (°C)	
	Starting	After ___ min	Starting	After ___ min
1				
2				
3				
4				
Total				
Average				

8·2 Rates of Chemical Reactions

What You'll Learn

► How to describe and measure the speed of a chemical reaction
► How chemical reactions can be speeded up or slowed down

Vocabulary
rate of reaction
inhibitor
catalyst

Why It's Important

► It helps to be able to speed up beneficial reactions and slow down destructive ones.

Figure 8-8 Some reactions are so slow you don't realize they are happening. Others happen explosively.

How fast?

Fireworks explode in the summer sky. A tree lies rotting in a forest. Two sets of chemical reactions are happening here—one fast and one slow. You've seen other examples of chemical reactions that take different amounts of time: the baking soda and vinegar reaction, a burning match, the gradual rusting of a car's fender. Why does one reaction in **Figure 8-8** take longer than the other? Can you measure how fast a reaction proceeds? Can anything be done to speed up or slow down a reaction?

Activation Energy

If a chemical reaction is to occur between two substances, the particles of those substances must bump into each other or collide. That makes sense, because to form new chemical bonds, atoms must be close together. But, not just any collision will do. The collision must be strong enough to cause a change to take place. This means that the reaction particles must smash into each other with a certain minimum amount of energy. Anything less, and the reaction will not occur. Why is this true? A reaction involves breaking bonds in the reactants and then recombining the atoms to form products. The process of breaking the bonds requires energy, so for the reaction to get underway, energy must be present at the beginning. This minimum amount of energy is called the activation energy of the reaction.

A It takes decades for the soft green coating to develop on copper statues. This coating is the result of exposure of copper to other elements in the air.

B The disappointing thing about fireworks is that these chemical reactions are over so quickly.

What about exothermic reactions? Is there an activation energy for reactions that release energy? In both exothermic and endothermic reactions, enough energy must be present at the start to break the original bonds, so even exothermic reactions have an activation energy. Consider the exothermic reaction between gasoline and oxygen gas. You know that gasoline burns readily to provide a lot of energy to move vehicles such as cars and buses. But, if gasoline is spilled when a car's gas tank is being filled, the gasoline doesn't burst into flames when it is exposed to air. It just forms a puddle on the ground and, in time, evaporates. In this case, the necessary activation energy is not available. But, if someone ignores the No Smoking sign in **Figure 8-9** or leaves the car's ignition on so that it creates a spark, it could be enough to supply the necessary activation energy and start an explosive reaction. Then, the energy that the reaction releases is enough to keep the reaction going.

Figure 8-9 A spark from a car's ignition or a cigarette could supply the activation energy needed to ignite spilled gasoline.

Reaction Rate

Many physical quantities are measured in terms of a rate. A rate tells you how much something changes over time. For example, speed is the rate at which you might run or ride your bike. It's the amount of distance you move divided by the time during which you were moving. Maybe you jog at a rate of 8 km per hour. Chemical reactions have rates, too. The **rate of reaction** is a measure of how fast a reaction occurs.

To find the rate of a reaction, you can measure either how quickly one of the reactants is disappearing or how quickly one of the products is appearing, as in **Figure 8-10.** Both measurements tell how the amount of a substance changes per unit of time. Reaction rate is important because the faster the product can be made, the lower the cost. However, sometimes fast rates of reaction are not desirable. In the case of the spoilage of food, the slower the rate, the longer the food will stay edible. What conditions control the rate of a reaction, and what can be done to change the rate?

Figure 8-10 As a population of green chameleons turns red, the rate of appearance of red chameleons is equal to the rate of disappearance of green chameleons.

Figure 8-11 Some fresh foods can be stored for a week or more at the temperature of the refrigerator. Other foods are still edible after storing for six months or a year at freezing temperatures. **How does temperature affect spoilage?**

Temperature Makes a Difference

What can you do to keep the food you buy at the store from spoiling? You can put it in the refrigerator or the freezer, as in **Figure 8-11.** The spoiling of food is a chemical reaction, and the temperature of the food affects the rate of this reaction. Most chemical reactions speed up at higher temperatures. This is because atoms and molecules are always in motion and the higher the temperature, the faster they move. Faster molecules collide with each other more often and with greater energy than slower molecules, so collisions are more likely in which there is enough energy to break the old bonds. This energy is the activation energy. The high temperature inside an oven speeds up the chemical reactions going on as the liquid batter of a cake changes into a spongy product. Lowering the temperature slows down most reactions. For example, if you caught a fish in the summer and put it into the freezer, you could eat it in the winter.

Concentration Affects Rate

The more reactants that are present, the greater the chance of collisions between them and the faster the reaction rate. It's like the situation in **Figure 8-12.** When you try to walk along a street that is full of people hurrying here and there, you're

Figure 8-12 Reactions occur faster when there are more particles to collide with each other.

 A Bumping and jostling are bound to happen when the sidewalk gets this crowded.

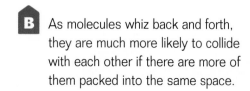 **B** As molecules whiz back and forth, they are much more likely to collide with each other if there are more of them packed into the same space.

liable to bump into other people. The amount of substance present in a certain volume is called the concentration of the substance. If you increase the concentration, you increase the number of particles of a substance per unit of volume. The particles are more crowded, so more collisions occur, which increases the rate of reaction.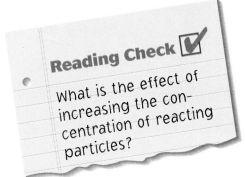

Particle Size Can Change the Rate

The size of the reactant particles also affects how fast the reaction can occur. Only the atoms or molecules on the outside of the piece of reactant material are in contact with the other reactants and can take part in the reaction. If the particles are large, most of the atoms are stuck inside and can't participate in the reaction. If the particles are small, more of the reactant atoms are at the surface and can react. When more atoms can take part in the reaction, the rate of reaction increases. Think about how easily you can start a campfire with thin, dry twigs. Even a large pile of twigs will easily catch fire and burn completely in a few minutes. Could you start a fire if you just had large logs and no tinder to burn? Probably not, but once started, a campfire of logs will burn more slowly, and sometimes die down with one log still slowly smoldering.

Reading Check

What is the effect of increasing the concentration of reacting particles?

Problem Solving

Changing Rates of Reaction

Chemists often try to make reactions go more quickly. The faster the reaction, the more product can be made in a given period of time and the lower the cost. In their search for faster reaction rates, chemists experiment with the conditions of the reaction such as the temperature, the concentration of the reactants, and the particle size of the reactants.

Examine the table that lists the conditions for two trials for each of the three reactions in column 1. List the factors that affect the rate of a reaction. Next, use your list to decide which of the trials for each reaction was faster.

Think Critically: In reaction 1, what additional change could be made in a third trial? Would it increase the reaction rate if the baking soda in

reaction 2 were dissolved in water? In reaction 3, what more could the chemist do to get more oxygen gas from hydrogen peroxide more quickly? What could be done to slow down reaction 3? Explain your answers.

Conditions for Reactions		
Chemical Reaction	**Trial 1**	**Trial 2**
1. Zinc reacts with hydrochloric acid.	The zinc is in chunks.	The zinc is powdered.
2. Baking soda reacts with acetic acid.	10% acetic acid is used.	5% acetic acid is used.
3. Three percent hydrogen peroxide breaks down into oxygen gas and water.	The reaction takes place at 50°C.	The reaction takes place at 25°C.

Mini Lab

Uncovering Inhibitors

Procedure

1. Cereals and crackers would be stale soon after you bought them if it were not for some common inhibitors that increase the shelf life of these products. The long chemical names for three such inhibitors are usually shortened to BHT, TBHQ, and tocopherols. Look at the ingredient lists on packages on your kitchen shelves and list products that contain one of these inhibitors.

2. A date on the top of the box tells you how long the product is considered fresh. Compare that date with the approximate date when the product was purchased to estimate shelf life.

Analysis

1. What is the average estimated shelf life of the products you examined?

2. Why is increased shelf life important?

Using Math

At the beginning of a reaction, there is no CO_2 present. After 50 s, the concentration of CO_2 is 66 g per liter. Calculate the average rate of reaction during this time in units of grams per liter per second.

LIFE SCIENCE
INTEGRATION ➤

Inhibitors—Slowing Down

Sometimes, reactions occur too quickly. Food and medications, for example, undergo chemical reactions that cause them to spoil or lose their effectiveness. Can these reactions be slowed down? A substance that slows down a chemical reaction is called an **inhibitor.** An inhibitor doesn't completely stop a reaction, but it makes the formation of a certain amount of product take longer. The boxes in which many cereals are sold contain the compound butyl hydroxytoluene, BHT. The presence of BHT in the packaging material slows the spoiling of the cereal and increases shelf life.

Catalysts—Speeding Up

Is it possible to speed up a chemical reaction? You could add a catalyst (KAT uh lihst). A **catalyst** is a substance that speeds up a chemical reaction but doesn't appear in the chemical equation because it is not permanently changed or used up. A reaction using a catalyst will not produce more product than a reaction without a catalyst, but it will produce the same amount of product faster. How does a catalyst work? Visualize catalysts as hands that hold molecules in the best possible position for the reaction to take place. By holding molecules in the best position for the reaction, the catalyst reduces the activation energy needed to start the reaction. When the activation energy is reduced, the reaction rate increases.

Enzymes Are Catalysts

Some of the most effective catalysts are at work in your body. These catalysts, called enzymes, speed up reactions needed for efficient cell functioning. They help your body convert food to fuel, build bone and muscle tissue, and convert extra energy to fat.

These are complex reactions. Without enzymes, they would occur at rates that are too slow to measure or they would not occur at all. Enzymes make it possible for your body to function. Enzymes function as catalysts by positioning the reacting molecules so that their structures fit together properly. One class of enzymes called proteases (PROH tee ays es) functions within cells to break down proteins and recycle the materials. Proteins are large, complex molecules that perform many important functions in living things. Proteases are used in common products, such as meat tenderizer and contact lens-cleaning solution, as shown in **Figure 8-13.** Why do you think these products would need to break down proteins?

Figure 8-13 Proteins from the eye collect on contact lenses and can cloud your view. Proteases in lens-cleaning solutions speed up the decomposition of proteins so that they can be removed from a lens.

Section Assessment

1. How would you measure the rate of a reaction?

2. For the following general reaction, A + B + energy → C, where A and B are gases, what will be the effect on the reaction rate of the following?
   a. increasing the temperature
   b. increasing the pressure
   c. adding more of A without adding more of B

3. **Think Critically:** Jars of spaghetti sauce are stored on shelves at the grocery store waiting to be purchased. When you take a jar home and use it, you break the air-tight seal on the top. These jars are labeled "refrigerate after opening." Explain why the jar can be stored on the shelf in the market but must be placed in the refrigerator after it is opened.

4. **Skill Builder**
   Observing and Inferring The rate of a reaction is affected by several factors. For example, the temperature of the reaction mixture can either speed up or slow down the reaction. Do the **Chapter 8 Skill Activity** on page 561 to investigate a chemical reaction. Then, infer the type of reaction you have observed and the effect temperature has on it.

Using Math

A chemical reaction is proceeding at a rate of 2 g of product per 45 s. How long will it take to obtain 50 g of product from the reaction?

Speeding Up a Reaction

Materials

- Test tubes (2)
- Test-tube rack
  *beaker to hold test tubes
- Graduated cylinder (25 mL)
- Small plastic spoon
- Hot plate
- Wooden splint
- Hydrogen peroxide, 3%, H_2O_2
- Manganese dioxide, MnO_2
- Beaker of hot water
- Bunsen burner
  *lighter

  *Alternate Materials

The equation for a chemical reaction tells you nothing about how fast the reaction occurs. One slow reaction is the breakdown of hydrogen peroxide, H_2O_2, into oxygen gas, O_2, and water. Is there a way to make this reaction go faster?

Chemists measure the rate of a chemical reaction by observing how quickly the reactants are used up or the products are formed. Testing the production of oxygen is a handy way to observe the rate of a reaction. A glowing wooden splint will relight and burn brightly when placed in oxygen.

What You'll Investigate

How is the rate of the breakdown of hydrogen peroxide affected when manganese dioxide, MnO_2, is added as a catalyst?

Goals

- **Observe** the decomposition of hydrogen peroxide.
- **Infer** how a catalyst changes the reaction rate.

Safety Precautions

CAUTION: *Hydrogen peroxide can irritate skin and eyes. Wear goggles, an apron, and gloves. Do not use more than 5 mL of hydrogen peroxide.*

Procedure

1. Pour 5 mL of hydrogen peroxide into each of two test tubes.

2. Place about ¼ teaspoonful of manganese dioxide in one of the test tubes.

3. Light the wooden splint. Blow out the flame and insert the glowing splint first into the test tube containing only hydrogen peroxide and then into the test tube containing the manganese dioxide.

4. Record your observations.

5. Place the two test tubes in a beaker of hot water and heat them on a hot plate until all the liquid has disappeared. Record your observations.

Conclude and Apply

1. **Describe** what happened when manganese dioxide was added to one of the test tubes.

2. In which test tube was gas produced more rapidly? How do you know?

3. How did you identify the gas?

4. What remained in the two test tubes after the liquid was driven off?

5. Does manganese dioxide fit the description of a catalyst? Give reasons for your answer.

6. The word *catalyst* is used in everyday conversation to describe special people. Write a sentence that illustrates what effect such people might have on others around them.

Using Proportions

The Mole

One job of a chemist is to determine the number of atoms needed to combine with other atoms or molecules to make new products. In real life, large numbers of atoms are involved in chemical reactions. So, chemists invented the mole to use as a counting unit, the way a baker uses the word *dozen*, meaning 12 of something. A mole of atoms contains 6.02×10^{23} atoms, and a mole of molecules contains 6.02×10^{23} molecules. This huge quantity is known as Avogadro's number. If you counted out 1 mole of peas, your pile would cover the United States to a depth of about 6 km. Let's see how chemists use the mole to solve problems.

Problem and Solution

Ammonia gas is made from nitrogen gas and hydrogen gas. This reaction is written as follows.

$$N_2 + 3H_2 \rightarrow 2NH_3$$

This balanced equation shows a chemist that 1 mole of nitrogen molecules reacts with 3 moles of hydrogen molecules and that 2 moles of ammonia molecules will be produced. If you wanted to produce 6 moles of ammonia from this reaction, how would you know how much hydrogen you needed?

1. From the balanced equation, you now know that the ratio of hydrogen molecules to ammonia molecules is 3:2.

2. The easiest way to find out your answer is to set up a proportion and calculate the cross product. Start with the ratio that is known. Set it equal to the ratio that has the unknown quantity. Then, solve the proportion.

$$\frac{3 \text{ moles } H_2}{2 \text{ moles } NH_3} = \frac{x}{6 \text{ mole } NH_3}$$

$$x = \frac{(3 \text{ moles } H_2)(6 \text{ moles } NH_3)}{2 \text{ moles } NH_3}$$

$$x = 9 \text{ moles } H_2$$

You would start with 9 moles of H_2 to produce 6 moles of NH_3.

Practice
PROBLEMS

1. How many moles of N_2 would be needed to produce 9 moles of NH_3 ?

2. How many moles of NH_3 would you produce if 5 moles of N_2 were used?

For a **preview** of this chapter, study this Reviewing Main Ideas before you read the chapter. After you have studied this chapter, you can use the Reviewing Main Ideas to **review** the chapter.

The Glencoe MindJogger, Audiocassettes, and CD-ROM provide additional opportunities for review.

8-1 EVIDENCE FOR CHEMICAL REACTIONS

Reactions are always occurring all around you. Many observable signs show that **chemical reactions** have occurred, including changes in color or odor, the release or absorption of heat or light, and the release of a gas. Sometimes, a solid called a precipitate forms when two clear liquids are mixed. Observations of the changes that occur are the basis for writing equations that describe chemical reactions. *Write down an example of a chemical reaction and describe the evidence that shows it has occurred.*

BALANCED CHEMICAL EQUATIONS

A chemical equation is a shorthand way of describing what happens in a chemical reaction. In a chemical equation, chemists use symbols to represent the **reactants** and **products** of a reaction. The reactants are placed on the left side of the equation with an arrow pointing toward the products on the right. The law of conservation of mass requires that chemical equations be balanced, meaning that the same number of atoms of each element must be found on each side of the equation. The chemical equation sometimes shows whether a reaction is **endothermic** or **exothermic.** *What is the difference between an endothermic and an exothermic reaction?*

HCCHHHOO NaHCOOO   NaCCHHHOO HHO COO

$$HC_2H_3O_2 + NaHCO_3 \longrightarrow NaC_2H_3O_2 + H_2O + CO_2$$

8-2   RATE OF REACTION

The **rate of reaction** is a measure of how quickly a reaction occurs. All reactions have an activation energy, which is a minimum amount of energy required to start the reaction. Reactions with low activation energies occur rapidly. Those with high activation energies occur slowly or not at all. Other factors that influence the rate of a chemical reaction are the temperature at which the reaction occurs, the concentration of the reactants, and the size of the particles of reactant. **Catalysts** are substances that can speed up a reaction without being used up. **Inhibitors** slow down the rate of reaction. *Why do many reactions occur more quickly at higher temperatures?*

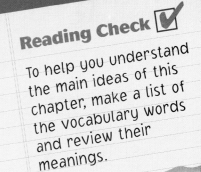

Reading Check ✔

To help you understand the main ideas of this chapter, make a list of the vocabulary words and review their meanings.

Career
CONNECTION

Dr. Lynda Jordan, Biochemist

Dr. Lynda Jordan is a biochemist working at North Carolina Agricultural and Technical State University. Dr. Jordan studies the enzyme phospholipase, an enzyme isolated from the cells of the human placenta. She is interested in finding out about the structure and function of the enzyme. Many people have diseases, such as diabetes, that are associated with this enzyme, so understanding how the enzyme functions is important. *How might an enzyme cause a disease in an organism?*

Chapter 8 Assessment

Using Vocabulary

a. catalyst
b. chemical reaction
c. endothermic reaction
d. exothermic reaction
e. inhibitor
f. product
g. rate of reaction
h. reactant

Explain the differences between terms in each of the following sets.

1. exothermic reaction, endothermic reaction
2. catalyst, rate of reaction
3. reactant, product
4. catalyst, inhibitor
5. chemical reaction, rate of reaction

Checking Concepts

Choose the word or phrase that best answers the question.

6. A balanced chemical equation must have the same number of atoms of each of these on both sides.
   A) atoms
   B) elements
   C) molecules
   D) compounds

7. Which is **NOT** a balanced equation?
   A) $CuCl_2 + H_2S \rightarrow CuS + 2HCl$
   B) $AgNO_3 + NaI \rightarrow AgI + NaNO_3$
   C) $2C_2H_6 + 7O_2 \rightarrow 4CO_2 + 6H_2O$
   D) $MgO + Fe \rightarrow Fe_2O_3 + Mg$

8. Which is a chemical change?
   A) Paper is shredded.
   B) Liquid wax turns solid.
   C) A raw egg is broken.
   D) Soap scum forms.

9. Reactions that release energy are which of the following?
   A) unbalanced
   B) balanced
   C) exothermic
   D) endothermic

10. Which is a false statement about the law of conservation of mass?
    A) The mass of reactants must equal the mass of products.
    B) All the atoms on the reactant side of an equation are also on the product side.
    C) It is not always necessary to have the same elements present on both sides of the equation.
    D) No atoms are lost, but only rearranged.

11. What is a way to decrease the rate of a chemical reaction?
    A) increase the temperature
    B) reduce the concentration of a reactant
    C) increase the concentration of a reactant
    D) add a catalyst

12. In order to slow down a chemical reaction, what should you add?
    A) catalyst
    B) salt
    C) inhibitor
    D) enzyme

13. Which is **NOT** evidence that a chemical reaction has occurred?
    A) The leaves turn red in fall.
    B) Steam condenses on a cold window.
    C) A strong odor comes from the exhaust pipe of a car.
    D) Bubbles of gas form when a tablet is placed in water.

14. What does **NOT** affect reaction rate?
    A) the law of conservation of mass
    B) activation energy
    C) particle size
    D) concentration

15. Which of the following does NOT describe a catalyst?
    A) It can be recovered after the reaction.
    B) It speeds up a reaction.
    C) It does not appear in the chemical equation.
    D) It can be used in place of an inhibitor.

Thinking Critically

16. Pickled cucumbers remain edible much longer than fresh cucumbers. Explain.

17. A test tube containing a substance becomes warmer when you add another substance to it. What can you infer from this observation?

18. A beaker of water standing in the sunlight becomes warm. Has a chemical reaction occurred? Explain.

19. Is 2Ag + S the same as Ag_2S? Explain.

Developing Skills

If you need help, refer to the Skill Handbook.

20. Interpreting Data: At 25°C, you measure the rate of a chemical reaction. You then increase the temperature to 100°C and find that the reaction rate is half as large as before. Does this reaction absorb or release energy? Explain.

21. Interpreting Scientific Illustrations: The two curves on the graph represent the concentrations of compounds A (blue) and B (red) during a chemical reaction.
A) Which compound is a reactant?
B) Which compound is a product?
C) During what time period is the concentration of the reactant changing most rapidly?

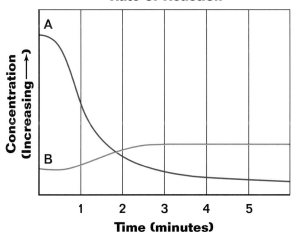

Rate of Reaction

Concentration (Increasing →)

A

B

Time (minutes)
1 2 3 4 5

THE PRINCETON REVIEW

Test-Taking Tip

Plan Your Work and Work Your Plan
Set up a study schedule for yourself well in advance of your test. Plan your workload so that you do a little each day rather than a lot all at once. The key to retaining information is to repeatedly review and practice it.

Test Practice

Use these questions to test your Science Proficiency.

1. Which of the following is **NOT** true?
A) All chemical reactions either release or absorb energy.
B) In all chemical equations, energy must be included either on the reactant or the product side.
C) Some reactions are important because they produce energy.
D) Reactions that produce energy are called exothermic.

2. In a balanced equation for a chemical reaction, each side of the equation must have all of the following except one. Choose the one that should **NOT** be included.
A) the same number and kind of elements
B) the same number of each kind of atom
C) the same number of molecules
D) the same mass

CHAPTER

9

Solutions

Chapter Preview

Skills Preview

Skill Builders

- Classify
- Sequence

Activities

- Observe and Infer
- Measure in SI

MiniLabs

- Compare and Contrast

Reading Check ☑

Several vocabulary words in this chapter share the same base word from a Latin term that means "to loosen or solve." Write and define the words that share this base word.

Explore Activity

Have you ever gone hiking in the mountains on a warm day and come across the entrance to a cave? A nice, cool cave is a welcome sight—almost as welcome as a cold fruit drink. Once inside a cave, you may see formations called stalagmites and stalactites. These large spikes hang down from the roof of the cave and stick upward from the cave floor. You might be surprised to learn that the formations inside the cave and the cold fruit drink have something in common—they both involve solutions. To understand how, you'll need to know how stalactites and stalagmites form.

Observe Stalagmite Growth

1. Wash and dry a glass dish or jar lid.

2. Using forceps, place a few small crystals of sodium acetate on the glass dish.

3. Slowly drip the solution provided by your teacher onto the crystals and observe what happens.

Science Journal

In your Science Journal, record what happens and describe how you think stalagmites might be formed on the floor of a cave.

What is a solution?

What You'll Learn

► The different types of solutions that can exist
► How solutions form

Vocabulary
mixture   solute
solution   solvent

Why It's Important

► The air you breathe, the water you drink, and even your own body are all solutions.

Substances

Atoms are the basic building blocks of matter on Earth. All the atoms of an element have the same number of protons. For example, the dark gray material inside your pencil is made up mostly of atoms that contain six protons—graphite, a form of carbon (not lead, as the name "pencil lead" might make you believe), as shown in **Figure 9-1.**

A compound is a type of matter made from atoms of two or more elements that are combined chemically. The ratio of the different atoms in a compound is always the same. For example, water is composed of the elements hydrogen and oxygen, and always in the ratio of two hydrogen atoms to one oxygen atom.

Elements and compounds are called substances and can't be broken down to simpler parts by ordinary physical processes, such as squeezing, grinding, or filtering. Only a chemical process can change a substance into one or more new substances. For instance, you can't separate water into hydrogen and oxygen by ordinary means. It takes a chemical process to break water down into the two elements.

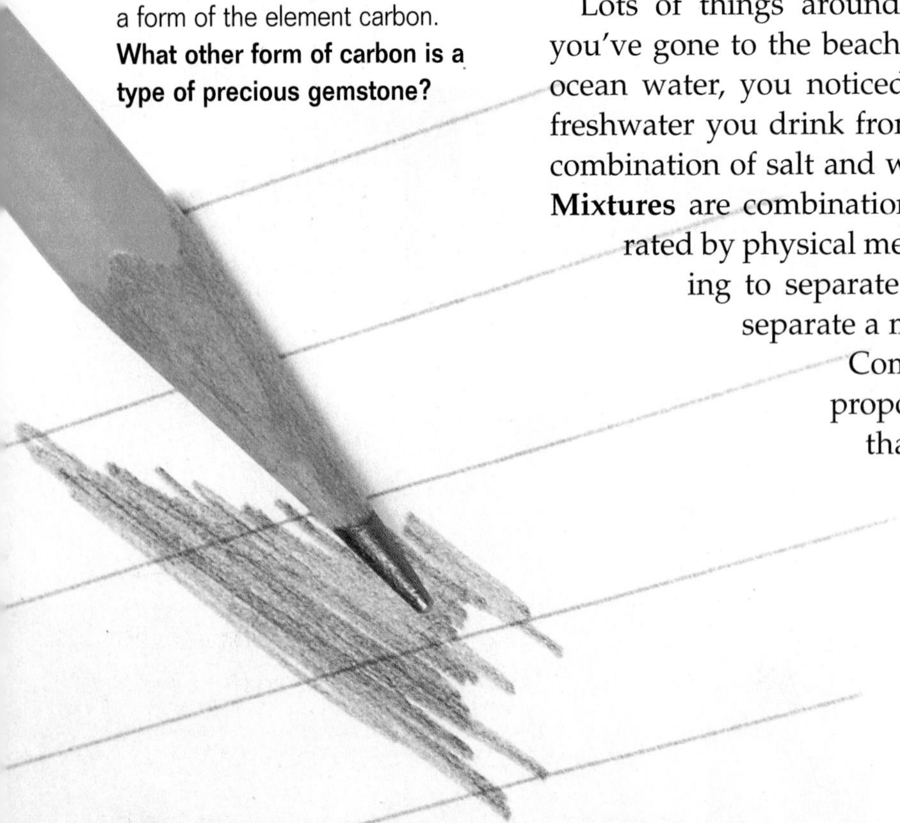

Figure 9-1 The "lead" in a wooden pencil is actually graphite, a form of the element carbon. **What other form of carbon is a type of precious gemstone?**

Mixtures

Lots of things around you are not pure substances. If you've gone to the beach and accidentally swallowed some ocean water, you noticed that it tasted salty—not like the freshwater you drink from a water fountain. Salt water is a combination of salt and water that is classified as a mixture. **Mixtures** are combinations of substances that can be separated by physical means. For example, you can use boiling to separate salt from water and a magnet to separate a mixture of iron filings and sand.

Compounds always contain the same proportions of the different substances that make them up, but mixtures don't. For example, if you're wearing clothing made of permanent-press fabric, it's a mixture of two fibers—polyester and cotton. Your permanent-press fabric may contain varying amounts of polyester and cotton, a fact that you can find out by looking at a label like the one in **Figure 9-2.**

Heterogeneous Mixtures

The prefix *hetero-* means "different." The substances that make up a heterogeneous mixture are not mixed evenly, so different parts of the mixture have different compositions. The different parts of a heterogeneous mixture are usually easy to tell apart. Think about a watermelon. If you cut the watermelon open, you can tell the difference between the part you eat and the seeds.

Homogeneous Mixtures

The prefix *homo-* means "the same." Accordingly, the composition of a homogeneous mixture is the same throughout. The substances that make up a homogeneous mixture are not usually easy to tell apart. For example, when you look at the salt water that you might have tasted at the beach, you can't see the salt. Salt water can be separated by physical means, though. If you boil salt water, the water will evaporate and form steam, but the salt will be left behind, as shown in **Figure 9-3.** The steam can be collected and cooled to make pure water. Some countries that don't have much freshwater but are close to salt water use this property of mixtures to supply their fresh drinking water. Another name for a homogeneous mixture is a **solution.**

Figure 9-2 The label on this garment tells you what mixture its fabric is made of.

Figure 9-3 When salt water boils, the water leaves as a gas but the salt remains behind. **Why did the water boil away while the salt did not?**

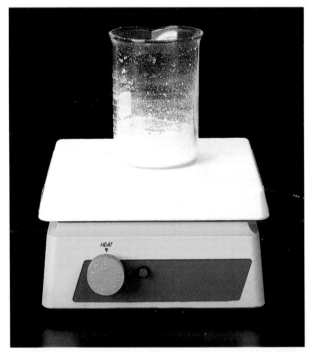

Think again about the cold fruit drink you enjoy on a warm day. What does the drink resemble most: a substance such as water? A watermelon? Salt water? It's liquid, like water, but it has a sweet flavor something like the watermelon. The fruit drink looks the same throughout, and you can't see the fruit substances in it. In fact, the molecules of water and the particles that give the drink its taste and sweetness are so small that they can't be seen, even with a microscope. The fruit drink is a solution. Use the **Field Guide to Kitchen Chemistry** at the end of this chapter to learn more about mixtures.

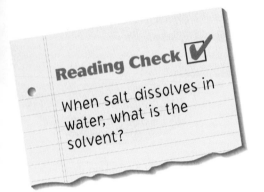

Reading Check

When salt dissolves in water, what is the solvent?

How Solutions Form

The manufacturer of the fruit drink probably combined several materials to make the drink. If crystals of solid were added to water, the crystals were separated into some combination of atoms, ions, and molecules. This process, forming a solution, is called dissolution. A solution is made up of two or more substances, one or more of which seem to disappear in the other. The substance that seems to disappear, or dissolves, is called the **solute.** The solute that you saw in **Figure 9-3** is salt. The substance that dissolves the solute is called the **solvent.** The solvent in **Figure 9-3** was water. A solution usually contains more solvent than solute. A substance that readily dissolves in another is said to be soluble. Therefore, you would say that salt is soluble in water. Similarly, one that does not readily dissolve is insoluble. ☑

Some soluble substances can be made to fall out of a liquid solution. When this happens, the solid formed is called a precipitate. One way this happens is by chemical reaction, as seen in **Figure 9-4.** In fact, you need look no further than your sink or shower to see a precipitate. Minerals are dissolved in your tap water, and when you combine them with soap, the product falls out of solution. The resulting precipitate, called soap scum, forms on your sink and the walls and floor of your tub or shower.

Figure 9-4 When you mix lead (II) nitrate and potassium iodide solutions, solid lead (II) iodide forms because it's insoluble in water. **Why doesn't solid potassium nitrate form, too?**

Table 9-1

Common Solutions			
Solution	**Solvent and State**	**Solute and State**	**State of Solution**
Earth's atmosphere	nitrogen/gas	oxygen/gas carbon dioxide/gas argon/gas	gas
Ocean water	water/liquid	salt/solid oxygen/gas carbon dioxide/gas	liquid
Carbonated beverage	water/liquid	carbon dioxide/gas	liquid
Brass	copper/solid	zinc/solid	solid

Now that you know about solutions and precipitates, can you better understand how stalactites, stalagmites, and a fruit drink are related? The fruit drink is a solution formed when certain substances dissolve in water. Stalactites and stalagmites form from solutions. How does this happen? The cave formations are the result of minerals dissolving in water as it flows through the soil and rocks at the top of the cave. The resulting solutions then form precipitates as they drip from the ceiling of the cave onto its floor.

Types of Solutions

So far, you've learned about only one kind of solution—one in which a solid solute dissolves in a liquid solvent. But, many kinds of solutions can involve combinations of solids, liquids, and gases. Several examples of types of solutions are described in **Table 9-1.** Would you be surprised to know that solutions are all around you and even in you? The water you drink, the gasoline you put in a car, the air you breathe, the blood in your arteries and veins, and the ground you walk on are all solutions of one type or another.

Gaseous Solutions

Gaseous solutions are solutions in which a smaller amount of one gas is dissolved in a larger amount of another gas. This is a gas-gas solution.

The air you breathe is a gaseous solution. Nitrogen makes up about 78 percent of dry air. Other gases in air include oxygen and smaller amounts of argon, carbon dioxide, neon, helium, krypton, hydrogen, xenon, and ozone. Nitrogen is considered to be the solvent, and the other gases are solutes.

EARTH SCIENCE
INTEGRATION

Erosion by Groundwater
Erosion by groundwater can be a major problem in areas that have large amounts of rainfall. As groundwater flows through soil and rocks, these substances can dissolve in the water and be carried away from their original locations. This dissolution by groundwater can lead to the formation of underground caves or sinkholes.

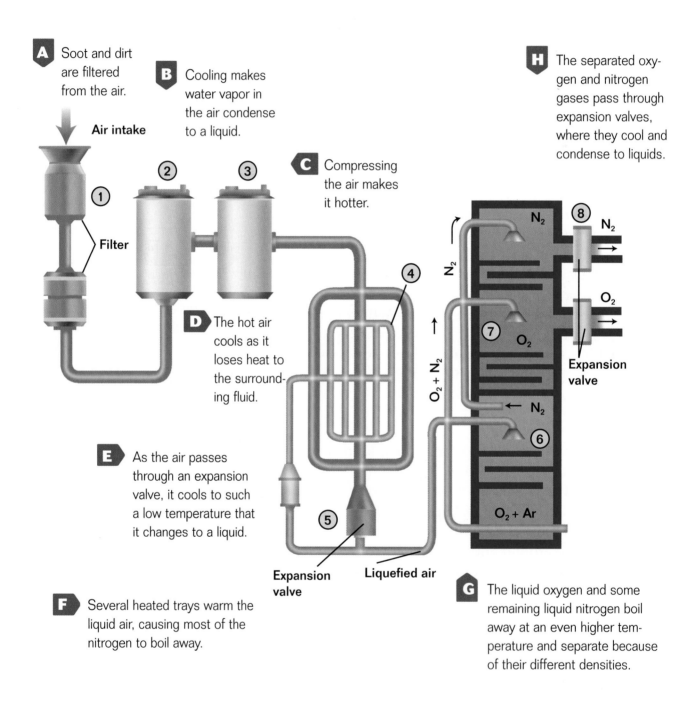

VISUALIZING
Air Fractionation

Figure 9-5 The gases in air can be separated by fractionation. The liquid oxygen formed by fractionation is used for life-support systems in hospitals and at high altitudes. Liquid nitrogen is used to manufacture fertilizers.

A Soot and dirt are filtered from the air.

Air intake

B Cooling makes water vapor in the air condense to a liquid.

C Compressing the air makes it hotter.

H The separated oxygen and nitrogen gases pass through expansion valves, where they cool and condense to liquids.

Filter

D The hot air cools as it loses heat to the surrounding fluid.

N_2

$O_2 + N_2$

N_2

O_2

N_2

O_2

Expansion valve

E As the air passes through an expansion valve, it cools to such a low temperature that it changes to a liquid.

N_2

$O_2 + Ar$

Expansion valve

Liquefied air

F Several heated trays warm the liquid air, causing most of the nitrogen to boil away.

G The liquid oxygen and some remaining liquid nitrogen boil away at an even higher temperature and separate because of their different densities.

Is it possible to separate the gases that make up air? If air is a solution, there should be some way to use physical means to separate the different gases that make it up. But, it's not easy or simple. For air, the separation process is called fractionation, which is described in **Figure 9-5.**

Liquid Solutions

You're probably most familiar with liquid solutions; that is, solutions in which the solvent is a liquid. The solute can be another liquid, a solid, or even a gas. Carbonated beverages are gas-liquid solutions. Carbon dioxide is the gas, and water is the liquid. The carbon dioxide gas gives the beverage its fizz and some of its tartness. Of course, the beverage normally contains other solutes too, like the compounds that give it its flavor and sweetness.

In a liquid-liquid solution, both the solvent and the solute are liquids. Vinegar, which you might put on your salad as a dressing, is a liquid-liquid solution made of 95 percent water (the solvent) and 5 percent acetic acid (the solute). In a solid-liquid solution, the solute is a solid and the solvent is a liquid. You've already learned about several solid-liquid solutions, such as a fruit drink, salt water, and the solutions that produce cave formations.

Solid Solutions

Solid solutions are solutions in which the solvent is a solid. A gas-solid solution can form when a gas-liquid solution is frozen and the gas remains in the solid that results. An example is a bottle of frozen carbonated beverage.

The most common solid solutions are solid-solid solutions—ones in which both the solvent and solute are solids. Solid-solid solutions containing two or more metals are commonly called alloys. Several alloys are shown in **Figure 9-6.**

Figure 9-6 Alloys are solid-solid solutions containing two or more metals. **Why are pots and pans that are used for cooking often made of stainless steel rather than pure iron?**

A This sterling silver pitcher is a solid-solid solution containing 92.5 percent silver and 7.5 percent copper.

B The brass that you see in musical instruments like trumpets, trombones, and tubas is made up of copper and zinc.

C To make this steel faucet more resistant to rusting, chromium and nickel are added. The resulting alloy is called stainless steel.

It's also possible to include elements that are not metals in alloys. Alloys containing the elements aluminum, gallium, and arsenic can give off light. The color of the light depends on the amounts of aluminum and gallium in the alloy. The blue sapphire, red ruby, and purple amethyst shown in **Figure 9-7** are solid solutions. Aluminum oxide, or silicon dioxide, contains trace amounts of other elements that give these gems their distinctive color.

Figure 9-7 Both the blue sapphire and the red ruby are gem-quality forms of the mineral corundum. The blue sapphire contains trace amounts of iron and titanium. The red ruby contains chromium. Trace amounts of iron in quartz gives the amethyst its color.

Section Assessment

1. Describe the differences between elements, compounds, and mixtures. Into which of these categories does a solution fall? Explain.

2. How is a container of hydrogen gas and oxygen gas different from a container of water in the gaseous state, known as water vapor?

3. **Think Critically:** Carbonated-beverage cans are made out of aluminum alloys with three different compositions. The body of the can is made of one alloy, the top of the can is made of a second alloy, and the tab you pull on to open the can is made of a third alloy. Which of these alloys do you think is the strongest? Which is the most flexible? Explain your answer.

4.  **Skill Builder**
   Comparing and Contrasting Compare and contrast the following types of solutions: the active material in a helium-neon laser (glows like a neon light), bronze (copper-tin), cloudy ice cubes, and ginger ale. If you need help, refer to Comparing and Contrasting in the **Skill Handbook** on page 532.

Science **Journal** Read about ancient peoples in a world history book. Record in your Science Journal the names of some of the eras of human existence that were named after the materials and alloys people used for making tools. Discuss why each new material was an improvement over the ones used before.

Aqueous Solutions

Water—The Universal Solvent

You've learned about a number of solutions that have water as a solvent—salt water, fruit drinks, the solutions that form stalactites and stalagmites, and vinegar. These solutions and the many others in which water is the solvent are called **aqueous** (AH kwee us) solutions. Because water can dissolve so many different solutes, chemists often call it the universal solvent. What is it about water that makes it such a great solvent?

Understanding Molecular Compounds

You'll better understand water and its properties by thinking back to what you learned about atoms and bonding. Atoms are neutral because they contain equal numbers of positively charged protons and negatively charged electrons. When atoms come together to form compounds, they often share electrons.

In water, the two hydrogen atoms share electrons with the single oxygen atom. Sharing electrons, called covalent bonding, results in molecular compounds; that is, compounds made up of molecules. If the atoms that make up a molecule share electrons equally, the atoms remain electrically neutral and the resulting molecule has an even distribution of positive and negative charges. Such a molecule is said to be nonpolar, as in **Figure 9-8.** However, that's not what happens with water. Water is a compound made up of H_2O molecules. Because the hydrogen atoms don't share electrons equally with the oxygen atom, polar covalent bonds are formed. So, one region of the water molecule has a somewhat positive charge while another region has a somewhat negative charge. Such a molecule is said to be polar.

What You'll Learn

► Why water is able to dissolve many substances
► Why solvents can dissolve some solutes but not others
► How to describe the concentration of a solution
► What factors affect a solution's maximum concentration

Vocabulary

aqueous	concentration
solubility	concentrated
saturated	dilute

Why It's Important

► Solutions, including the liquids that you drink and bodily fluids like blood, allow your body to function.

Oxygen molecule

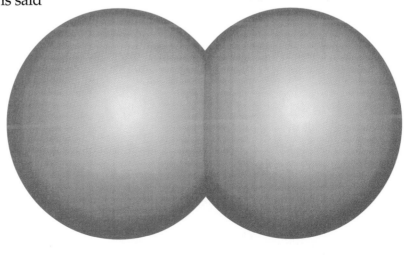

Figure 9-8 Because the two oxygen atoms in an O_2 molecule share electrons equally, the molecule is nonpolar. **Why is the nitrogen molecule, N_2, nonpolar?**

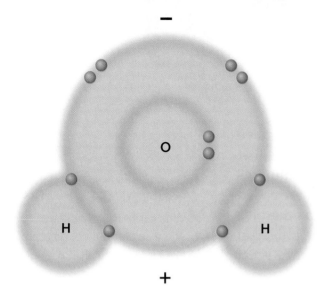

Figure 9-9 In the water molecule, the oxygen atom attracts electrons more than the hydrogen atoms, making the oxygen side of the molecule somewhat negative.

Figure 9-10 Sodium chloride dissolves in water because opposite charges attract each other. Once dissolved, water molecules surround the sodium and chloride ions. **What part of the water molecule attracts the positive calcium ions when calcium chloride dissolves in water?**

Understanding Ionic Compounds

An ionic compound is formed when one or more of the bonding atoms loses electrons and one or more of the bonding atoms gains electrons. That's what happens when sodium combines with chlorine to form table salt, which is sodium chloride. Each sodium atom loses one electron and becomes a positively charged sodium ion. Each chlorine atom gains one electron, becoming a negatively charged chloride ion. The formula NaCl tells you that sodium chloride contains equal numbers of sodium ions and chloride ions.

How Water Dissolves Things

Now, think about the properties of water and the properties of ionic compounds as you visualize how an ionic compound dissolves in water. Because water molecules are polar, as shown in **Figure 9-9,** they can attract both positive and negative ions. Water dissolves ionic compounds by literally pulling apart the ions, as shown with table salt in **Figure 9-10.** The more positive ends of water molecules are attracted to salt's negative chloride ions, while the more negative ends of water molecules are attracted to the positive sodium ions.

Water can dissolve a molecular compound such as sugar because sugar contains many polar bonds. Sugar molecules are polar, just like water molecules. Similar to the dissolving of ionic compounds, the more positive ends of water molecules are attracted to the more negative portions of sugar molecules, and the more negative ends of water molecules are attracted to the more positive portions of sugar molecules. If you've ever added sugar to your iced tea, you know the result: sugar dissolves in water.

Solubility

When you stir a spoonful of sugar into your iced tea, the sugar dissolves, but the spoon doesn't. Why are some substances soluble in a certain solvent while others are not? What determines how much solute can be dissolved in a solvent? **Solubility** is the term used to describe how much solute dissolves in a given amount of solvent.

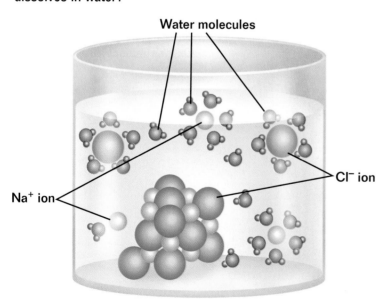

Water molecules

Cl⁻ ion

Na⁺ ion

A When a mixture of baby oil (colorless) and water (dyed blue) is shaken and then sits for a time, the oil and water separate into layers.

B Olive oil (greenish-gold) and safflower oil (nearly colorless) mix with water and remain mixed upon sitting.

Figure 9-11 Some liquids mix with each other more readily than others do. **Why doesn't gasoline mix with water?**

Like Dissolves Like

Water dissolves many things, but it can't dissolve everything. When trying to predict which solvents can dissolve which solutes, chemists use the rule of thumb that "like dissolves like." This statement means that dissolution of the solute occurs when the solvent and the solute are similar. In the case of sugar and water, both are made up of polar molecules, so sugar is soluble in water. In the case of salt and water, the water molecule is like a charged particle because it has excess positive charge at one end and excess negative charge at the other end. ☑

Have you ever heard the expression "they don't mix, like oil and water"? When baby oil and water are mixed, they separate rather than forming a solution, as shown in **Figure 9-11A.** Baby oil is a mixture of nonpolar molecules, so it is unlike water. You've probably noticed the same thing about the oil-and-water solutions that make up many salad dressings. Oils generally dissolve better in solvents that have nonpolar molecules. Some other oils, though, such as olive oil and safflower oil, are made up of molecules that are more polar. Because these oils are more like water, they mix with it more readily, as in **Figure 9-11B.**

Reading Check ☑
Are sugar molecules polar or nonpolar?

How much will dissolve?

Solubility often is given as the amount of a substance that can dissolve in 100 g of solvent at a given temperature. Some solutes are highly soluble, meaning that a large amount of solute can be dissolved in 100 g of solvent. For example, 315 g of potassium chromate can be dissolved in 500 g of water at 25°C, **Figure 9-12**. However, some solutes are not very soluble, meaning that only a small amount of solute can be dissolved in 100 g of solvent. For example, only 0.00025 g of barium sulfate will dissolve in 100 g of water at 25°C. Barium sulfate and other compounds with extremely low solubilities are usually said to be insoluble in water.

Saturated Solutions

You would say that calcium carbonate, commonly called limestone, is insoluble in water. However, 0.0014 g of calcium carbonate dissolves in 100 g of water at 25°C. Such a solution, one that contains all of the solute that it can hold under the given conditions, is called a **saturated** solution. If any more solute is added to a saturated solution, the extra solute will not dissolve. If the solution is a solid-liquid solution, the extra solute added will settle to the bottom of the container. It's important for you to know that solubility does not tell you *how fast* a solute will dissolve. A solute dissolves faster when the solution is stirred or shaken. Increasing temperature and surface-area contact between solute and solvent also makes a solute dissolve faster.

Of course, it's possible to make solutions that have less solute than they would need to become saturated. Such solutions are called unsaturated solutions. An example of an unsaturated solution would be one containing 50 g of sugar in 100 g of water at 25°C. That's much less than the 204 g of sugar the solution would need to be saturated. If a saturated solution is cooled slowly, sometimes the excess solute remains dissolved for a period of time. Such a solution is said to be supersaturated.

Using Math

In a laboratory, a flask of sodium chloride solution contains 60 g of sodium chloride in 1.0 L of solution. If 75 mL of this solution are poured into a beaker, how many grams of solute are contained in the beaker?

Figure 9-12 Potassium chromate is so soluble in water that the entire pile of the compound shown can dissolve in the water in the flask. **What is another compound that is highly soluble in water?**

Concentration

The **concentration** of a solution tells you *how much* solute is present compared to the amount of solvent. If you don't need to know exactly what the concentration is, you can describe the solution in relative terms as being either concentrated or dilute. A **concentrated** solution is one that contains a large amount of solute per given amount of solvent. A **dilute** solution is one that contains a small amount of solute per given amount of solvent. A comparison of concentrated and dilute solutions is shown in **Figure 9-13.**

Suppose you're in the hospital and your doctor decides to administer an intravenous (IV) solution. Would you feel safe if the doctor simply ordered a "dilute IV solution" or a "concentrated IV solution"? Absolutely not! Those terms would not be exact enough. As is true in this case and many others, it's often necessary to specify the exact concentration of a solution. One way is to state the percentage of the volume of the solution that is made up of solute and the percentage made up of solvent. A fruit-drink label may advertise that the drink is 20 percent fruit juice. This means that the remaining 80 percent is water and other substances such as sweeteners and flavorings. This drink is more concentrated than another brand that contains ten percent fruit juice, and it's more dilute than pure juice, which is 100 percent juice.

Observing Gas Solubility

Procedure

1. Obtain any size bottle of a thoroughly chilled, carbonated beverage.
2. Carefully remove the cap from the bottle with as little agitation as possible.
3. Quickly cover the opening with an uninflated balloon. Use tape to secure and seal the balloon to the top of the bottle.
4. **CAUTION:** *Be careful not to point the bottle at anyone.* Gently agitate the bottle from side to side for two minutes and observe the size of the balloon.
5. Set the bottle of soft drink in a container of hot tap water for ten minutes and observe the final size of the balloon.

Analysis

1. Compare and contrast the amounts of carbon dioxide gas released from the cold and warm soft drinks.
2. Why does the soft drink contain a different amount of carbon dioxide when warmed than it does when chilled?

Figure 9-13 The cherry drink on the left is more concentrated than the one on the right. Canned fruit is sometimes packed in light sugar syrup and sometimes in heavy sugar syrup. **Which syrup is more concentrated?**

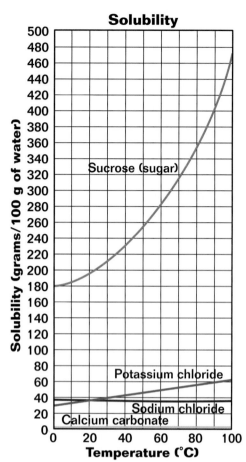

Solubility

Solubility (grams/100 g of water)

Sucrose (sugar)

Potassium chloride

Sodium chloride

Calcium carbonate

Temperature (°C)

Factors That Affect Solubility

The solubility of many solutes changes if you change the temperature of the solvent. This effect is shown in **Figure 9-14.** If you raise the temperature of water, you can add more sugar before the solution becomes saturated.

Another factor can change solubility. In gas-liquid solutions, if the pressure of the gas is increased, its solubility also is increased. You can see this in action when you open a bottle of carbonated beverage. Before you open the bottle, you don't see any bubbles in the liquid. But when you open the bottle, bubbles are suddenly visible as the liquid fizzes. When the bottle was originally filled, extra carbon dioxide gas was squeezed into the space above the liquid. This increased the pressure in the bottle and forced most of the gas into solution in the liquid. When you open the cap, the extra pressure is released into the air and the solubility of the gas in the liquid becomes less. The carbon dioxide gas comes out of solution by forming small bubbles that float to the top of the soft drink and make it fizz.

Figure 9-14 This solubility graph tells how much of four substances can dissolve in 100 g of water at various temperatures.

Section Assessment

1. Why is water called the universal solvent? Why does it have these properties?

2. The new bottles of concentrated laundry detergent are much smaller than the old bottles, but the labels claim they can clean the same amount of clothing. Explain how this might be so.

3. **Think Critically:** Why can the fluids used to dry-clean clothing remove grease from clothes even when water cannot?

4. **Skill Builder**
   Separating and Controlling Variables Scientists pay close attention to controls, dependent variables, and independent variables when they design experiments. Do the **Chapter 9 Skill Activity** on page 562 to learn how to identify controls and variables.

Using Computers

Spreadsheet Use a spreadsheet to make a graph showing the solubility of potassium nitrate on the vertical axis and temperature on the horizontal axis. What is the approximate solubility of potassium nitrate in water at 25°C? If you need help, refer to page 550.

Growing Crystals

If you create a supersaturated solution of alum and then introduce a seed crystal, the alum in solution will attach to the seed crystal and make it grow.

What You'll Investigate

How does a crystal grow in a supersaturated solution?

Goals

- **Observe** the formation of a large alum crystal from a supersaturated solution.

Safety Precautions

Procedure

1. Pour water into the 150-mL beaker to the 100-mL mark.

2. Heat the water on a hot plate to a temperature of 45°C.

3. Dissolve 25 g of alum powder in the heated water.

4. Use the heatproof mitt to remove the beaker from the hot plate and set it on your laboratory table.

5. **Measure** and record the initial size of the alum seed crystal.

6. Tie one end of a thin string or wire around the seed crystal and the other end to a support stick.

7. Place the seed crystal support stick across the top of the beaker so that the seed crystal is submerged just below the surface of the solution.

8. Allow the solution to sit overnight.

9. The following day, **measure** and record the size of your alum crystal again. If you wish, let the solution sit overnight again and then repeat the measurement.

Materials

- Heat-resistant beaker (150 mL)
- Alum powder
- Balance
- Hot plate
- Stirring rod
- Heatproof mitt
  *beaker tongs
- Alcohol thermometer
- Metric ruler

  *Alternate Materials

Conclude and Apply

1. **Compare and contrast** the size of the crystal after one day to the crystal's original size.

2. Where does the extra crystal material come from?

3. Why does the crystal grow?

Alum Crystal Data	
Day	**Size of Crystal**

9•3 Acids and Bases

Acids

You've probably enjoyed a glass of cold lemonade on a warm summer day. What gives lemonade its thirst-quenching, sour taste—a taste shared by many other foods, including vinegar, dill pickles, orange juice, and grapefruit? Acids cause the sour taste of the foods shown in **Figure 9-15**. **Acids** are substances that contain hydrogen and produce hydronium ions when they dissolve in water. Hydronium ions are positively charged and have the formula H_3O^+. How do acids produce hydronium ions? When acids are dissolved in water, they release positively charged hydrogen ions, H^+. The H^+ ions then combine with water molecules to form hydronium ions, as shown in **Figure 9-16**.

Properties of Acidic Solutions

Sour taste is one of the properties of acidic solutions. The taste allows you to detect the presence of acids in your food. Even though you can identify acidic solutions by their sour taste, you should NEVER use taste to test for the presence of acids. In fact, some acids can cause burns and damage body tissues.

Acidic solutions can conduct electricity because they contain ions. Acidic solutions are corrosive, which means they can eat away at certain substances. The solutions of some acids react strongly with certain metals, forming metallic compounds and hydrogen gas and leaving holes in the metal in the process.

When carbon dioxide from the air dissolves in water, carbonic acid is formed. Because carbon dioxide is dissolved in water to produce carbonated beverages, these beverages contain carbonic acid. The stalagmite and stalactite formations you saw earlier in the chapter involved carbonic acid solutions, too. Naturally formed carbonic acid in the soil begins to dissolve the calcium carbonate that makes up most of the

What You'll Learn

▶ What acids and bases are
▶ Properties of acidic and basic solutions
▶ Why some acids and bases are stronger than others
▶ What happens when acids and bases are brought together

Vocabulary

acid   indicator
base   neutralization
pH

Why It's Important

▶ Many common products work because they are acids or bases.

Figure 9-15 Vinegar, dill pickles, and citrus fruits taste sour because they contain acids.
Why do some apples taste more tart than others?

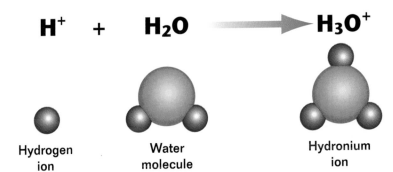

$$H^+ \ + \ H_2O \ \longrightarrow \ H_3O^+$$

Hydrogen ion — Water molecule — Hydronium ion

Figure 9-16 When hydrogen ions from acids combine with water molecules, hydronium ions are formed.

limestone rock in the cave. When drops of the resulting solution cling to the roof of the cave and evaporate, they create the hanging rock formations called stalactites. When drops of the solution fall onto the floor of the cave and evaporate, they form stalagmites, which look like upside-down stalactites. This same kind of reaction occurs when acid rain, which can form from air pollution and other sources, falls on statues and eats away at the stone, as shown in **Figure 9-17.**

Uses of Acids

You're probably familiar with many acids. Vinegar, which is used in salad dressing and in making pickles, contains acetic acid. Lemons and oranges have a sour taste because they contain citric acid. Your body needs ascorbic acid, which is vitamin C. Ants that sting inject formic acid to cause pain in their victims.

Try at Home

Mini Lab

Observing a Nail in a Carbonated Drink

Procedure

1. Observe the initial appearance of the iron nail.
2. Pour some of the carbonated soft drink into a cup or beaker, filling it about twice as deep as the nail is long.
3. Drop the nail into the soft drink and observe what happens.
4. Leave the nail in the soft drink overnight and observe it again the next day.

Analysis

1. Describe what happened when you first dropped the nail into the soft drink and the appearance of the nail the following day.
2. Based upon the fact that the soft drink was carbonated, explain why you think the drink reacted with the nail as you observed.

Figure 9-17 Acid rain has eaten away some of the stone in these columns at the Acropolis in Athens, Greece. **Why is acid rain usually more of a problem near or downwind of industrial areas?**

Acids are often used in batteries because their solutions conduct electricity and because the ions they produce can react in certain ways. Sulfuric acid is used in the production of fertilizers, steel, paints, and plastics. Because sulfuric acid is an important ingredient in automobile batteries, it is sometimes called battery acid. Hydrochloric acid, which is known commercially as muriatic acid, is used in a process called pickling. Pickling removes impurities from the surfaces of metals. Hydrochloric acid also can be used to clean mortar from brick walls. Nitric acid is used in the production of fertilizers, dyes, plastics, and explosives.

Bases

The ammonia solutions that people sometimes use to clean windows have properties that are distinctly different from those of acidic solutions. Ammonia is called a base. **Bases** are substances that produce hydroxide ions when they dissolve in water. Hydroxide ions are negatively charged and have the formula OH^-.

Properties of Basic Solutions

Most soaps are bases, and if you think about how you use soap, you can figure out some of the properties of basic solutions. Basic solutions feel slippery to the touch. While acids in water solution taste sour, bases taste bitter—as you know, if you have ever accidentally gotten soap in your mouth.

Like acids, bases are corrosive. Touch or taste tests should NEVER be used to test for bases because they can cause burns and damage tissue. Like acidic solutions, basic solutions contain ions and can conduct electricity. Unlike acidic solutions, basic solutions usually do not react with metals.

Uses of Bases

Bases give soaps and many other cleaning products, as shown in **Figure 9-18,** some of their useful properties. That's because the hydroxide ions produced by bases can interact strongly with certain substances, such as dirt and grease. Ammonia is a part of many household cleaners and also is used in the manufacture of fertilizers, fibers, and plastics.

Antacid tablets, chalk, oven cleaner, and many other familiar products and substances contain bases. Magnesium hydroxide is a base found in some

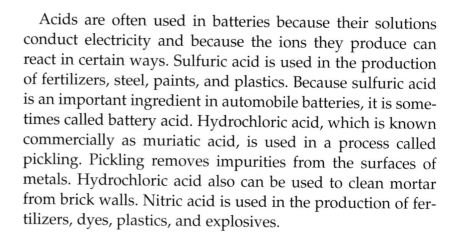

*inter*NET
CONNECTION

Visit the Glencoe Science Web Site at **www.glencoe.com/ sec/science/ca** for more information about acids and their uses.

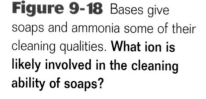

Figure 9-18 Bases give soaps and ammonia some of their cleaning qualities. **What ion is likely involved in the cleaning ability of soaps?**

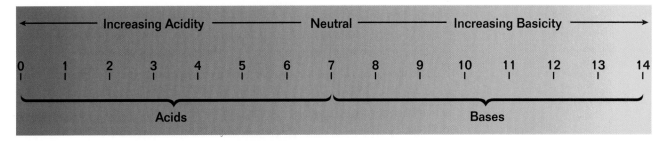

Increasing Acidity — Neutral — Increasing Basicity

0 1 2 3 4 5 6 7 8 9 10 11 12 13 14

Acids   Bases

antacids. Your blood is a basic solution. Calcium hydroxide, a base that is often called lime, is used to mark the lines on athletic fields. Calcium hydroxide is also found in chalk, mortar, plaster, and paving materials, and it can be used to treat lawns and gardens that have acidic soil. Sodium hydroxide, also known as lye, is a strong base that can cause burns and other health problems. Lye is used to make soap, clean ovens, and unclog drains.

Figure 9-19 The pH scale is a quick way to classify a solution as acidic, basic, or neutral. **Does an ammonia solution have a pH above 7 or below 7?**

pH

If you've seen someone test the water in a swimming pool, you know that the water's pH is important to the safety of swimmers. You've probably heard of pH-balanced shampoo. A solution's **pH** is a measure of how acidic or basic the solution is. The pH scale generally ranges from 0 to 14. More acidic solutions have lower pH values, and a solution with a pH of 0 is highly acidic. A solution that has a pH of 7 is neutral. More basic solutions have higher pH values, and a solution with a pH of 14 is extremely basic, as shown in **Figure 9-19.** ☑

The pH of a solution is directly related to its concentrations of hydronium ions and hydroxide ions. As shown in **Figure 9-20,** acidic solutions have more hydronium ions than hydroxide ions. Neutral solutions have equal numbers of the two ions. Basic solutions have more hydroxide ions than hydronium ions.

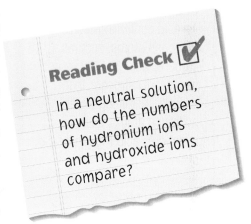

Reading Check ☑

In a neutral solution, how do the numbers of hydronium ions and hydroxide ions compare?

Figure 9-20 What makes a pH 7 solution neutral?

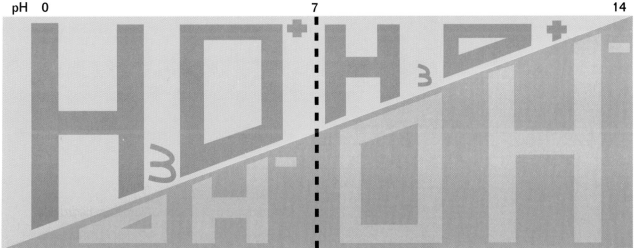

pH 0   7   14

The pH scale is not a simple linear scale like mass or volume. For example, if one book has a mass of 2 kg and a second book has a mass of 1 kg, the mass of the first book is just twice that of the second. However, a change of 1 pH unit represents a tenfold change in the acidity of the solution. For example, if one solution has a pH of 1 and a second solution has a pH of 2, the first solution is not just twice as acidic as the second. Rather, it's ten times more acidic! In a similar way, a solution with a pH of 12 is 100 times more basic than one with a pH of 10.

pH and Strengths of Acids and Bases

Sometimes, acids and bases can be confusing. On one hand, you've learned that acids give foods a sour taste. On the other hand, acids can cause burns and damage tissue. Both are properties of acids, but what's the difference between food acids and the acids that can burn you? The acids have different strengths. The acids in food are fairly weak acids, while the dangerous acids are strong acids. The strength of an acid is related to the number of hydronium ions it produces when it dissolves to form a solution. For the same concentration, a strong acid forms more hydronium ions in solution than a weak acid. More hydronium ions mean the strong-acid solution has a lower pH than the weak-acid solution. Similarly, the strength of a base is related to the number of hydroxide ions it produces when it dissolves to form a solution. The relative strengths of some common acids and bases are shown in **Table 9-2.**

Indicators are compounds that react with acidic and basic solutions to produce certain colors. For that reason, indicators can help you find out how acidic or basic a solution is. Some indicators, such as litmus, are soaked into paper strips. When litmus paper is placed in an acidic solution, it turns red. But, when placed in a basic solution, litmus paper turns blue.

CHEMISTRY
INTEGRATION

Strong and Weak Acids
An acid containing more hydrogen atoms, such as carbonic acid (H_2CO_3), is not necessarily stronger than an acid containing fewer hydrogen atoms, such as hydroiodic acid (HI). An acid's strength is related to how many hydronium ions it *does* produce—not to how many it *could* produce. In this comparison, for example, hydroiodic acid is stronger than carbonic acid.

Table 9-2

Strengths of Some Acids and Bases		
Strength	**Acid**	**Base**
Strong	Hydrochloric	Sodium hydroxide
	Sulfuric	Potassium hydroxide
	Nitric	
Weak	Acetic	Ammonia
	Carbonic	Aluminum hydroxide
	Ascorbic	Iron(III) hydroxide

Some indicators can change through a wide range of colors, with each different color appearing at a different pH value.

Acid rain can result from the introduction of acid-forming compounds into the air by power plants. This rain falls across the countryside and into bodies of water. Many lakes have become unfit for fish to live in because much of the lake water comes from acid rain.

LIFE SCIENCE
◄ INTEGRATION

Neutralization

Perhaps you've heard someone complain about heartburn or an upset stomach after eating a large meal. To feel better, the person may have taken an antacid. How do antacids work?

Heartburn or stomach discomfort is caused by excess hydrochloric acid in the stomach. Hydrochloric acid helps break down the food you eat, but too much acid can irritate your stomach or digestive tract. The antacid product, often made from the base magnesium hydroxide, neutralizes the excess acid. **Neutralization** (new truh luh ZAY shun) is the interaction that occurs between acids and bases in which the properties of each are canceled out by the other.

*inter*NET
CONNECTION

Visit the Glencoe Science Web Site at **www.glencoe.com/ sec/science/ca** for more information about acid rain.

Problem Solving

The Statue Mystery

When members of the art museum's board of directors returned for their annual meeting, they happened to look at the old marble and metal statues in front of the museum. They noticed that the previously beautiful statues were deteriorating badly. They suspected that acid rain might be the problem.

To check their hypothesis, they designed and carried out an experiment that produced the following results. First, when marble chips are placed in a dilute sulfuric acid solution, gas bubbles form and the chips dissolve slowly. (Sulfuric acid is a component of acid rain.)

Then, when mossy zinc is placed in a dilute sulfuric acid solution, a rapid reaction occurs. (Zinc is a component of the metal in statues.) Many gas bubbles form, and the zinc dissolves quickly.

Think Critically: Infer how the damage to the statues may have occurred based on the results of the experiment. Research and explain some ways that the museum's board of directors and other segments of society, such as energy companies, might minimize the problems caused by acid rain.

How does neutralization happen? Remember that each water molecule contains two hydrogen atoms and one oxygen atom. When one hydronium ion reacts with one hydroxide ion, the product is simply two water molecules, **Figure 9-21.** This reaction occurs during acid-base neutralization, in which equal numbers of hydronium ions and hydroxide ions react to produce water. Water has a pH of 7, which means that it's neither acidic nor basic.

In the case of an antacid that contains magnesium hydroxide, the excess hydrochloric acid combines with magnesium hydroxide to form water and magnesium chloride. Water is neutral. Magnesium chloride, the other substance formed, is neither an acid nor a base. Magnesium chloride is called a salt. Salts have a number of uses in your body. Calcium salts are needed for healthy teeth and bones. Iron salts are found in your blood. Other salts are needed for muscle function and the control of fluid balance in your body's cells.

Figure 9-21 When acidic and basic solutions react, hydronium ions react with hydroxide ions to form water molecules.

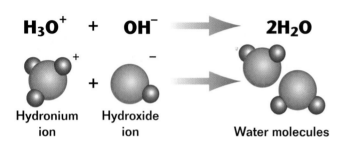

H_3O^+ + OH^- ⟶ $2H_2O$

Hydronium ion   Hydroxide ion   Water molecules

Section Assessment

1. Why do acidic and basic solutions conduct electricity?

2. Name three acids that are important in industry. Give one use for each.

3. What is the pH of pure water at 25°C?

4. **Think Critically:** Strong acids are used in many industrial applications, but they can be hazardous to humans. How do you think a company that uses a strong acid would handle a situation in which that acid spills onto the factory floor?

5. **Skill Builder**
   Sequencing Arrange the following list of solutions in order from most basic to most acidic. If you need help, refer to Sequencing in the **Skill Handbook** on page 526.

   Tomato juice, pH 5   Milk of magnesia, pH 10.5
   Baking soda, pH 9   Seawater, pH 8
   Lemon juice, pH 2   Drain cleaner, pH 13

Using Math

How much more acidic is a solution with a pH of 2 than one with a pH of 6? How much more basic is a solution with a pH of 13 than one with a pH of 10?

Making Paper

Paper vs. Rock

Your backpack may feel heavy, but suppose it were loaded with stone tablets instead of paper? Before the invention of paper, ancient people wrote on stone. By 3500 B.C., Egyptians were making a type of paper from the papyrus plant. Later, people created another form of paper, called parchment, from animal skins.

The Chinese (left) were using vegetable fibers to make paper by the beginning of the second century A.D. The paper made from these fibers was so valuable that the process of making it was kept secret for 500 years. Only when the Arabs in Samarkand (a city in what is now Uzbekistan) captured Chinese papermakers did the rest of the world learn how to manufacture paper. With the invention of the printing press, paper became even more important. In 1798, the invention of papermaking machines made it possible to mass-produce paper.

Perfecting Paper

Early paper had one major problem—the wood pulp used to make paper had impurities and fibers that had to be broken down. To do this, paper manufacturers began to boil the wood pulp with various chemicals. This process often made the paper acidic. Because acidic paper is fragile, examples of early paper are rare.

Today, alkalis, a mixture of soluble salts, are used to strengthen paper and to improve the way it feels. Papermaking plants (right) make most paper from wood. Cloth rags are used to make fine writing paper and artists' paper. Some papers can be recycled and used again.

Science JOURNAL

In your Science Journal, write about how life would change if there were no paper available. Would computers be able to fill the gap?

Testing pH Using Natural Indicators

Materials

- Small test tubes (9)
- Test-tube rack
- Concentrated red cabbage juice in a dropper bottle
- Labeled bottles containing: household ammonia, baking soda solution, soap solution, hydrochloric acid solution, white vinegar, colorless carbonated soft drink, sodium hydroxide, drain cleaner solution, distilled water
- Grease pencil

You have learned that certain substances, called indicators, change color when the pH of a solution changes. Indicators can be used to determine the approximate pH of a solution and to show changes in pH. The juice from red cabbage is one of these substances.

What You'll Investigate

How can you use red cabbage juice as an indicator to determine the relative pH of solutions? Why do the solutions of some bases have higher pH values than solutions of other bases? What ion is involved in the cleaning process?

Goals

- **Determine** the relative pH values of several common solutions.
- **Compare** the strengths of several common acids and bases.

Safety Precautions

Use caution when working with acids and bases. Wear laboratory aprons and safety goggles.

Cabbage Juice Data	
Cabbage Juice Color	**Relative pH**
bright red	strong acid
red	medium acid
reddish-purple	weak acid
purple	neutral
blue-green	weak base
green	medium base
yellow	strong base

Procedure

1. **Design** a data table in which you can record the names of the solutions to be tested, the colors caused by the added cabbage juice indicator, and the relative pH values of the solutions.

2. Mark each test tube with the identity of the solution it will contain.

3. Fill each test tube about halfway with the solution to be tested. **CAUTION:** *If you spill any liquids on your skin, rinse the area immediately with water. Alert your teacher if any liquid is spilled in the work area.*

4. Add ten drops of the cabbage juice indicator to each of the solutions to be tested. Gently agitate or wiggle each test tube to mix the cabbage juice with the solution.

5. **Observe** and record the color of each solution in your data table.

Conclude and Apply

1. **Compare** your observations with the cabbage juice color table. Record the relative pH of each solution tested in your data table.

2. **Classify** which solutions were acidic and which were basic.

3. Which solution was the weakest acid? The strongest base?

4. **Predict** what ion might be involved in the cleaning process based upon your pH values for the ammonia, soap, and drain-cleaner solutions.

5. **Form a hypothesis** that explains why the sodium hydroxide solution had a much higher pH than an ammonia solution of approximately the same concentration.

FIELD GUIDE to Kitchen Chemistry

FIELD ACTIVITY

For a week, use this field guide to help you identify the mixtures and changes you see in your kitchen. Observe the preparation of at least one meal each day. In your Science Journal, record the day of the week, what meal is being prepared, and a description of the types of mixtures, chemical changes, and physical changes you observe.

It's early morning in the kitchen, and chemistry surrounds you. Breakfast—with its wake-up sights and smells—is almost ready. Freshly squeezed orange juice, hot tea, yogurt with strawberries, butter, and syrup wait on the counter. Eggs and pancakes sizzle on the griddle. Slices of bread are toasting. Some foods are liquids. Others are solids. Most are mixtures. Some are undergoing delectable changes while you watch. Using this field guide, you can identify the different types of mixtures that you drink and eat, and the chemical and physical changes that occur as foods are prepared.

How Mixtures Are Classified

Mixtures contain two or more substances that have not combined to form a new substance. The proportions of the substances that make up a mixture can vary. Mixtures are classified as either homogeneous or heterogeneous.

- You cannot see the substances in a homogeneous mixture no matter how closely you look.
- You easily can identify the substances that are in a heterogeneous mixture.

Homogeneous Mixtures—Solutions

Much of the chemistry in your kitchen takes place in solutions. Because solutions are homogeneous mixtures, you can't see their different parts. Both tea and syrup are solutions of solids dissolved in liquids.

Acids

Many foods contain acids or acidic solutions. One noticeable property of an acidic solution is its sour taste. Of course, you should never taste a solution simply to determine if it's acidic! For example, lactic acid gives yogurt its sour taste. While fruits such as oranges, lemons, and apples contain many other substances that are not acidic, citric acid gives them their tartness or sour taste. Acidic solutions have pH values below 7.

Heterogeneous Mixtures

You can see the different parts of most heterogeneous mixtures. For example, strawberries are clearly visible in the yogurt.

How Changes Are Classified

A change to a substance can be classified as either a chemical or physical change. A chemical change is one in which one or more new substances are formed. When a physical change occurs, the identity of the substance does not change.

Protein Denaturation

The proteins in a raw egg are folded into balls, sheets, and coils. Heating the egg breaks some of the bonds holding the proteins in these tight shapes. As cooking continues, the proteins unravel and begin forming weak bonds with other proteins, causing the egg to solidify.

Chemical Changes

Chemical changes can be recognized by the following signs.
- The color changes.
- A solid forms when solutions are mixed.
- Heat or light is absorbed or released.
- An odor forms or changes.
- A gas is released.

Gas Production

The bubbles you see in pancake batter are caused by a chemical change in the batter. Baking powder is a mixture containing mostly baking soda and an acidic substance. When water is added to baking powder, the acidic solution that forms reacts with baking soda to make carbon dioxide gas.

Browning

Browning is a chemical change in which sugars and proteins in foods form new flavors and smells. Browning produces the barbecue flavors of foods cooked on a grill and the caramelized flavor of a roasted marshmallow.

Physical Changes

You can recognize a physical change when one of the following occurs.
- The substance changes shape.
- The substance changes size.
- The substance changes form. For example, a liquid changes to a solid or gas.

Melting

The pad of butter is changing from a solid to a liquid. Melting occurs because heat from the warm toast weakens and breaks bonds between the molecules in the butter.

Freezing

An ice-and-salt brine cools the liquid mixture of cream, sugar, and flavorings inside an ice-cream freezer. Most of the water in the mixture freezes into small ice crystals, and air bubbles give the solid mixture its smooth, creamy texture.

Boiling

Popcorn kernels contain 11 to 14 percent water. When the kernels are heated, the liquid water changes to steam. The steam creates pressure that bursts the kernels. The hot steam also cooks the starchy interior of the corn, forming a light, crisp, and edible snack.

For a **preview** of this chapter, study this Reviewing Main Ideas before you read the chapter. After you have studied this chapter, you can use the Reviewing Main Ideas to **review** the chapter.

The Glencoe MindJogger, Audiocassettes, and CD-ROM provide additional opportunities for review.

Section 9-1 SOLUTIONS

Materials can be elements, compounds, or mixtures. A **solution** is a homogeneous **mixture** in which the components cannot be distinguished easily. **Solutes** dissolve in **solvents** to form solutions. Solutions are classified as gaseous, liquid, or solid. *What is the difference between a compound and a mixture or solution?*

Section 9-2 AQUEOUS SOLUTIONS

Water is known as the universal solvent because it can dissolve many solutes. This is possible because water molecules are polar. The **concentration** of a solution is a measure of the amount of solute in a particular volume of solvent. Solutions can be unsaturated, **saturated,** or supersaturated. *What kind of substances cannot be dissolved by the polar molecules that make up water? Explain why.*

Water molecules

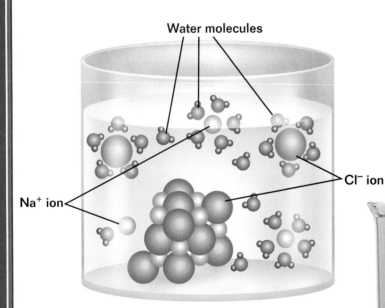

Na⁺ ion

Cl⁻ ion

SOLUBILITY

The maximum amount of solute that can be dissolved in a given amount of solvent at a particular temperature is called the **solubility** of the solute. Temperature and pressure can affect solubility. *How do you describe a solution that contains the maximum amount of solute possible under a given set of conditions?*

Reading Check ✔

Suggest one or two additional illustrations for this chapter and explain why they would be valuable.

Section 9-3 ACIDS AND BASES

Acids produce hydronium ions when dissolved in water, forming acidic solutions. **Bases** produce hydroxide ions when dissolved in water, forming basic solutions. Acidic and basic solutions have many distinctive properties. *List two properties of acidic solutions and two properties of basic solutions.*

pH

In aqueous solutions, **pH** expresses the concentrations of hydronium ions and hydroxide ions. Solutions with pH values below 7 are acidic. Solutions with a pH of 7 are neutral. Solutions with pH values above 7 are basic. *How do the acidities of two solutions with pH values of 3 and 5 compare?*

NEUTRALIZATION

In a neutralization reaction, an acid reacts with a base to form water and a salt. **Neutralization** cancels the properties of the acid and base as they are reacting and produces a neutral solution. *What salt will be formed when hydrochloric acid neutralizes aluminum hydroxide?*

$$H_3O^+ \ + \ OH^- \longrightarrow 2H_2O$$

Hydronium ion $+$ Hydroxide ion $\longrightarrow$ Water molecules

Chapter 9 Assessment

Using Vocabulary

a. acid
b. aqueous
c. base
d. concentrated
e. concentration
f. dilute
g. indicator
h. mixture
i. neutralization
j. pH
k. saturated
l. solubility
m. solute
n. solution
o. solvent

Each of the following sentences is false. Make the sentence true by replacing the italicized word with a word from the list above.

1. A *base* is substance that produces hydronium ions in solution.
2. A measure of how much solute is in a solution is its *solubility*.
3. The amount of a substance that can dissolve in 100 g of solvent is its *pH*.
4. The *solvent* is the substance that dissolves to form a solution.
5. The reaction between an acidic and a basic solution is called *concentration*.

Checking Concepts

Choose the word or phrase that best answers the question.

6. What is the solid substance that falls out of a solution?
   A) polymer   C) reactant
   B) ion   D) precipitate

7. What has a pH greater than 7?
   A) salt   C) acidic solution
   B) basic solution D) solid

8. When chlorine is dissolved in pool water, what is the water?
   A) the alloy   C) the solution
   B) the solvent D) the solute

9. A solid may become less soluble in a liquid when you decrease what?
   A) stirring   C) temperature
   B) pressure   D) container size

10. Which acid is used in the industrial process known as pickling?
    A) hydrochloric C) sulfuric
    B) carbonic   D) nitric

11. At different pH values, indicators change what?
    A) odor   C) color
    B) smell   D) taste

12. What is formed by combining negative ions from an acid and positive ions from a base?
    A) a salt   C) lime
    B) lye   D) steel

13. Bile, a body fluid involved in digestion, is acidic, so its pH is what?
    A) 11   C) less than 7
    B) 7   D) greater than 7

14. Which of the following is a solution?
    A) pure oxygen in a firefighter's tank
    B) an oatmeal raisin cookie
    C) copper
    D) vinegar

15. Which of the following is potentially most dangerous to human skin?
    A) neutral solution
    B) concentrated basic solution
    C) dilute basic solution
    D) dilute acidic solution

Thinking Critically

16. Why do deposits form in the steam vents of irons in some parts of the country?

17. Is it possible for a solution to be both saturated and dilute? Explain your answer.

18. In which type of container is orange juice more likely to keep its freshly squeezed taste, a metal can or a paper carton? Explain.

19. Knowing what you do about the relative amounts of iron and carbon in regular steel, which do you think is the solvent? Which is the solute? Explain.

20. Water molecules can break apart to form H⁺ ions and OH⁻ ions. Water is known as an amphoteric substance, which is something that can act as an acid or a base. Explain how this can be so.

Developing Skills

If you need help, refer to the **Skill Handbook.**

21. **Making and Using Graphs:** Using the solubility graph below, estimate the solubilities of potassium chloride and sugar in grams per 100 g of water at 70°C.

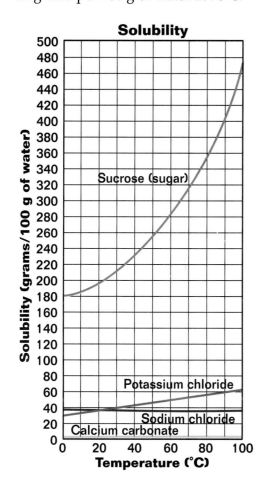

THE PRINCETON REVIEW

Test-Taking Tip

Make Yourself Comfortable When you take a test, try to make yourself as comfortable as possible. You will then be able to focus all of your attention on the test.

Test Practice

Use these questions to test your Science Proficiency.

1. Which of the following statements about acids is false?
   A) Metals can be eaten away by acids.
   B) Acids release hydroxide ions when dissolved in solution.
   C) Sour tastes can be a result of acids being present.
   D) Acids help in the digestion of food.

2. Which of the following approaches might be of use if you want to dissolve more potassium nitrate in 100 g of water?
   A) Increase the pressure.
   B) Decrease the amount of time you take to add the potassium nitrate.
   C) Increase the size of the container.
   D) Increase the temperature of the water.

3. A carbonated soft drink contains carbonic acid. Why does a carbonated soft drink have a higher pH than hydrochloric acid?
   A) The soft drink contains a sweetener.
   B) Carbonic acid is stronger than hydrochloric acid.
   C) Hydrochloric acid is stronger than carbonic acid.
   D) Carbonic acid contains more hydrogen atoms than hydrochloric acid.

Carbon Chemistry

Chapter Preview

Skills Preview

Skill Builders

- Sequence
- Make and Use a Graph

Activities

- Form a Hypothesis

MiniLabs

- Make a Model

Reading Check ✔

Review or find out the meanings of these word parts so you will better understand this chapter: *carbo–*, *hydro–*, *iso–*, *poly–*, *–mer*, *–ane*, *–ene*.

Explore Activity

This family is going on a picnic, and they're taking along a lot of stuff. Besides the picnic basket full of food, there are the baseball gloves, tennis rackets, towels and blankets, and the beach chairs. Different as they are, these items all share one thing in common—they contain the element carbon. Even many parts of the minivan are made of compounds that contain carbon. What is special about carbon that allows it to form so many different compounds?

Infer Carbon's Bonding

CAUTION: *Do not eat foods used in your activity.*

1. Insert four toothpicks into a small clay or plastic foam ball so that the toothpicks are evenly spaced around the sphere. The ball represents a carbon atom. The toothpicks represent chemical bonds.

2. Use raisins to represent hydrogen atoms, grapes to represent chlorine atoms, and gumdrops to represent fluorine atoms. Make models of molecules by adding any combination of raisins, grapes, and gumdrops to the toothpicks.

3. Compare your models with those of other class members.

Science Journal

Draw each model and write the formula for it. Did you make all the models that were possible with the materials you had? Did the class make all that were possible? What can you infer about the number of compounds a single carbon atom can form with only three kinds of atoms?

10·1 Simple Organic Compounds

What You'll Learn

▶ Why carbon is able to form many compounds
▶ How saturated and unsaturated hydrocarbons differ
▶ How to identify isomers of organic compounds

Vocabulary
organic compound
hydrocarbon
saturated hydrocarbon
unsaturated hydrocarbon
isomer

Why It's Important

▶ Plants, animals, and most of the things that are part of your life are made of organic compounds.

Figure 10-1 Organic substances contain carbon.

Organic Compounds

One way to classify the substances that are a part of your life is shown in **Figure 10-1.** Some substances are made by living organisms, for example, leaves and wood. Other substances, such as most rocks and minerals, are not and have never been alive. Most of the substances associated with living things contain the element carbon. Scientists used to think that this group of substances could be produced only by living plants and animals, so these carbon-containing substances were called organic compounds. The word *organic* means "derived from a living organism." But, in 1828, a German scientist formed the organic compound urea from substances that were not organic compounds. Scientists then realized that living organisms are not necessary to form organic compounds. Now, most compounds that contain carbon are called **organic compounds.**

Atoms form chemical bonds and thus obtain the stability of a noble gas with eight electrons in their outer energy level. A carbon atom has four electrons in its outer energy level, so it forms four covalent bonds with as many as four other atoms. A single covalent bond is a pair of electrons that is shared between two atoms. One of carbon's most frequent partners in covalent bonds is hydrogen.

A Most of the substances in the photo are organic. Although some are, or were, alive, others were manufactured.

B The substances in this photo are mostly composed of elements other than carbon.

Hydrocarbons

Many compounds are made of carbon and hydrogen alone. A compound in which the only elements are carbon and hydrogen is called a **hydrocarbon.** The simplest hydrocarbon is methane, sometimes called natural gas. If you have a gas stove or gas furnace in your home, the fuel that may be burned in these appliances is methane. It consists of a single carbon atom covalently bonded to four hydrogen atoms. Methane's formula is CH_4. **Figure 10-2** shows a model of the methane molecule and its structural formula. In a structural formula, the lines between one atom and another atom represent pairs of electrons shared between the atoms. A single line represents one pair of electrons.

Now, visualize one of the hydrogen atoms being plucked from a methane molecule, as in **Figure 10-3A.** A fragment of the molecule called a methyl group, $-CH_3$, would remain. The methyl group can then form a single bond with another methyl group. If two methyl groups bond with each other, the result is the two-carbon hydrocarbon ethane, C_2H_6, which is shown with its structural formula in **Figure 10-3B.**

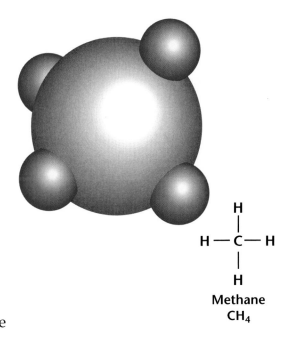

Methane
CH_4

Figure 10-2 This simple molecule is the first of a long list of hydrocarbon molecules.

Figure 10-3 Here's a way to visualize the building up of larger hydrocarbons. **Would it matter which hydrogen atom was plucked off?**

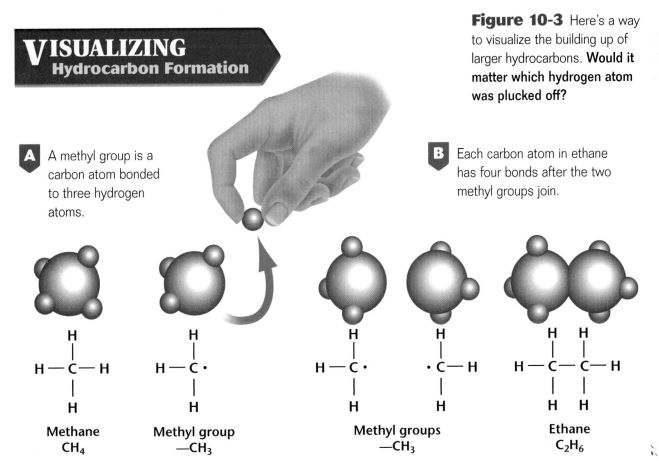

VISUALIZING
Hydrocarbon Formation

A A methyl group is a carbon atom bonded to three hydrogen atoms.

B Each carbon atom in ethane has four bonds after the two methyl groups join.

Methane
CH_4

Methyl group
$-CH_3$

Methyl groups
$-CH_3$

Ethane
C_2H_6

Figure 10-4 Propane and butane are two useful fuels.

A When propane burns, it releases energy for cooking food and warmth. It's the fuel used in camp stoves and heaters.

B In addition to its use as lighter fuel, butane is used in making many products.

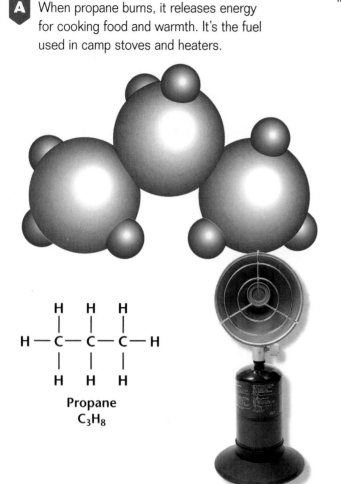

Propane
C_3H_8

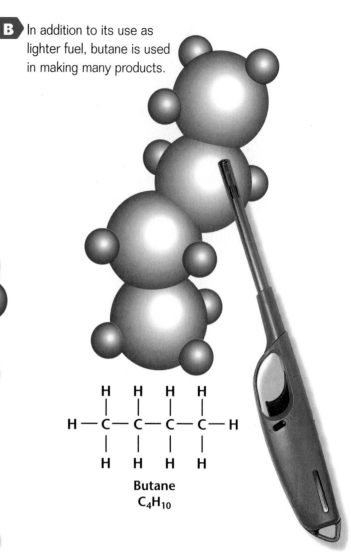

Butane
C_4H_{10}

EARTH SCIENCE
INTEGRATION

Petroleum from Dinosaurs
Petroleum is a mixture of hydrocarbons that was formed from aquatic plants and animals—perhaps even dinosaurs—that lived hundreds of millions of years ago. With the right temperature and pressure, dead plant and animal matter, buried deep under Earth's surface, is decomposed to form petroleum. Why is petroleum a nonrenewable resource?

Saturated Hydrocarbons

Methane and ethane are the first two members of a family of molecules in which carbon and hydrogen atoms are joined by single covalent bonds. When all the bonds in a hydrocarbon are single bonds, the molecule is called a **saturated hydrocarbon.** You can visualize the formation of larger hydrocarbons in the same way you visualized the formation of ethane. A hydrogen atom is removed from ethane and replaced by a –CH_3 group. Propane is the third member of the series. Butane, with four carbon atoms, is the fourth.

These short hydrocarbon chains have low boiling points, so they evaporate and burn easily. That makes methane a good fuel for your stove or furnace. Propane is used in gas grills and in hot-air balloons. Butane is a fuel for camp stoves and lighters. You can see the structures of these hydrocarbons in **Figure 10-4.** Some long-chain hydrocarbons have more than 50 carbon atoms. Longer hydrocarbons are used as oils, waxes, or in asphalt. **Table 10-1** lists the names and the chemical formulas of a few of the smaller saturated hydrocarbons.

Unsaturated Hydrocarbons

Carbon also forms hydrocarbons with double and triple bonds. In a double bond, two pairs of electrons are shared between two atoms, and in a triple bond, three pairs of electrons are shared. Hydrocarbons with double or triple bonds are called **unsaturated hydrocarbons.** Ethene, or ethylene, the simplest unsaturated hydrocarbon, has two carbon atoms joined by a double bond. Propene, or propylene, is an unsaturated hydrocarbon with three carbons. Some unsaturated hydrocarbons have more than one double bond. Butadiene has four carbon atoms and two double bonds. The structures of ethylene, propylene, and butadiene are shown in **Figure 10-5.**

Table 10-1

	The Structures of Hydrocarbons	
Name	Structural Formula	Chemical Formula
Methane		CH_4
Ethane		C_2H_6
Propane		C_3H_8
Butane		C_4H_{10}
Hexane		C_6H_{14}

Figure 10-5 You'll find unsaturated hydrocarbons in many of the products you use every day.

Ethylene
C_2H_4

Propylene
C_3H_6

Butadiene
C_4H_6

A Ethylene helps ripen fruits and vegetables. It's also used to make milk and soft-drink bottles.

B This detergent bottle contains the tough plastic polypropylene made from propylene.

C Butadiene made it possible to replace natural rubber with synthetic rubber.

Figure 10-6 In the welder's torch, ethyne (acetylene) is combined with oxygen to form a mixture that burns, releasing intense light and heat. The two carbon atoms in ethyne are joined by a triple bond. **Why is the oxygen important?**

$$H - C \equiv C - H$$

Ethyne or Acetylene
C_2H_2

Unsaturated hydrocarbons also may have triple bonds, as you can see in the structure of ethyne (ETH ine) shown in **Figure 10-6.** Ethyne, commonly called acetylene, is a gas used for welding because it produces high heat as it burns in a mixture with oxygen in the welding torch.

Hydrocarbon Isomers

Suppose you want to redecorate your room but you can't get new furniture or posters for the walls. One thing you can do is rearrange all of the things that you already have. Even though your room contains the same items, it is different from before. The atoms in an organic molecule also can have different arrangements but still have the same formula. Compounds that have the same chemical formula but different structures are called **isomers** (I suh murz). Two isomers, butane and isobutane, are shown in **Figure 10-7.** Notice that their formulas are the same. But, because of their different structures, they

Try at Home

Mini Lab

Modeling Isomers

Procedure

1. Construct a model of pentane, C_5H_{12}. Use toothpicks for covalent bonds and small balls of different colored clay for carbon atoms and hydrogen atoms.

2. Using the same collection of atoms, build a molecule with a different arrangement of the atoms. Are there any other possibilities?

3. Make a model of hexane, C_6H_{14}.

4. Arrange the atoms of hexane in different ways.

Analysis

1. How many isomers of pentane did you build? How many isomers of hexane?

2. Do you think there are more isomers of heptane, C_7H_{16}, than hexane? Why or why not?

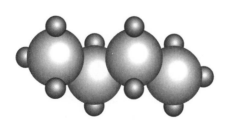

Figure 10-7 Butane and isobutane have the same formula, C_4H_{10}, but they are different in their structure and properties.

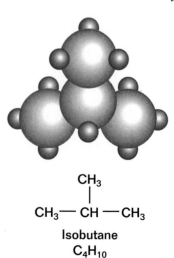

$$CH_3 - CH_2 - CH_2 - CH_3$$
Butane
C_4H_{10}

$$
\begin{array}{c}
CH_3 \\
| \\
CH_3 - CH - CH_3
\end{array}
$$
Isobutane
C_4H_{10}

have different chemical and physical properties. As the size of a hydrocarbon molecule increases, the possibilities for isomers also increase. ✓

Hydrocarbons in Rings

You may be thinking that all hydrocarbons are chains of carbon atoms with two ends. But, no rule states that a molecule must have two ends. Just as a rope can be tied together to form a loop, some molecules can occur in rings. You can see the structures of two different molecules in **Figure 10-8.** The carbon atoms bond together to form closed rings containing five and six carbons. The prefix *cyclo-* in their names tells you that the molecules are cyclic or ring shaped.

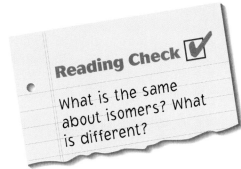

Reading Check ✓ What is the same about isomers? What is different?

Cyclopentane
C_5H_{10}

Cyclohexane
C_6H_{12}

Figure 10-8 Visualize a hydrogen plucked from the carbon atoms on both ends of a pentane or hexane chain. Then, the two end carbons form a bond with each other. **How does the formula for cyclohexane differ from the formula for hexane?**

Section Assessment

1. Explain the difference between a saturated hydrocarbon and an unsaturated hydrocarbon, and give an example of each.

2. From the structure of the carbon atom, explain the large number of compounds that can be formed by carbon.

3. **Think Critically:** Are propane and cyclopropane isomers? Use diagrams and formulas to explain your answer.

4. **Skill Builder**
   Making and Using Graphs Make a graph using the information in **Table 10-1.** For each compound, plot the number of carbon atoms on the *x*-axis and the number of hydrogen atoms on the *y*-axis. Use your graph to predict the formula for the saturated hydrocarbon that has 11 carbon atoms. If you need help, refer to Making and Using Graphs in the **Skill Handbook** on page 529.

Using Math

The general formula for saturated hydrocarbons is C_nH_{2n+2} where *n* can be any whole number except zero. Use the general formula to determine the formula for a saturated hydrocarbon with 25 carbon atoms.

10·2 Other Organic Compounds

What You'll Learn

▶ How new compounds are formed by substituting hydrocarbons
▶ The classes of compounds that result from substitution

Vocabulary
hydroxyl group
carboxyl group
amino group
amino acid

Why It's Important

▶ Many organic compounds that you use every day have been made by chemists.

Substituted Hydrocarbons

Suppose you pack an apple in your lunch every day. One day, you have no apples, so you substitute a pear. When you eat your lunch, you'll notice a difference in the taste and texture of your fruit. Chemists make substitutions, too. They change hydrocarbons to make compounds called substituted hydrocarbons. To make a substituted hydrocarbon, one or more hydrogen atoms are taken off and replaced by atoms such as the halogens, or by groups of atoms. Such changes result in compounds with chemical properties different from the original hydrocarbon. When one or more chlorine or fluorine atoms are added to methane in place of hydrogens, new compounds are formed like the ones in **Figure 10-9.**

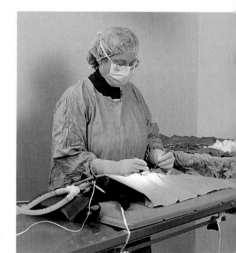

Figure 10-9 Chlorine can replace from one to four of methane's hydrogen atoms.

C The trichloromethane, or chloroform, molecule has three chlorine atoms that replace hydrogen atoms in methane. Chloroform is used as a veterinary anesthetic

$$H - \overset{\overset{\displaystyle Cl}{|}}{\underset{\underset{\displaystyle Cl}{|}}{C}} - Cl$$

Trichloromethane or chloroform
$CHCl_3$

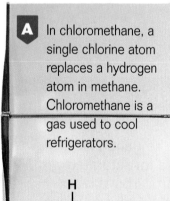

A In chloromethane, a single chlorine atom replaces a hydrogen atom in methane. Chloromethane is a gas used to cool refrigerators.

$$H - \overset{\overset{\displaystyle H}{|}}{\underset{\underset{\displaystyle H}{|}}{C}} - Cl$$

Chloromethane
CH_3Cl

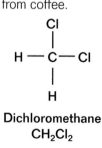

B Dichloromethane forms when two hydrogen atoms are replaced by chlorine atoms. Dichloromethane is used to remove caffeine from coffee.

$$H - \overset{\overset{\displaystyle Cl}{|}}{\underset{\underset{\displaystyle H}{|}}{C}} - Cl$$

Dichloromethane
CH_2Cl_2

D Carbon tetrachloride is a fully substituted methane molecule. It is a poisonous substance that was formerly used as a dry-cleaning solvent.

$$Cl - \overset{\overset{\displaystyle Cl}{|}}{\underset{\underset{\displaystyle Cl}{|}}{C}} - Cl$$

Carbon tetrachloride
CCl_4

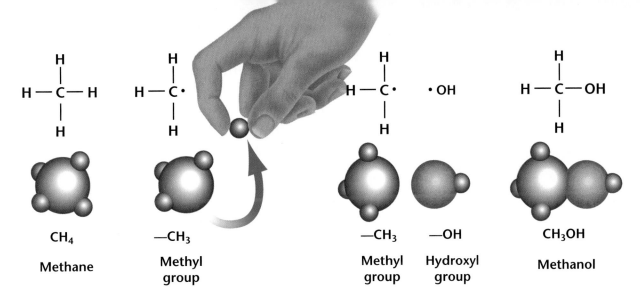

CH₄

Methane

—CH₃

Methyl
group

—CH₃

Methyl
group

—OH

Hydroxyl
group

CH₃OH

Methanol

Alcohols

Groups of atoms also can be added to hydrocarbons to make different compounds. The **hydroxyl group** (hi DROX ul) is made up of an oxygen atom and a hydrogen atom joined by a covalent bond. It is represented by the formula –OH. When a hydroxyl group replaces a hydrogen atom in a hydrocarbon, an alcohol forms. **Figure 10-10** shows the formation of the alcohol methanol as a hydrogen in the methane molecule is replaced by a hydroxyl group.

Larger alcohol molecules are formed by adding more carbon atoms to the chain. Ethanol is an alcohol produced naturally when sugar in corn, grains, and fruit ferments. It is a combination of ethane and an –OH group. Isopropyl alcohol forms when the hydroxyl group is substituted for a hydrogen on the middle carbon of propane rather than one of the end carbons. You've probably used isopropyl alcohol to disinfect injuries. **Table 10-2** lists several alcohols with their structures and uses.

Figure 10-10 After the methane molecule loses one of its hydrogens, it has an extra electron to share, as does the hydroxyl group. **What kind of bond do they form?**

*inter***NET**
C O N N E C T I O N

Visit the Glencoe Science Web Site at **www.glencoe.com/ sec/science/ca** for more information about substituted hydrocarbons.

Table 10-2

Three Common Alcohols			
	Methanol	**Ethanol**	**Isopropyl Alcohol**
Uses	H—C—OH with H above and H below	H—C—C—OH with H,H above and H,H below	H—C—C—C—H with H,H,H above and H,OH,H below
Fuel	yes	yes	no
Cleaner	yes	yes	yes
Disinfectant	no	yes	yes
Manufacturing chemical	yes	yes	yes

Carboxylic Acids

Remember the reaction between vinegar and baking soda? The reactant in vinegar is acetic acid. You can think of acetic acid as the hydrocarbon methane with a carboxyl group substituted for a hydrogen. A **carboxyl group** (car BOX ul) consists of a carbon atom, two oxygen atoms, and a hydrogen atom. Its formula is –COOH. When a carboxyl group is substituted in a hydrocarbon, the substance formed is called a carboxylic acid. The simplest carboxylic acid is methanoic acid, commonly called formic acid. Formic acid consists of a single hydrogen atom and a carboxyl group. You can see the structures of formic acid and acetic acid in **Figure 10-11.** Some ants produce formic acid naturally. When they sting you, they inject formic acid into your skin.

Methanoic or formic acid
HCOOH

Ethanoic or acetic acid
CH₃COOH

Figure 10-11 Ants make the simplest carboxylic acid, formic (methanoic) acid. **How do the structures of formic acid and acetic acid differ?**

You can probably guess that many other carboxylic acids are formed from longer hydrocarbons. Many carboxylic acids occur in foods. Citric acid is found in citrus fruits such as oranges and grapefruit. Lactic acid is present in milk.

Amines

Amines are a group of substituted hydrocarbons formed when an amino group replaces a hydrogen atom. An **amino group** (uh ME no) is a nitrogen atom joined by covalent bonds to two hydrogen atoms. It has the formula –NH₂. Methylamine, shown in **Figure 10-12,** is formed when one of the hydrogens in methane is replaced with an amino group. A more complex amine that you may have experienced is the novocaine your dentist uses to numb the pain of dental work.

Amino groups are important because they are a part of many biological compounds.

Figure 10-12 Complex amines account for the strong smells of cheeses such as these, as well as the odor of other decaying organic matter.

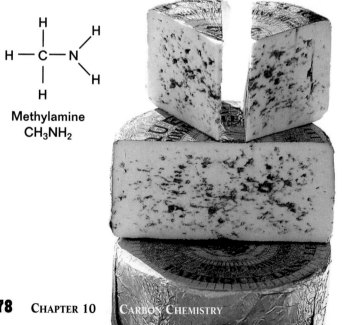

Methylamine
CH₃NH₂

Amino Acids

You have seen that a group can be substituted onto one end of a chain to change the molecule. It's also possible to substitute groups on both ends of the chain, and even to replace hydrogen atoms bonded to carbon atoms in the middle of the chain. When both an amino group (–NH₂) and a carboxyl group (–COOH) replace hydrogens on the same carbon atom in a molecule, a special type of compound known as an amino acid is formed. **Amino acids** are the building blocks of proteins, which are an important class of biological molecules needed by living cells. Twenty different amino acids bond together in different combinations to form the variety of proteins that are needed in the human body. Glycine and alanine are shown in **Figure 10-13.** Glycine is the simplest amino acid. It is a methane molecule in which one hydrogen atom has been replaced by an amino group and another has been replaced by a carboxyl group. The other 19 amino acids are formed by replacing the highlighted hydrogen atom with different groups. For example, in alanine, the hydrogen atom is replaced by a methyl ($-CH_3$) group.

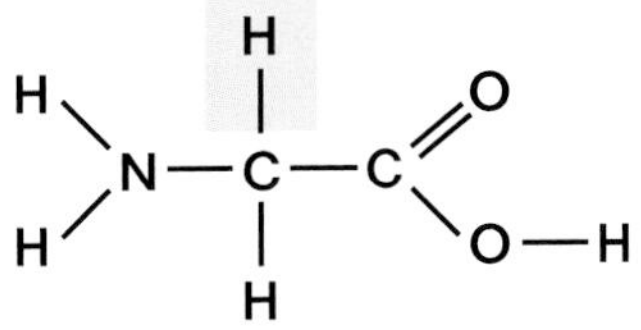

Glycine

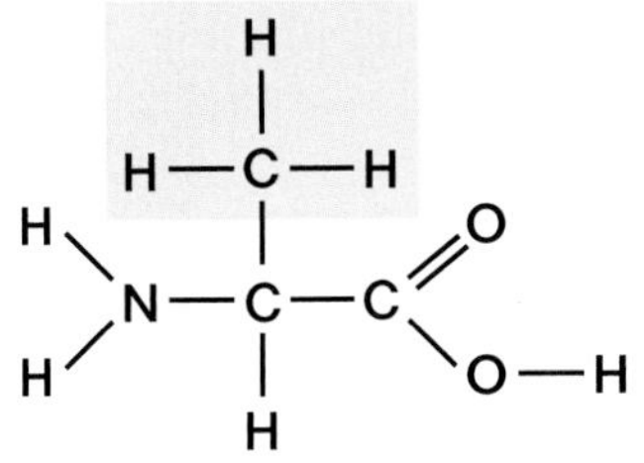

Alanine

Figure 10-13 The amino acids glycine and alanine are the simplest building blocks of proteins.

Section Assessment

1. The nonstick coating found on some pots and pans is made from tetrafluoroethylene, a substituted hydrocarbon in which all four of the hydrogen atoms of ethylene are replaced by fluorine. Draw the structural formula for this molecule.

2. In what way is an amino acid different from a carboxylic acid?

3. How do the 20 amino acids differ from each other?

4. **Think Critically:** Both of the substituted hydrocarbons, chloromethane and dichloromethane, result from the replacement of hydrogen atoms with chlorine atoms. Predict which of these compounds will have the lower boiling point. Explain.

5. **Skill Builder**
   Making Models A substituted hydrocarbon can be made by removing a hydrogen atom from a carbon and putting another atom or group in its place. Do the **Chapter 10 Skill Activity** on page 563 to make models of substituted hydrocarbons.

Using Computers

Word Processing Use the table function in a word processing program to make a table listing the classes of substituted hydrocarbons in this section: halogen-substituted hydrocarbons, alcohols, carboxylic acids, amines, and amino acids. List the substituted group(s) for each class and give the name and formula of a molecule that belongs in each class. If you need help, refer to page 544.

Conversion of Alcohols

Materials

- Test tube and stopper
- Test-tube rack
- Potassium permanganate solution (1 mL)
- Sodium hydroxide solution (1 mL)
- Ethanol (3 drops)
- pH test paper
- Graduated cylinder

Wine will spoil when the ethanol it contains is exposed to air and the bacteria *Acetabactor.* Is this spoilage a chemical change?

What You'll Investigate

What changes occur when ethanol is exposed to conditions like those produced by exposure to air and bacteria?

Goals

- **Observe** a chemical change in an alcohol.
- **Infer** the product of the chemical change.

Procedure

Wash your hands after completing the experiment.

1. Measure 1 mL of potassium permanganate solution and pour it into a test tube. Measure 1 mL of sodium hydroxide solution and add it to the test tube. **CAUTION:** *Handle these chemicals with care. Immediately flush any spills with water and call your teacher.*

2. **Dip** a piece of pH paper into the mixture in the test tube. **Record** the result in your Science Journal.

3. **Add** three drops of ethanol to the test tube. Put a stopper on the test tube and gently **shake** it for one minute.

4. Place the test tube in a test-tube rack and **observe** what happens. Record any changes you notice during the next five minutes.

5. **Test** the sample with pH paper again. **Record** what you observe.

6. **Dispose** of the solutions as directed by your teacher.

Conclude and Apply

1. Did a chemical reaction take place? What leads you to **infer** this?

2. Alcohols may undergo a chemical reaction to form carboxylic acids in the presence of potassium permanganate. If the alcohol used is ethanol, what would you **predict** to be the chemical formula of the acid produced?

Alcohol Conversion	
Procedure Step	**Observations**
Step 2	
Step 4	
Step 5	

Nature's Medicines and the Organic Chemist

Nature's Medicine Chest

Plants have long been used as sources of medicine. Ancient Egyptian, Chinese, and Indian writings describe many plant-based treatments for diseases of the eyes, skin, and internal organs. In the inset, a thirteenth-century Arabic manuscript shows six healing herbs. Sap of both the piñon pine (left) and ponderosa pine tree was used by Native Americans to prevent infection in wounds.

Tree Bark to Drugstore

A chemical compound called quinine is found in the bark of the Cinchona tree. Long before Europeans arrived in the New World, native people in the Andes mountain region of South America used Cinchona bark to treat malaria, a disease that still afflicts millions of people worldwide. Around 1630, Jesuit priests in Peru learned from their native neighbors how to grind the bark and mix it with water to make an effective malaria remedy. For centuries, Cinchona bark was the world's only weapon against malaria.

Advances in organic chemistry have made it possible to synthesize, or put together, many medicinal compounds obtained from plants. In 1908, chemists identified the chemical formula of quinine as $C_{20}H_{24}N_2O_2$, but it wasn't until 1944 that quinine was synthesized in the laboratory.

The Search Continues

Today, the search goes on for new medicines derived from plants. When a plant compound shows promise in treating a disease, chemists often use computer models to help figure out its structure. Then, they try to synthesize that compound in the laboratory. The new medicine must then be tested for safety and effectiveness—a process that can take many years before the medicine reaches your local drugstore.

interNET CONNECTION

Visit the Glencoe Science Web Site at **www.glencoe.com/sec/ science/ca** to find more information about taxol, aspirin, and codeine. Prepare a presentation that includes the identity of the natural remedy and the medicine's uses.

What You'll Learn

► How large organic molecules are made
► The roles of organic molecules in the body
► Why eating the recommended amounts of certain foods is important for maintaining health

Vocabulary
polymer   carbohydrate
protein   lipid

Why It's Important

► Your diet may affect how you feel.

What's a polymer?

Now that you know about some simple organic molecules, you can begin to learn about more complex biological molecules. These are organic substances found in milk, muscle, and blood, and some common materials such as the nonstick coating on a frying pan or the nylon in your jacket. All of these substances contain large molecules called polymers. A **polymer** is a molecule made up of many small organic molecules that link up with each other to form a long chain. The name polymer comes from the Greek words *poly*, which means "many," and *meros*, which means "part."

In **Figure 10-14,** you can see what happens in the polymerization of ethylene. Polymerization (pah lih mer i ZAY shun) is a chemical reaction that occurs between many small molecules when they link to form long chains. The ethylene molecule, C_2H_4, is an unsaturated hydrocarbon, so there is a double bond between the carbon atoms. One of the bonds in the double bond breaks in each ethylene molecule. The two carbon atoms then form new bonds with carbon atoms in other ethylene molecules. This process goes on as a chain reaction that results in the formation of a much larger molecule called polyethylene. It is a polymer that is used to make many products, such as plastic bottles. Polyethylene is an example of a synthetic polymer, but many polymers occur naturally. Some of them play important roles in keeping your body healthy.

Figure 10-14 Small molecules link into long chains to form polymers.

A The carbon atoms that were joined by the double bond each have an electron to share with another carbon in another molecule of ethylene.

B The process goes on until a huge molecule is formed.

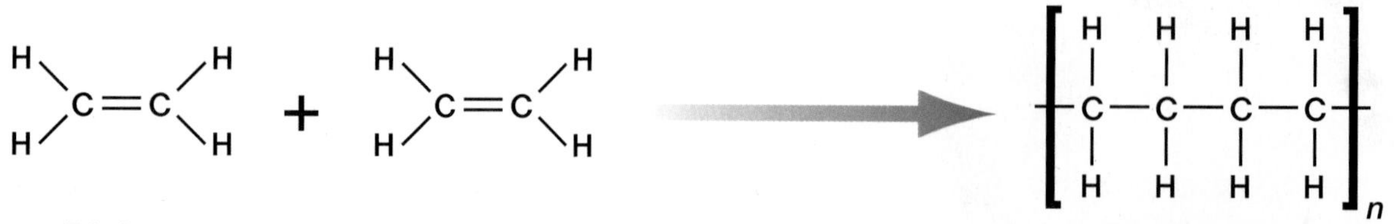

Ethylene   Ethylene   Polyethylene

Proteins Are Polymers

You've probably heard about proteins when you've been urged to eat healthy foods. A **protein** is a polymer that consists of a chain of individual amino acids linked together. Your body cannot function properly without them. Proteins serve as catalysts and speed up chemical reactions in cells. Some proteins make up the structural materials in ligaments, tendons, muscles, cartilage, hair, and fingernails. Hemoglobin, which carries substances through the blood, is a protein.

The different functions in your body are performed by different proteins. Your body makes many of these proteins by assembling 20 amino acids in different ways. Eight of the amino acids that are needed to make proteins cannot be produced by your body. These amino acids, which are called essential amino acids, must come from the food you eat. That's why your diet should include a wide variety of protein-rich foods, some of which are shown in **Figure 10-15.**

Try at Home
Mini Lab

Summing Up Protein

Procedure

1. Make a list of the foods you ate during the last 24 hours.
2. Use the data your teacher gives you to find the total number of grams of protein in your diet for the day. Multiply the grams of protein in one unit of food by the number of units of food you ate.

Analysis

1. The recommended daily allowance (RDA) of protein for girls, 11 to 14 years old, is 46 g per day. For boys, 11 to 14 years old, the RDA is 48 g per day. Was your total greater or less than the RDA?
2. Which of the foods you ate supplied the largest amount of protein? What percent of the total did that food supply?

Figure 10-15 These are a few of the foods you might eat in order to supply your body with the eight amino acids it needs. **How can you be sure that you aren't missing any proteins?**

Glycine   Alanine

Figure 10-16 Both ends of an amino acid can link with another amino acid. **What molecule is released in the process?**

Reading Check ✔

Describe how proteins are formed from amino acids.

Figure 10-17 These athletes are eating a meal high in carbohydrates. **How will this help them in the next day's race?**

The process by which your body converts amino acids to proteins is shown in **Figure 10-16.** In this reaction, the amino group of the amino acid alanine forms a bond with the carboxyl group of the amino acid glycine, and a molecule of water is released. Each end of this new molecule can go on to form similar bonds with another amino acid. The process continues in this way until the amino acid chain, or protein, is complete. ✔

Carbohydrates

The day before a race, marathon runners like the ones in **Figure 10-17** often eat large amounts of pasta. What's in pasta and other foods like bread and fruit that makes them good choices for prerace eating? These foods contain sugars and starches, which are members of the family of organic compounds called carbohydrates. A **carbohydrate** is an organic compound that contains only carbon, hydrogen, and oxygen in a ratio of two hydrogen atoms to one oxygen atom and one carbon atom. In the body, carbohydrates are broken down into simple sugars that the body can use for energy. In effect, the marathon runners are storing energy for the next day's race.

Sugars

If you like chocolate-chip cookies or ice cream, then you're familiar with sugars. They are the substances that make both fresh fruit and candy sweet. Simple sugars are carbohydrates containing five, six, or seven carbon atoms arranged in a ring. The structures of glucose and fructose, two common simple sugars, are shown in **Figure 10-18.** Glucose forms a six-carbon ring. It is found in many naturally sweet foods, such as grapes.

Glucose

Fructose

Figure 10-18 Glucose and fructose are simple six-carbon carbohydrates found in many fresh foods and in packaged foods. **Name some products that contain these sugars.**

Problem Solving

Comparing Sweetness

There are natural sugars, and there are artificial sweeteners. Natural sugars include sucrose, glucose, fructose, maltose, and lactose. Artificial sweeteners are compounds unrelated to sugars. They include saccharin, aspartame, and acesulfame. They are not all equally sweet. If you taste equal amounts of aspartame and sucrose, the aspartame will taste 200 times sweeter than sucrose. Assume sucrose has a sweetness index of 100. A sweetness index is a measure of how sweet a compound is. Compared with sucrose, other sweeteners have the following sweetness indices: glucose, 70; fructose, 170; maltose, 30; lactose, 16; saccharin, 40 000; aspartame, 20 000; acesulfame, 20 000.

Solve the Problem

1. Determine how many times sweeter than sucrose each sweetener is. You can figure this out by taking the ratio of the sweetness index of any sweetener to the sweetness index of sucrose. For example, aspartame's sweetness index is 20 000. The ratio of 20 000/100 = 200, so aspartame is 200 times sweeter than sucrose. For a sweetener with a

sweetness index of 50, the ratio would be 50/100 = 1/2. This sweetener is one half as sweet as sucrose. Present your results in a table with three columns. List the eight sweeteners in the first column. List their sweetness indices in the second column. In the third column, show how many times sweeter each sweetener is than sucrose.

2. Make a bar graph that compares the sweetness indices of the sweeteners.

3. Which sugar is the sweetest? Which artificial sweetener is the sweetest?

4. How much maltose would match the sweetness of one teaspoon of sucrose?

Think Critically: Why might a person choose to use an artificial sweetener rather than a natural sugar?

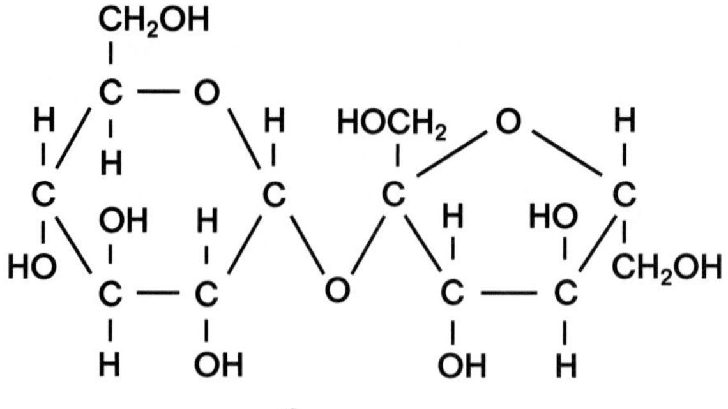

$$CH_2OH$$

Sucrose

Figure 10-19 Sucrose is a molecule of glucose combined with a molecule of fructose. **What small molecule must be added to sucrose when it separates to form the two six-carbon sugars?**

Fructose is the sweet substance found in ripe fruit and honey. It is often made into corn syrup and added to many foods as a sweetener. The sugar you probably have in your sugar bowl or use in baking a cake is sucrose. Sucrose, shown in **Figure 10-19,** is a combination of the two simple sugars glucose and fructose. In the body, sucrose cannot move through cell membranes. It must be broken down into glucose and fructose to enter cells. Inside the cell, these simple sugars are broken down further to provide energy for cell functions.

Starches

Starches are large carbohydrates that exist naturally in grains such as rice, wheat, and corn. Starches are polymers of glucose molecules in which hundreds or thousands of sugar molecules may be joined together. Because each sugar molecule releases energy when it is broken down, starches are sources of large amounts of energy.

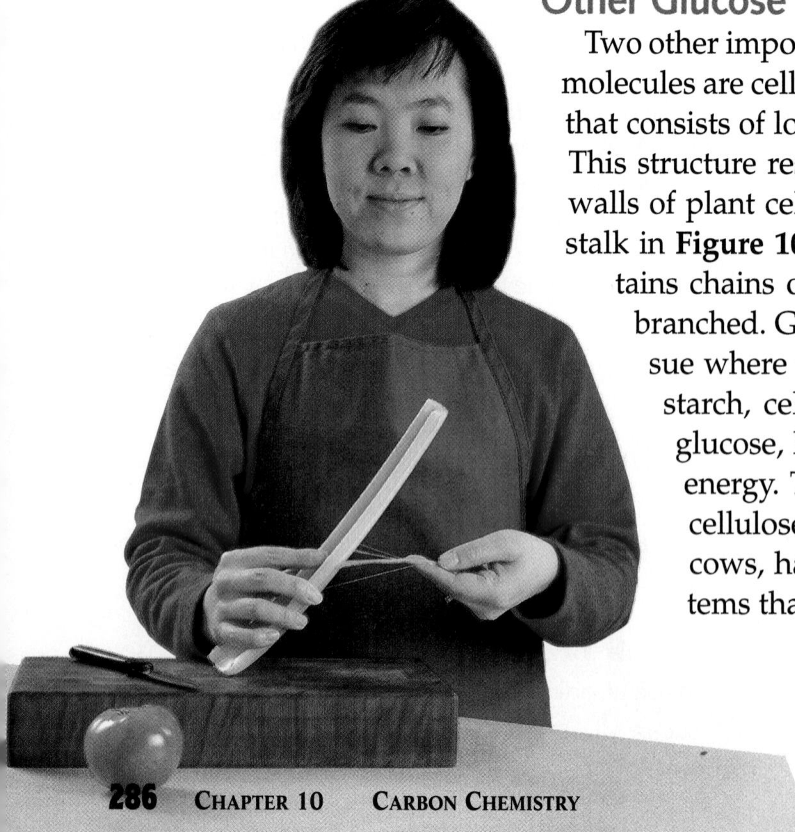

Other Glucose Polymers

Two other important polymers that are made up of glucose molecules are cellulose and glycogen. Cellulose is a polymer that consists of long chains of glucose units linked together. This structure results in long, stiff fibers that make up the walls of plant cells, like the strands that pull off the celery stalk in **Figure 10-20.** Glycogen is a polymer that also contains chains of glucose units, but the chains are highly branched. Glycogen molecules are found in animal tissue where their function is to store energy. Although starch, cellulose, and glycogen are all polymers of glucose, humans can't use all of them as sources of energy. The human digestive system can't convert cellulose into sugars. Grazing animals, such as cows, have microorganisms in their digestive systems that break down cellulose into sugars.

Figure 10-20 Your body cannot break down long cellulose fibers on celery, but your health can benefit from eating a certain amount of fiber.

Lipids

Many of the foods you eat contain lipids, for example, butter, salad dressings, ice cream, cheese and meat. A **lipid** is an organic compound that contains the same elements as carbohydrates—carbon, hydrogen, and oxygen—but in different proportions. They are composed of three long-chain carboxylic acids bonded to an alcohol called glycerol that has three –OH groups. Lipids are commonly called fats and oils, but they also are found in greases and waxes like the beeswax in **Figure 10-21.**

Lipids Store Energy

Lipids store energy in their bonds, just as carbohydrates do, but they are a more concentrated source of energy than carbohydrates. If you eat more food than your body needs to supply the energy for your usual activities, the excess energy from the food is stored by producing lipids.

How can energy be stored in a molecule? The chemical reaction that produces lipids is endothermic. An endothermic reaction is one in which energy is absorbed. That means that energy is stored in the chemical bonds of lipids. When your body needs energy, the bonds are broken and energy is released. This process protects your body in times when you need extra energy or in times when you may not be able to eat. If you regularly eat more food than you need, large amounts of lipids will be produced and stored as permanent fat on your body.

interNET CONNECTION

Visit the Glencoe Science Web Site at **www.glencoe.com/ sec/science/ca** for more information about lipids.

Using Math

One gram of carbohydrates releases 4 Calories of energy and 1 g of lipids releases 9 Calories. If your daily diet provides 400 g of carbohydrates and 100 g of lipids, how many Calories of energy will be available to you?

Figure 10-21 Fats and oils are not the only kinds of lipids. Wax is a lipid that is harder than fat. Bees secrete wax from a gland in the abdomen to form beeswax, which is part of the honeycomb.

Saturated and Unsaturated Lipids

Not all lipids are the same. Remember the difference between saturated and unsaturated hydrocarbons? Unsaturated molecules have one or more double or triple bonds between carbon atoms. Lipid molecules may be saturated or unsaturated. As you can see in **Figure 10-22A,** when a lipid is saturated, the acid chains are straight because all the bonds are single bonds. They are able to pack together closely. A compact arrangement of the molecules is typical of a solid. These solid lipids are called saturated fats.

When a lipid is unsaturated, as in **Figure 10-22B,** the molecule bends wherever there is a double bond. This prevents the chains from packing close together, so these lipids tend to be liquid oils. They are called unsaturated fats.

Scientists and doctors have observed that people who eat a diet high in saturated fats have a high rate of cardiovascular problems such as heart disease. Unfortunately, many foods containing both saturated and unsaturated fats are available so that you can choose the foods you want to include in your diet.

Figure 10-22 Whether a lipid is a liquid or a solid depends on the type of bonds.

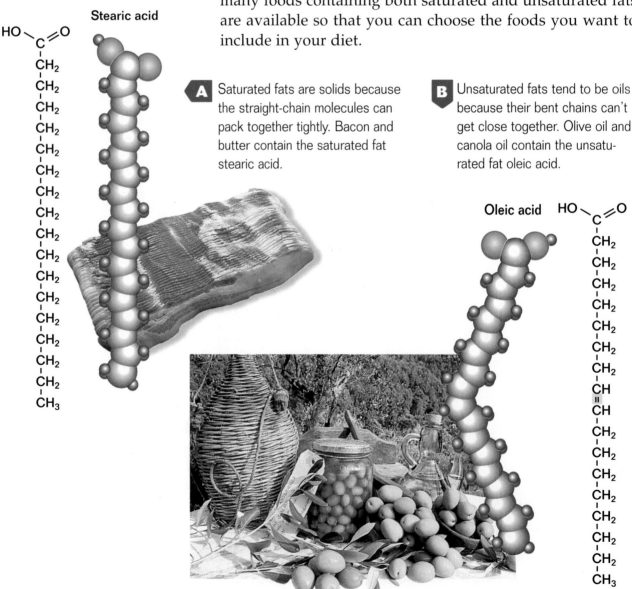

A Saturated fats are solids because the straight-chain molecules can pack together tightly. Bacon and butter contain the saturated fat stearic acid.

B Unsaturated fats tend to be oils because their bent chains can't get close together. Olive oil and canola oil contain the unsaturated fat oleic acid.

Cholesterol

Cholesterol is a complex lipid present in foods that come from animals, such as meat, butter, eggs, and cheese. Even if you don't eat foods containing cholesterol, your body makes its own supply. Your body needs cholesterol for building cell membranes. Cholesterol is not found in plants, so oils derived from plants are free of cholesterol. However, the body can convert fats in these oils to cholesterol.

High cholesterol levels in the blood can lead to the buildup of deposits of cholesterol on the inside walls of arteries. This condition, known as atherosclerosis, is shown in **Figure 10-23.** When arteries become clogged, the flow of blood is restricted, which results in high blood pressure. This, in turn, can lead to heart disease. Eating less saturated fat and cholesterol can help to lower cholesterol levels in the blood and reduce the risk of heart problems.

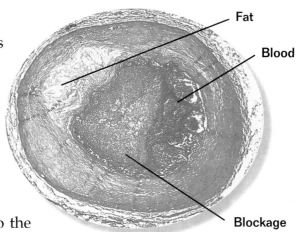

Fat

Blood

Blockage

Figure 10-23 This view of an artery shows atherosclerosis, a dangerous condition in which arteries in the body become clogged. Deposits build up on the walls of the artery leaving less room for blood to flow.

Section Assessment

1. Describe the process by which large organic molecules such as proteins are made. What other product is formed along with a protein molecule?

2. Identify some of the roles of carbohydrates, proteins, and lipids in the functioning of your body.

3. How are cellulose and glycogen different from sugars and starches?

4. **Think Critically:** Explain why even people who eat a healthy diet may gain weight if they don't get enough exercise.

5. **Skill Builder**
   Forming a Hypothesis A chemist who planned to do experiments on refrigerants opened a valve on a tank that was supposed to contain the gas tetrafluoroethylene. He was surprised to find that no gas was released. When he opened the tank, he found a waxy, white solid. Form a hypothesis about how this white solid came to be inside the tank and what happened to the gas. If you need help, refer to Forming a Hypothesis in the **Skill Handbook** on page 534.

Science Journal
In your Science Journal, make a record of all the foods you eat during one day. Write a paragraph identifying the foods that contain proteins, carbohydrates (identify both starches and sugars), and lipids.

Design Your Own Experiment

Activity 10·2

Detecting Fats and Starches

Possible Materials

- Paper grocery bag
- Iodine solution in dropper bottle
- Marker
- Scissors
- Liquid cooking oil
- Bread
- Raw potato slice
- Cooked bacon
- Cheese
- Cracker
- Cooked egg white
- Potato chip

It's important to know what's in the foods you eat. Simple tests can show which foods contain carbohydrates and which contain fats. When rubbed on brown paper, foods that contain fats leave a grease spot, just as they make your hands feel greasy. When a drop of iodine solution is placed on foods containing starches, they turn dark blue.

Recognize the Problem

How will you find out which foods contain starch? Which contain fat?

Form a Hypothesis

How will you and your group use procedures that you know to test foods to determine which foods contain starch, fat, or both?

Goals

- **Predict** which foods contain starch and which contain fat.

- **Observe** the tests on each food to determine the presence of starch and fat.

Safety Precautions

CAUTION: *Iodine is poisonous.* Do NOT eat food used in a laboratory experiment. Dispose of all food after your experiment.

Test Your Hypothesis

Plan

1. **Predict** which foods contain starch and which contain fat.

2. Reread the opening paragraph of the experiment. How can you use that information to plan your experiment? You know that cooking oil is a fat and bread contains starch. Testing these foods will result in a positive test. Can you use these positive tests as a comparison to other tests?

3. **Write** the procedure you will use to test your hypothesis.

4. **Copy** the data table in your Science Journal.

Do

1. Make sure your teacher approves your plan and your data table before you begin your experiment.

2. Make your predictions and then carry out your plan.

3. Immediately **record** all your observations and results in your data table.

Analyze Your Data

1. **Describe** the evidence that allowed you to **infer** that fat was present in the food.

2. **Describe** the evidence that showed that starch was present.

Draw Conclusions

1. Which of the foods you tested contain carbohydrates? Which contain fat?

2. Did any foods contain both carbohydrates and fat?

3. Were your predictions correct?

Predictions and Tests for Fat and Starch			
Food	Prediction	Paper Bag	Iodine
oil			
bread			
potato			
bacon			

For a **preview** of this chapter, study this Reviewing Main Ideas before you read the chapter. After you have studied this chapter, you can use the Reviewing Main Ideas to **review** the chapter.

The Glencoe MindJogger, Audiocassettes, and CD-ROM provide additional opportunities for review.

Section 10-1 COMPOUNDS OF CARBON AND HYDROGEN

Hydrocarbons are compounds containing only carbon and hydrogen. If a hydrocarbon has only single bonds, it is called a **saturated hydrocarbon.** A hydrocarbon chain can be lengthened by substituting a methyl group for a hydrogen. **Isomers** are compounds with the same chemical formula but different structures, and so they have different properties. *Draw the structural formulas of butane and isobutane.*

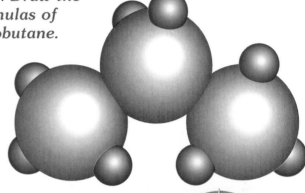

UNSATURATED HYDROCARBONS

Unsaturated hydrocarbons have one or more double or triple bonds. The simplest unsaturated hydrocarbons are ethylene and propylene. Each has one double bond and is used to form useful polymers. Butadiene has two double bonds and is used to make synthetic rubber. *Draw the structural formula for an unsaturated hydrocarbon with five carbon atoms and two double bonds.*

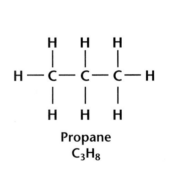

Propane
C_3H_8

H — C ☰ C — H

Ethyne or Acetylene
C_2H_2

Reading Check ✓

Choose a major illustration, such as Figure 10-4, and explain three things you learned from it.

Section

10-2 SUBSTITUTED HYDROCARBONS

Hydrocarbons may be substituted with other atoms such as the halogens, or with groups of atoms. An alcohol is formed when a **hydroxyl group** is substituted for a hydrogen in a hydrocarbon. A carboxylic acid is made when a **carboxyl group** is substituted. An amine is formed when an **amino group** is substituted. An **amino acid** contains both an amino group and a carboxyl group substituted on the same carbon atom. Substituted hydrocarbons have different physical and chemical properties from the unsubstituted hydrocarbons. *List three functional groups and give their chemical formulas.*

Section

10-3 MOLECULES OF LIFE

Biological compounds are complex, substituted hydrocarbons that make up living things. Many biological compounds are large molecules called **polymers,** which are made up of small repeating units. **Proteins** serve a variety of functions, including catalyzing many cell reactions and providing the structural material for many parts of the body. **Carbohydrates** and **lipids** are both energy sources and the means of storing energy. Eating a healthy diet is important. *List different types of carbohydrates.*

Chapter 10 Assessment

Using Vocabulary

a. amino acid
b. amino group
c. carbohydrate
d. carboxyl group
e. hydrocarbon
f. hydroxyl group
g. isomer
h. lipid
i. organic compound
j. polymer
k. protein
l. saturated hydrocarbon
m. unsaturated hydrocarbon

Answer the following questions about the Vocabulary words.

1. Explain the difference between an amino group and an amino acid.
2. How does a hydroxyl group differ from a carboxyl group?
3. How can an organic compound be an isomer?
4. What is the connection between a polymer and a protein?
5. What do carbohydrates and lipids have in common?

Checking Concepts

Choose the word or phrase that best answers the question.

6. A certain carbohydrate molecule has ten oxygen atoms. How many hydrogen atoms does it contain?
   A) five   C) ten
   B) 20   D) 16

7. Which is **NOT** a group that can be substituted in a hydrocarbon?
   A) amino   C) hydroxyl
   B) carboxyl   D) lipid

8. Which chemical formula represents an alcohol?
   A) CH_3COOH C) CH_3OH
   B) CH_3NH_2 D) CH_4

9. Which can build up in arteries and lead to heart disease?
   A) cholesterol   C) glucose
   B) fructose   D) starch

10. What is an organic molecule that contains a triple bond called?
    A) polymer
    B) saturated hydrocarbon
    C) isomer
    D) unsaturated hydrocarbon

11. What is the name of the substituted hydrocarbon with the chemical formula CH_2F_2?
    A) methane   C) difluoromethane
    B) fluoromethane   D) trifluoromethane

12. Excess energy is stored in your body as which of the following?
    A) proteins   C) lipids
    B) isomers   D) saturated hydro-carbons

13. What are produced by reactions between carboxylic acids and glycerol?
    A) lipids   C) sugars
    B) proteins   D) carbohydrates

14. Which is a chemical formula that represents an amino acid?
    A) CH_3COOH C) NH_2CH_2COOH
    B) CH_3NH_2 D) CH_4

15. Which is a ring-shaped molecule?
    A) acetone   C) cyclopentane
    B) Freon   D) dichloroethane

Thinking Critically

16. Some drugs that were obtained from trees and plants are now manufactured. Do you think these manufactured drugs can be the same as the natural products? Explain.

17. Ethanol is used as a fuel for cars. Would you have predicted that ethanol would burn and produce energy? Explain.

18. Candle wax is one of the longer hydro-carbons. What do you think are the products of the burning of candle wax?

19. In the polymerization of proteins, water molecules are produced as part of the reaction. But, in the polymerization of ethylene, no water is produced. Explain.

Developing Skills

If you need help, refer to the **Skill Handbook.**

20. **Recognizing Cause and Effect** Marathon runners go through a process known as hitting the wall. They have used up all their stored glucose and start using stored lipids as fuel. What is the advantage of eating lots of complex carbohydrates the day before a race?

21. **Using a Graph** The graph shows the boiling points of some saturated hydrocarbons with from one to five carbon atoms. How does boiling point depend upon the number of carbon atoms? What would you predict would be the approximate boiling point of hexane, a hydrocarbon with six carbon atoms?

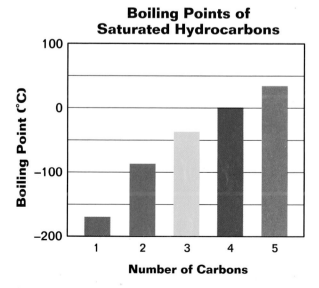

Boiling Points of Saturated Hydrocarbons

THE PRINCETON REVIEW

Test-Taking Tip

Study in Quiet It's best to study in an environment similar to the one in which you'll be tested. Blaring stereos, video game machines, chatty friends, and beepers are not allowed in the classroom during test time. So, why get used to them when you study?

Test Practice

Use these questions to test your Science Proficiency.

1. Which of the following is an unsaturated hydrocarbon?
   A) propane
   B) hexane
   C) ethene
   D) methane

2. When biological compounds are digested by the human body, which of the following processes does **NOT** occur?
   A) Carbohydrates are broken down into simple sugars.
   B) Excess energy released from food is stored as lipids.
   C) Proteins are broken down into lipids.
   D) Sugars are broken down to provide energy to cells.

3. Which of the following describes isomers?
   A) They contain a hydroxyl group.
   B) They occur in rings.
   C) They have the same formula but different structures.
   D) They have different formulas but the same structures.

3

Forces
and
Motion

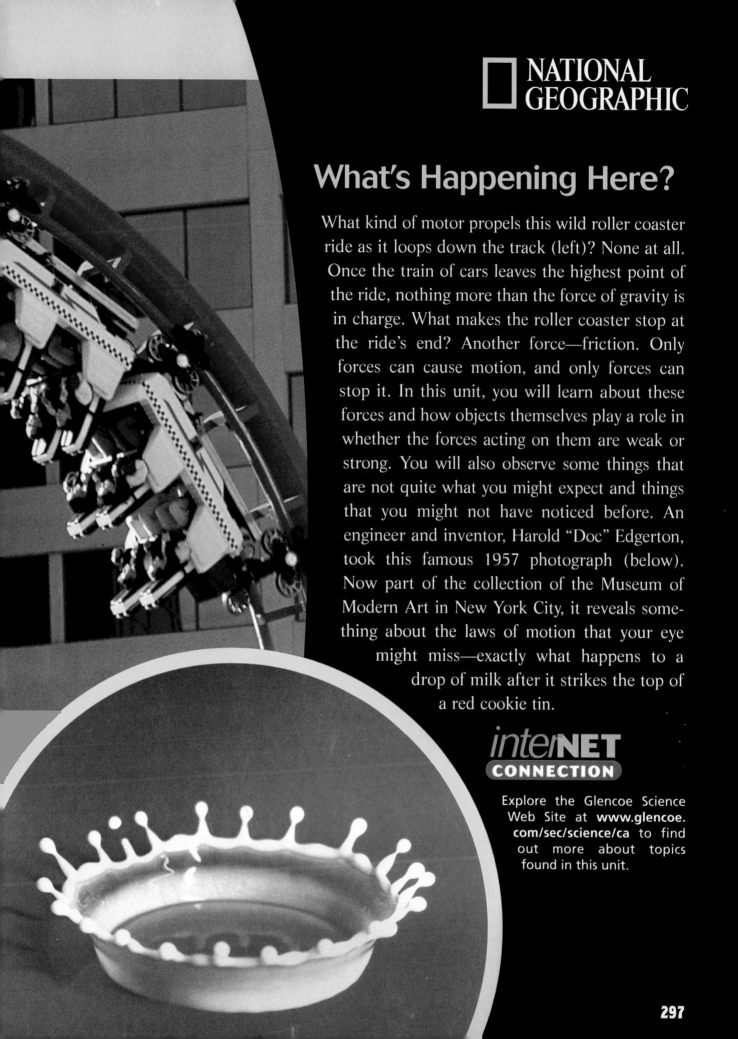

What's Happening Here?

What kind of motor propels this wild roller coaster ride as it loops down the track (left)? None at all. Once the train of cars leaves the highest point of the ride, nothing more than the force of gravity is in charge. What makes the roller coaster stop at the ride's end? Another force—friction. Only forces can cause motion, and only forces can stop it. In this unit, you will learn about these forces and how objects themselves play a role in whether the forces acting on them are weak or strong. You will also observe some things that are not quite what you might expect and things that you might not have noticed before. An engineer and inventor, Harold "Doc" Edgerton, took this famous 1957 photograph (below). Now part of the collection of the Museum of Modern Art in New York City, it reveals something about the laws of motion that your eye might miss—exactly what happens to a drop of milk after it strikes the top of a red cookie tin.

interNET CONNECTION

Explore the Glencoe Science Web Site at **www.glencoe. com/sec/science/ca** to find out more about topics found in this unit.

Chapter Preview

Skills Preview

Skill Builders
- Measuring in SI
- Observe and Infer

Activities
- Use Numbers
- Design an Experiment

MiniLabs
- Use Numbers
- Observe and Infer

Reading Check ✓

Before reading the chapter, list the vocabulary terms. Note what you think each word means. As you read, revise your definitions.

Explore Activity

It's your turn. You chalk up the end of your pool cue and take aim. If you make the break just right, the balls will scatter just how you want them to. You might have observed the collision of two or more balls when playing pool, croquet, or pinball. With practice and understanding, players learn to control the motions of the balls. Science can explain the motion.

Compare Collisions

1. Use a piece of paper with a fold in the middle to make a track and a ruler with a groove to make a ramp.

2. Lean the ruler against a binder or a book to give it a slope. Place the base of the ramp on the track.

3. Put a target marble at the bottom of the ramp. Mark its starting position.

4. Let a second marble, the shooter, roll down the ramp from about 10 cm up and hit the target marble. Mark on the paper where both marbles go.

5. Repeat the experiment, starting the shooter higher up the ramp.

In your Science Journal, describe your experiment and what you discovered. Did both marbles always move? When did they move farthest?

11·1 What is motion?

Change in Position

What You'll Learn

► How to calculate speed
► How to calculate velocity and acceleration

Vocabulary
speed
displacement
velocity
acceleration

Why It's Important

► Most of the changes you observe are the result of matter in motion.

As you stand on a street corner, you can sense how fast all the vehicles and pedestrians are moving by watching them change position. If something is moving slowly, such as a snail crossing a wall, its slow motion is obvious. By observing for just a short time, you know it will take hours for it to change its position from one end of the wall to the other. At the other extreme, a race car changes its position in a flash. A car can be moving so fast that you have a hard time following it. By observing for a short time, you know it can cover a lot of track in a hurry. It is easy to get a rough idea of an object's motion from familiar experiences, as shown in **Figure 11-1.**

To better describe an object's motion, numbers are used. The rate of change of position is called **speed.** You can describe an object's motion with its speed at one instant, as police radar does. Or, you can describe the average speed for a journey. Average speed is found by dividing the total distance traveled by the time it takes.

$$\text{average speed} = \frac{\text{distance}}{\text{time}}$$

If you ran 50 m in 20 s, the average speed was as follows.

$$\frac{50 \text{ m}}{20 \text{ s}} = 2.5 \text{ m/s}$$

Your average speed was 2.5 m/s.

In the example above, you might have started out slowly, at a steady speed, slowed to turn around, and

Figure 11-1 Speed is the rate of change of position.

A This rhinoceros beetle might walk 0.08 m in 10 s, for an average speed of 0.008 m/s.

B This cheetah might run 300 m in 10 s, for an average speed of 30 m/s.

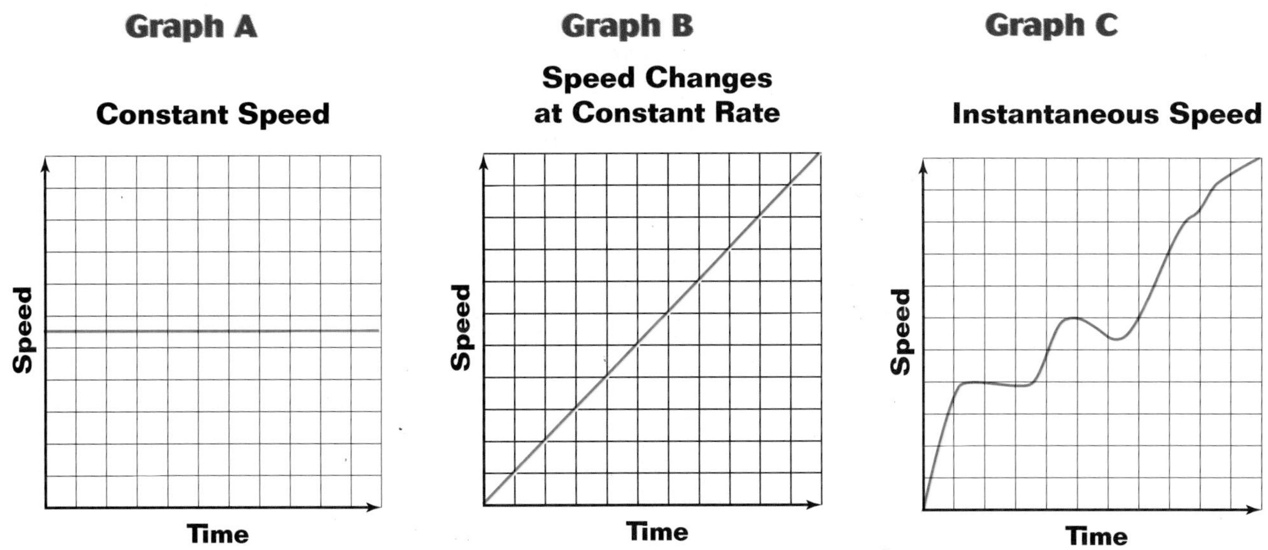

Graph A

Constant Speed

Speed

Time

Graph B

Speed Changes at Constant Rate

Speed

Time

Graph C

Instantaneous Speed

Speed

Time

stopped suddenly to avoid hitting a wall. If you were concerned with the details of your motion, you might record your speed every few seconds over the course of the run. You might also record the direction at those times, tell where you ran, and indicate when you speeded up or slowed down. In this chapter, you will usually be concerned with average speed, or with speed that is increasing or decreasing in a steady, predictable way. You can compare the ways of describing motion in the graphs in **Figure 11-2.**

Displacement

Saying you ran 2.5 m/s is often all you need to know. But where did you go? The direction of motion can be important. **Displacement** measures the change in position of an object. It includes direction. Only the starting and ending points are used to find displacement. This is illustrated in **Figure 11-3.** If you tell a friend you moved 20 m to the left, you are describing your displacement.

Figure 11-2 Graph A shows constant speed. When you use average speed to make calculations, you treat it as a constant speed. Constant acceleration is illustrated in Graph B. The actual speed increases over time. In this case, the average speed is the same as the constant speed in Graph A. Graph C shows the details of a speed changing over time. **Compare the initial and final speeds in Graphs B and C.**

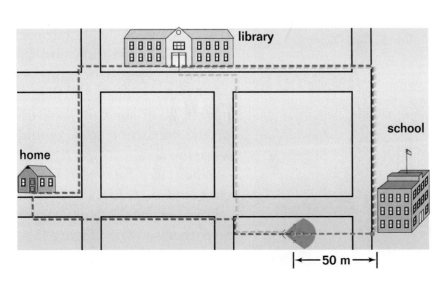

Figure 11-3 Three students (red line, blue line, orange line) walk from school to the ball diamond. In each case, the displacement is 50 m west. The distances traveled depend on the routes each student chose. **How does the distance traveled in each case compare to the displacement?**

|← 50 m →|

Velocity

The rate of change of displacement is **velocity** (vel AH seh TEE). Velocity includes both speed and direction. For example, you might say, "We drove west at 30 km/h." In this case, 30 km/h is the speed and west at 30 km/h is the velocity. *Velocity* is often used as a synonym for *speed*, but in science velocity and speed mean two different things.

$$\text{average velocity} = \frac{\text{displacement}}{\text{time}}$$

$$v = \frac{d}{t}$$

In this equation, v stands for average velocity and d for displacement. ☑

Average speed is not always equal to average velocity. For example, if you run around a 1-km track in six minutes (0.1 hour), your distance traveled is 1 km. However, your displacement for the whole trip around the track is 0 because you end up where you started. Your initial and final positions are identical. So, despite the fact that you ran the whole track, there is no change in position.

$$\text{average speed} = \frac{\text{distance}}{\text{time}} \qquad \text{average velocity} = \frac{\text{displacement}}{\text{time}}$$

$$= \frac{1 \text{ km}}{0.1 \text{ h}} \qquad\qquad\qquad = \frac{0 \text{ km}}{0.1 \text{ h}}$$

$$= 10 \text{ km/h} \qquad\qquad\qquad = 0 \text{ km/h}$$

Your average speed is 10 km/h, but your average velocity is 0 km/h.

Velocity gives much more information than speed when measuring motion. The directional part is important. You have seen examples of velocity. For example, when weather reporters track a hurricane, they give its position and its velocity. The direction is needed for someone to determine if he or she is in the path of the hurricane and should leave the area.

When the *Pathfinder* spacecraft landed on Mars in 1997, it released a small robot named Sojourner, shown in **Figure 11-4.** The robot had to be guided

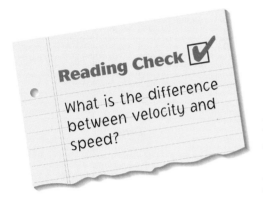

Reading Check ☑

What is the difference between velocity and speed?

Figure 11-4 Controllers gave Sojourner careful instructions on how to roll away from the *Pathfinder* spacecraft after its cushioned landing on Mars. **Why was the robot's speed important? Why was its direction important?**

around large boulders and then moved up against rocks in order to study them. Sojourner could not carry out its mission without ground controllers on Earth knowing both its position and its velocity.

Relative Motion

Motion is always described relative to a frame of reference. For example, the *Sojourner* robot in **Figure 11-4** starts at the spacecraft *Pathfinder.* A displacement might be described as "4 m north of *Pathfinder.*" Another reference frame, such as the rock Scooby Doo, could have been chosen. People also must agree on directions. *Forward* and *left* can have different meanings, depending on which way you are facing.

For motion back and forth along a line, people sometimes use positive and negative numbers. For example, +3 would mean three steps forward, and –5 would mean five steps back. If you make both displacements, you will be two steps back from where you started, as shown in **Figure 11-5.** This is true no matter which order you do the displacements.

Velocity is also relative. Imagine watching a train moving 20 km/h north relative to the ground. If you are standing on the sidewalk, the train appears to be moving at 20 km/h north. If you are riding in a car going north at 15 km/h, the train appears to be moving more slowly, at 5 km/h north. If you are riding in a car going south at 15 km/h, the train appears to zip by at 35 km/h. The motion of the train relative to the ground is the same in each case. Only your frame of reference changes.

Positive and negative numbers are used to indicate motion forward and backward or right and left. **Figure 11-6** shows an example of how to compute relative velocity.

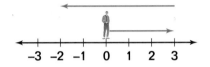

Figure 11-5 If you take 3 steps forward and 5 steps back, you will be 2 steps back from your starting point. **What happens if you take 4 steps left and 1 step right?**

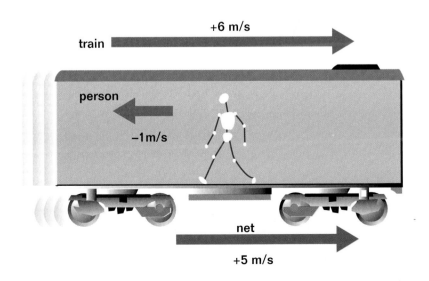

Figure 11-6 The velocity of the walker relative to the ground is 5 m/s forward.

Acceleration

When you're riding in a car that takes off quickly from a stop sign, you feel your body press back against the seat. When you stop, your body is pushed forward against the seat belt. You can sense motion when you accelerate. **Acceleration** is the rate of change of velocity. Speeding up, slowing down, and turning are all forms of acceleration. To find the average acceleration, use the following formula.

$$\text{average acceleration} = \frac{\text{change in velocity}}{\text{time}}$$

$$a = \frac{v_2 - v_1}{t}$$

For example, if an object takes 2 s to go from velocity 0 to velocity +4 m/s, the average acceleration is found as follows.

$$\frac{4 \text{ m/s} - 0 \text{ m/s}}{2 \text{ s}} = +2 \text{ m/s}^2$$

The average acceleration is +2 m/s².

You can rearrange the formula to find the change in velocity given the acceleration and time, as illustrated in **Figure 11-7.** The direction of the acceleration is important.

When an object accelerates in the direction it is moving, the object speeds up, as shown in **Figure 11-7A.** If an object is moving to the right and you accelerate it to the right, it goes to the right at a greater velocity.

Acceleration in the direction opposite to its motion slows an object down, as shown in **Figure 11-7B.** If an object is moving forward and you accelerate it backward, its velocity decreases. For example, friction accelerates an object opposite to the direction of motion, slowing it down.

Acceleration and Distance

When an object accelerates in the direction of motion, it covers more distance in each second than it did in the previous second. An object that starts at rest and accelerates at a for time t covers a distance given by the following formula.

$$\text{distance} = 0.5(\text{acceleration})(\text{time})^2$$
$$d = 0.5at^2$$

Mini Lab

Calculating Acceleration

Procedure

1. Mark off a course. Place tape at the following number of meters from start: 0, 0.1, 0.4, 0.9, 1.6, 2.5, and 3.6.
2. Work with a partner. While one of you claps a slow, steady beat, the other should move along the course, stepping on one piece of tape for each clap.
3. Measure the time between claps.
4. Experience negative acceleration by moving through the course from 3.6 to 0 while your partner claps a steady beat.

Analysis

1. As you move through this course forward and backward, how does your velocity change?
2. Calculate the change in displacement (velocity) and the change in velocity (acceleration) for each time interval. For example, if your claps were about 3 s apart, then you would go from 0 to 0.1 m in 3 s for a velocity of 0.03 m/s, and the acceleration would be (0.03 m/s − 0)/(3 s) = 0.01 m/s².

Figure 11-7 Determine the direction of acceleration and velocity. Find the change in velocity. Then, find the new velocity.

A You are biking at 2 m/s and accelerate forward 0.3 m/s² for 2 s.

change in velocity = acceleration × time
$$= (0.3 \text{ m/s}^2)\,(2 \text{ s})$$
$$= 0.6 \text{ m/s}$$

Add the change in velocity to the initial velocity.

2 m/s + 0.6 m/s = 2.6 m/s

Your new velocity is 2.6 m/s forward. **What would your velocity be if you now accelerated at 0.1 m/s² for 5 s?**

B You are biking at 2 m/s and accelerate backward (brake) at –0.5 m/s² for 2 s.

change in velocity = acceleration × time
$$= (-0.5 \text{ m/s}^2)\,(2 \text{ s})$$
$$= -1 \text{ m/s}$$

Add the change in velocity to the initial velocity.

2 m/s – 1 m/s = 1 m/s

Your new velocity is 1 m/s forward. **If you now accelerate at –0.3 m/s² for 1.5 s, what will your new velocity be?**

Table 11-1

Accelerating from Rest at 1 m/s^2		
Time (s)	Velocity (m/s) $v = at$	Distance (m) $d = 0.5at^2$
0	0	0.0
1	1	0.5
2	2	2.0
3	3	4.5
4	4	8.0

The velocity and distance of an object accelerating at a constant rate of 1 m/s^2 are given in **Table 11-1.** Note that if the acceleration is opposite to the direction of motion, the object will cover less and less distance in each time interval until it comes to a stop.

Graphing Motion

Graphs can help to explain motion. For example, the graph in **Figure 11-8** describes a bike ride along a street.

a. You start at rest.

b. You accelerate at 0.3 m/s^2 for 10 s.

c. You are now biking at 3 m/s. You maintain this speed for 30 s, until you come to a hill.

d. You start uphill. You slow down at –0.2 m/s^2 until you come to a stop. How long does this take?

e. You remain stopped for 5 s.

f. When you let off the brakes, you start to coast backward. You accelerate backward at –0.2 m/s^2 for 2 s.

g. You squeeze hard on the brakes with an acceleration of 0.4 m/s^2 until you come to a stop. Note that the acceleration is positive because it is opposite to a negative velocity.

Figure 11-8 The graph shows velocity vs. time for a bike ride. **When is acceleration positive? When is it negative? When is it zero? How can you tell?**

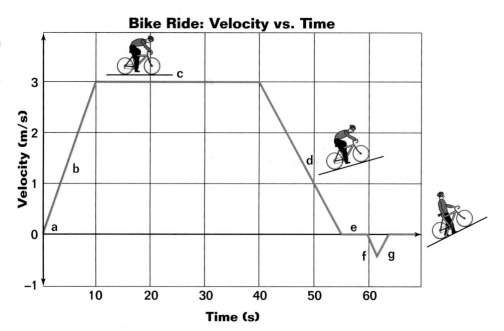

Bike Ride: Velocity vs. Time

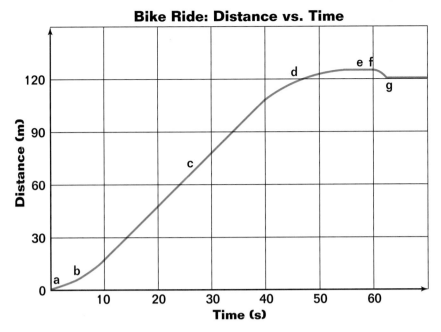

Bike Ride: Distance vs. Time

Figure 11-9 The information in Figure 11-8 also can be conveyed in a distance-time graph, as shown here. Notice that when the acceleration is 0, the distance-time graph is a straight line. When you find the slope of the line (the rate of change of distance), you find the velocity. **What is the acceleration in part c of the graph?**

Compare the velocity-time graph in **Figure 11-8** with the distance-time graph in **Figure 11-9**. Both convey information about the same bike ride. The distance-time graph shows your displacement and how it changed (velocity). The velocity-time graph shows your speed and how it changed. Both describe your motion.

Section Assessment

1. Belayneh Dinsamo of Ethiopia set a world's record in the 1988 Rotterdam Marathon. He ran the 42.2-km course in 2.114 hours. What was his average speed?

2. A bicyclist starts at rest. She starts to pedal, and after 8 s she is traveling forward at 4 m/s. Find her acceleration, including the direction.

3. The bicyclist in question 2 continues to pedal at 4 m/s. Draw a velocity-time graph of her motion from 0 s to 15 s.

4. **Think Critically:** Suppose you are in-line skating forward at 1.5 m/s. Suddenly, another person bumps you, giving you an acceleration of 0.5 m/s² for 1 s. What other information do you need to determine your velocity after the push?

5. **Skill Builder**
   Using Numbers Do the **Chapter 11 Skill Activity** on page 564 to calculate average velocity based on measurements from a scientific illustration.

Using Math

A car is traveling due north at 20 m/s. It brakes with an acceleration of –4 m/s² for 3 s. What is its final velocity?

The Tortoise and the Hare

Possible Materials

- Stopwatch
  *clock or watch with second hand
- Meterstick or another way of measuring position
- Calculator
  *Alternate Materials

The tortoise and the hare is an old fable. The tortoise and the hare have a race. The tortoise plods slowly and steadily along. The hare alternately zips ahead, then stops for a while. Even though the hare is faster, the tortoise wins the race. The hare's velocity at any moment can be higher than the tortoise's, but over the course of the race, the tortoise's average velocity is greater than the hare's.

Recognize the Problem

You will design two racing strategies. One will involve slow, steady movement. The other will involve rapid starts, stops, and pauses. Compare and contrast the two types of motion.

Form a Hypothesis

Based on what you know about motion, state a hypothesis about how the tortoise's average speed and average velocity compare to those of the hare.

Goals

- **Measure** the positions of two different racers.
- **Calculate** their average speeds.
- **Use** a position-time graph.

Safety Precautions

Work where there is enough space to jog safely.

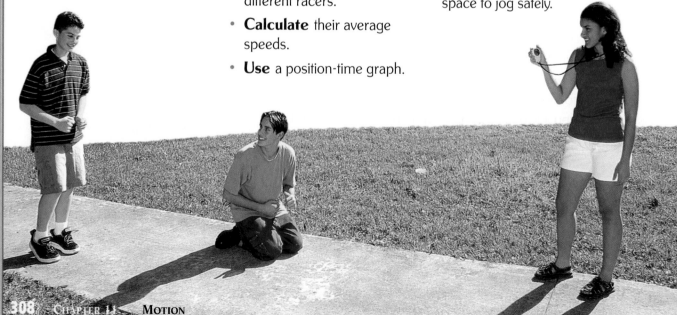

Test Your Hypothesis

Plan

1. **Find** a location for your race. Measure the distance.

2. Choose a racer to play the tortoise and one to be the hare. The tortoise should walk the course slowly. **Time** the tortoise and **calculate** the average velocity.

3. The hare will have two different strategies. Both will involve jogging part of the time at a constant speed. **Find** a reasonable speed for the jogging hare.

4. **Design** the first hare strategy. The hare will either jog at constant speed or stand still. For

example, the hare might jog for 5 s, rest for 10 s, and so on. Try to make a plan that lets the tortoise win the race.

5. **Design** a second hare strategy. This time, the hare will jog forward and backward. For example, the hare might jog forward 5 s, back 5 s, and so on. Again, try to let the tortoise win the race.

6. In both plans, ignore the hare's acceleration. Assume that the hare is moving at constant speed or is at rest.

Do

1. Make sure your teacher approves your plan before you proceed.

2. **Run** the two races of hare vs. tortoise. One person should use a timer to call out *start, 5, 10,* and so on at 5-s intervals.

(Longer intervals are fine if you have a long course.)

3. While doing the experiment, **record** your observations. Who won? When was the tortoise ahead? When was the hare ahead?

Analyze Your Data

1. **Calculate** the average velocity of each racer for both races.

2. **Calculate** the average speed of each racer for both races.

3. Use a distance-time graph to **compare and contrast** the distances the hare ran in the two races.

Draw Conclusions

1. If you know the speed of two racers at any moment, can you **predict** the outcome of a race? Explain.

2. **Compare and contrast** the different types of motion seen in the races.

What You'll Learn

▶ How to find an object's momentum
▶ How to use the law of conservation of momentum to understand collisions

Vocabulary

mass
inertia
momentum
law of conservation of momentum

Why It's Important

▶ The conservation of momentum explains collisions between objects, whether they are pool balls or atoms.

Mass and Inertia

The universe consists of matter in motion. **Figure 11-10** shows some familiar examples. The stars you see, the air you breathe, the ground you walk on, and the eyes you read with all are made of matter. The quantity of matter is measured as **mass.** The unit of mass is the kilogram. From the tiniest particles, such as atoms, to the largest objects, such as stars, all are made of matter.

Mass plays an important role when you study motion. In the 1600s, Galileo Galilei studied motion. He noticed that objects with a lot of mass were more difficult to move and, once moving, were just as difficult to stop. If you have ever had to help push a stalled car out of the road, you know just how difficult it can be to get it moving. Once it's moving, it's easy to keep it moving as long as the ground is flat. The effort to stop the car is just as great as the effort to get it moving.

Compared to pushing a car, pushing your bicycle is easy. It hardly takes any effort because the bicycle has a small mass. Galileo used the word inertia (in ER sha) to describe how easy or difficult it is to change an object's motion. **Inertia** measures an object's tendency to remain at rest or stay in constant motion. A measure of the inertia of an object is its mass. By pushing on different objects, you can compare their masses by seeing how easy they are to move.

Figure 11-10 Your world is filled with matter in motion.

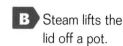 **A** People can move their bodies, as well as objects such as this bat and ball.

 **B** Steam lifts the lid off a pot.

Momentum

When Sir Isaac Newton began to organize his ideas to explain force and motion, he kept returning to the same two quantities—mass and velocity. He decided that these two quantities are the most important things to know when you want to understand an object's motion. He called the product of mass and velocity **momentum.** Momentum has the symbol p. Using m for mass, the formula is as follows.

$$\text{momentum} = \text{mass} \times \text{velocity}$$
$$p = mv$$

Because momentum includes velocity, it has direction. Momentum points in the direction of motion, just like velocity. Positive and negative signs are used to indicate momentums in opposite directions. You can add momentums, as shown in **Figure 11-11.**

Momentum, Newton said, was the quantity of motion. If you know this quantity, then you can begin to understand exactly how objects move.

When a fast-moving baseball is zipping straight toward your head, you know you'd better duck! Moving at up to 200 km/h (56 m/s), the speeding ball could seriously injure you. Even if you caught the ball with a glove, your hand

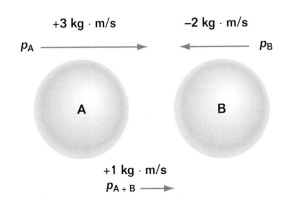

Figure 11-11 The momentum of this system, balls A and B, is the sum of the individual momentums.

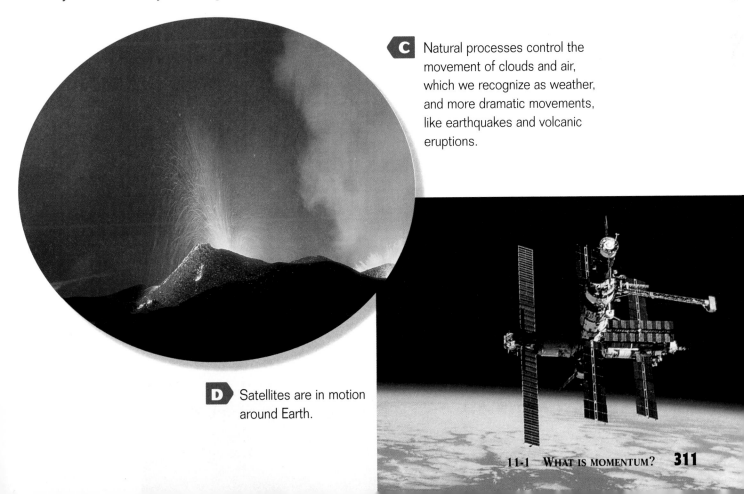

C Natural processes control the movement of clouds and air, which we recognize as weather, and more dramatic movements, like earthquakes and volcanic eruptions.

D Satellites are in motion around Earth.

would feel a sting when it hit. That ball has momentum. The momentum of a baseball with a mass of 0.125 kg moving at this speed is found using the momentum formula.

$$\text{momentum} = \text{mass} \times \text{velocity}$$

$$p = mv$$
$$= (0.125 \text{ kg}) \times (56 \text{ m/s})$$
$$= 7.0 \text{ kg} \cdot \text{m/s}$$

The ball's momentum is 7.0 kg · m/s. An answer that includes direction might say the ball is moving toward the spectator in Section 1A, Row 7, Seat 23 with a momentum of 7.0 kg · m/s.

Momentum does not have a standard unit. You can use kg · m/s, g · m/s, kg · km/h, or whatever combination of mass and velocity units is most useful. (The symbol · means "times.") But, if you are making calculations with more than one momentum, be sure to use the same units for each.

Table 11-2 is a list of common objects that all have a momentum of 7 kg · m/s. Compare these objects with the speeding baseball. You can see that a mosquito with little mass needs a lot of velocity to have the same momentum. At the other extreme, a massive truck has the same momentum when barely moving. This is why, when you ride in a car on the highway, a collision with a truck is more dangerous than an insect colliding with your windshield.

Table 11-2

Common Objects with a Momentum of 7 kg · m/s		
Object	Mass (kg)	Speed (m/s)
mosquito	0.000001	7 000 000
Ping-Pong ball	0.005	1 400
bullet	0.02	350
bowling ball	7	1
seventh grader	50	0.14
18-wheeler	12 000	0.0006

Conservation of Momentum

When you hit a ball with a bat, you change the ball's motion. If the ball has a great deal of inertia, its velocity will not change quickly. For example, if you hit a bowling ball with a bat in the same way you would hit a baseball, the bowling ball's velocity will not change much. The baseball has much less inertia, so it's easier to change its motion. Newton discovered that in both cases, however, the momentum is the same. The two balls get the same quantity of motion from the bat as long as the action (or push) is the same and lasts for the same amount of time.

Once moving, which ball is easier to stop? It takes just as much force, applied for the same amount of time, to stop each ball. It would be like running a movie backward. Force applied in one direction gives a certain momentum, and force in the opposite direction during an equal amount of time stops that momentum.

Momentum is conserved. In every situation you can imagine, from atoms smashing in particle accelerators to stars exploding in a galaxy, the momentum of the collection of objects involved does not change. If no outside forces act on a group of objects, the momentum of the whole group will never change. This is called the **law of conservation of momentum.** If one object slows down, it's because it hit another object. The object it hit then moves faster. The one object lost just as much momentum as the other one gained, so there's no change overall. This law is illustrated in **Figure 11-12.** ☑

Reading Check ☑

What is the law of conservation of momentum?

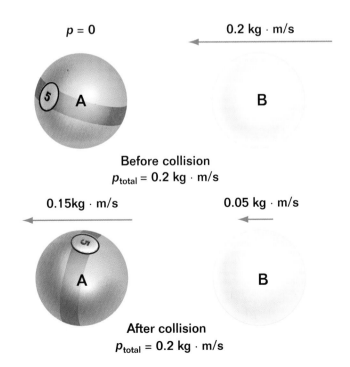

$p = 0$

0.2 kg · m/s

A

B

Before collision
$p_{total} = 0.2$ kg · m/s

0.15kg · m/s

0.05 kg · m/s

A

B

After collision
$p_{total} = 0.2$ kg · m/s

Figure 11-12 The total momentum is 0.2 kg · m/s before and after the balls collide because momentum is conserved. **How could you predict the white ball would slow down after the collision?**

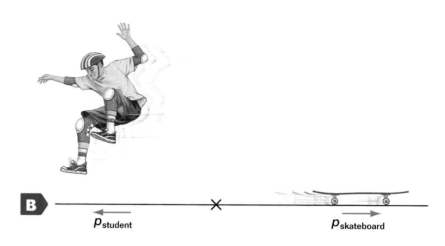

Figure 11-13 The student-skateboard systems in A and B have a momentum of 0. When the student jumps, the momentum of the system is conserved.

$p_{student}$ $p_{skateboard}$

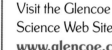
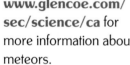

Visit the Glencoe Science Web Site at **www.glencoe.com/sec/science/ca** for more information about meteors.

Examples of Momentum Conservation

The system of skateboard and rider in **Figure 11-13** has a momentum of 0 before and after the skateboarder jumps. In **Figure 11-13B,** the momentum of the person is equal and opposite to the momentum of the board, so they cancel. The opening pages of this chapter show a rack of pool balls being scattered by a cue ball. The shooter applies an outside force on the cue ball when he or she hits it. The cue ball gains momentum from the stick. When the cue ball hits the rack, it slows down as it collides with the other balls. The cue ball loses momentum as the other balls gain a nearly equal amount of momentum. In a perfect system, the balls would bounce around the table without stopping until an outside force acted. When you play pool, the outside force of friction causes the balls to slow down and eventually stop.

Problem Solving

Observing Inertia

Mass is usually measured with a beam balance or a spring scale. A beam balance compares a known mass to an unknown mass. A spring scale measures the pull (or push) of the mass on a spring. Sometimes, you need to measure mass without these simple lab tools. For example, scientists who study meteor craters can't weigh the meteor. Astronomers can't weigh a comet. They need other ways to determine mass.

Get a number of balls that are about the same size. Place them on a flat surface. Make a hypothesis about their relative masses without handling them. (For

example, blue is heaviest, then red, then silver, and green is lightest.) Use one of the balls as a control ball. Place the other balls one at a time at the bottom of a ramp. Launch the control ball from the same point on a ramp to collide with each of these balls. (Launching from the same point ensures that the control ball will have approximately the same velocity each time.) Observe the collisions and the inertia of each ball.

Think Critically: How can you tell the mass order with this method? What can you do to make this more accurate?

The law of conservation of momentum can help you figure out what happens in a collision. Using the break in pool as an example, you could calculate where every ball is going to go if you knew the momentum of the cue ball and the exact position of all the balls before the collision. You might need a computer to help with the calculations, but you would not need to know anything else.

The particles in a gas are sometimes modeled as tiny billiard balls. The particles have an average speed, which is determined by the temperature of the gas. But, individual particles might have speeds higher or lower than this value. If the system is at rest, the sum of the momentums of the individual particles is zero. In this model, momentum is conserved in each collision. When a fast particle hits a slow molecule, the momentum of each may change, but the total momentum for the pair remains constant. **Figure 11-14** illustrates how the collisions of the particles with the walls of the container provide the pressure of the gas.

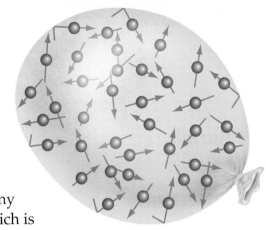

Figure 11-14 The particles in a gas can be modeled as colliding balls. When the particles collide with the balloon, they give the balloon its shape.

CHEMISTRY
◄ **INTEGRATION**

Section Assessment

1. A 140-kg lineman from your favorite team comes charging at you. He is running at full speed of 10 km/h. Suppose your mass is 50 kg. How fast must you be moving to stop his forward motion?

2. You see a film where one pool ball rolls forward and hits another. The first ball stops and the second moves off with the same momentum as the first ball. Can you tell whether the film is being run backward or forward?

3. **Think Critically:** Every day, Earth is hit by 1 million kg of matter from outer space. Most of this is in the form of grains of dust that hit Earth with an average speed of about 10 km/s. Give some reasons why we don't notice a change in the motion of Earth.

4.  **Skill Builder**
   Interpreting Scientific Illustrations The illustration shows the momentums before and after a collision. What is the momentum of B after the collision? If you need help, refer to Interpreting Scientific Illustrations in the **Skill Handbook** on page 538.

Science Journal
Explain how your momentum changes over the course of a bike ride around your block.

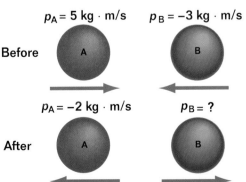

$p_A = 5$ kg · m/s $p_B = -3$ kg · m/s

Before   A   B

$p_A = -2$ kg · m/s $p_B = ?$

After   A   B

Comparing Collisions

Materials
- Small marbles (5)
- Large marbles (2)
- Metersticks (2)

You've played games that involve bouncing balls against each other, the walls and floor, and various pieces of sports equipment. How do these collisions work?

What You'll Investigate

How do the masses and velocities of marbles before a collision affect the velocities of the marbles after a collision?

Goals

- **Make** a hypothesis about how momentum changes.
- **Compare and contrast** different collisions.

Procedure

1. You want to limit this study to motion along a straight line. Use the metersticks to make a track, as shown in the photo. The sticks should be a little farther apart than the width of the largest marble you are using in each collision.

2. Set a small marble in the center of the track. Shoot another small marble as fast as you can down the track. Repeat. **Describe** the collision.

3. Repeat step 2 with two large marbles.

4. Repeat step 2 with a small shooter marble and a large target.

5. Repeat step 2 with a large shooter marble and a small target.

6. Repeat step 2 shooting two small marbles at each other.

7. Repeat step 2 shooting one small and one large marble at each other.

8. Repeat step 2 using four small, touching marbles as the target and one small marble as the shooter.

Conclude and Apply

1. **Compare and contrast** the various types of collisions.

2. How did you **separate and control variables?**

What is energy?

Energy

A final way to describe motion is with energy. **Energy** is the ability to cause change. If you look back at all the examples of motion in this chapter, you will see that all involve change.

The energy of matter in motion is **kinetic energy.** Where does kinetic energy come from? It comes from other forms of energy. Chemical energy is found in the bonds between atoms. You use it to move your body, as in **Figure 11-15.** Nuclear energy is contained in the bonds in the nucleus. Electromagnetic energy includes electricity, magnetism, and light. Heat is the transfer of thermal energy. All of these can cause change.

Energy can be transferred between objects. A soccer player has chemical energy in her muscles from the food she ate. The chemical energy is released as she accelerates her leg. Her leg now has kinetic energy. When her foot kicks the ball, the kinetic energy of her foot is used to accelerate the ball. Her foot and leg lose kinetic energy as the ball gains the same amount of kinetic energy. The ball soars downfield and eventually stops. The ball's kinetic energy turns to heat energy as it heats up the atoms and molecules of the ball, air, and ground. Eventually, these hot particles will bounce into other particles and spread the heat everywhere.

It can be difficult to follow the trail of energy. People became especially interested in defining and understanding energy when steam engines started to be used to do work. James Joule discovered the **law of conservation of energy,** which states that energy cannot be created or destroyed, but is only transformed from one form to another. ✔

What You'll Learn

▶ What energy is, and some of its forms
▶ How to find kinetic and gravitational potential energy
▶ What the law of conservation of energy is and how to use it

Vocabulary
energy
kinetic energy
law of conservation
  of energy
gravitational potential
  energy

Why It's Important

▶ Natural processes involve the transfer of energy.

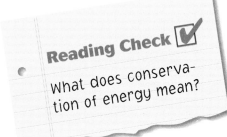

Reading Check ✔
What does conservation of energy mean?

Figure 11-15 Chemical energy is contained in your muscles. It is transformed to kinetic energy when you use your muscles to produce motion.

Figure 11-16 Heat energy from the sun is transformed to chemical energy in the bamboo. When the animal eats the bamboo, it gains chemical energy, which it can transform to kinetic energy.

The total amount of energy in the whole universe never changes. Only the different forms in which energy appears change, as shown in **Figure 11-16.** As you study the flow of energy, as in the case of the soccer ball, you will eventually find that all the energy has been transformed into heat and seems to have disappeared. It really hasn't, but it has been lost from the object that had it at first.

To show how energy is transferred by friction, drop a basketball from shoulder height. After it bounces on the ground, it will not return to the height of your shoulders. When it bounces a second time, it won't return to the height of the first bounce. The bounces will keep getting shorter and shorter until the ball lies still on the ground. If there were no friction, the ball would bounce up and down from the same height forever.

Calculating Kinetic Energy

Kinetic energy is the energy an object has due to its motion. It depends on the object's mass and velocity. You can calculate the amount of kinetic energy using the following formula.

$$\text{kinetic energy} = \frac{1}{2}(\text{mass})(\text{velocity})^2$$

$$KE = \frac{1}{2}mv^2$$

KE represents kinetic energy; *m*, mass; and *v*, velocity. The unit of energy is the joule (J), $1 \text{ J} = 1 \text{ kg} \cdot \text{m}^2/\text{s}^2$. It is named for James Joule.

MiniLab

Observing Energy Transfer

Procedure

1. Tie a weight to a long string. Hang the string and weight from the ceiling. Adjust the string until the weight is just above the floor.
2. Pull the weight to one side until it is 1 m high. Gently let go of the weight. Do not push it.
3. Observe the motion of the weight.

Analysis

1. Calculate the gravitational potential energy of the weight before it was released.
2. Where did the weight have the greatest kinetic energy? The least?
3. What happened as *GPE* decreased? Increased? Explain.

Potential Energy

Potential energy is the stored energy of position or condition. Many forces can store energy this way. A book on the edge of a desk has potential energy due to gravity. If you knock it off, it will accelerate toward the ground. A paper clip held near a magnet also has potential energy. If you let go of it, it will accelerate toward the magnet. The positive and negative charges in a battery have potential energy. When you run a wire between them, the negative charges move. A squashed spring has potential energy. If you release it, it will accelerate.

Anything that can fall has the ability to create change. **Gravitational potential energy,** or *GPE,* is the energy an object could change to kinetic energy if it falls. An object's *GPE* depends on its mass, *m,* and the height it can fall, *h.*

$$GPE = (\text{force of gravity})(\text{height})$$

$$GPE = mgh$$

The *g* represents the acceleration due to gravity, 9.8 m/s^2.

You have experience with gravitational potential energy. How many times have you held your arms over your head to protect it from something falling? The more massive the object or the farther it falls, the more you cringe, hoping it does not hit you on the head.

Figure 11-17 shows how energy changes when a ball is dropped. When you first release the ball, it has a certain gravitational potential energy, *mgh,* and no kinetic energy. Just before it hits the ground, its *GPE* is 0. All the *GPE* has been converted to kinetic energy. At any point along the way, it's part *GPE* and part *KE.* But everywhere the total amount of energy is the same.

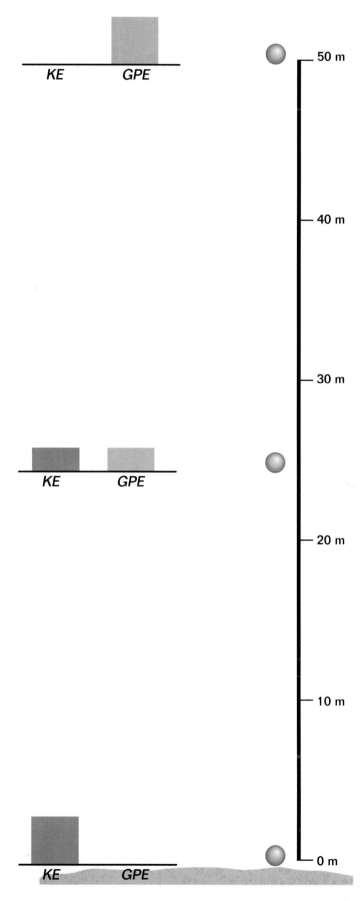

Figure 11-17 As the ball falls, gravitational potential energy is converted to kinetic energy.

Figure 11-18 Energy is transferred on a long slide. **Where is a rider's potential energy least? Greatest? Where is a rider's kinetic energy least? Greatest? Does the total energy change?**

interNET
CONNECTION

Visit the Glencoe Science Web Site at **www.glencoe.com/ sec/science/ca** for more information about energy.

Figure 11-18 shows a slide. As you ride down, potential energy is transferred to kinetic energy. When you climb back up, you use kinetic energy to gain potential energy. Because this is a real system, some energy is transferred to heat. But none is lost or gained: energy is conserved.

Section Assessment

1. Suppose you and your bicycle have a total mass of 70 kg. You are moving at 10 m/s. How much kinetic energy do you and the bicycle have?

2. When you bring your bicycle to a stop, where does the kinetic energy it had go?

3. **Think Critically:** Suppose you hold a strong magnet 1 cm away from the refrigerator door. Is there potential energy in this system? What happens when you let go of the magnet?

4. **Skill Builder**
   Observing and Inferring Use the conservation of energy to explain what happens when you drop a ball and it bounces back up. If you throw the ball downward instead of dropping it, do you expect it to bounce higher or lower than when you dropped it? Why? If you need help, refer to Observing and Inferring in the **Skill Handbook** on page 532.

Using Computers

Database Use on-line databases to investigate a particular source of energy, such as oil, solar, or alternative fuels. If you need help, refer to page 545.

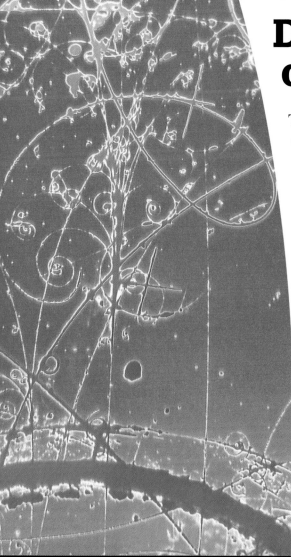

Science
JOURNAL

The track at right was made by a particle in a high-energy accelerator. Scientists used the law of conservation of momentum to propose that the particle must have thrown off another particle, called a neutrino, which doesn't leave a track. In your Science Journal, explain why the conservation of momentum law suggests this is so.

Discovery of the Neutrino

The law of conservation of momentum states that when no outside forces act on a system, the momentum of the system is conserved. The law of conservation of energy states that energy is not created or destroyed, only transferred from one object to another. These seemingly simple ideas are behind some of the most important scientific discoveries, including that of a tiny particle called a neutrino.

Tracking Particles

To find the momentum and energy of small particles, scientists study the tracks the particles leave in detectors (left). A track depends on the mass, charge, and initial momentum of the particle.

Around 1930, scientists discovered that one type of particle track (lower right) showed a sudden change of direction and speed. When the particle turned, it did not hit anything and no new outside force acted on it. Scientists predicted that a new particle, one they couldn't detect, was being ejected, carrying off momentum and energy. The new particle was called a neutrino, which means "little neutral particle."

The Mysterious Neutrino

Scientists thought the neutrino had no electric charge and no mass. Neutrinos leave no track in detectors. Direct evidence for the neutrino did not come until 1956. In 1998, scientists in Japan showed that neutrinos do have mass, though that mass has not yet been measured. Neutrinos are a topic of current research in science. Yet, they still obey the basic laws you learn in science class.

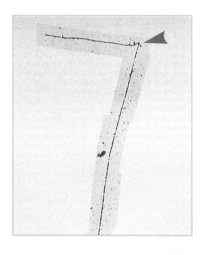

Chapter 11 Reviewing Main Ideas

For a **preview** of this chapter, study this Reviewing Main Ideas before you read the chapter. After you have studied this chapter, you can use the Reviewing Main Ideas to **review** the chapter.

The Glencoe MindJogger, Audiocassettes, and CD-ROM provide additional opportunities for review.

Section

11-1 VELOCITY AND ACCELERATION

An object's motion can be described by **velocity.** Velocity gives the rate of change of position, or **speed,** and the direction of motion. An object's change in motion is described with **acceleration,** the rate of change of velocity. Acceleration can act in the direction of motion, opposite to the direction of motion, or at an angle. *How are speed and velocity related to position and time?*

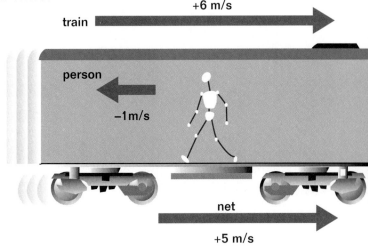

train   +6 m/s

person   −1m/s

net   +5 m/s

Section

11-2 MASS AND INERTIA

Mass is the amount of matter in an object and it is a measure of the object's **inertia.** *How does the inertia of a freight train moving at 10 km/h compare with your inertia while you bicycle at the same speed?*

+3 kg · m/s   −2 kg · m/s

p_A ⟶   ⟵ p_B

A   B

+1 kg · m/s
p_{A+B} ⟶

MOMENTUM

Momentum is the quantity of motion for an object. Knowing this value gives you an idea of how powerfully the object could collide with another object. *If your mass is 60 kg and you travel in a car moving at 100 km/h, what is your momentum?*

Reading Check ✓

Explain how direction plays a role in the different concepts studied in this chapter.

CONSERVATION OF MOMENTUM

If no outside forces act on a group of objects, the momentum of the group will not change. The momentum of individual objects in the group may change, as collisions transfer momentum between objects, but the total momentum of the group remains unchanged. *What happens to the momentum of a small ball that strikes a large ball and stops?*

11-3 CONSERVATION OF ENERGY

Energy is the ability to cause change. It takes many forms. **Gravitational potential energy, kinetic energy,** and heat are familiar examples. Energy cannot be created or destroyed, only transferred from one form to another. *A bouncing ball eventually comes to a stop. Where did the kinetic energy go?*

Chapter 11 Assessment

Using Vocabulary

a. acceleration
b. displacement
c. energy
d. gravitational potential energy
e. inertia
f. kinetic energy
g. law of conservation of energy
h. law of conservation of momentum
i. mass
j. momentum
k. speed
l. velocity

For each set of terms below, explain the relationship that exists.

1. inertia, mass
2. displacement, velocity
3. velocity, acceleration
4. kinetic energy, gravitational potential energy
5. mass, momentum

Checking Concepts

Choose the word or phrase that best answers the question.

6. When an object accelerates, what can it do?
   A) speed up   C) change direction
   B) slow down   D) all of the above

7. What is the rate of change of position?
   A) velocity   C) displacement
   B) acceleration   D) momentum

8. Where is the kinetic energy of a falling object greatest?
   A) top of fall   C) middle of fall
   B) bottom of fall   D) it doesn't change

9. What is the rate of change of velocity called?
   A) momentum   C) acceleration
   B) mass   D) force

10. When no outside forces act on a system of objects, what do the objects do?
    A) conserve momentum
    B) do not conserve momentum
    C) come to rest
    D) continue with the same velocity

11. What is a possible unit of momentum?
    A) kg   C) $kg \cdot m/s^2$
    B) $kg \cdot m$ D) $kg \cdot m/s$

12. What is the gravitational potential energy of a 3-kg object 8 m above the ground?
    A) 24 J   C) 96 J
    B) 36 J   D) 235 J

13. Which of the following is **NOT** conserved?
    A) mass   C) energy
    B) acceleration   D) momentum

14. What is the momentum of an object with mass 50 kg moving at 20 km/h?
    A) $1000 \; kg \cdot km/h$ C) $5000 \; kg \cdot km/h$
    B) $2000 \; kg \cdot km/h$ D) $20\,000 \; kg \cdot km/h$

15. What is the kinetic energy of a 60-kg diver falling at 10 m/s?
    A) 300 J   C) 3000 J
    B) 600 J   D) 5880 J

Thinking Critically

16. When a wrecking ball hits a wall, it is usually moving at about 10 km/h, which is not very fast. Explain how this ball can knock down a solid wall.

17. When you rub your hands together, what energy was transformed to produce heat?

18. An 80-kg person decides to jump off the back end of a 30-kg canoe. His friend measures the speed of the canoe after he jumps to be 0.8 m/s. The canoe was initially at rest. What rule would you use to find the speed of the person who jumped?

19. If the canoe accelerates from 0 to 0.8 m/s in 0.2 s, what is the acceleration?

20. A ball has a potential energy of 180 J and a kinetic energy of 0 J. After falling 2 m, it has a potential energy of 135 J. What is its kinetic energy at this point?

Developing Skills

If you need help, refer to the **Skill Handbook**.

21. Using Numbers: An in-line skater is going north at 2 m/s. After accelerating smoothly for 9 s, she is going south at 1 m/s. What was her acceleration, including direction?

22. Concept Mapping: Complete the concept map with the following phrases: *kinetic energy, chemical energy (plant), chemical energy (animal),* and *solar energy.*

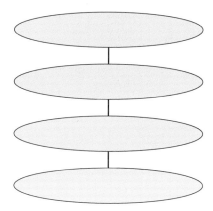

23. Recognizing Cause and Effect: Before a collision, a 1-kg ball is moving left at 0.4 m/s and a 2-kg ball is at rest. After the balls collide, only the 2-kg ball is in motion. What is its velocity? How do you know?

24. Making and Using Graphs: Make a distance-time graph for an object moving with constant velocity 4 m/s. Go from 0 s to 5 s.

Test-Taking Tip

Warm Up Before the Race On the day of your exam, arrive at the site early enough to relax, get settled, and go over your notes. It will give you time to relax and prepare your mind for the test.

Test Practice

Use these questions to test your Science Proficiency.

1. Before a collision, a system of three balls has a momentum of +8 kg · m/s. After the collision, one ball has a momentum of −2 kg · m/s and one ball has a momentum of +5 kg · m/s. What is the momentum of the third ball?
A) +5 kg · m/s
B) +13 kg · m/s
C) +1 kg · m/s
D) −1 kg · m/s

2. An object is displaced from a position 2 m north of you to a position 6 m south. The displacement takes 2 s. What is the velocity of the object?
A) 1 m/s north
B) 2 m/s north
C) 3 m/s south
D) 4 m/s south

3. A rock falls 10 m down a cliff. Where is its gravitational potential energy greatest?
A) at the top of the fall
B) at the bottom of the fall
C) at the midpoint of the fall
D) no change in *GPE*

Force and Newton's Laws

Chapter Preview

Skills Preview

Skill Builders
- Concept Mapping

Activities
- Design an Experiment

MiniLabs
- Measure in SI

Reading Check ✔

As you read, make a chart of the examples used to help explain each of Newton's laws. Add one or two examples of your own for each law.

Explore Activity

Bobsleds go fast—very fast, as you know if you've ever watched one speed down its icy run. At the top of the run, the bobsledders exert a force on the sled to accelerate it. Then they jump in, and the force of gravity accelerates them down. The team members use their bodies as well as the brakes and steering mechanism to change the sled's motion, slowing it or turning it. The motion of the sled can be understood with Newton's laws of motion.

Define Motion

1. Lean one end of a meterstick on top of three books. This is your ramp. Put one side of the ramp against a wall so the marbles won't roll off.

2. Tap a marble so it rolls up the ramp. Measure how far up the ramp it travels before rolling back.

3. Repeat step 2 using two books, one book, and zero books. The same person should tap the marble each time, trying to keep the force constant.

Make a table and record the motion of the marble for each ramp height. What do you think would happen if you could send a marble along a perfectly smooth, flat path?

12•1 Newton's First Law

What You'll Learn

► How to recognize a force
► What balanced and net forces are
► Newton's first law of motion
► How friction works

Vocabulary
force
net force
balanced forces
unbalanced forces
Newton's first law
  of motion
friction

Why It's Important

► Newton's first law is the basis of all motion, from a bike moving at constant speed to the motion of the planets.

Force

When an object accelerates, it changes its motion. It can speed up, slow down, or turn. If an object accelerates, a force must be acting on it. A **force** is a push or a pull. Some examples of forces are shown in **Figure 12-1.** For example, when you throw a ball, your hand exerts a force on the ball, and you accelerate the ball forward. After the ball leaves your hand, gravity exerts a force on it, causing its path to curve downward. When the ball hits the ground, the ground exerts a force, stopping the ball and perhaps bouncing it back up.

The force of a magnet can move a paper clip. Earth's gravitational field can also move the paper clip. Or, you can move the paper clip by picking it up. All of these are examples of forces acting on the paper clip.

Suppose you hold a paper clip near a magnet. You, the magnet, and gravity all exert forces on the clip. A **net force** is the total force felt by an object. The object will accelerate in the direction of the net force. The clip does not move because the net force is zero.

Figure 12-1 Each of these pictures shows a force working.

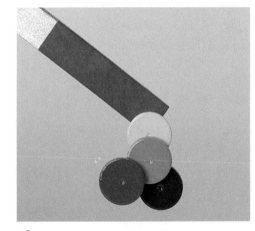

B The force of the magnet on the metal disks is strong enough to pull them off the table.

C The force stored in the spring will stop the door as it opens.

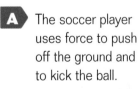

A The soccer player uses force to push off the ground and to kick the ball.

If you push gently on one side of the book in **Figure 12-2,** and a friend pushes hard on the other side, the net force is toward you, so the book will move toward you.

A force can act on an object without causing it to accelerate. Right now gravity is pulling you down and your chair is pushing you up. Your motion isn't changing, so the forces are *balanced*. Two or more forces are **balanced forces** if their effects cancel each other and they do not cause a change in an object's motion. An example is shown in **Figure 12-3.** If the forces on an object are balanced, the net force is zero. If the forces are **unbalanced forces,** the net force is not zero, and the object accelerates. An object can be in motion and have no net force acting on it. If you push a hockey puck across the ice, your hockey stick accelerates it by exerting a force. When you stop exerting that force, the puck keeps moving at constant speed across the ice until the force of friction slows it down. All the forces acting on the puck are balanced while its motion doesn't change.

Figure 12-2 The sum of all the forces acting on an object is the net force.

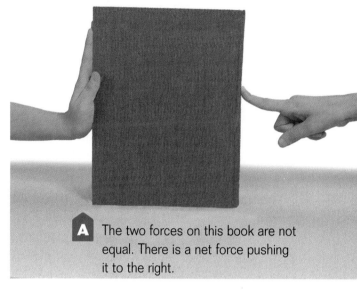

A The two forces on this book are not equal. There is a net force pushing it to the right.

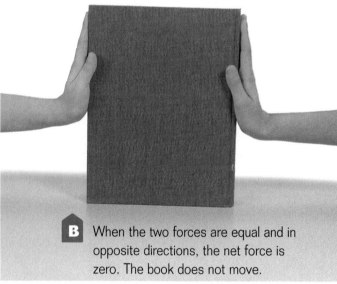

B When the two forces are equal and in opposite directions, the net force is zero. The book does not move.

Figure 12-3 Acrobats exert forces to hold each other in position. All the forces are balanced, so the acrobats do not move. **What will happen if the forces become unbalanced?**

CHEMISTRY
INTEGRATION

Electric Force
A neutral atom has balanced electric forces. An ion has charge and can accelerate other ions or electrons. It has a net electric force. When two negatively charged ions repel each other, is this an example of force? How do you know?

Newton's First Law of Motion

In 1635, when Galileo Galilei was 70 years old, he was placed under house arrest for claiming that the planets, including Earth, orbit the sun and that Earth rotates once each day. His claim troubled many people. "How can Earth be moving?" they thought. "If it does, then our water glasses should fall over!" Galileo's view was revolutionary. He spent the remaining seven years of his life confined to his home. About thirty years later, Isaac Newton would build on Galileo's work and begin to change the way people thought about the world.

Galileo said the reason the water glass does not fall over is because Earth has always been moving around the sun and spinning on its axis in a smooth manner. If Earth suddenly stopped rotating, everything that is not strongly attached to the ground would spill. **Figure 12-4** gives another example.

Newton used Galileo's ideas about motion in what is now called **Newton's first law of motion.** It states, "An object will remain at rest or move with constant velocity until it is acted upon by a net force." This also is called Newton's law of inertia.

A Thought Experiment

Galileo discovered this scientific law by thinking about a ball rolling up a ramp, as in the Explore Activity. If the ramp is steep, the ball will not travel far before it stops. As the ramp

Figure 12-4 An object in motion remains in motion.

B If the vehicle suddenly stops, the drink spills. This demonstrates Newton's first law: a body in motion continues in motion unless acted on by a net force.

A When you travel by car, train, or plane at constant speed, you can hold a glass of soda or set it next to you. You, the glass, the liquid, and the car are all traveling at the same speed.

Figure 12-5 Friction acts against the motion between objects.

A Without friction, the climber would slide down the slope.

is lowered closer and closer to level, the ball will go farther and farther up the ramp. If the ramp is then made perfectly smooth and level, the ball should continue moving forever if nothing disturbs it.

You can try this by rolling a bowling ball on a large, level surface, like your school gymnasium floor. A slight push will easily send the ball across the room at nearly constant speed.

What happens when you repeat the experiment on a rough or uneven surface, like grass or a thick carpet? The ball slows down. Something disturbs the ball's motion. A force must be acting on the ball.

Friction

Galileo said an object in motion remains in motion until a net (or unbalanced) force acts on it. The unbalanced force that brings nearly everything to a stop is **friction,** the rubbing force that acts against motion between two touching surfaces. There are a number of different forms of friction, but they all have one thing in common. They always act against an object's direction of motion, as shown in **Figure 12-5.** Friction will never speed up an object. If you rub your hand against a tabletop, you can feel the friction push against the direction your hand is moving. If you rub back the other way, you can feel the direction of friction change so it is again acting against your hand's motion.

B If you are in motion, friction slows you down, like this baseball player.

Reading Check ✔

What is friction?

interNET CONNECTION

Visit the Glencoe Science Web Site at **www.glencoe.com/ sec/science/ca** for more information about the study of motion.

Older Ideas About Motion

It took a long time to understand force. People once thought the natural state of an object was rest. For an object to be in motion, something had to be continuously moving it. As soon as the force stopped, nature would bring the object to rest.

Galileo understood that constant motion is as natural as rest. If he could remove friction, an object would continue to move with constant motion. He did a series of experiments where he pushed an object across smoother and smoother surfaces and found that the object would go farther and farther. He reasoned that if he could make the surface perfectly smooth and flat, the object would never slow down. You can repeat this experiment yourself at home or at school.

Static Friction

Another experiment can demonstrate static friction. Place an eraser on your ruler. Start to tip the ruler, as shown in **Figure 12-6.** The eraser does not start to slide right away, but stays in place until the ruler reaches a certain angle. The friction that prevents an object from moving when a force is applied is called static friction. It is static friction that makes it possible to walk. Every step taken pushes against Earth. Without friction, you'd slip and fall.

Have you ever tried to push something heavy, like a refrigerator? When you begin to push, nothing happens. Static friction balances your force. As you push harder and harder, the object will suddenly give way and move. When the object begins to move, you are exerting a force too great for static friction to balance.

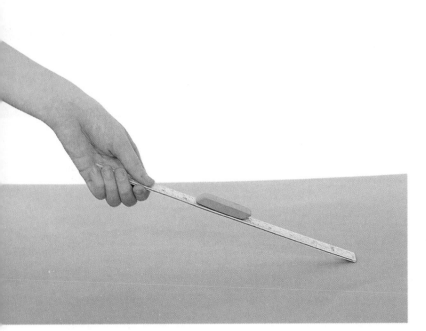

Figure 12-6 Static friction holds the eraser in place on the ruler. **What will happen when the net force due to gravity is greater than the force of static friction?**

Sliding Friction

Static friction keeps an object at rest. Sliding friction slows down an object that slides. If you push an object across the room, there is sliding friction between the bottom of the object and the floor. You have to keep pushing to overcome the force of sliding friction. The brake pads in a car use sliding friction against the wheels to slow the car. Bicycle brakes, shown in **Figure 12-7A,** work the same way. Skidding tires, shuffling shoes, and rubbing hands are all common forms of sliding friction.

Figure 12-7 A bicycle uses sliding friction and rolling friction.

A Sliding friction is used to stop this bicycle tire. Friction between the brake pads and the wheel brings the wheel to a stop.

B Rolling friction with the ground pushes the bottom of the bicycle tire back so the wheel rolls forward.

Rolling friction

Rolling Friction

The wheel helps reduce sliding friction, but even the best wheel cannot completely remove this force. In fact, another kind of friction, rolling friction, is needed to make a wheel turn. There is friction between the ground and the part of a bike tire in contact with the ground, as shown in **Figure 12-7B**. Rolling friction pushes back so that the tire rolls forward. Sometimes, when a bike hits a patch of ice or wet leaves, there is not enough friction between the tire and ground to spin the tire, and the bike skids.

Spin a wheel with your hand and you can feel the friction between your hand and the wheel. If the wheel were coated in oil, your hand would slip off and it would be difficult to get enough friction to start the wheel in motion.

Air Resistance

When you ride a bicycle, the air pushes your hair and clothes back. Whether you are biking, walking, or riding in a car, air pushes against you. This is air resistance. Air resistance acts on the forward moving part of an object, such as the front of a car. It acts against the direction of motion and gets stronger as an object goes faster.

When you first start to pedal, your legs provide the force to push the bicycle forward. The air resistance is low, and you can accelerate fairly quickly. As you go faster, the air resistance gets stronger. Eventually, the air resistance (and road friction) balance your pedaling force, so you move at constant velocity.

Mini Lab

Defining Rolling Friction

Procedure

1. Attach a spring scale to a wheeled object such as a skateboard.
2. Pull the skateboard across the room at a steady speed. Observe the reading on the spring scale.

Analysis

1. What did the spring scale read when you started? What did it read as you moved at constant speed? When you stopped?
2. What is the force of rolling friction in this example? (Assume air resistance is so small it can be ignored.)

Figure 12-8 Engineers design cars, bike helmets, and other items so that they have as little air resistance as possible.

Whatever type, friction plays a role in nearly every real-life situation, as shown in **Figure 12-8.** It is one key in understanding and applying Newton's laws. Friction is a force that is always present, though it can be reduced and sometimes ignored.

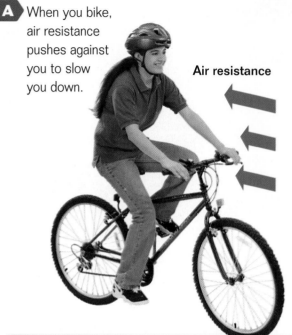

A When you bike, air resistance pushes against you to slow you down.

Air resistance

B When driving a car at high speed, overcoming the force of air resistance takes most of the energy used in gas.

Section Assessment

1. A car maintains a speed of 20 km/h as it turns to the left. Is a force acting on the car? Explain.

2. Explain why friction made it difficult to discover Newton's first law of motion.

3. **Think Critically:** In the following situations, are the forces balanced or unbalanced? How can you tell?

   a. You push a box of books until it is moving at 0.5 m/s.

   b. You continue to push the box of books across the floor at 0.5 m/s.

   c. You stop pushing the box, and it comes to a stop.

4.  **Skill Builder**
   Comparing and Contrasting
   Compare and contrast static friction, sliding friction, and rolling friction. If you need help, refer to Comparing and Contrasting in the **Skill Handbook** on page 532.

Science Journal
Most of the meteors that reach Earth's atmosphere burn up on the way down. Friction between the meteor and the atmosphere produces a huge amount of heat. Research how the space shuttle is protected from friction when it reenters Earth's atmosphere. Report your findings in your Science Journal.

Newton's Second Law

Force and Acceleration

Are you ever afraid to share your ideas in class? Newton did not like to write about his discoveries because he was afraid he would be criticized. A fellow scientist encouraged Newton to publish his discoveries about motion. Newton reluctantly agreed and wrote *The Principia*.

The central theme for *The Principia* was Newton's description of forces and how they act, now called Newton's laws of motion. If you know how a force acts on an object, you can calculate anything you would like to know about its motion in the future as well as the past. Newton used the laws to calculate the motions of the planets.

Newton presented the answers to many complex problems. He calculated the orbits of the planets around the sun and the effect of Jupiter's gravity pulling on Saturn. He then asked an astronomer if he had noticed Saturn's motion change unexpectedly when it passed near Jupiter. The motion had changed and by just the amount Newton calculated. Newton's laws are still used to understand and predict motion today.

The change in Saturn's motion depended on the direction of Jupiter's force. As **Figure 12-9** shows, you must know the direction of a force to know what effect it will have.

What You'll Learn

► Newton's second law of motion
► Why the direction of force is important

Vocabulary
Newton's second law of motion
normal force

Why It's Important

► Newton's second law explains how any object, from a swimmer to a satellite, moves when any force acts on it.

Figure 12-9 The boy is moving at constant speed. When the girl gives him a gentle push, will he speed up, slow down, or turn to one side? You have to know the direction of a force to understand how it will affect motion.

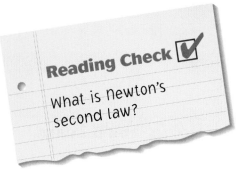
Newton's first law of motion describes the motion of an object with no net force acting on it. **Newton's second law of motion** states, "An object acted upon by a net force will accelerate in the direction of the force according to the following equation." ✔️

$$\text{acceleration} = \frac{\text{net force}}{\text{mass}}$$

$$a = \frac{F_{net}}{m} \text{ or } F_{net} = ma$$

In this equation, a is the acceleration, m is the mass, and F_{net} is the net force. Force is measured in newtons, abbreviated N; $1 \text{ N} = 1 \text{ kg} \cdot \text{m/s}^2$. If force acts on a small mass and a large mass, the small mass accelerates more. For example, if you try to push an empty box across the floor, you can accelerate it faster than if the box is packed with books.

Using Math

A force of 30 N acts on a 6-kg mass. What is the acceleration? If a 0.5-kg mass accelerates at 9.8 m/s², what is the force?

Newton's Second Law and Momentum

Momentum is equal to mass times velocity. When a net force acts on an object, the object's momentum changes. For example, when the bicyclist in **Figure 12-10** brakes, he exerts a force to reduce his velocity. When he reduces his velocity, he reduces his momentum.

The longer a net force acts the greater the change in momentum. The change in momentum, $p_2 - p_1$, is the difference between the object's momentum before and after the force acts. This is described by the following formula.

$$\text{Force} \times \text{time} = \text{change in momentum}$$

$$Ft = p_2 - p_1$$

Because $p_1 = mv_1$ and $p_2 = mv_2$, you can substitute mv_1 and mv_2 in the equation above.

$$Ft = mv_2 - mv_1$$

The force that acts on an object is related to the initial velocity, v_1, and final velocity, v_2, of the object.

Notice that the force can be positive or negative. Force is defined relative to a frame of reference. In the example in **Figure 12-10,** the positive direction is defined as forward. A force that slows the bike is directed backward, so such a force is negative.

Balanced Forces

While you are reading this sentence, you are probably sitting in a chair. Are forces acting on you now? Newton's first law says that if you're at rest, all the

Figure 12-10 This bicyclist uses the brakes to slow down. His velocity before and after he brakes is forward. **In what direction is the force?**

forces acting on you are balanced. Gravity is pulling you down. Your chair is pushing you up. The outward force from a surface, such as the upward force provided by your chair, is called the **normal force.** *Normal* means at a right angle. On a flat surface, the normal force is straight up and balances your weight. The normal force is supplied by the strength of the surface—in this case, the chair. If you put a heavy weight on a rickety chair, the chair might not be able to provide enough normal force to balance the weight. Then, the chair breaks.

When the surface is tilted, the normal force is reduced, as shown in **Figure 12-11.** The normal force no longer balances the weight. If friction doesn't balance this net force (look back at **Figure 12-5A**), you will start moving downhill.

Figure 12-11 The normal force acts outward from a surface. On a hill, the normal force is less than your weight, and not opposite in direction. The forces are not balanced, so there is a net force parallel to the hill.

Using Math

Force and Change in Momentum

Example Problem
A bicyclist exerts a net force of 24 N and accelerates from 2 m/s to 4 m/s. Find the time needed to do this if the bicycle and rider have a mass of 90 kg.

Problem-Solving Steps
1. What is known? velocity before and after, $v_1 = 2$ m/s and $v_2 = 4$ m/s, mass $m = 90$ kg, force $F = -24$ N
2. What is unknown? time t
3. Use the equation $Ft = mv_2 - mv_1$.
4. **Solution:**
$$Ft = mv_2 - mv_1$$
$$(24 \text{ N})t = (90 \text{ kg})(4 \text{ m/s}) - (90 \text{ kg})(2 \text{ m/s})$$
$$(24 \text{ kg} \cdot \text{m/s}^2)t = 180 \text{ kg} \cdot \text{m/s}$$
$$t = 7.5 \text{ s}$$

The bicyclist takes 7.5 s to reach the new speed.

Practice Problem
The same bicyclist exerts a force on the brakes to slow from 4 m/s to 0 m/s. This takes 12 s. What was the force?
Strategy Hint: Is the force positive or negative?

Figure 12-12 The force of air resistance on these skydivers pushes them up. The force of gravity pulls them down. When the forces are equal, the skydivers fall at a constant speed. This speed is called terminal velocity.

Another example of balanced forces is an object moving at constant speed, such as the bicyclist in **Figure 12-8.** Even falling objects eventually reach a constant speed due to air resistance. *Terminal velocity* is the speed an object reaches when the force of gravity is balanced by the force of air resistance, as shown in **Figure 12-12.** When parachutists jump from an airplane, they will fall for a long time before opening the parachutes. As they accelerate downward, the air resistance against each parachutist's body gets stronger until terminal velocity is reached. If a jumper falls spread eagle, the terminal velocity is about 215 km/h. If a jumper falls in a jack knife, the terminal velocity could be 320 km/h. Although this is very fast, it is still constant. When the speed is constant, the forces acting must be balanced.

Once the parachute is opened, the upward force of air resistance on the open parachute is much greater than the downward force of gravity. The forces are unbalanced and the increased air resistance will slow the parachutist down to a safer terminal velocity of about 18 km/h.

Unbalanced Forces

When the forces acting on an object are not balanced, the object accelerates in the direction of the net force. It might speed up, slow down, or turn.

Figure 12-13 The force and acceleration are to the left. **If the puck has a mass of 0.2 kg and the hockey stick exerts a force of 100 N for 0.1 s, what is the final speed of the puck, v_2?**

Speeding Up

If you look back at all of the examples of objects speeding up, you'll notice there's something pushing or pulling the object in the direction it is moving. The direction of the push or pull is the direction of the force. It is also the direction of the acceleration. Force is in the same direction as the velocity if the object is speeding up, as shown in **Figure 12-13.**

For example, if an object is at rest or moving in a positive direction, and it is accelerated at +4 m/s², it will go +4 m/s faster every second the force acts. You accelerate like this when you fall. Your velocity increases downward by 9.8 m/s every second. This is a rapid change that

v_2 F

Figure 12-14 When you catch a ball, you exert a force opposite to the direction of the ball's motion. **If you exert a force of 40 N on a 0.5-kg ball moving at 10 m/s, how long does it take to stop the ball?**

produces high speeds in just seconds. If you have ever jumped off a high-diving platform, you know how quickly you speed up.

Slowing Down

To slow down an object you have to push or pull it against the direction it is moving. An example is given in **Figure 12-14.** This time the force is opposite to the velocity. If the velocity is positive, then the acceleration is negative and makes the velocity less and less.

When a platform diver hits the water, the water provides a large force that slows the diver down. If the diver doesn't have the correct form when entering the water, this force can hurt. You may have experienced this. Water normally seems easy to move around, but when you hit it quickly, its tendency is to remain at rest. It pushes up against you as you enter the water. The force of the water against your body can stop it about five times faster than the pull of gravity accelerated it.

Turning

Sometimes forces and motion are not in a straight line. If a net force acts at an angle to the direction of motion, an object will follow a curving path. Its velocity will change because the direction of motion changes. The object might be going slower, faster, or at the same speed after the turn.

If you jump straight forward from a diving board you will not continue straight across the pool at that height. The force of gravity accelerates you downward, at a right angle to your direction of motion.

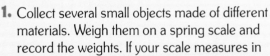

Measuring Buoyant Force

Procedure

1. Collect several small objects made of different materials. Weigh them on a spring scale and record the weights. If your scale measures in kilograms rather than newtons, multiply by 10 m/s^2 to get the force in newtons.

2. Now, attach each object to the spring scale and place the object in water. Compare the force reading on the scale with the weights you found in step 1.

Analysis

1. Compare the differences in the weights.

2. How would you find the buoyant force exerted upward on each object by the water?

Your body follows a curving path in the air, as shown in **Figure 12-15.**

Acceleration makes motion exciting because you can feel the change. Pushing then pulling, fast then slow, up then down—these are the action words of force and acceleration. They are what make a day at the amusement park or the swimming pool so much fun.

Figure 12-15 When a diver jumps forward, she doesn't keep moving in a straight line. Gravity exerts a force perpendicular to her motion, turning her.

Section Assessment

1. A human cannonball with a mass of 80 kg is fired out of a cannon with a force of 6400 N. The force lasts for 0.32 s. Find the acceleration and final speed.

2. You are riding on your bicycle at a speed of 20 km/h when you decide to stop pedaling. Draw a simple picture of you on your bicycle. Using arrows to represent forces, draw and label all the forces acting on you as you coast along. If it takes you a minute to stop, at what rate did you accelerate?

3. **Think Critically:** Explain how you can determine the direction of a force by watching an object's change in motion.

4. 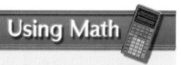 **Skill Builder**
   Making and Using Tables The gravitational force on the surface of each planet in our solar system is different. Do the **Chapter 12 Skill Activity** on page 565 and use a table to find out what you would weigh on different planets.

Using Math

A ball of mass 5 kg is moving at 2 m/s. A force takes 4 s to stop the ball. Find the force.

Science&Math

Applying the Pythagorean Theorem

One way to represent a force is with a vector. A vector is an arrow that points in the direction of the force and is proportional in length to the size of the force. For example, a 3-N force to the left can be represented on paper by a 3-cm arrow pointing left. Vectors also can represent other quantities that have number and direction, such as displacement, velocity, momentum, and acceleration.

Adding Vectors

You can represent all the forces acting on an object with vectors. When all the vectors are connected tip-to-tail, the vector for the total force is drawn from the end of the chain to the head, as follows.

Problem

A boat is moving east at 10 km/h relative to the water. The water is flowing south at 6 km/h relative to the shore. Find the velocity of the boat relative to the shore.

Solution

1. Make a sketch of the situation. Note that the vectors are at right angles.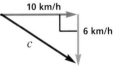

2. The two velocities form two sides of a right triangle. To find the boat's actual velocity, find the length of the hypotenuse. Use the Pythagorean theorem, $c^2 = a^2 + b^2$.

3. Substitute 10 and 6 for a and b, and solve for c.

$$c^2 = a^2 + b^2$$
$$= (10 \text{ km/h})^2 + (6 \text{ km/h})^2$$
$$= 136 \text{ (km/h)}^2$$
$$c = \sqrt{136 \text{ km}^2/\text{h}^2} = 11.7 \text{ km/h}$$

So, the boat is moving at about 12 km/h relative to the land.

Practice PROBLEMS

1. A plane is flying north at 500 km/h. A wind is blowing toward the east at a speed of 60 km/h. What is the actual speed of the plane?

2. You push on the front of a box with a force of 5 N. Your friend pushes on the left side of the box with a force of 12 N. What is the total force on the box? Use an arrow to show the direction of the force.

3. A ball is thrown with a forward velocity of 4 m/s and an upward velocity of 1 m/s. Find the total velocity of the ball.

Modeling Motion in Two Directions

Possible Materials

- Masking tape
- Stopwatch
  *watch or clock with a second hand
- Meterstick
  *metric tape measure
- Spring scales marked in newtons (2)
- Plastic lid
- An egg in its shell
  *Alternate Materials

When you move a computer mouse across a mouse pad, how does the rolling ball tell the computer cursor to move in the direction you push the mouse? Inside the housing for the mouse's ball, there are two or more rollers that the ball rubs against as you move the mouse. They measure up-and-down motion and back-and-forth motion. What happens to the rollers when you move diagonally and at different angles?

Recognize the Problem

Place an egg on something that will slide, such as a plastic lid. The container is called a *skid.* Lay out a course to follow on the floor. Can you move an egg from one point to another using forces in only two directions?

Form a Hypothesis

How can you combine forces to move in a straight line, along a diagonal, or around corners? Write a plan for moving your egg along the path.

Goals

- **Move** the skid across the ground using two forces.
- **Measure** how fast the skid can be moved.
- **Determine** how smoothly the direction can be changed.

Safety Precautions

Be careful not to drop the egg.

Test Your Hypothesis

Plan

1. **Lay out** a course that involves two directions, such as the course shown in the photo.

2. **Attach** two spring scales to the skid. One will always pull straight forward. One will always pull to one side. You cannot turn the skid. If one scale is pulling toward the door of your classroom, it must always pull in that direction. (It can pull with zero force, if needed, but it can't push.)

3. How will you handle movements along diagonals and turns?

4. How will you measure speed?

5. **Experiment** with your skid. How hard do you have to pull to counteract sliding friction at a given speed? How fast can you accelerate? Can you stop suddenly without spilling the egg, or do you need to slow down?

6. **Write a plan** for moving your egg along the course by pulling only forward and to one side. Be sure you understand your plan and have considered all the details.

Do

1. Make sure your teacher approves your plan before you proceed.

2. **Try** moving your egg along the path.

3. **Modify** your plan, if needed.

4. **Organize** your data so it can be used to run your course.

5. **Test** your results with a new route.

Analyze Your Data

1. What was the difference between the two routes? How did this affect the forces you could use on the egg?

2. How did you **separate and control variables** in this experiment?

3. Was your hypothesis supported? Explain.

Draw Conclusions

1. What happens when you combine two forces at right angles?

2. If you could pull on all four sides (front, back, left, right) of your skid, could you move anywhere along the floor? **Make a hypothesis** to explain your answer.

12•3 Newton's Third Law

Action and Reaction

What You'll Learn

▶ Newton's third law of motion

Vocabulary
Newton's third law
of motion

Why It's Important

▶ Newton's third law can help
you understand motion from
walking to launching rockets.

Newton's first two laws explain everything about the motion of a single object. If the forces acting on the object are balanced, the object will remain at rest or stay in motion with constant velocity. If the forces are unbalanced, the object will accelerate in the direction of the net force.

Newton's final law describes the connection between the object supplying the force and the object receiving the force. **Newton's third law of motion** states, "Forces always act in equal but opposite pairs." Another way of saying this is "For every action, there is an equal but opposite reaction." This means that one object can't supply a force (action) without the object it is acting on causing a return force (reaction), as shown in **Figure 12-16.**

Figure 12-16 When one ice-skater pulls on the second, the second pulls back just as hard. The forces are equal and opposite.

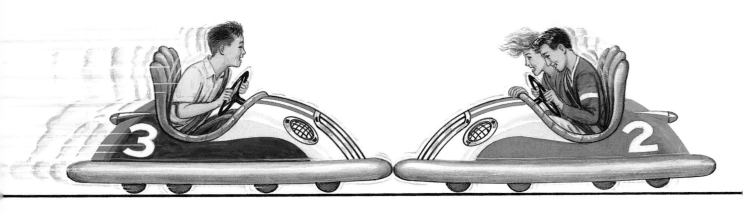

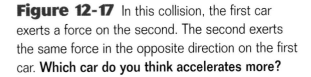

Figure 12-17 In this collision, the first car exerts a force on the second. The second exerts the same force in the opposite direction on the first car. **Which car do you think accelerates more?**

Fun with Newton

Imagine you're driving a bumper car and are going to ram into your two friends in another car, head-on, as shown in **Figure 12-17.** Initially, your friends are at rest. When your bumper meets theirs, its surface pushes against their bumper's surface. Their car accelerates in the direction you forced it to move—backwards. By Newton's third law, their car pushes you with an equal and opposite force, which is directed toward you. This causes your car to slow down because the force was against your motion. Action-reaction forces are always the same size but are in opposite directions and act on different objects.

There is no delay in time between the action and the re-action. They occur at the same time. If you touch your nose with your finger, your nose and finger sense the touch at exactly the same time. These are action-reaction forces. As soon as you remove your finger, the nerves in both your finger and nose will sense this. Also, when you touch your nose, your head moves in the direction of the finger's push, and the finger slows down as the nose pushes back. Why doesn't your head's motion change as drastically as your finger's motion?

Usually, you don't notice the action-reaction that goes on as you move about. You know how to use these forces from experience. You have been learning this since you learned to sit up or roll over. When you start looking, you notice action-reaction pairs all around you.

Using Math

Two students pull on each other. The 45-kg student has an acceleration of 0.2 m/s². What is the acceleration of the 50-kg student? Use action force = reaction force.

*inter*NET CONNECTION

Visit the Glencoe Science Web Site at **www.glencoe.com/ sec/science/ca** for more information about the physics of living things.

Force of ground against shoe

Force of shoe against ground

Figure 12-18 The force of the ground on your foot is equal and opposite to the force of your foot on the ground. If you push down harder, the ground pushes up harder.

Reading Check

If the action force is the pull of Earth on a diver, what is the reaction force?

LIFE SCIENCE

INTEGRATION ▶

Large and Small

Another reason it's easy to miss the action-reaction pair is because one of the objects is often much more massive and appears to remain motionless when a force acts on it. It has so much inertia, or tendency to remain at rest, that it hardly accelerates. Walking is a good example. When you walk forward, you push backward on the ground. Your shoe pushes Earth backward, and Earth pushes your shoe forward, as shown in **Figure 12-18.** Earth has so much mass, it does not noticeably move when you push it. You have very little mass compared to Earth. Earth pushes you forward with enough acceleration to make you move. The forces are the same but in opposite directions. If you step on something that can move easily, like a skateboard, you can see it being pushed back.

One subtle example of action-reaction is falling to the ground after jumping off a diving board or a step. Earth's gravity pulls a diver down with an acceleration of 9.8 m/s². The reaction is the diver pulling Earth up. The forces are equal but opposite. Why don't you notice Earth being moved by this force? The person's mass is a tiny fraction of Earth's mass, so Earth's acceleration is a tiny fraction of the person's acceleration. ☑

More Examples of Newton's Third Law

Have you ever stuck your hand out a car window and felt the wind push your hand back? Did it take a lot of strength to keep your hand steady? Why was it hard to hold your hand still? The answer is because air has mass. Your hand exerts a force forward on the air, and the air exerts an equal and opposite force back against your hand. The faster the car is going, the more force you have to exert to equal the force of the air.

When a bird flies, its wings push the air down and backward along a diagonal. In reaction, the air pushes the bird upward and forward, as shown in **Figure 12-19A.** If you could see the air, you would see it accelerate quickly as the bird pushes it. Air has little inertia. The bird is more massive than the air and does not accelerate as much.

When you paddle a canoe, there is little friction between the canoe and the water. To move the canoe forward, you push water back with your paddle. The paddle has a large enough surface to push a lot of water. Although it is hard to

Figure 12-19 When a bat flies or a fish swims, they also push on the air or water around them. **What pushes back?**

A The bird's wings push down on the air, which pushes up on the wing. In a wind tunnel, you could see how the bird's wings push on the air. Without air to push on, the bird couldn't fly.

see the water move, you can see currents form on the surface as the water is pushed backwards, as in **Figure 12-19B.** The water accelerates backwards and reacts by pushing forward on the paddle. Because the paddle is attached to you and you are attached to the canoe, the canoe accelerates in the forward direction. The same thing happens when you use your arms to swim. Can you think of another example of action-reaction?

B The paddle pushes back on the water, and the water pushes forward on the paddle.

Section Assessment

1. You sit on the floor and push a skateboard with a force of 6 N. If your mass is 60 kg, what is the force the skateboard exerts on you? In what direction is the force?

2. A hockey puck is at rest on the ice. What two forces are acting on it? You now hit the puck across the ice. While you are hitting the puck, what forces act on it? What else has a change of motion when the puck is hit?

3. **Think Critically:** Suppose you are an astronaut on the space shuttle. What would happen if you pushed against a chair that was not bolted to the floor? Why is pushing against a chair that is bolted down different?

4. **Skill Builder**
   Using Numbers A person standing on a canoe throws a cement block over the side. The action force on the cement block is 60 N. The reaction force is on the person and canoe. Their total mass is 100 kg. What is their acceleration? If you need help, refer to Using Numbers in the **Skill Handbook** on page 543.

Science Journal
Some people have trouble understanding Newton's third law. They reason, "If every action has an equal and opposite reaction, nothing will ever move." Explain why objects can still move. (Consider whether the forces act on the same object or on different objects.)

Balloon Races

Materials

- Balloons of different sizes and shapes
- Drinking straws
- String
- Tape
- Meterstick
- Stopwatch or clock

Going into space captures people's imaginations. Rockets use Newton's third law to propel them. In this experiment, you will compare different balloon rocket designs. The balloon rocket is powered by escaping air, using Newton's third law. Its motion is determined by Newton's first and second laws.

What You'll Investigate

How does Newton's third law accelerate different balloon rockets?

Goals

- **Measure** the speed of a balloon rocket.
- **Describe** how Newton's laws explain a rocket's motion.

Procedure

1. Run a string across the classroom to make a rocket path. Leave one end loose so you can easily place the rockets on the string.

2. **Make** a balloon rocket according to the photo. Don't tie the balloon closed. Let it run down the track. **Measure** its distance and time.

3. Repeat step 2 with different balloons.

Conclude and Apply

1. **Compare and contrast** the distances traveled. Which rocket went the greatest distance?

2. **Calculate** the average speed for each rocket. **Compare and contrast** them. Which rocket has the greatest average speed?

3. **Infer** what aspects of these rockets made them travel far or fast.

4. **Draw** a diagram showing all the forces acting on a balloon rocket.

5. Use Newton's laws of motion to **explain** the motion of a balloon rocket from launch until it comes to a stop.

Describing Motion

The Laws of Motion

With Newton's laws and the law of conservation of momentum, summarized in **Table 12-1**, almost any motion problem can be solved. In most everyday problems, if you know an object's motion and all the forces acting on it, you can figure out how the object will move in the future and how it moved in the past. It can be exciting to make a prediction using Newton's laws and then see your prediction confirmed by experiment. **Figures 12-20** and **12-21** give examples of complex motions that can be analyzed with Newton's laws.

Table 12-1

The Laws of Motion	
Newton's first law	An object will remain at rest or continue moving with constant velocity until it is acted upon by a net force.
Newton's second law	An object acted upon by a net force will accelerate in the direction of the force according to the following equation. $$a = \frac{F_{net}}{m}$$
Newton's third law	Forces occur in equal but opposite pairs. (For every action, there is an equal but opposite reaction.)
Law of conservation of momentum	In a system where no outside forces act, the total momentum before and after a collision stays the same.

What You'll Learn

► How to use the law of conservation of momentum and Newton's laws of motion to describe and analyze motion

Why It's Important

► All the motion you observe, whether the moon in orbit or a fast-turning in-line skater, can be understood with these laws.

Figure 12-20 When the child pushes off the wall, the wall pushes against the child—Newton's third law. Conservation of momentum explains why the adult will be pushed back when she catches and slows the child. They glide back together. This demonstrates Newton's first law. Eventually friction with the water will slow them according to Newton's second law. **Can you find another example of Newton's third law?**

VISUALIZING Newton's Laws

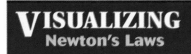

Figure 12-21 Athletes don't do calculations before they jump, run, or throw, but understanding how the laws of motion work can help you improve your game. Newton's laws are all seen on a bobsled run.

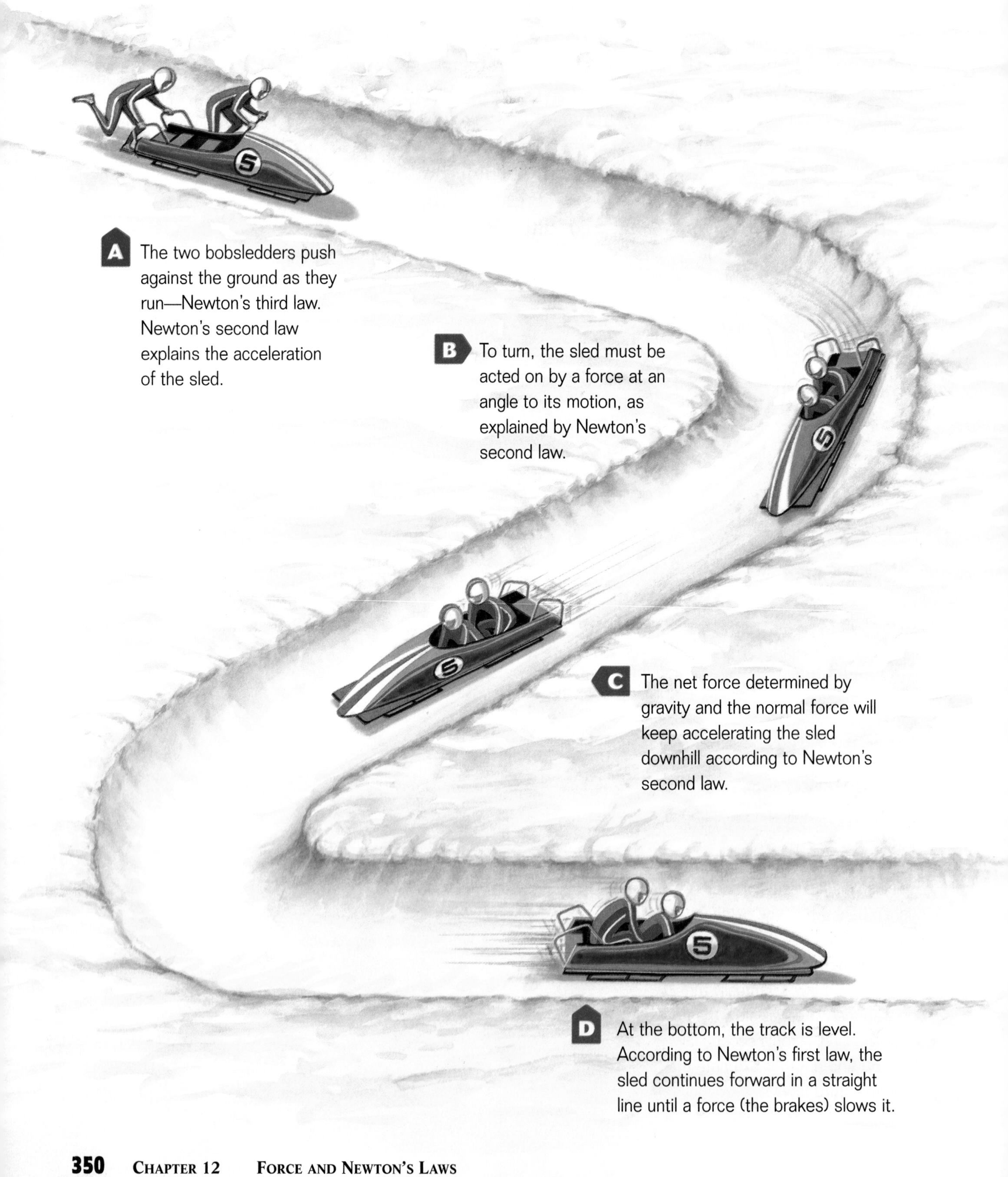
A The two bobsledders push against the ground as they run—Newton's third law. Newton's second law explains the acceleration of the sled.
B To turn, the sled must be acted on by a force at an angle to its motion, as explained by Newton's second law.
C The net force determined by gravity and the normal force will keep accelerating the sled downhill according to Newton's second law.
D At the bottom, the track is level. According to Newton's first law, the sled continues forward in a straight line until a force (the brakes) slows it.

Throwing and Catching a Ball

What happens when you can't use friction to hold yourself in one spot? Imagine you are standing on ice skates and the effect of friction is small. Suppose your friend exerts a forward force of 60 N for 1 s to throw a 15-kg ball, as shown in **Figure 12-22.** You can find the forward velocity of the ball.

$$\text{force} \times \text{time} = \text{mass} \times \text{velocity}$$

$$Ft = mv$$

$$(60\text{ N})(1\text{ s}) = (15\text{ kg})(v)$$

$$60\text{ kg} \cdot \text{m/s} = (15\text{ kg})(v)$$

$$v = 4\text{ m/s}$$

The ball is moving at 4 m/s.

What happens when you catch the ball? Use the law of conservation of momentum. Assume you have a mass of 50 kg.

$$\text{momentum before} = \text{momentum after}$$

$$\frac{\text{momentum of}}{\text{ball before}} = \frac{\text{momentum of you}}{\text{and ball after}}$$

$$m_1v_1 = m_2v_2$$

$$(15\text{ kg})(4\text{ m/s}) = (15\text{ kg} + 50\text{ kg})(v_2)$$

$$60\text{ kg} \cdot \text{m/s} = (65\text{ kg})(v_2)$$

$$v_2 = 0.9\text{ m/s}$$

You and the ball go backward at about 0.9 m/s.

Mini Lab

Measuring Force Pairs

Procedure

1. Work in pairs. Each person needs a spring scale.

2. Hook the two scales together. Each person should pull back on a scale. Record the two readings. Pull harder and record the two readings.

3. Continue to pull on both scales, but let the scales move toward one person. Do the readings change?

4. Try to pull in such a way that the scales have different readings.

Analysis

1. What can you conclude about the pair of forces in each situation?

2. Explain how this experiment demonstrates Newton's laws.

Figure 12-22 When you try to catch a ball without friction to hold you still, the law of conservation of momentum describes how you and the ball move backwards with the same momentum the ball alone had before the collision. **What would happen to your speed if you threw the ball back to your friend?**

Figure 12-23 If the engine compartment were closed, the gas inside would collide evenly with all sides, and it would stay at rest. But, the opening at the bottom of the engine lets the gas moving down escape. To get out, the gas must first bounce off the top of the compartment. The force down is equal to the force up.

Rocket Launch

The launching of the space shuttle is a spectacular use of Newton's third law. Three rocket engines supply the force of lift, called thrust. Just before launch, the shuttle's weight is about 20 million N. Nearly all of this is highly explosive rocket fuel.

When the rocket fuel is ignited, the burning creates a hot, fast-moving gas. Particles of gas push against the inside of the engine but can only escape out the bottom of the engine, as shown in **Figure 12-23.** The hard wall of the engine pushes the gas molecules downward when they bounce off of it. The upward push on the shuttle is the action. The downward push on the gas is the reaction. The forces are equal but opposite.

Gas particle

Engine compartment

Problem Solving

Modeling Motion in Space

Astronaut Jim Lovell, who flew on *Gemini 7* and *12* and *Apollo 8* and *13,* explains how underwater training for astronauts started.

The attempts to work outside a spacecraft on *Gemini* flights *9, 10,* and *11* were disasters. Every time the astronauts touched the spacecraft it seemed to repel them, and the astronauts became fatigued and hot, fighting to maintain position. We forgot Newton's third law of motion: "For every action there is an equal and opposite reaction." On Earth, gravity is so overwhelming that we don't notice the reaction. But in zero gravity the reaction is noticeable.

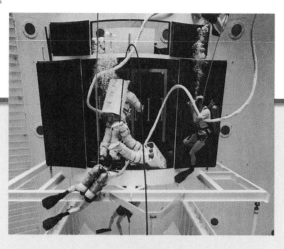

. . . Someone had the brilliant idea that a person. . . underwater would be a good substitute for an astronaut in zero gravity . . . [With this technique] we established the proper handholds and footholds, tools, and movement techniques that are still used today.

Think Critically: Explain how each of Newton's laws would affect your motion working outside a spacecraft in orbit.

Steering a Rocket

The space shuttle steers using the same principle that it does to launch. Little engines located all around its surface can fire in different directions. When the pilot wants to turn the shuttle's nose to the right, he or she will fire an engine on the front left and back right. The action-reaction is due to Newton's third law. According to Newton's second law, the reaction force will move the nose to the right and the tail to the left, as shown in **Figure 12-24A.**

The astronauts also have a backpack that works the same way, shown in **Figure 12-24B.** It uses cold rather than hot gas. Remember Newton's first law—once turning, how does an astronaut stop from turning?

Newton's laws are the keys to understanding motion. They aren't complicated, but you must think carefully to fully understand how they work. As you see how these laws are used to explain familiar motions, you can start to use them to analyze more complicated motions.

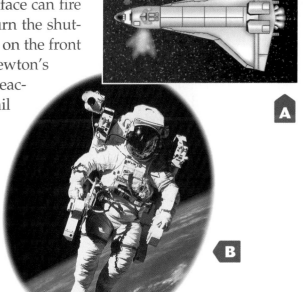

Figure 12-24 A stream of gas in one direction moves the shuttle (A) or astronaut (B) in the opposite direction.

Section Assessment

1. You catch a 0.2-kg baseball moving at 30 m/s. It takes you 0.4 s to bring it to a stop. What force did you use? If the ball is moving in a positive direction, is the force in a positive or negative direction?

2. A player throws a baseball. The ball flies forward and downward toward another player. The second player catches the ball. Explain how Newton's laws are involved in each of these three motions.

3. **Think Critically:** You can use the law of conservation of momentum to analyze a collision in which two balls roll together, collide, then roll apart. Explain what is happening in this collision using Newton's laws of motion.

4. **Skill Builder**
   Recognizing Cause and Effect Explain how cause and effect apply to Newton's second law. If you need help, refer to Recognizing Cause and Effect in the **Skill Handbook** on page 533.

Using Math

Look at **Figure 12-22.** Suppose the ball has a mass of 10 kg. Find its velocity if the throw is still 60 N for 1 s. Find your velocity after catching the ball.

For a **preview** of this chapter, study this Reviewing Main Ideas before you read the chapter. After you have studied this chapter, you can use the Reviewing Main Ideas to **review** the chapter.

The Glencoe MindJogger, Audiocassettes, and CD-ROM provide additional opportunities for review.

Section

12-1 FORCE

A **force** is a push or a pull. *How can you tell that a net force is acting on an object?*

NEWTON'S FIRST LAW

Newton's first law states that objects in motion tend to stay in motion and objects at rest tend to stay at rest unless acted upon by a **net force.** *Why don't we see objects in motion on Earth tending to stay in motion forever?*

Section

12-2 NEWTON'S SECOND LAW

Newton's second law states that an object acted upon by a net force will accelerate in the direction of this force according to the equation $a = F_{net}/m$. *If a baseball bat hits a bowling ball, why doesn't the bowling ball accelerate as quickly as a baseball that is hit just as hard?*

Reading Check ✓

List three questions someone might ask about force and the changes it causes. Then answer the questions.

Section
12-3 NEWTON'S THIRD LAW

Newton's third law states that forces are always applied in equal but opposite pairs between two objects. *What is meant by "equal but opposite pairs?" Use an example to explain.*

Section
12-4 LAWS OF MOTION

The laws of motion can be used to completely describe and understand most of the motion you observe. *Explain how each of Newton's three laws is involved when you jump off a diving board into a pool.*

Chapter 12 Assessment

Using Vocabulary

a. balanced forces
b. force
c. friction
d. net force
e. Newton's first law of motion
f. Newton's second law of motion
g. Newton's third law of motion
h. normal force
i. unbalanced forces

Each phrase below describes a science term from the list. Write the term that matches the phrase describing it.

1. the outward force a surface supplies to support an object
2. the forces acting on a body cancel each other
3. forces occur in equal and opposite pairs
4. the sum of the forces on an object
5. the force needed to turn a wheel

Checking Concepts

Choose the word or phrase that best answers the question.

6. How can Newton's third law be simply stated?
   A) action-reaction
   B) balanced-unbalanced
   C) inertia
   D) before-after

7. What is the rubbing when one surface moves against another surface called?
   A) terminal velocity
   B) friction
   C) normal force
   D) inertia

8. What is the combination of units for the newton?
   A) m/s^2
   B) $kg \cdot m/s$
   C) $kg \cdot m/s^2$
   D) kg/m

9. Which of the following has no direction?
   A) force
   B) acceleration
   C) momentum
   D) mass

10. What is a push or a pull a simple definition of?
    A) force
    B) momentum
    C) acceleration
    D) inertia

11. What is the type of friction important to walking?
    A) static friction
    B) sliding friction
    C) rolling friction
    D) air resistance

12. An object is accelerated by a net force in what direction?
    A) at an angle to the force
    B) in the direction of the force
    C) in the direction opposite to the force
    D) Any of these is possible.

13. If you exert a net force of 8 N on a 2-kg object for 3 s, what is the object's change in momentum?
    A) $12 \ kg \cdot m/s$
    B) $13 \ kg \cdot m/s$
    C) $24 \ kg \cdot m/s$
    D) $48 \ kg \cdot m/s$

14. You push against a wall with a force of 5 N. What is the force vector of the wall on your hands?
    A) 0 N
    B) 2.5 N
    C) 5 N
    D) 10 N

15. You are on a bike. Which of the following is an example of balanced forces?
    A) You pedal to speed up.
    B) You turn at constant speed.
    C) You coast to slow down.
    D) You pedal at constant speed.

Thinking Critically

16. A baseball is pitched east at 40 km/h. The batter hits it west at 40 km/h. Did the ball accelerate? Explain.

17. Frequently, we don't notice the pair of forces acting between two objects because one of the objects is Earth. How are the forces acting on Earth hidden?

18. A car is parked on a hill. The driver starts the car, accelerates until the car is driving at constant speed, drives at constant speed, then brakes to put the brake pads in contact with the spinning wheels. Explain how static friction, sliding friction, rolling friction, and air resistance are seen in this example.

19. You hit a hockey puck and it slides across the ice at constant speed. Is there a force keeping it in motion? Explain.

20. Newton's third law describes the forces between two colliding objects. Use this connection to explain the forces acting when you kick a soccer ball.

Developing Skills

If you need help, refer to the **Skill Handbook.**

21. **Making Models:** Explain why Galileo's thought experiment of rolling balls along a flatter and flatter ramp is a model of motion. Could the predicted motion ever be seen in a real experiment?

22. **Interpreting Scientific Illustrations:** Is there a net force acting on the object shown?

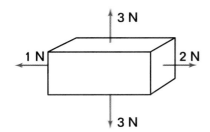

23. **Using Numbers:** An object of mass 0.4 kg accelerates at 2 m/s^2. Find the force.

24. **Recognizing Cause and Effect:** Use Newton's third law to explain why a rocket accelerates on takeoff.

THE PRINCETON REVIEW

Test-Taking Tip

Become an Expert on What You Fear Most If you think you can't remember all of the information, don't run away. Instead, consider it a challenge, meet the problem head-on, and you'll be surprised at how easy it is to conquer even the toughest concepts.

Test Practice

Use these questions to test your Science Proficiency.

1. Two students, Molly and Brian, are sitting in identical desk chairs with rollers. Molly weighs 40 kg and Brian weighs 60 kg. Brian quickly shoves Molly's chair, causing both chairs to move. During the push, while Brian's hand touched Molly's chair, which of the following is true?
   A) Neither student exerts a force on the other.
   B) Brian's force on Molly is larger.
   C) Molly's force on Brian is larger.
   D) Both students exert the same amount of force on each other.

2. You are standing in an elevator that is moving upward with constant velocity. What can you conclude about the forces acting on your body?
   A) The normal force of the floor is greater than the gravitational force.
   B) The normal force of the floor is less than the gravitational force.
   C) The normal force of the floor is equal to the gravitational force.
   D) No forces are acting.

CHAPTER 13

Work and Simple Machines

Chapter Preview

Section 13-1
What is work?
Section 13-2
Simple Machines

Skills Preview

Skill Builders
- Classify
- Compare and Contrast

Activities
- Design an Experiment
- Make a Model

MiniLabs
- Measure in SI
- Compare and Contrast

Reading Check ✔

Before you begin this chapter, write down what you already know about machines such as the lever, ramp, pulley, and wheel and axle.

Explore Activity

Two of the world's greatest buildings, monuments to humanity's progress, were built using very different tools. The Great Pyramid at Giza in Egypt shown at the left was built nearly 5000 years ago using blocks of limestone moved into place by hand with tools such as ramps and levers. In comparison, the Sears Tower in Chicago was built in 1973 using tons of steel that were hoisted into place by gasoline-powered cranes. Both structures were the tallest at the time they were built. But, the work done by each builder was drastically different.

Compare Forces

1. Balance a ruler on an eraser or lump of clay. At one end, place something heavier than the ruler, such as a paperback book. This is the load.

2. Using one finger, push down on the free end of the ruler to lift the load.

3. Repeat the experiment, placing the eraser or clay in various positions. Observe how much force is needed in each instance to lift the load.

Science Journal

In your Science Journal, describe what you discovered. How did the different distances between the load and eraser affect the force needed to lift the load?

13•1 What is work?

What You'll Learn

▶ How to determine if work is being done
▶ What work is and how it's calculated
▶ How power is related to work

Vocabulary
work
power

Why It's Important

▶ Whenever you lift, push, or pull something, you do work. If you understand work, you can learn to make work easier.

Work

What does *work* mean to you? You may think of household chores; a job at an office, factory, or farm; or the homework you do every night. Scientists also use the word *work*. When a force produces motion parallel to the direction of the force, **work** is done in the scientific sense. The following examples illustrate this definition of work.

When the motion is in the direction of the force, positive work is done. When you throw a ball, you do positive work on the ball, as shown in **Figure 13-1A.** When you pull a sled, you do positive work on the sled.

When the motion is opposite to the direction of the force, negative work is done. When you catch a ball, as shown in **Figure 13-1B,** you exert a force opposite to the ball's motion to bring it to a stop. You do negative work on the ball. When you pull a sled, friction acts against the sled's motion to slow it. Friction does negative work on the sled.

A force at a right angle to the direction of motion cannot perform work. When you carry the ball off the field, you exert an upward force to balance gravity, but the direction of motion is forward, at a right angle to the force. You do no work on the ball. When you pull a sled, the ground exerts a

Figure 13-1

A The player's arm exerts a forward force on the ball during the throw. The ball moves forward. Force and motion are in the same direction, so the player does *positive work* on the ball.

B The player's arm exerts a forward force to stop the ball. The ball and glove are moving backward. Force and motion are in opposite directions, so the player does *negative work.*

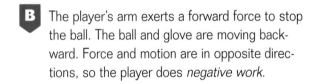

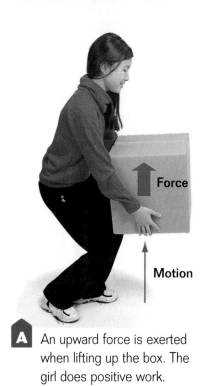

A An upward force is exerted when lifting up the box. The girl does positive work.

B An upward force is exerted while moving the box forward. No work is done.

C An upward force is exerted while lowering the box. The girl does negative work.

normal force upward on the sled, but that force does no work. **Figure 13-2** gives examples of positive work, no work, and negative work.

When you pick up a book bag, you do positive work. The force you exert and the motion of the book bag are in the same direction. When you walk to school at a steady speed carrying your book bag, you do no work on the book bag. Your upward force on the book bag does not act along the direction of motion.

Gravity can do work on an object. After a thrown ball leaves your hand, you no longer exert a force on it. Therefore, you do no work on it. However, gravity does work, pulling the ball toward Earth. Gravity's work is negative when the ball is going up (motion up, force down) and positive when the ball is going down (motion down, force down).

Another example of a situation where a force does no work is an object in orbit, as in **Figure 13-3.** The sun's gravity is pulling Earth toward the sun with a lot of force. But, Earth does not move toward the sun. Instead, it moves at a right angle to the sun's pull. No movement occurs parallel to the direction of the force, so the force does no work.

Effort Doesn't Always Equal Work

When a person applies force using muscles, work may or may not be done. It takes work to lift a heavy barbell, but not to hold it over your head. In either case, you would say you were working hard. But, for work to be done, the object must move.

Figure 13-2 To hold a box, you exert an upward force equal to gravity's downward force. **What would happen if the girl in C exerted no upward force on the box?**

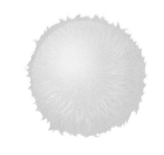

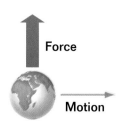

Figure 13-3 When force is at a right angle to the direction of motion, the force does no work.

Figure 13-4 The net force is at an angle to the direction of motion. Only the part of the force parallel to the direction of motion contributes to the work done.

Figure 13-5 Try pushing straight down on a book, pushing straight from one side, and pushing down and to the side. In each case, the downward force does no work. **Does the normal force of the desk on the book do work? Explain.**

CHEMISTRY
INTEGRATION

Work and Energy
Work transfers energy through motion. All forms of energy can do work. For example, chemical energy in your muscles is converted to kinetic energy when you run.

Force in Two Directions

Imagine you have been asked to mow the lawn. As you push the mower, you are exerting a force on it, as shown in **Figure 13-4.** Notice how the force acts through the handle of the mower at an angle to the direction the mower is moving.

By pushing at an angle, you push a little bit downward while also pushing forward. Because the downward push doesn't make the mower move down, no work is done by the downward force. The force in the forward direction moves the mower forward. Only this part of the net force does work. **Figure 13-5** shows another example.

Measuring Work

The formula for work, using W for work, F for force, and d for distance, is as follows.

$$\text{Work} = \text{Force} \times \text{distance}$$
$$W = Fd$$

Work is measured in joules, abbreviated J. This unit is named in honor of James Prescott Joule, who discovered how work and heat are related in engines. One joule is equal to 1 newton times 1 meter ($1\ \text{J} = 1\ \text{N} \cdot \text{m} = 1\ \text{kg} \cdot \text{m}^2/\text{s}^2$).

It takes about 100 N of force to push a lawn mower forward. You also are pushing down with about this same amount of force, but that effort does no work. At the end of mowing a typical lawn, you might have walked 1000 m. The work done is found as follows.

$$\text{Work} = \text{Force} \times \text{distance}$$
$$W = Fd$$
$$= (100\ \text{N})(1000\ \text{m})$$
$$= 100\ 000\ \text{J}$$

The work done is 100 000 N · m, or 100 000 J.

Now, find the work done to lift a 1000-kg car 10 m. Recall that to lift an object takes an upward force of mg, the object's mass times the acceleration due to gravity. Use $g = 10$ m/s^2.

$$\text{Work} = \text{Force} \times \text{distance}$$
$$\begin{aligned} W &= Fd \\ &= mgd \\ &= (1000 \text{ kg})(10 \text{ m/s}^2)(10 \text{ m}) \\ &= 100\ 000 \text{ kg} \cdot \text{m}^2/\text{s}^2 \\ &= 100\ 000 \text{ J} \end{aligned}$$

It seems incredible that mowing the lawn requires the same work as lifting the car. It all depends on how you do the work. Exerting a small force for a long distance can accomplish the same work as exerting a large force for a short distance. The Egyptians used this idea to build the pyramids. Today, tools are designed using the same basic ideas. A wrench makes it easier to remove a nut because you can use less force while pushing over a greater distance. ☑

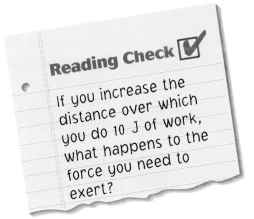

Reading Check ☑

If you increase the distance over which you do 10 J of work, what happens to the force you need to exert?

Power

What does it mean to be powerful? Like work, power is often used in everyday conversation. A person who can motivate people is considered a powerful leader. In science, **power** describes the rate at which work is being done. It measures how much work is being done in a certain period of time, usually a second. It is calculated using the following formula.

$$\text{Power} = \frac{\text{Work done}}{\text{time to do it}}$$

This can be shortened using P for power, W for work, and t for time.

$$P = \frac{W}{t}$$

The unit for power is called the watt, abbreviated W. This unit is named in honor of James Watt, the inventor of an improved and practical version of the steam engine. One watt is equal to 1 joule per second (1 W = 1 J/s).

Power is often used to describe engines. Humanity's ability to harness large amounts of power in huge engines has made it possible to construct buildings like the Sears Tower in Chicago. But, power also can be used to describe the effort put out by animals or people.

Try at Home

Mini Lab

Measuring Work and Power

Procedure

1. Measure the mass of a book.
2. Go to a ramp or stairway. Measure the vertical height of the ramp or stairs.
3. Time yourself walking slowly up with the book.
4. Time yourself walking quickly up with the book.

Analysis

1. Calculate and compare the work done on the book in each case.
2. Calculate and compare the power used to lift the book in each case.
3. Would it always require twice as much power to lift twice as much mass up the stairs? Explain.

Using Math

Calculating Power

Example Problem

A mountain rises 1300 m from its base. A 50-kg hiker steadily works her way to the top in about two hours. How much power does she supply to make the climb?

Problem-Solving Steps

1. What is known? mass $m = 50$ kg, $g = 10$ m/s^2, distance $d = 1300$ m, time $t = 2$ h $= 7200$ s. The force is equal to her weight, mg.

2. What is unknown? power, P

3. Use the equation $P = \dfrac{W}{t} = \dfrac{Fd}{t}$.

4. **Solution:** $P = \dfrac{Fd}{t} = \dfrac{mgd}{t} = \dfrac{(50 \text{ kg})(10 \text{ m/s}^2)(1300 \text{ m})}{7200 \text{ s}} = 90$ W

She supplies 90 W to reach the top.

Practice Problem

You push with a force of 25 N for a distance of 12 m. This takes half a minute. What power did you supply?

Strategy Hint: Check that your answer is in the proper units.

Section Assessment

1. How much work would it take to lift a 1000-kg limestone block to the very top of the Great Pyramid, 146 m above the ground?

2. If it takes 50 minutes to cut a lawn, and the work required is 100 000 J, how much power, in watts, is used?

3. **Think Critically:** Explain how you know that work is being done on an object.

4. **Skill Builder**

   Classifying A boy accelerates from a stop to a running speed while holding a ball. He carries the ball as he runs at constant speed. He throws the ball, exerting a force for 65 cm. Then, the ball is thrown back to him, and he stops it by exerting a force for 20 cm. In each case, is positive work, negative work, or no work done on the ball by the boy? If you need help, refer to Classifying in the **Skill Handbook** on page 525.

Using Math

A 7460-W engine is used to lift an I beam weighing 1000 kg up 145 m. How much work must the motor do to lift this mass at constant speed? How long will it take? Is this a reasonable amount of time? Explain.

Activity 13·1

Building the Pyramids

Materials

- Wood block
- Tape
- Spring scale
- Ruler
- 3-ring binder
- Meterstick
- Books

The workers who built the Great Pyramid at Giza needed to move 2.3 million blocks of limestone. Each block weighed more than 1 metric ton. The designers knew how to use ramps to reduce the force needed to lift the blocks into place.

What You'll Investigate

How does the force needed to lift a block a certain height depend on the distance traveled?

Goals

- **Model** the method that was probably used to build the pyramids.
- **Compare** the force needed to lift a block straight up with the force needed to pull it up a ramp.

Procedure

1. Use a pile of books to **model** a half-completed pyramid. **Measure** the height.

2. The wooden block **models** a block of stone. Attach it to the spring scale and **measure** the force needed to lift it straight up the side of the books.

3. Use a binder to **model** a ramp. **Measure** the ramp. **Measure** the force needed to pull the block up the ramp. Be sure to pull parallel to the ramp. Repeat the experiment with at least two other ramp lengths. Fill in the table.

Conclude and Apply

1. What happens to the force needed as the distance increases?

2. **Compare and contrast** your results for each case.

3. **Calculate** the work in each case.

4. How could you modify your setup to use less force?

Ramp Data		
Distance (cm)	Force (N)	Work (J)

Simple Machines

What is a machine?

The modern day is an age of machines. A *machine* is a device that makes work easier by changing the size or direction of the force applied to it. Try opening a can of soup without a can opener. Not only would it take you a long time to get it open, but also the mess made would leave you with little to eat. The can opener, shown in **Figure 13-6,** is a machine that focuses the force of your hand to the area where force is needed. The can opener turns a small force into a large force. Interestingly, the can was invented 130 years before the opener. It stored food so well, it was immediately put to use without a convenient way to get it open. For a long time, a hammer and chisel were used to open cans.

A **simple machine** is a machine with only one movement. Simple machines are the simplest form of tools. They include the inclined plane, lever, wheel and axle, and pulley. A **compound machine** is a combination of simple machines. The can opener is a compound machine that combines several simple machines. Examples of simple and compound machines are shown in the **Field Guide to Machines** at the end of this chapter.

Mechanical Advantage

You can't get something for nothing. The work produced by a machine can never be greater than the work put into it. With the can opener, your hand supplies a force to one end of the handle to dig a blade into the lid of a can. The can opener magnifies your force by increasing the distance over which you can exert that force. **Figure 13-7** illustrates how your arm can be used to magnify the force of your shoulder muscles.

Figure 13-6 The can opener changes the small force of your hand on the handles to a large force on the blade that cuts into the can.

A Hold your arm bent rigidly against your body. Throw a ball using only your shoulder muscles.

B Hold your arm out rigidly from your body. Throw the ball again using only your shoulder muscles.

The force you exert is called the **effort force,** F_e. The force you must overcome is the **resistance force,** F_r. In a can opener, the effort force is provided by your hand and the resistance force is provided by the strength of the can's lid. An ideal can opener would transmit all of your effort force into useful work with no losses. The work done on an ideal machine is the same as the work produced by the machine—work in equals work out. Real machines always spend some of the effort force overcoming friction or other losses. The work done by the effort force is that force multiplied by the distance over which the effort is exerted. The work done by the resistance force is that force multiplied by the distance over which the resistance is exerted. An example is shown in **Figure 13-8.**

Figure 13-7 Your shoulder muscles can generate a certain amount of forward force. Your arm lets you exert that force over a greater distance, magnifying the work done. **Which position would you use to throw a ball?**

Work in = Work out

$$F_e d_e = F_r d_r$$

Figure 13-8 To lift a loaded wheelbarrow (d_r), you must overcome the resistance force (F_r) of the weight. If you lift the handles three times as high as the center of the wheelbarrow is raised (d_e), you can use one-third the effort force (F_e) you would need without the machine.

Using Math

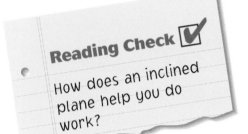

What does it mean if the mechanical advantage is 1? Less than 1? Greater than 1?

The principle, work in = work out, is used in every simple machine. As you increase the effort distance, you decrease the effort force needed.

How do you determine the effort force needed to do work with a simple machine? The **mechanical advantage,** *M.A.,* compares the effort force applied to a machine to the resistance force that it must overcome. This is calculated as a ratio.

$$\text{Mechanical Advantage} = \frac{\text{Resistance Force}}{\text{Effort Force}}$$

$$M.A. = \frac{F_r}{F_e}$$

The mechanical advantage tells you the number of times a machine increases the effort force. If a can opener increases an effort force of 20 N to overcome a resistance force of 140 N, *M.A.* = 140 N/20 N = 7. You normally want a large mechanical advantage. Most simple machines discussed in the rest of the section are designed to make work easier by giving you a mechanical advantage.

Reading Check ✔

How does an inclined plane help you do work?

Inclined Plane

Ramps may have enabled the ancient Egyptians to build their pyramids. In order to move limestone blocks weighing more than 1000 kg apiece, archaeologists hypothesize that the Egyptians built enormous ramps, similar to those used by motorists to enter a highway. An **inclined plane** is a sloped surface, more commonly called a ramp. It allows you to lift a heavy load by using less force over a greater distance. A ramp supports some of the object's weight. ✔

Figure 13-9 Using an inclined plane, an effort force of 300 N over 5 m can do the same work as 1500 N over 1 m. **What is the mechanical advantage of the ramp?**

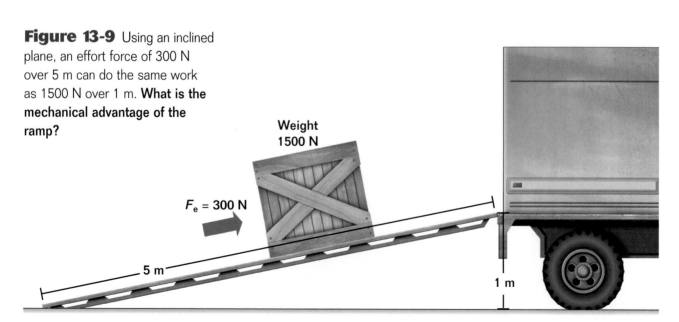

Weight
1500 N

$F_e = 300$ N

5 m

1 m

Imagine having to lift a 150-kg (1500-N) refrigerator 1 m off the ground onto a truck. This would require (1500 N)(1 m) = 1500 J of work, because you are doing work against gravity. What would help? If you used a 5-m-long ramp, as shown in **Figure 13-9,** the effort distance would be five times farther than the distance straight up. That means the effort force would be now five times less than it was, or 300 N. The inclined plane lets you push a greater distance but with less force. The mechanical advantage of an inclined plane is the length of the inclined plane divided by its height. In this example, the ramp has a mechanical advantage of 5.

Wedge

A **wedge** is a moving inclined plane. It can have one or two sloping sides. A knife, shown in **Figure 13-10,** is an example of a wedge. Your front teeth are wedges. They are designed for cutting. If you examine the teeth of carnivores and herbivores, you will see that carnivores' teeth are more wedge-shaped because they must cut more. Herbivores' teeth are designed for grinding. Scientists can determine what a fossilized animal ate when it was living by examining the teeth.

Screw

A **screw** is an inclined plane wrapped around a shaft, as shown in **Figure 13-11.** It looks like a road that wraps around a mountain. It's a lot easier to make your way up a slope gradually than to go straight up the side. When you screw a fixture into the wall, each turn of the screwdriver pushes the screw a little farther. If the length of the thread wrapped around a screw is four times as long as the screw, the screw has a mechanical advantage of 4. You still have to do the same amount of work, but it is spread out over four times the distance and you can use one-fourth the force.

Figure 13-10 A knife might move downward 10 mm to separate the two sides of the red pepper by 0.5 mm. **What is the mechanical advantage of the knife?**

LIFE SCIENCE
◄ **INTEGRATION**

Figure 13-11 The thread around a screw is an inclined plane. **If the thread is 4 cm long and the screw is 1 cm high, what is the mechanical advantage?**

Figure 13-12 A small effort force (F_e), exerted over a large distance (d_e), can move a large resistance force (F_r) a short distance (d_r). **If a lever has a mechanical advantage of 2, what effort force is needed to balance an 80-N resistance force?**

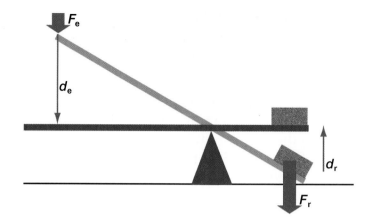

*inter*NET
CONNECTION

Visit the Glencoe Science Web Site at **www.glencoe.com/ sec/science/ca** for more information about early tools.

Lever

The lever was probably the first simple machine to be invented by prehistoric humans. A **lever** is a rod or plank that pivots about a point. The pivot point is called a **fulcrum.** A digging stick (or modern shovel) is a lever. Baseball bats, brooms, and teeter-totters are also levers.

A heavy load can be lifted a short distance using a small force over a great distance. This is illustrated in **Figure 13-12.** Again, $F_e d_e = F_r d_r$. For the lever to become balanced, the force times the distance from the fulcrum on each side must be equal. Different types of levers are shown in **Figure 13-13.**

Problem Solving

Calculating Work

The first screw was not used to fasten two pieces of wood together, but to raise water. The figure shows one of these devices, called Archimedes' screw. A long tube is wrapped around a cylinder. One end of the tube can go into the water. The other end empties into a container at the top.

As the wheel turns at the top, it dips the tube into the water, so water flows into the tube. As the wheel turns, the water flows along the tube. The water cannot flow out of the bottom of the tube because it would have to go over the top of the screw to get there. Water is moved up along the tube until it reaches the top.

Think Critically: Suppose you have an Archimedes' screw with a cylinder diameter 30 cm. If the tube wraps around the cylinder 40 times, about how long is the tube? If the screw raises water 3 m, what is the mechanical advantage of the machine?

Figure 13-13 In the formula $F_e d_e = F_r d_r$, the distance of each force from the fulcrum can substitute for the distance moved up and down. When $F_e d_e = F_r d_r$, the lever is in balance.

There are three classes of levers, depending on the location of the effort, load, and fulcrum. For each of them, $F_e d_e = F_r d_r$.

A In a first-class lever, such as a pan balance, the fulcrum is between the effort and the load.

F_e

B In a second-class lever, such as a wheelbarrow, the load is between the fulcrum and the effort.

F_e

C In a third-class lever, such as a baseball bat, the effort is between the fulcrum and the load. This lever allows you to apply the resistance force over a greater distance.

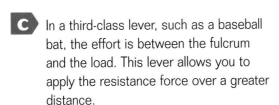

F_e

Figure 13-14 A potter's wheel is an example of a wheel and axle. A small force on the outside wheel keeps it spinning.

Wheel and Axle

Have you ever tried to turn a doorknob by holding onto the narrow base of the knob? It is hard to move. The doorknob magnifies the force of your hand. It is an example of a **wheel and axle,** two rigidly attached wheels that rotate together. It was invented around 3500 B.C. to turn a potter's table, as shown in **Figure 13-14.** With a small force at the edge of the wheel, the potter could easily keep the table turning as the pottery was shaped.

A wheel and axle is like a circular lever, as shown in **Figure 13-15.** The center is the fulcrum, and the wheel and axle turn around it.

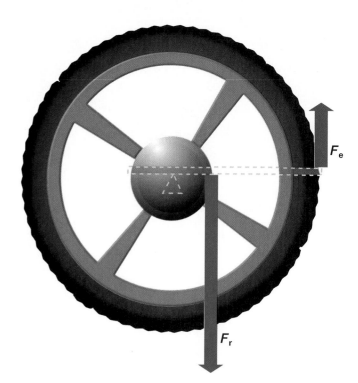

Figure 13-15 The mechanical advantage of

a wheel and axle is $\dfrac{\text{radius of wheel}}{\text{radius of axle}}$. A small

force on the wheel is transformed into a large force on the axle.

Observing Mechanical Advantage—Pulleys

Procedure 🥽

1. Give broomsticks or dowels to two students to hold. Tie a 3-m long rope to the middle of one stick. Wrap the rope around both sticks four times, leaving about 0.5 m gap between the sticks. The broomsticks are now pulleys.

2. Give the end of the rope to a third student.

3. While the two students pull the broomsticks apart, have the third student pull on the rope.

4. Observe what happens. Repeat using only two wraps of the rope and then using eight wraps.

Analysis

1. Describe what you observed. Could the students hold the sticks apart?

2. Compare and contrast the results with two, four, and eight turns of the rope around the pulleys.

3. With four turns of rope, what length of rope must be pulled to move the pulleys 10 cm closer together? What is the mechanical advantage of this pulley system?

Pulley

To raise a window blind, you pull down on a cord. The blind uses a pulley to change the direction of the force needed. A **pulley** is a surface, such as a wheel, that redirects force using a rope. It allows you to pull down to lift a weight rather than having to lift directly upward, as shown in **Figure 13-16.** You can use your body's weight to help supply effort. A rope thrown over a railing or tree branch can be used as a crude pulley system. This arrangement has a mechanical advantage of one, which means the effort and resistance forces are the same. The only advantage of using a simple pulley is that it is easier on your back. A large mechanical advantage can be created if more than one pulley is used. A double-pulley system is shown in **Figure 13-17,** with one pulley attached to a solid support and the other pulley attached to the load.

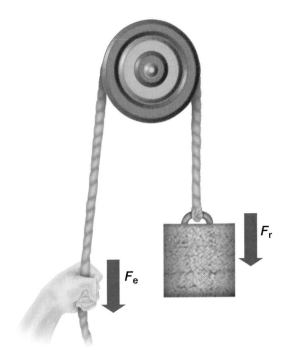

Figure 13-16 A simple pulley changes the direction of the effort force needed to move the load. **What is its mechanical advantage?**

Figure 13-17 In this double-pulley system, the ceiling supports some of the load.

A The person must provide an effort force equal to half the resistance force. The forces along the ropes on either side of a pulley must be equal.

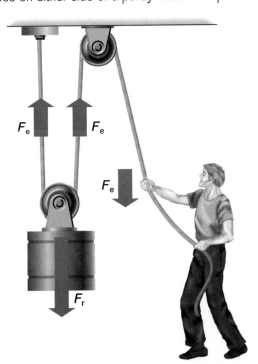

B After pulling 1 m of rope, the load is 0.5 m higher.

Each support rope is 0.5 m shorter.

This rope is 1 m longer.

0.5 m

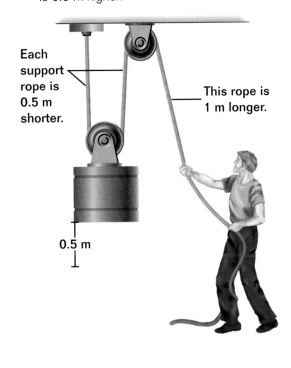

Efficiency

This chapter has calculated the forces and mechanical advantages of ideal machines, which lose nothing to friction or other problems. Real machines always have some loss. The **efficiency** of a machine is its ability to convert the work input, W_{in}, into the work the machine is designed to do, called work output, W_{out}. Efficiency is a percentage and is given by the following formula.

$$\text{efficiency} = \frac{W_{out}}{W_{in}} \times 100$$

An ideal machine has an efficiency of 100 percent. No real machine is perfectly efficient because some friction always steals away part of the work input and converts it to heat. The lever is nearly 100 percent efficient. Even the human body is fairly efficient in converting its chemical energy to useful work. A car is only about 20 percent efficient in converting the chemical potential energy released from the gasoline exploding in the engine into the kinetic energy of movement. Most of the energy is lost as the heat escapes from the hot engine and from friction in the car's many moving parts.

Visit the Glencoe Science Web Site at **www.glencoe.com/ sec/science/ca** for more information about designing machines.

Section Assessment

1. The Great Pyramid is 146 m high. How long would a ramp need to be to run from the top of the pyramid to the ground and have a mechanical advantage of 4?

2. A lever is used to lift a load with a resistance force of 500 N. The load is 1 m from the fulcrum. How far from the fulcrum must an effort force of 250 N be applied to lift the load?

3. If you put 8000 J of work into a machine with efficiency 60 percent, how much work will you get out?

4. **Think Critically:** Your arm and hand are a compound machine. Identify the simple machines that make it compound. Be creative. Use this machine to explain why it is easier to hold a heavy object close to your body rather than at arm's length.

5. 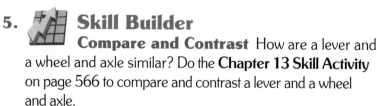 **Skill Builder**
   Compare and Contrast How are a lever and a wheel and axle similar? Do the **Chapter 13 Skill Activity** on page 566 to compare and contrast a lever and a wheel and axle.

In your Science Journal, explain how the lever, inclined plane, and wheel and axle are used in a can opener.

Using Electronic Calculators

A pocket calculator is a specialized computer programmed to solve arithmetic problems. The parts of a typical calculator include a power supply, a keypad for entering numbers and calculation commands, and a screen for displaying input numbers and calculation results. The brain of the calculator is a tiny silicon chip. This chip, the calculator's processing unit, performs arithmetic operations.

PARTS OF A CALCULATOR

1 Batteries or solar cells provide electricity.

2 Pressing a number on the keypad closes a contact between the key and the circuit board beneath it. The closed contact allows an electrical signal specific to that key to flow from the circuit board to a storage area in the calculator's processing unit.

3 The processing unit's storage area, or memory, holds all input information until the entire problem has been entered and is ready for processing.

4 With each key stroke, an electrical signal also flows from the processing unit to the screen, which displays the number or symbol.

5 When one of the function keys such as addition or multiplication is pressed, its unique signal is also sent to the processing unit for storage. In simple calculators, this information is not displayed on the screen.

6 Pressing the equal sign sends a signal to the processing unit, instructing it to perform the calculation stored in its memory. The result is sent to the screen for display.

Career CONNECTION

Interview someone in your community who works in an electronics-related field. Find out what the person did to get involved in that career.

Thinking Critically

1. What are some similarities and differences between pocket calculators and computers?

2. A calculator does exactly what you tell it to do. How can this be limiting? How can it help?

Pulley Power

Possible Materials

- Single- and multiple-pulley systems
- Nylon rope
- Steel bar to support the pulley system
- Meterstick
  metric tape measure
- Variety of weights to test pulleys
- Force spring scale
- A brick
  heavy book
- Balance or scale

Alternate Materials

It would have taken decades to build the Sears Tower without the aid of a pulley system attached to a crane. Hoisting the 1-ton I beams to a maximum height of 110 stories required tremendous lifting forces and precise control of the beam's movement.

Recognize the Problem

How can you use a pulley system to reduce the force needed to lift a load?

Form a Hypothesis

Write a hypothesis about how pulleys can be combined to make a system of pulleys to lift a heavy load, such as a brick. Consider the efficiency of your system.

Goals

- **Design** a pulley system.
- **Measure** the mechanical advantage and efficiency of the pulley system.

Safety Precautions

The brick could be dangerous if it falls. Don't stand under it.

Test Your Hypothesis

Plan

1. **Decide** how you are going to support your pulley system.

2. How will you measure the effort force and the resistance force? How will you determine the mechanical advantage? How will you measure efficiency?

3. **Experiment** by lifting small weights with a single pulley, double pulley, and so on. How efficient are the pulleys?

4. Use the results of step 3 to **design** a pulley system to lift the brick.

Do

1. Make sure your teacher has approved your plan before you proceed.

2. **Assemble** the pulley system you designed. You may want to **test** it with a smaller weight before attaching the brick.

3. **Measure** the force needed to lift the brick. How much rope must you pull to raise the brick 10 cm?

Analyze Your Data

1. **Calculate** the theoretical mechanical advantage of your pulley system. (You can refer to the **Field Guide to Machines** at the end of this chapter.)

2. **Calculate** the actual mechanical advantage of your pulley system.

3. **Calculate** the efficiency of your pulley system.

Draw Conclusions

1. **Explain** how increasing the number of pulleys increases the mechanical advantage.

2. How could you modify the pulley system to lift a weight twice as heavy with the same effort force used here?

3. **Compare** this real machine with an ideal machine.

FIELD GUIDE *to Machines*

FIELD *ACTIVITY*

For a week, use this field guide to identify machines that people use in everyday life. Many of the machines you will see are combinations of two or more simple machines. Try to identify all of the simple machines that make up the compound machine. Use the examples on the next pages to estimate the mechanical advantages of each machine.

Whenever and wherever work needs to be done, you can be sure that some type of a machine is involved. The joints in your body are simple machines that allow you to run, jump, bend, and lift. But, the amount of force your body can exert is limited. Machines have been developed that increase or change the direction of the force you can produce. Machines do not change the amount of work done. They only make doing work easier.

How Machines Are Classified

The more you look, the more you will discover machines being used in daily living. Machines can be divided into two categories, simple or compound. Simple machines are all variations of two basic machines—the lever and the inclined plane.

A compound machine is a combination of two or more simple machines. Most machines that you observe people using will be compound machines.

It takes the same amount of work to climb any route to the top of the mountain. It takes much less force when you use the switchback trail.

Simple Machines

Mechanical advantage is a measure of how much help a machine is going to be when you do work. You can estimate mechanical advantage (*M.A.*) for a simple machine by using the formulas below. The formulas give only estimates of *M.A.* because some of the force you apply to a machine must be used to overcome friction. The greater the *M.A.*, the more the machine increases your force.

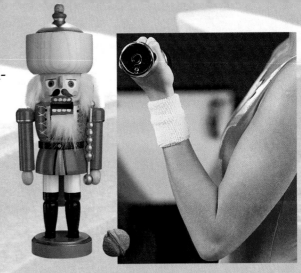

The Lever

$$M.A. = \frac{\text{length of the effort arm}}{\text{length of the resistance arm}}$$

F_r F_e

Resistance arm   Effort arm

The Pulley

$M.A.$ = number of ropes supporting the object

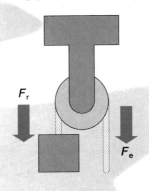

F_r

F_e

The Wheel and Axle

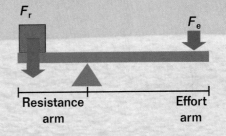

$$M.A. = \frac{\text{radius}_e}{\text{radius}_r}$$

radius$_r$

radius$_e$

F_e

F_r

The Inclined Plane

$$M.A. = \frac{\text{length of slope}}{\text{height of slope}}$$

The Wedge

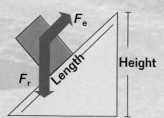

$$M.A. = \frac{\text{height}}{\text{width}}$$

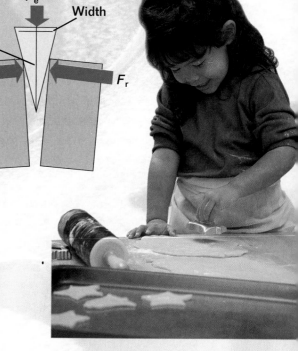

The Screw

$$M.A. = \frac{2\pi\,(\text{radius of circular path})}{\text{gap between ridges}}$$

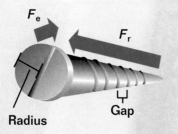

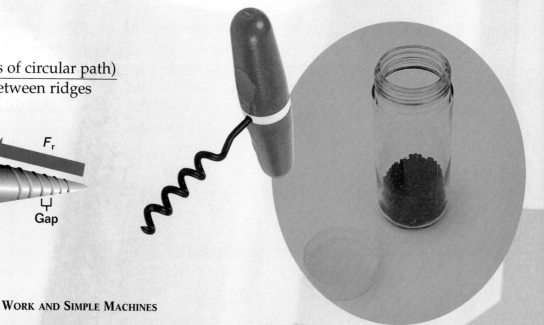

Recognizing Compound Machines

Scissors may look simple, but a pair of scissors is actually a compound machine. Two levers and two wedges combine to make an excellent cutting tool.

A compound machine is made up of two or more simple machines linked together. To estimate the mechanical advantage of a compound machine, multiply the mechanical advantages of each simple machine in the compound machine.

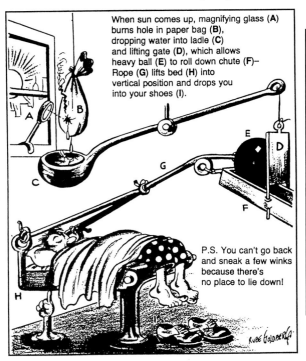

No More Oversleeping

When sun comes up, magnifying glass (**A**) burns hole in paper bag (**B**), dropping water into ladle (**C**) and lifting gate (**D**), which allows heavy ball (**E**) to roll down chute (**F**)— Rope (**G**) lifts bed (**H**) into vertical position and drops you into your shoes (**I**).

P.S. You can't go back and sneak a few winks because there's no place to lie down!

RUBE GOLDBERG

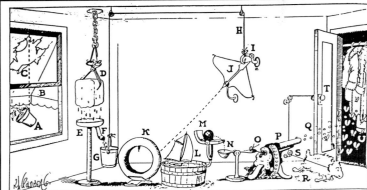

THE PROFESSOR EMERGES FROM THE GOOFY BOOTH WITH A DEVICE FOR THE EXTERMINATION OF MOTHS. START SINGING. LADY UPSTAIRS, WHEN SUFFICIENTLY ANNOYED, THROWS FLOWER POT (A) THROUGH AWNING (B). HOLE (C) ALLOWS SUN TO COME THROUGH AND MELT CAKE OF ICE (D). WATER DRIPS INTO PAN (E) RUNNING THROUGH PIPE (F) INTO PAIL (G). WEIGHT OF PAIL CAUSES CORD (H) TO RELEASE HOOK (I) AND ALLOW ARROW (J) TO SHOOT INTO TIRE (K). ESCAPING AIR BLOWS AGAINST TOY SAILBOAT (L) DRIVING IT AGAINST LEVER (M) AND CAUSING BALL TO ROLL INTO SPOON (N) AND PULL STRING (O) WHICH SETS OFF MACHINE GUN (P) DISCHARGING CAMPHOR BALLS (Q). REPORT OF GUN FRIGHTENS LAMB (R) WHICH RUNS AND PULLS CORD (S), OPENING CLOSET DOOR (T). AS MOTHS (U) FLY OUT TO EAT WOOL FROM LAMB'S BACK THEY ARE KILLED BY THE BARRAGE OF MOTH BALLS.
IF ANY OF THE MOTHS ESCAPE AND THERE IS DANGER OF THEIR RETURNING, YOU CAN FOOL THEM BY MOVING.

Look at the drawings of these two compound machines. Rube Goldberg used simple machines to invent complicated ways to do simple things. Name the simple machines used in the drawings.

For a **preview** of this chapter, study this Reviewing Main Ideas before you read the chapter. After you have studied this chapter, you can use the Reviewing Main Ideas to **review** the chapter.

The Glencoe MindJogger, Audiocassettes, and CD-ROM provide additional opportunities for review.

Section

13-1 WORK

A force does **work** when an object is moved parallel to the direction in which a force is applied. If the force and movement are in the same direction, as when you push a door closed, the work is positive. If the force and movement are in opposite directions, as when you push on a door to prevent it from closing too fast, the work is negative. Only the part of the force along the direction of motion does work.

No work is done when an object is carried forward at constant speed (there is distance but no force in that direction), when an object is held (there is a force but no distance), and when an object is swung in a circle (motion is at a right angle to the direction of force). *Is work done when you climb up the stairs? Explain.*

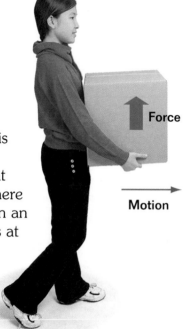

Force

Motion

Forward force

Downward force

Net force

Motion

CALCULATING WORK AND POWER

Work is calculated using the equation $W = Fd$. The unit of work is the joule, $1\ J = 1\ N \cdot m$. Only the force exerted parallel to the direction of motion is included in the calculation. **Power** measures the rate at which work is done. It is defined as follows.

$$P = \frac{W}{t}$$

The unit of power is the watt, $1\ W = 1\ J/s$. *If you do 48 J of work for a distance of 6 m, how much force do you apply? In what direction? If it takes 12 s, what is the power?*

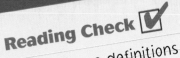

Reading Check ☑️

Write science definitions for *work, power, force,* and *efficiency.* Compare them to the common usage definitions of these words.

Section

13-2 SIMPLE MACHINES

A machine reduces the **effort force** needed to counter a **resistance force.** The work is the same, $F_e d_e = F_r d_r$. The **inclined plane, wedge, screw, lever, wheel and axle,** and **pulley** are **simple machines,** which have only one motion.

Mechanical advantage measures the decrease in effort force needed as follows.

$$M.A. = \frac{F_r}{F_e}$$

The larger the mechanical advantage, the more resistance force you can overcome with a given effort force. Because all machines have some loss to friction or heat, **efficiency,** is always less than 100 percent.

$$\text{Efficiency} = \frac{W_{out}}{W_{in}} \times 100$$

If a pulley system has a mechanical advantage of 4, how much rope will you have to pull to lift an 80-kg object 4 m?

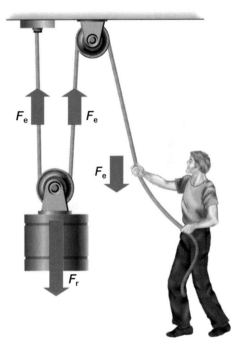

CONNECTION

Yvonne Ho Cardinale, Hydroelectric Engineer

As a hydroelectric engineer, Yvonne Ho Cardinale designs and maintains hydroelectric power plants, which use water stored behind a dam to make electricity. Her tasks include predicting how much electricity a plant can generate based on weather factors. She monitors weather stations and measures snow depth. Then, she uses computer models to help her decide how much water to save behind the dam so that power is produced when it is needed. *If the power plant produces less power, would a motor do work more quickly or slowly?*

Chapter 13 Assessment

Using Vocabulary

a. compound machine
b. efficiency
c. effort force
d. fulcrum
e. inclined plane
f. lever
g. mechanical advantage
h. power
i. pulley
j. resistance force
k. screw
l. simple machine
m. wedge
n. wheel and axle
o. work

Each phrase below describes a science term from the list. Write the term that matches the phrase describing it.

1. comparison of work in to work out
2. force put into a machine
3. a point about which a lever pivots
4. two rigidly attached wheels
5. a comparison of the effort force and resistance force for a machine

Checking Concepts

Choose the word or phrase that answers the question.

6. What is an example of a simple machine?
   A) baseball bat
   B) pair of scissors
   C) can opener
   D) car

7. When friction slows an object, what type of work does the force of friction do?
   A) positive work
   B) negative work
   C) no work
   D) both positive and negative work

8. An ax is a compound machine that includes what?
   A) a lever and wedge
   B) two levers
   C) a wedge and a pulley
   D) a lever and a screw

9. How can the unit for work be written?
   A) W · s
   B) kg · m^2/s^2
   C) N · m
   D) all of the above

10. A force of 8 N is exerted over 2 m to stop an object. What is the work done?
    A) 4 J
    B) −4 J
    C) 16 J
    D) −16 J

11. If a machine takes in 50 J and puts out 45 J, what is its efficiency?
    A) 0.9 percent
    B) 1.1 percent
    C) 90 percent
    D) 111 percent

12. A ramp decreases which of the following?
    A) height
    B) effort force
    C) resistance force
    D) effort distance

13. In which example is gravity doing work?
    A) an apple falling
    B) a planet in orbit
    C) a box on a table
    D) a bike rolling on a flat road

14. A force of 30 N exerted over a distance of 3 m does how much work?
    A) 3 J
    B) 10 J
    C) 30 J
    D) 90 J

15. A wheel with a radius of 20 cm is attached to an axle with a radius of 1 cm. An effort force of 100 N on the wheel counters a resistance force of what on the axle?
    A) 5 N
    B) 200 N
    C) 500 N
    D) 2000 N

Thinking Critically

16. Does gravity do positive or negative work on a falling object? Explain.

17. A doorknob is an example of a wheel and axle. Explain why turning the knob is easier than turning the axle.

18. The ground does 1600 J of work to stop a falling ball in 0.05 m. What force was needed?

19. How much effort force is required to lift an 11 000-N I beam using a pulley system with a mechanical advantage of 20?

20. A lever has a 9-N load 1.5 m from the fulcrum. Where should a 0.5-N effort force be applied to balance the load?

Developing Skills

If you need help, refer to the **Skill Handbook**.

21. Observing and Inferring: Suppose a lever is in balance. Would this arrangement be in balance on the moon, where the force of gravity is less? Explain.

22. Measuring in SI: At the 1976 Olympics, Vasili Aleseev shattered the world record for weight lifting when he lifted 2500 N from the floor to over his head, a point 2 m above the ground. It took him about 5 s to complete the lift. How much work did he do? What was his power?

23. Making and Using Graphs: A pulley system has a mechanical advantage of 5. Make a graph of the possible combinations of effort force and resistance force.

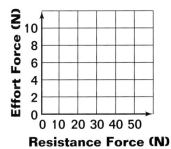

24. Designing an Experiment: Design an experiment to measure the efficiency of the ground in rebounding a basketball.

THE PRINCETON REVIEW

Test-Taking Tip

Study Sterile It's best to study in an environment similar to the one in which you'll be tested. Blaring stereos, video game machines, chatty friends, and beepers are not allowed in the classroom during test time. So why get used to them?

Test Practice

Use these questions to test your Science Proficiency.

1. A student exerts 150 W of power for 30 s. How much work is done?
   A) 50 J
   B) 75 J
   C) 300 J
   D) 4500 J

2. A block is pulled across the table with a rope, as shown. Which force does work?
   A) the normal force
   B) the force of gravity
   C) the upward force on the rope
   D) the sideways force on the rope

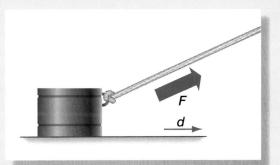

Interactions
in the
Physical
World

NATIONAL GEOGRAPHIC

What's Happening Here?

In a warehouse in Salt Lake City, Utah, these table tennis players (left) are "wired for action." They are also equally matched. How so? Because they share a brain! The engineer on the right is directing all the action. Each of the engineer's movements is transferred electronically to the robot named Sarcos. In this unit, you will learn how compound machines, such as robots, are made from simple machines. You will also learn how electrical energy can accomplish such feats. You will explore another way energy moves in the form of electromagnetic waves, including radio, micro-waves, and light. Telescopes, such as this one at Kitt Peak, Arizona (below), are used to collect light from distant objects. How do mirrors and lenses help magnify images, and how can scientists study light from the stars? These are a few of the questions you will explore in this unit.

interNET CONNECTION

Explore the Glencoe Science Web Site at **www.glencoe.com/sec/ science/ca** to find out more about topics found in this unit.

Chapter Preview

Skills Preview

Skill Builders
• Map Concepts
• Compare and Contrast

Activities
• Classify
• Measure in SI

MiniLabs
• Compare and Contrast
• Observe

Reading Check ✓

As you read, jot down ways your life would change if there were no waves. What would your life be like? Could you live at all?

Explore Activity

Think about a beautiful autumn day. You are sitting by a lake in a park. You hear music coming from a nearby school band practicing for a big game. A fish jumps out of the water and falls back making a splash. You see a circle of waves that move away from the fish's entry point. The circular waves pass by a floating leaf that fell from a tree nearby. How does the leaf move in response to the waves?

Observe Wave Behavior

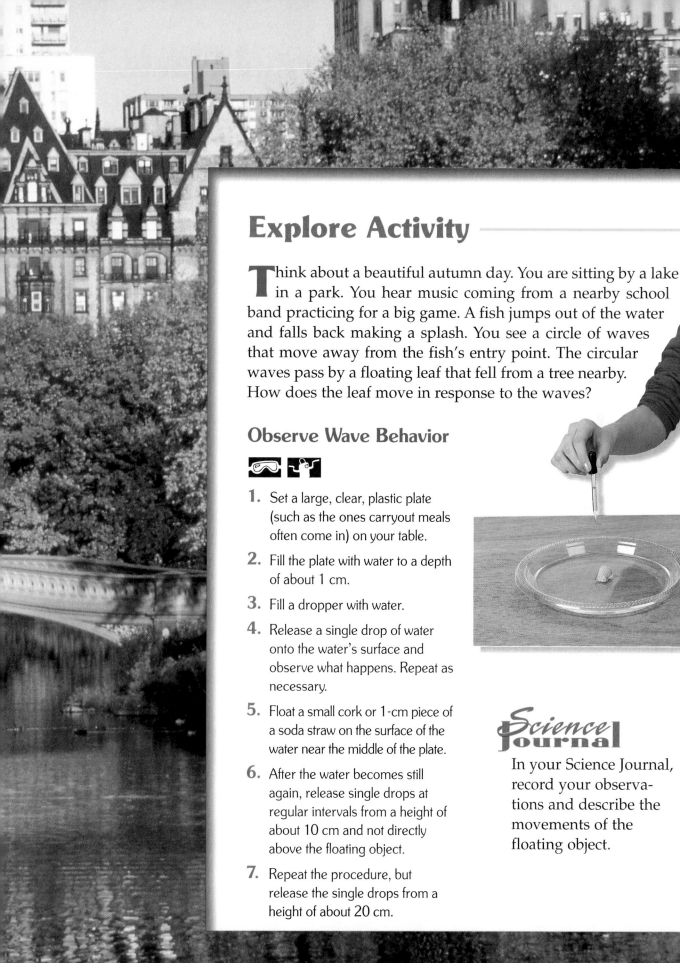

1. Set a large, clear, plastic plate (such as the ones carryout meals often come in) on your table.

2. Fill the plate with water to a depth of about 1 cm.

3. Fill a dropper with water.

4. Release a single drop of water onto the water's surface and observe what happens. Repeat as necessary.

5. Float a small cork or 1-cm piece of a soda straw on the surface of the water near the middle of the plate.

6. After the water becomes still again, release single drops at regular intervals from a height of about 10 cm and not directly above the floating object.

7. Repeat the procedure, but release the single drops from a height of about 20 cm.

Science Journal

In your Science Journal, record your observations and describe the movements of the floating object.

389

14•1 What are waves?

What You'll Learn

▶ Waves carry energy, not matter
▶ The difference between transverse waves and compressional waves

Vocabulary
wave
mechanical wave
electromagnetic wave
transverse wave
compressional wave

Why It's Important

▶ You can hear music because of waves.

Waves Carry Energy

In the Explore Activity, you saw that falling drops of water can move a floating object. You know that you can make something move by giving it a push or pull. But, the drops didn't hit the floating object. How did the energy from the falling drops travel through the water and move the object? Did you also notice that the ripples that moved in circles from the drop's entry point had peaks and valleys? These peaks and valleys make up water waves.

Waves are regular disturbances that carry energy through matter or space without carrying matter, as shown in **Figure 14-1A.** You also transfer energy when you throw a basketball or baseball to a friend. But, there is an important difference between a moving ball and a moving wave. As shown in **Figure 14-1B,** throwing a ball involves the transport of matter as well as energy.

Mechanical Waves

How does a wave carry energy but not matter? Here is one example you already know about. Sound travels as one type of wave motion. The sounds from a CD player reach your ears when the speakers vibrate back and forth and make sound waves.

Figure 14-1 The wave and the ball both carry energy.

A Waves on the water's surface carry energy from place to place, but the water itself moves mostly up and down.

B When you throw a ball to a friend, the ball carries both energy and matter. **What is another example of a moving object carrying both energy and matter?**

The sound waves transfer energy to anything in their path. When the waves reach your ears, they make your eardrums vibrate, as in **Figure 14-2.** If you've ever felt your house shake after a clap of thunder, you know that sound waves can carry large amounts of energy.

Waves that require matter to carry energy are called **mechanical waves.** The matter through which a mechanical wave travels is called a medium. A mechanical wave travels as energy is transferred from particle to particle in the medium. For example, a sound wave travels through the air because energy is transferred from gas molecule to gas molecule. Without a medium, you would not hear sounds. For example, sound waves can't travel in outer space. Imagine that you're standing on the moon. A person standing near you is telling you what she sees. But because there is no air on the moon to carry the sound, you won't hear a word she says—even if she yells at the top of her lungs.

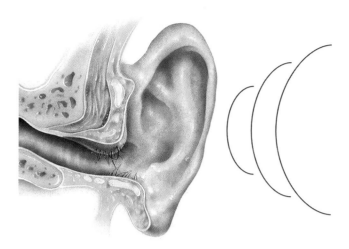

Figure 14-2 When you hear a sound, it's because sound waves traveling through the air make your eardrums vibrate.

Water Waves

Water waves—like the ones you made in the Explore Activity—are also mechanical waves. Each falling water drop touched water molecules when it hit the water's surface. Thus, the droplet's energy was carried from molecule to molecule through the water. Remember that the molecules of water do not move forward along with the wave. Rather, the water's surface moves up and down. In this same way, the wave transfers energy to a boat or other floating object, as shown in **Figure 14-3.** Absorbing some of the energy, the object bobs up and down and moves slowly away from the source of the wave.

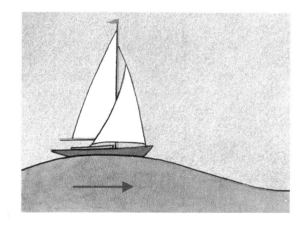

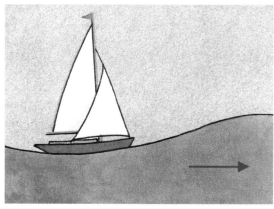

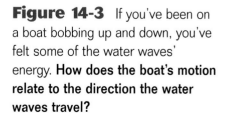
Figure 14-3 If you've been on a boat bobbing up and down, you've felt some of the water waves' energy. **How does the boat's motion relate to the direction the water waves travel?**

Visit the Glencoe Science Web Site at **www. glencoe.com/sec/ science/ca** for more information about electromagnetic waves.

Electromagnetic Waves

When you listen to the radio, watch TV, or use a microwave oven to cook, you use a different kind of wave—one that doesn't need matter as a medium.

Waves that do not require matter to carry energy are called **electromagnetic waves.** Electromagnetic waves can travel through air. They can even travel through the solid walls of your home. These are the kind of waves that bring you radio and TV programs. Electromagnetic waves also can travel through space to carry information to and from spacecraft. The X rays a doctor uses to see if you broke a bone and the light that carries the sun's energy to Earth are also electromagnetic waves.

Reading Check

What are the highest points of transverse waves called?

Transverse Waves

In a mechanical **transverse wave,** matter moves back and forth at right angles to the direction the wave travels. All electromagnetic waves are transverse waves. You can make a model of a transverse wave. Tie one end of a rope to a doorknob. Hold the other end in your hand. Now, shake the end in your hand up and down. By adjusting the way you shake the rope, you can create a wave that seems to vibrate in place.

Does the rope appear to move toward the doorknob? It doesn't really move toward the door, because if it did, you also would be pulled in that direction. What you see is energy moving along the "rope" wave. You can see that the wave has peaks and valleys at regular intervals. As shown in **Figure 14-4,** the high points of transverse waves are called crests. The low points are called troughs. ☑

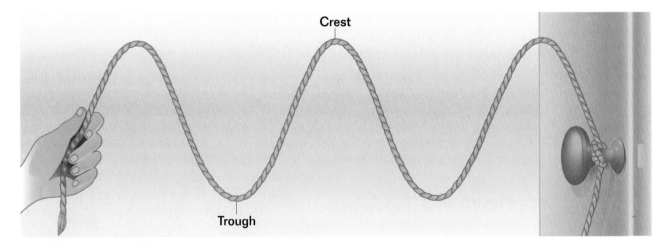

Crest

Trough

Figure 14-4 What does the vibrating rope carry from the hand to the door?

Figure 14-5 Sound waves are compressional

 A This compressional wave carries energy along the spring, while the spring itself vibrates forward and backward.

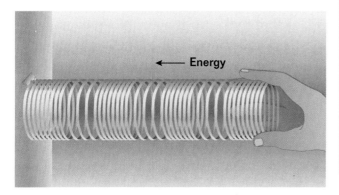

← Energy

B Vibrating strings make compressional waves that carry the harp's music to your ears. **What do you think vibrates to make compressional waves when a musician plays a trumpet?**

Compressional Waves

Mechanical waves can be either transverse or compressional. In a **compressional wave,** matter in the medium moves forward and backward in the same direction the wave travels. You can make a compressional wave by squeezing together and releasing several coils of a coiled spring toy, as shown in **Figure 14-5A.** When a compressional wave travels along a coiled spring, does the whole spring move along with the wave? If you tied a string around a single coil, you could watch that coil's movement as the wave passes. You would see that the coil moves forward and backward as the wave passes. So, like transverse waves, compressional waves carry only energy forward along the spring. The matter of the spring does not move along with the wave.

Sound Waves

Sound waves are compressional waves. How do you make sound waves when you talk or sing? If you hold your fingers against your throat while you hum, you can feel vibrations. These vibrations are actually the movements of your vocal cords. If you touch a stereo speaker while it's playing, you can feel the vibrations of the speaker, too. The sounds produced by the harp shown in **Figure 14-5B** are made when the strings of the instrument are made to vibrate.

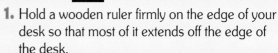

Comparing Sounds

Procedure 👓

1. Hold a wooden ruler firmly on the edge of your desk so that most of it extends off the edge of the desk.
2. Pluck the free end of the ruler so that it vibrates up and down. Pluck it easily at first, then with more energy.
3. Repeat step 2, moving the ruler about 1 cm further onto the desk. Continue until only about 5 cm extend off the edge.

Analysis

1. Compare the loudness of the sounds produced by using little energy with those using more energy.
2. Compare the pitches produced by the longer and shorter lengths of the object.

Making Sound Waves

How do vibrating vocal cords, strings, and other objects make sound waves? To find out, look at the drumhead stretched over the open end of the drum shown in **Figure 14-6.** When the drumhead moves upward, it touches some of the invisible particles that make up the air. When everything is quiet, the air particles are spaced about the same distance apart. But when the drumhead moves up, it pushes the air particles together. These groups of particles that are squeezed together are called a compressional. When the drumhead moves downward, the air particles have more room and move away from each other. A place where particles are spaced far apart is called a rarefaction (rar uh FAK shun).

Figure 14-6 A vibrating drumhead makes compressions and rarefactions in the air. **How do your vocal cords make compressions and rarefactions in air?**

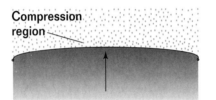

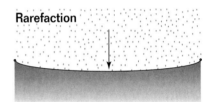

Section Assessment

1. Give one example of a transverse wave and one example of a compressional wave.

2. Why can't a sound wave travel from a satellite to Earth?

3. Is light a mechanical wave or an electromagnetic wave? A transverse wave or a compressional wave?

4. **Think Critically:** How is it possible for a sound wave to transmit energy, but not matter?

5. **Skill Builder**
   Concept Mapping Create a concept map that shows the relationships between the following: *waves, mechanical waves, electromagnetic waves, compressional waves,* and *transverse waves.* If you need help, refer to Concept Mapping in the **Skill Handbook** on page 526.

Using Computers

Word Processing Use word-processing software to write short descriptions of the waves you encounter during a typical day. If you need help, refer to page 544.

Wave Properties

Amplitude

Waves have characteristics that you can see and measure. For example, you can describe a wave in a lake or ocean by how high it rises above, or falls below, the normal water level. This is called the wave's amplitude. The **amplitude** of a transverse wave is one-half the distance between a crest and a trough, as shown in **Figure 14-7A.** In a compressional wave, the amplitude is greater when the particles of the medium are squeezed closer together in each compression and spread farther apart in each rarefaction.

Amplitude and Energy

A wave's amplitude is important. It is a measure of the energy the wave carries. For example, the waves that make up bright light have greater amplitudes than the waves that make up dim light. Waves of bright light carry more energy than the waves that make up dim light. In a similar way, loud sound waves have greater amplitudes than soft sound waves. Loud sounds carry more energy than soft sounds.

If you've seen pictures of a hurricane that strikes a coastal area, you know that the waves caused by the hurricane can damage anything that stands in their path. Waves with large amplitudes carry more energy than waves with smaller amplitudes. The waves caused by the hurricane have much more energy than the small waves or ripples on a pond, as you can see in **Figure 14-7B.**

What **You'll Learn**

▶ What wave frequency and wavelength are
▶ Waves travel at different speeds

Vocabulary
amplitude
wavelength
frequency

Why **It's Important**

▶ A wave's energy depends on its amplitude.

Figure 14-7 A wave's amplitude is a measure of how much energy it carries.

A The higher the crests (and the lower the troughs) of a wave, the greater the wave's amplitude is.

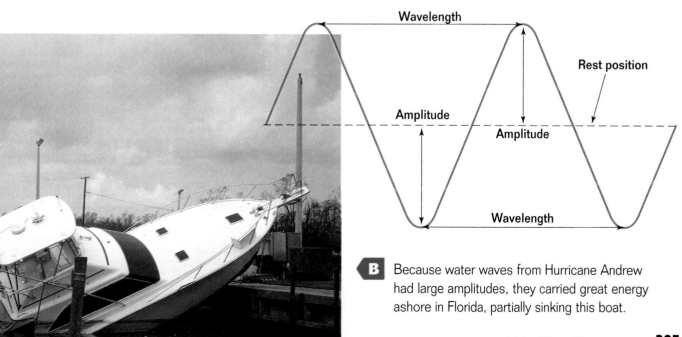

B Because water waves from Hurricane Andrew had large amplitudes, they carried great energy ashore in Florida, partially sinking this boat.

Tsunamis are huge sea waves that are caused by under-water earthquakes or volcanic eruptions. Because of their large amplitudes, tsunamis carry tremendous amounts of energy. They cause great damage when they move ashore.

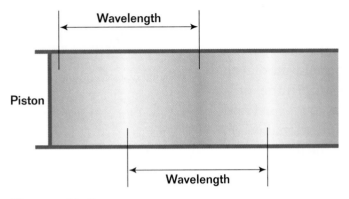

Figure 14-8 The wavelength of a compressional wave is measured from one compression or rarefaction to the next. **When the piston moves to the right, does it make a compression or a rarefaction?**

Figure 14-9 The wavelengths and frequencies of electromagnetic waves vary greatly. **Which waves have longer wavelengths, radio waves or visible light waves?**

Wavelength

Another way to describe a wave is by its wavelength. **Wavelength** is the distance between a point on one wave and an identical point on the next wave—from a crest to a crest or from a trough to a trough, as shown in **Figure 14-7A.** For a compressional wave, the wavelength is the distance between adjacent compressions or rarefactions, as shown in **Figure 14-8.**

Wavelength is an important characteristic of a wave. For example, the difference between red light and green light is that they have different wavelengths. Like all electromagnetic waves, light is a transverse wave. The wavelength of visible light determines its color. In this example, the wavelength of red light is longer than the wavelength of green light. Some electromagnetic waves, like X rays, have short wavelengths. Others, like microwaves in an oven, have longer wavelengths. The range of wavelengths of electromagnetic waves is shown in **Figure 14-9.**

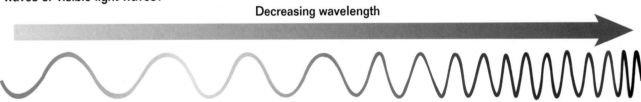

Decreasing wavelength

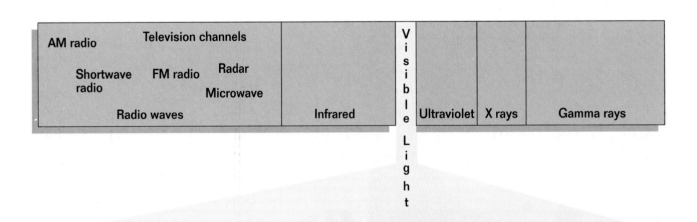

AM radio | Television channels | | Visible Light | | | |
Shortwave radio | FM radio | Radar | | | | |
| | Microwave | | | | |
Radio waves | | | Infrared | Ultraviolet | X rays | Gamma rays |

Frequency

The **frequency** of a wave is the number of waves that pass a given point in 1 s. Frequency is measured in waves per second, or hertz (Hz). For a given speed, waves with longer wavelengths have lower frequencies. Fewer long waves pass a given point in 1 s. Waves with shorter wavelengths have higher frequencies because more waves pass a given point in 1 s. Frequency is illustrated in **Figure 14-10A** and **B**.

The wavelength of an electromagnetic light wave determines the color of the light. In a sound wave, the frequency (associated with its wavelength) determines the pitch. Pitch is the highness or lowness of a sound. A flute makes musical notes with a high pitch. A tuba produces notes with a low pitch. When you sing "do re mi fa so la ti do," both the pitch and frequency increase from note to note. In other words, high-pitched sound waves have high frequencies. Low-pitched sound waves have low frequencies. ☑

PHYSICS
INTEGRATION

Global Positioning Systems
Maybe you've used a global positioning system (GPS) receiver to determine your location while driving, boating, or hiking. Earth-orbiting satellites send out electromagnetic radio waves that give the satellites' exact locations and times of transmission. The GPS receiver calculates the distance to each satellite and displays your location to within about 16 m.

Wave Speed

You've probably watched a distant thunderstorm approach on a hot summer day. You see a bolt of lightning flash between a dark cloud and the ground. Do the sound waves, or thunder, produced by the lightning bolt reach your ears at the same instant you see the lightning? If the thunderstorm is many kilometers away, several seconds may pass between the time you see the lightning and you hear the thunder. This happens because light travels much faster in air than sound does. Light is an electromagnetic wave that travels through air at about 300 million m/s. Sound is a mechanical wave that travels through air at about 340 m/s.

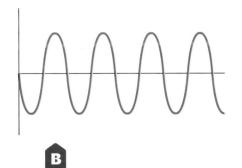

Reading Check ☑

What determines the pitch of a sound?

Figure 14-10 Wave A has a longer wavelength and a lower frequency than wave B. **Why does a wave with a long wavelength have a low frequency?**

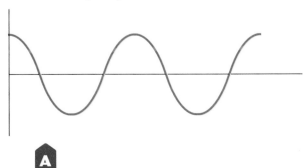

A

B

Determining Wave Speed

You can calculate the speed of a wave by multiplying its frequency by its wavelength. For example, suppose you know that a sound wave has a frequency of 266 Hz and a wavelength of 1.29 m. (Remember that 266 Hz means that 266 sound waves pass a given point in 1 s.) The wave's speed is given by the following calculation.

$$\text{wave frequency} \times \text{wavelength} = \text{wave speed}$$
$$266 \text{ Hz} \times 1.29 \text{ m} = 343 \text{ m/s}$$

The speed of the wave is 343 m/s.

Light waves don't always travel at the same speed. For example, the speed of light waves is slightly higher in empty space than in air. And, light waves travel only about 200 million m/s in glass. You can see that this is much slower than the speed light travels in air. The speed of sound waves varies, too. Have you ever heard sounds while swimming underwater? Have you ever put your ear against a wall or on the ground to hear something more clearly? If you have, you may have noticed something interesting. Sound travels faster in liquids and solids than in gases like air.

Using Math

You can calculate the speed of a wave in meters per second (m/s) by multiplying the wave's frequency in hertz (Hz) by its wavelength in meters (m). This calculation is possible because 1 Hz = 1/s. For example, 266 Hz × 1.29 m = 266 1/s × 1.29 m = 343 m/s.

Section Assessment

1. Why is the statement "The speed of light is 300 million m/s" not always correct?

2. How does the frequency of a wave change as its wavelength changes?

3. In what part of a compressional wave are the particles spaced farthest apart?

4. Why is a sound wave with a large amplitude more likely to damage your hearing than one with a small amplitude?

5. **Think Critically:** Explain the differences between the waves that make up bright green light and dim red light.

6. **Skill Builder**
   Interpreting Scientific Diagrams
   Scientific diagrams can help you understand wave properties. Do the **Chapter 14 Skill Activity** on page 567 to learn about a compressional wave, its parts, and its wavelength.

Using Math

If a sound wave traveling through water has a speed of 1470 m/s and a frequency of 2340 Hz, what is its wavelength?

Waves on a Spring

Materials
- Long, coiled spring toy
- Meterstick
- Stopwatch
- Piece of colored yarn (5 cm)

Waves are rhythmic disturbances that carry energy through matter or space. Studying waves can help you understand how the sun's energy reaches Earth and sounds travel through the air.

What You'll Investigate

In this activity, you will create transverse and compressional waves on a coiled spring and investigate some of their properties.

Goals

- **Create** transverse and compressional waves on a coiled spring.
- **Investigate** wave properties such as speed and amplitude.

Procedure

1. **Prepare a data table** such as the one shown.

2. Work in pairs or groups and clear a place on an uncarpeted floor about 6 m long and 2 m wide.

3. While one team member grasps one end of the coiled spring toy with one hand, another team member should stretch it to the length suggested by the teacher. **Measure** the length of the coiled spring toy. **CAUTION:** *Coiled springs can be damaged permanently by over-stretching or tangling. Be careful to follow the teacher's instructions.*

4. **Create** a wave by having one team member make a quick sideways snap of the wrist. Time several waves as they travel from one end of the coiled spring toy to the other. Record the average time in your data table.

5. Repeat step 4 using waves that have slightly larger amplitudes.

6. Use one hand to squeeze together about 20 of the coils near you. **Observe** what happens to the unsqueezed coils. Release the coils and **observe** what happens.

7. Quickly push one end of the coiled spring toward your partner, then pull it back to its original position.

8. Tie the piece of colored yarn to a coil near the middle of the coiled spring toy. Repeat step 7, **observing** what happens to the string.

Wave Data	
Length of stretched spring toy	
Average time for a wave to travel from end to end—step 4	
Average time for a wave to travel from end to end—step 5	

Conclude and Apply

1. **Classify** the wave pulses you created in steps 4 and 5 and those you created in steps 6 to 8 as compressional or transverse.

2. **Calculate** and **compare** the speeds of the waves in steps 4 and 5.

3. **Classify** the unsqueezed coils in step 6 as a compression or a rarefaction.

4. **Compare and contrast** the motion of the yarn in step 8 with the motion of the wave. Did the coil that had the yarn attached to it move along the coiled spring toy or did the wave's energy pass through that coil?

Wave Behavior

Reflection

What You'll Learn

▶ Waves can reflect from some surfaces
▶ How waves usually change direction when they move from one material into another
▶ Waves are able to bend around barriers

Vocabulary

reflection   diffraction
refraction   interference

Why It's Important

▶ Without wave reflection, you couldn't read the words on this page.

You've probably yelled to a friend across a gymnasium or down a long hallway. When you did this, you might have heard an echo of your voice. What property of sound caused the echo?

When you look in a mirror, what property of light lets you see your face? Both the echo of your voice and the face you see in the mirror are caused by wave reflection. **Reflection** occurs when a wave strikes an object or surface and bounces off. An echo is reflected sound. Sound reflects from all surfaces. Your echo bounced off the walls, floor, ceiling, furniture, and people. In old western movies, light reflected off a mirror was often used to send a message over long distances. When you see your face in a mirror, as shown in **Figure 14-11A,** reflection occurs. Light from your face hits the mirror and reflects back to your eyes.

A mirror is smooth and even. However, when light reflects from an uneven or rough surface, you can't see an image because the reflected light scatters in many different directions, as shown in **Figure 14-11B.**

Figure 14-11

A If light didn't reflect from you and the mirror, you wouldn't be able to see yourself in the mirror.

B The building at the far left has a rough surface that scatters light in different directions. Its surface is not smooth and shiny like the building on the right, which is mirror-like. **Why should a mirror's reflective surface be made as smooth as possible?**

Refraction

You've already seen that a wave changes direction when it reflects from a surface. Can a wave change its direction at other times? Perhaps you've used a magnifying glass to examine your skin, an insect, a coin, or a stamp. An object appears larger when viewed through a magnifying glass. This happens because the light rays from the object change direction when they pass from the air into the glass. They change direction again when they pass from the glass into the air. The bending of a wave as it moves from one medium into another is called **refraction.**

Refraction and Wave Speed

The speed of a wave is different in different substances. For example, light waves move slower in water than in air. Refraction occurs when the speed of a wave changes as it passes from one substance to another. As shown in **Figure 14-12A** and **B,** a line has been drawn perpendicular to the water's surface. This line is called the normal.

Try at Home

Mini Lab

Observing How Light Refracts

Procedure

1. Fill a large, opaque drinking glass or cup nearly to the brim with water.

2. Place a white soda straw in the water at an angle, with approximately one-third of its length extending out of the water.

3. Looking directly down into the cup from above, observe the straw where it meets the water.

4. Placing yourself so that the straw angles to your left or right, slowly back away about 1 m. If necessary, lower your head until you eliminate any unwanted glare from the water's surface. Observe the straw as it appears above, at, and below the surface of the water.

Analysis

1. Describe the straw's appearance as you looked directly down on it.

2. Compare the straw's appearance above and below the water's surface when you looked at it from the side. Draw a diagram and explain the apparent effect.

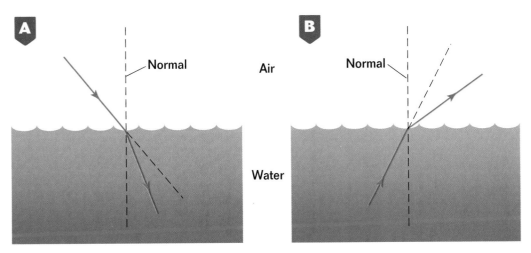

Figure 14-12 As the light ray in A passes from air into water, it refracts toward the normal. As the light ray in B passes from water into air, it refracts away from the normal.

When a light ray passes from air into water, it slows down and bends toward the normal. The more the light ray slows, the more its direction changes. When the ray passes from water into air, it speeds up and bends away from the normal.

You notice refraction when you look at an angle into a lake or pond and spot a fish near the bottom. Refraction makes the fish appear to be closer to the surface and farther away from you than it really is, as shown in **Figure 14-13.** Refraction also gives diamonds and other gems their wonderful sparkle. **Figure 14-14** illustrates how refraction and reflection produce a rainbow when light waves from the sun pass into and out of water droplets in the air.

Reading Check ✔

What produces a rainbow?

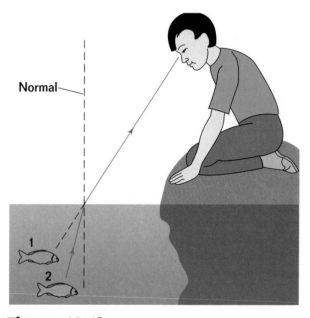

Normal

1

2

Figure 14-13
Refraction makes the fish at location 2 appear to be at location 1.

Diffraction

It's time for lunch. You're walking down the hallway to the cafeteria. As you near the open door, you can hear people talking and the clink and clank of tableware. But how do the sound waves reach your ears before you get to the door? The sound waves must be able to bend around the corners of the door, as shown in **Figure 14-15A. Diffraction** is the bending of waves around a barrier.

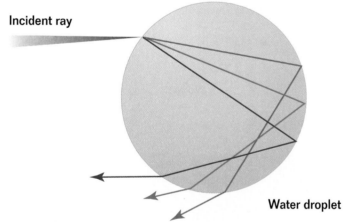

Incident ray

Sunlight

Water droplet

Figure 14-14 Light rays refract when they enter and leave a raindrop, and they reflect from the far side of the drop. Because different colors refract at different angles, they leave the drop separated into the colors of the spectrum. (Ray angles have been shown larger than they actually are for clarity.) **Which color of light shown on the diagram refracts most?**

Figure 14-15 Sound waves and light waves diffract differently through an open door.

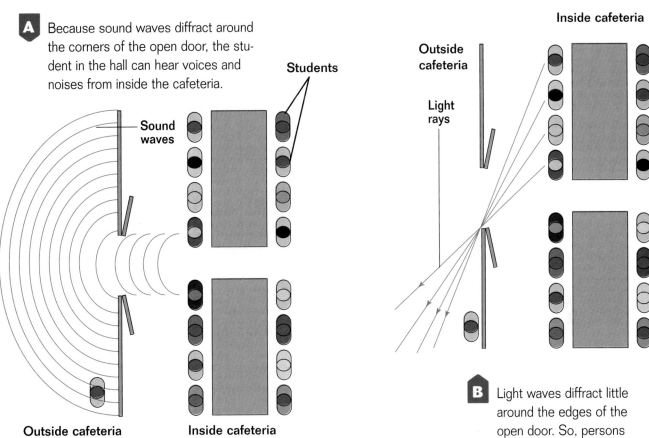

A Because sound waves diffract around the corners of the open door, the student in the hall can hear voices and noises from inside the cafeteria.

Students

Sound waves

Outside cafeteria

Inside cafeteria

Inside cafeteria

Outside cafeteria

Light rays

B Light waves diffract little around the edges of the open door. So, persons inside the cafeteria can be seen only when the student in the hall meets light rays streaming through the door. **How does diffraction explain why a boat inside a harbor rocks slightly from water waves outside the harbor?**

Diffraction of Light

Can light waves diffract, too? You can't see your friends in the cafeteria until you reach the open door, so the light waves must not diffract as much as the sound waves, as shown in **Figure 14-15.**

Are light waves able to diffract at all? As a matter of fact, light waves do bend around the edges of an open door. You can see some effects of light diffraction when you view a bright light through a small slit such as the one between two pencils held close together. However, the amount the light bends is extremely small. As a result, the diffraction of light is far too small to allow you to see around the corner into the cafeteria. The reason that light waves don't diffract much when they pass through an open door is that the wavelengths of visible light are much smaller than the width of the door. Sound waves that you can hear have much longer wavelengths. They bend more readily around the corners of an open door. Waves diffract best when the wavelength of the wave is similar in size to the barrier or opening.

Interference

Imagine a marching band that has only one of each kind of instrument. When this band performs on a football field, will it fill the stadium with sound? Having several of each instrument play the same notes at the same times produces much louder and more spectacular music. For example, the sound waves of many trumpets combine to make sound waves with larger amplitudes. The sound produced by many trumpets is therefore louder than the sound from a single trumpet. The ability of two or more waves to combine and form a new wave when they overlap is called **interference** (ihn tur FEER uns).

Constructive interference occurs when waves meet, for example, crest to crest and trough to trough. The amplitudes of these combining waves add together to make a larger wave, as shown in **Figure 14-16A, B,** and **C.** Destructive interference occurs, for example, when the crest of one wave meets the trough of another wave. In destructive interference, the amplitudes of the combining waves make a smaller wave. Sometimes, they produce no wave at all, as shown in **Figure 14-16D, E,** and **F** on the next page.

Reflected light waves sometimes produce interesting interference patterns. The colorful interference patterns that result from the microscopic pits in compact discs are one example.

interNET CONNECTION

Visit the Glencoe Science Web Site at **www. glencoe.com/sec/ science/ca** for more information about wave interference.

Problem Solving

Scattering Light

Why is the sky blue and the sunset red? Surprisingly, both effects have the same cause. Sunlight contains all colors of the visible spectrum. When sunlight passes through Earth's atmosphere, particles in the air scatter some colors more than others. Shorter-wavelength violet and blue light waves are scattered most, green and yellow waves a little, and longer-wavelength orange and red light waves even less.

The sky appears blue during the day because the scattered blue light waves reflect to your eyes from dust particles and water droplets in the air. However, at sunrise and sunset, the sky appears red because light waves from the sun pass through more of the atmosphere before reaching Earth's surface. With so much of the blue and violet light scattered away, only the orange and red waves reach your eyes.

Think Critically: You've seen the beautiful array of colors in a rainbow on a day that has both sunshine and water droplets in the air. You've viewed the colorful light pattern from a compact disc. What do the blue color of the daytime sky, the red color of a sunset, a multicolored rainbow, and the light pattern from a compact disc have in common? How are they different?

Figure 14-16

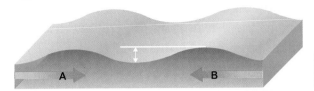

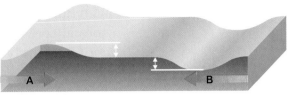

A Constructive Wave Interference
Crests of waves A and B approach each other from different directions. The waves have equal amplitudes.

D Destructive Wave Interference
A crest of wave A and trough of wave B approach each other from different directions. The amplitude of A equals the amplitude of B.

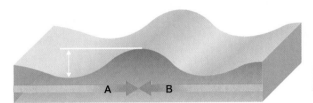

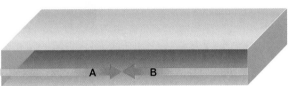

B When crests A and B meet, they briefly form a new wave, A + B, which has an amplitude equal to the sum of the amplitudes of the two waves.

E When the waves meet, they briefly form a new wave, A + B, which has an amplitude of zero for an instant.

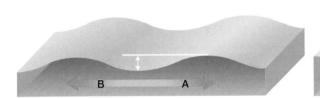

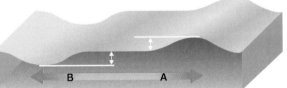

C The waves have passed through each other unchanged.

F The waves have passed through each other unchanged. **Compare and contrast constructive and destructive interference.**

Useful Interference

You may have seen someone cut grass with a power lawn mower or cut wood with a chain saw. In the past, many people who've performed these tasks have damaged their hearing because of the loud noises produced by these machines. Today, ear protectors can reflect and absorb some of the noise from lawn mowers and chain saws. The ear protectors lower the amplitudes of the harmful waves. The smaller-amplitude waves that reach the ears no longer damage eardrums.

Pilots of small planes have had an interesting problem. They couldn't shut out all the noise of the plane's motor. If they did, they wouldn't be able to hear instructions from air-traffic controllers. Engineers invented special earphones that contain electronic circuits. These circuits produce sound frequencies that destructively interfere with engine noise that might be harmful.

However, the sound frequencies produced do not interfere with human voices, allowing the pilot to hear and understand normal conversation. In these examples, destructive interference can be a benefit, as shown in **Figure 14-17.**

Figure 14-17 Some airplane pilots use ear protectors that muffle engine noise but don't block human voices. People who operate chain saws need ear protectors that greatly reduce the engine noise that could be harmful.

Section Assessment

1. White objects reflect light. Why don't you see your reflection when you look at a building made of rough, white stone?

2. If you're standing on one side of a building, how are you able to hear the siren of an ambulance on the other side of the building?

3. What behavior of light enables magnifying glasses and contact lenses to bend light rays and help people see more clearly?

4. **Think Critically:** Why don't light rays that stream through an open window into a darkened room spread evenly through the entire room?

5. **Skill Builder**
   Comparing and Contrasting When light rays pass from water into a certain type of glass, the rays refract toward the normal. Compare and contrast the speed of light in water and in the glass. If you need help, refer to Comparing and Contrasting in the **Skill Handbook** on page 532.

Science **Journal**
Look and listen carefully as you travel home from school or walk down the street where you live. What examples of wave reflection and refraction do you notice? Describe each of these in your Science Journal, and explain whether it's an example of reflection or refraction.

Graphing Waves

Constructive and Destructive Interference

Waves have special characteristics. The wavelength is the horizontal distance between a point on one wave and an identical point on the next wave. The amplitude is the vertical distance from the crest (or trough) of a wave to a position halfway between crest and trough.

When two waves meet in such a way that a new wave with greater amplitude is formed, it is called constructive interference. If the new wave formed has a smaller amplitude than either original wave or an amplitude of zero, it is called destructive interference.

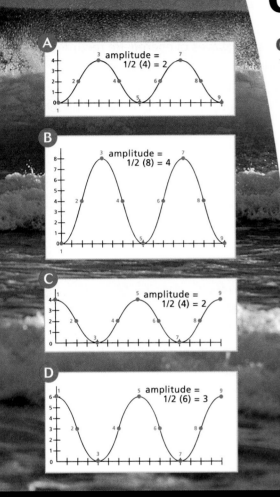

Problem

Draw a graph for the new wave formed by combining Waves A and B.

Solution

Notice that nine points on each wave are labeled with red dots and numbers. These points will be used to graph the new wave.

To graph the new wave formed by combining Waves A and B, find nine points for the new graph by adding the "height" of Waves A and B at each labeled point.

Point 1 (new): height of Wave A point 1 + height of Wave B point 1 = 0 + 0 = 0.

Point 2 (new): height of Wave A point 2 + height of Wave B point 2 = 2 + 4 = 6.

Point 3 (new): height of Wave A point 3 + height of Wave B point 3 = 4 + 8 = 12.

Continuing the process, you'll find that the remaining points have heights 6, 0, 6, 12, 6, and 0. A graph for the new wave looks like this:

To find a wave's amplitude, count the vertical units between the lowest and highest points on the graph and divide by 2. Because the new wave has greater amplitude (6) than either Wave A (2) or B (4), this problem is an example of constructive interference.

Practice
PROBLEMS

In the following problems, draw the graph and determine whether each is a case of constructive or destructive interference.

1. Draw a graph for the new wave formed by combining Waves B and D.

2. Draw a graph representing the combination of Waves C and D.

3. Draw a graph representing the combination of Waves A and C.

4. Draw graphs for two waves of your choice. Show the new wave formed by combining the two.

Activity 14•2

Doing the Wave

When an earthquake occurs, the waves of energy are recorded at points all over the world by instruments called seismographs. By comparing the data that they collected from their seismographs, scientists discovered that the interior of Earth must be made of layers of different materials. How did the seismographs tell them that Earth is not the same medium all the way through?

Materials

- Coiled spring toy
- Stopwatch
  * clock with a second hand
- Meterstick
- Tape

  * Alternate Materials

Recognize the Problem

Can the speed of a wave be used to identify the medium through which it travels?

Form a Hypothesis

Think about what you know about the relationship between the frequency, wavelength, and speed of a wave in a medium. **Make a hypothesis** about how you can measure the speed of a wave within a medium and use that information to identify an unknown medium.

Goals

- **Measure** the speed of a wave within a coiled spring toy.
- **Predict** whether the speed you measured will be different in other types of coiled spring toys.

Data Sources

Go to the Glencoe Science Web Site at **www.glencoe.com/sec/science/ca** for more information, hints, and data collected by other students.

Wave Data

Trial	Length spring was stretched (m)	Number of crests	Wavelength (m)	Number of vibrations timed	Number of seconds vibrations were timed (s)	Wave speed (m/s)
1						
2						
3						

Test Your Hypothesis

Plan 👓

1. **Make a data table** in your Science Journal like the one shown.

2. **Write** a detailed description of the coiled spring toy you are going to use. Be sure to include its mass and diameter, the width of a coil, and what it is made of.

3. **Decide** as a group how you will **measure** the frequency and length of waves in the spring toy. What are your variables? Which variables must be controlled? What variable do you want to measure?

4. Repeat your experiment three times.

Do

1. Make sure your teacher approves your plan before you begin.

2. Carry out the experiment as you have planned.

3. While you are doing the experiment, **record** your observations and measurements in your data table.

Analyze Your Data

1. **Calculate** the frequency of the waves by dividing the number of vibrations you timed by the number of seconds you timed them. Record your results in your data table.

2. Use the following formula to **calculate** the speed of a wave in each trial.

   wavelength $\times$ wave frequency = wave speed

3. **Average** the wave speeds from your trials to determine the speed of a wave in your coiled spring toy.

Draw Conclusions

1. **Post** the description of your coiled spring toy and your results on the Glencoe Science Web Site.

2. **Compare and contrast** your results with the results of other students.

3. How does the type of coiled spring toy and the length it was stretched affect the wave speed? Was your hypothesis supported?

4. Would it make a difference if an earthquake wave were transmitted through Earth's solid mantle or the molten outer core?

For a **preview** of this chapter, study this Reviewing Main Ideas before you read the chapter. After you have studied this chapter, you can use the Reviewing Main Ideas to **review** the chapter.

The Glencoe MindJogger, Audiocassettes, and CD-ROM provide additional opportunities for review.

Section

14-1 WAVES CARRY ENERGY

Waves are rhythmic disturbances that carry energy but not matter. **Mechanical waves** can travel only through matter. Other waves, called **electromagnetic waves,** can travel through space. *What kind of waves carry the sun's energy to Earth? An earthquake's energy through Earth?*

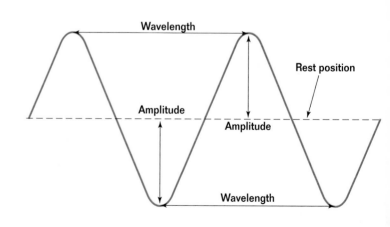

TRANSVERSE AND COMPRESSIONAL WAVES

In a mechanical **transverse wave,** matter in the medium the wave travels through moves back and forth at right angles to the direction the wave travels. In a **compressional wave,** matter in the medium moves forward and backward in the same direction as the wave. *Why doesn't a sound wave travel through space?*

Section

14-2 AMPLITUDE, FREQUENCY, AND WAVELENGTH

Waves can be described by their characteristics. The **amplitude** of a transverse wave is one half the distance between a crest and a trough. **Wavelength** is the distance between a point on one wave and an identical point on the next wave. The **frequency** of a wave is the number of waves that pass a given point in 1 s. *How is the amplitude of a wave related to the amount of energy it carries?*

Wavelength

Rest position

Amplitude

Amplitude

Wavelength

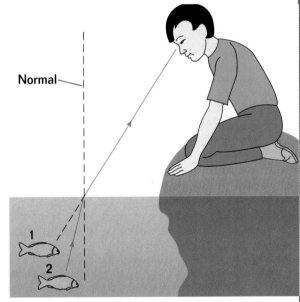

Section
14-3 REFLECTION
Reflection occurs when a wave strikes an object or surface and bounces off. You can see your image in a mirror because of reflection. *How does wave reflection explain echoes in a large canyon?*

REFRACTION
The bending of a wave as it moves from one medium into another is called **refraction**. A wave changes direction, or refracts, when its speed changes. *In what situation does a wave not change its direction when it passes from one medium into another?*

Normal

DIFFRACTION AND INTERFERENCE
The bending of waves around a barrier is called **diffraction**. The ability of two or more waves to combine and form a new wave when they overlap is called **interference**. *What kind of interference produces waves with the largest amplitudes?*

Using Vocabulary

a. amplitude
b. compressional wave
c. diffraction
d. electromagnetic wave
e. frequency
f. interference
g. mechanical wave
h. reflection
i. refraction
j. transverse wave
k. wave
l. wavelength

Using the list above, replace the underlined words with the correct Vocabulary words.

1. <u>Diffraction</u> is the change in direction of a wave.
2. The type of wave that has rarefactions is a <u>transverse wave</u>.
3. The distance between two adjacent crests of a transverse wave is the <u>frequency</u>.
4. The greater the <u>wavelength</u> of a wave, the more energy the wave carries.
5. A <u>mechanical wave</u> can travel through space.

Checking Concepts

Choose the word or phrase that best answers the question.

6. What is the material through which mechanical waves travel?
   A) charged particles
   B) space
   C) a vacuum
   D) a medium

7. What is carried from particle to particle in a water wave?
   A) speed   C) energy
   B) amplitude   D) matter

8. What are the lowest points on a transverse wave called?
   A) crests   C) compressions
   B) troughs   D) rarefactions

9. What determines the pitch of a sound wave?
   A) amplitude   C) speed
   B) frequency   D) refraction

10. What is the distance between adjacent wave compressions?
    A) one wavelength   C) 1 m/s
    B) 1 km   D) 1 Hz

11. What occurs when a wave strikes an object or surface and bounces off?
    A) diffraction   C) a change in speed
    B) refraction   D) reflection

12. What is the name for a change in the direction of a wave when it passes from one medium into another?
    A) refraction   C) reflection
    B) interference   D) diffraction

13. What type of wave is a sound wave?
    A) transverse
    B) electromagnetic
    C) compressional
    D) refracted

14. When two waves overlap and interfere destructively, what does the resulting wave have?
    A) a greater amplitude
    B) more energy
    C) a change in frequency
    D) a lower amplitude

15. What is the difference between blue light and green light?
    A) They have different wavelengths.
    B) One is a transverse wave and the other is not.
    C) They travel at different speeds.
    D) One is mechanical and the other is not.

Thinking Critically

16. Explain what kind of wave, transverse or compressional, is produced when an engine bumps into a string of coupled railroad cars on a track.

17. Is it possible for an electromagnetic wave to travel through a vacuum? Through matter? Explain your answers.

18. Why does the frequency of a wave decrease as the wavelength increases?

19. Why don't you see your reflected image when you look at a white, rough surface?

20. If a cannon fires at a great distance from you, why do you see the flash before you hear the sound?

Developing Skills

If you need help, refer to the **Skill Handbook**.

21. **Using Numbers:** A microwave travels at the speed of light and has a wavelength of 0.022 m. What is its frequency?

22. **Forming a Hypothesis:** Form a hypothesis that can explain this observation. Waves A and B travel away from Earth through Earth's atmosphere. Wave A continues on into space, but wave B does not.

23. **Recognizing Cause and Effect:** Explain how the object shown below causes compressions and rarefactions as it vibrates in air.

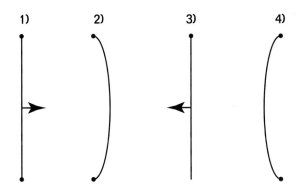

24. **Comparing and Contrasting:** AM radio waves have wavelengths between about 200 m and 600 m, while FM radio waves have wavelengths of about 3 m. Why can AM radio signals often be heard behind buildings and mountains while FM radio signals cannot?

THE PRINCETON REVIEW

Test-Taking Tip

Don't Cram If you don't know the material by the week before the test, you're less likely to do well. Set up a time line for your practice and preparation so that you're not rushed. Then, you will have time to deal with any problem areas.

Test Practice

Use these questions to test your Science Proficiency.

1. Two sounds have the same pitch, but one is louder than the other. What is different about the two sounds?
   A) their amplitudes
   B) their frequencies
   C) their wavelengths
   D) their speeds

2. What produces the colors seen when light reflects from CDs?
   A) wavelength
   B) interference
   C) refraction
   D) compression

3. The speed of a light ray increases as it passes at an angle from one medium into another. What happens to the ray?
   A) Its direction does not change.
   B) It travels along the normal.
   C) It bends toward the normal.
   D) It bends away from the normal.

4. What kind of waves requires a medium?
   A) all transverse waves
   B) only some compressional waves
   C) all electromagnetic waves
   D) all mechanical waves

Light, Mirrors, and Lenses

Chapter Preview

Skills Preview

Skill Builders

- Form a Hypothesis
- Compare and Contrast

Activities

- Observe and Infer
- Use Scientific Methods

MiniLabs

- Observe and Infer
- Form a Hypothesis

Reading Check ☑

As you read this chapter, list vocabulary terms that are also used in other subject areas, such as *medium* and *frequency*. Explain the meaning of these terms.

Explore Activity

What do you see when you look around you? Everything you see results from light waves that enter your eye. These light waves are emitted by objects like the sun or light-bulbs and are reflected by objects such as trees, books, people, and furniture. Laser beams like the ones shown here are also made of light waves. Lenses and mirrors can cause light waves to change direction and make objects seem larger or smaller. What happens to light as it passes from one material to another?

Observe Light Bending

1. Place two paper cups next to each other and put a penny in the bottom of each cup.

2. Stand so you can look straight down into both cups.

3. Fill one of the cups with water and observe what happens to the penny in that cup.

4. Slide the cup with no water away from you just until you can no longer see the penny.

5. Have your partner pour water into this cup and observe what seems to happen to the penny.

Science Journal

In your Science Journal, record your observations. Did adding water make the cup look deeper or shallower?

415

15•1 Properties of Light

What is light?

Have you ever dropped a rock on the smooth surface of a pond and watched the ripples spread outward, as shown in **Figure 15-1?** You produced a wave. The wave was all the ripples made by the rock striking the water. The impact of the rock added energy to the water. As the ripples spread out, they carried some of that energy.

Light also carries energy. A source of light like the sun or a lightbulb gives off light waves, just as the rock hitting the pond caused ripples to spread out from the point of impact. The ripples spread out only on the surface of the pond, but light waves spread out in all directions from the light source as shown in **Figure 15-2.**

Sometimes, it is easier to talk about just one narrow beam of light traveling in a straight line, which is called a **light ray.** You can think of a source of light as emitting light rays that are traveling away from the source in all directions.

However, light waves are different from ripples on a pond. If the pond dried up and there was no water, there could be no ripples. Waves on a pond need a material in which to travel—water. Any material in which a wave travels is called a **medium.** Light is a special type of wave called an electromagnetic wave. An **electromagnetic wave** is a wave that does not need a medium in which to travel. Electromagnetic waves can travel in a vacuum, as well as in materials such as air, water, and glass.

What You'll Learn

▶ The wave nature of light
▶ How light interacts with materials
▶ Why objects appear colored

Vocabulary
light ray
medium
electromagnetic wave
reflection
wavelength
frequency

Why It's Important

▶ Most of what you know about your surroundings comes from information carried by light waves.

Figure 15-1 Ripples on the surface of a pond are produced by an object hitting the water. As the ripples spread out from the point of impact, they carry energy.

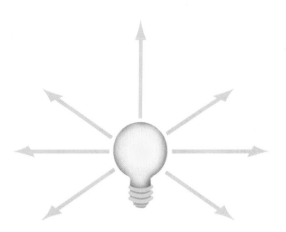

Light and Matter

Have you ever been in a closed room with no windows? You can see nothing until you turn on a light or open a door and let in light from outside. Unlike a candle flame, a lightbulb, or the sun, most objects do not give off light on their own. These objects can be seen only if light waves from another source bounce off the object and into your eyes, as shown in **Figure 15-3.** The process of light striking an object and bouncing off is called **reflection.** Right now, you can see these words because light is reflecting from the page and into your eyes. ☑

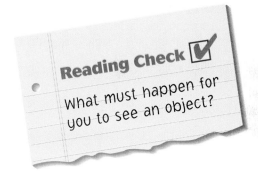

Reading Check ☑

What must happen for you to see an object?

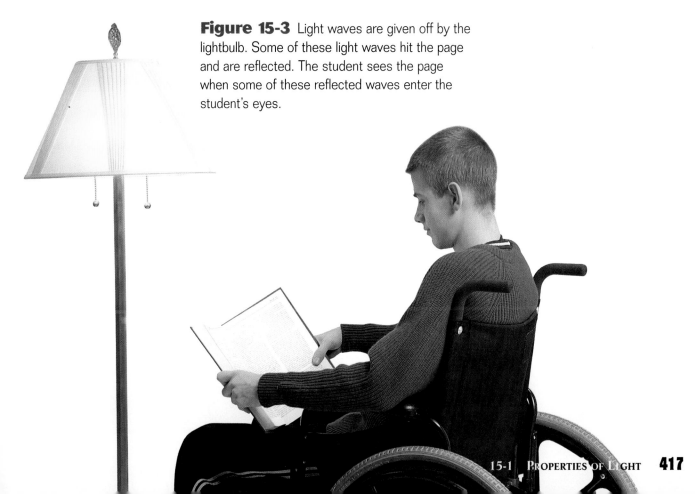

Figure 15-3 Light waves are given off by the lightbulb. Some of these light waves hit the page and are reflected. The student sees the page when some of these reflected waves enter the student's eyes.

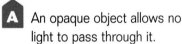
A An opaque object allows no light to pass through it.

B A translucent object allows some light to pass through it.

C A transparent object allows almost all light to pass through it.

Figure 15-4 Materials are opaque, translucent, or transparent depending on how much light passes through them.

Opaque, Translucent, and Transparent

When light waves strike an object, some of the light can be absorbed by the object, some of the light is reflected, and some of the light may pass through the object. How much light is absorbed, reflected, and passes through the object depends on what the object is made of.

Materials that let no light pass through them are *opaque* (oh PAYK). You cannot see other objects through opaque objects. Materials, such as glass, that allow nearly all the light to pass through are *transparent.* You can clearly see other objects through transparent materials. Other materials allow only some light to pass through so objects behind them cannot be seen clearly. These materials, such as waxed paper or frosted glass, are *translucent* (trans LEW sent). Examples of opaque, translucent, and transparent objects are shown in **Figure 15-4.**

Figure 15-5 Like all waves, ripples on a water surface have a wavelength.

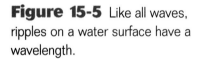
A The wavelength is the distance between ripples.

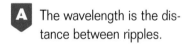
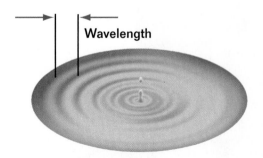

B A cross section of the water surface is shown. The energy added by the impact of the rock causes water to pile up at each ripple.

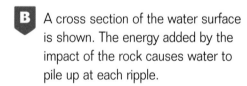
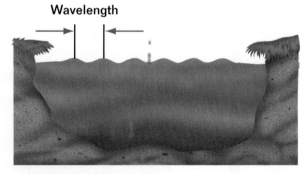

The Electromagnetic Spectrum

Light waves, like all waves, have a property called wavelength. Look at **Figure 15-5.** For ripples on a pond, the **wavelength** is the distance between the tops of two adjacent ripples. The number of wavelengths that pass a point in one second is the **frequency** of the wave. For waves that travel at the same speed, frequency and wavelength are related. As the wavelength decreases, the frequency increases.

The electromagnetic waves you see as light are part of the electromagnetic spectrum. **Figure 15-6** shows how electromagnetic waves are classified according to their wavelengths. All electromagnetic waves travel with a speed of about 300 million m/s in a vacuum. Electromagnetic waves also carry energy, just like the ripples in the pond. The energy carried by an electromagnetic wave increases as the wavelength decreases and the frequency increases.

Of all the electromagnetic waves, radio waves carry the least energy. They have wavelengths longer than about 1 cm. Television signals, as well as AM and FM radio signals, are types of radio waves. You can't see these waves with your eyes, nor can you sense them in any other way, but they are being absorbed, reflected, and transmitted by your body even as you read this! The highest-energy radio waves are called microwaves.

Earth's Ozone Layer
Ozone is formed high in Earth's atmosphere by sunlight striking oxygen molecules. However, chemical compounds called CFCs, which are used in air conditioners and refrigerators, can remove ozone from the ozone layer. To prevent this, the use of CFCs is being phased out. Visit the Glencoe Science Web Site at **www.glencoe.com/sec/science/ca** for more information about the effects of CFCs on the ozone layer.

Figure 15-6 Electromagnetic waves are classified according to their wavelengths and frequencies. Visible light is only a small section of the electromagnetic spectrum.

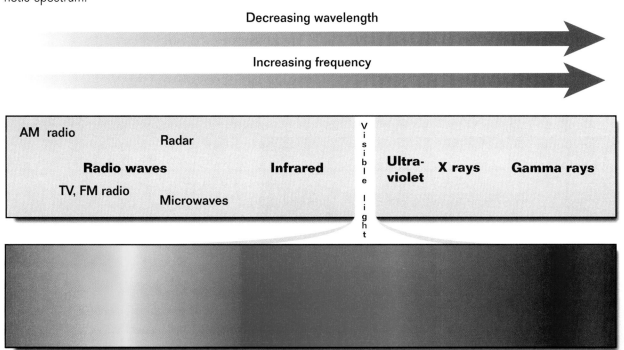

Viewing Colors Through Color Filters

Procedure

1. Obtain sheets of red, green, and blue construction paper.
2. Obtain a piece of red cellophane and green cellophane.
3. Look at each sheet of paper through the red cellophane and record the color of each sheet.
4. Look at each sheet of colored paper through the green cellophane and record the color of each sheet.
5. Hold both pieces of cellophane together and look at each sheet of colored paper. Record the color of each sheet.

Analyze

Explain why the sheets of paper changed color when you looked at them through the pieces of cellophane.

Electromagnetic waves with wavelengths less than radio waves, but greater than visible light, are called infrared waves. You can't see these waves either, but they are emitted by the sun and make your skin feel warm.

The sun also emits ultraviolet waves that carry enough energy to damage living cells. Earth's atmosphere contains a layer of a compound called ozone that blocks most of the sun's ultraviolet waves from reaching Earth's surface. Still, exposure to those ultraviolet waves that do get through can cause sunburn. Exposure to these waves over a long period of time can lead to early aging of the skin and possibly skin cancer.

Visible light is the narrow range of the electromagnetic spectrum that we can detect with our eyes. What we see as different colors are electromagnetic waves of different wavelengths. Red light has the longest wavelength (lowest frequency), and blue light has the shortest wavelength (highest frequency).

Color

Why does grass look green or a rose look red? The answer has to do with the way objects absorb and reflect light. The light from the sun or a lightbulb may look white, but it is actually a mixture of light waves of all visible colors from red to blue, as shown in **Figure 15-7.** When all these colors are mixed together, the eye and the brain do not distinguish the individual colors but interpret the mixture as being white.

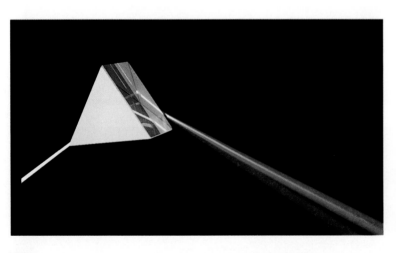

Figure 15-7 A beam of white light passing through a prism is separated into a spectrum of all the visible colors.

Figure 15-8

A Examine the pair of gym shoes and socks as seen under white light. **Why do the socks appear blue under white light?**

B The same shoes and socks were photographed through a red filter. **Why do the blue socks appear black when viewed under red light?**

When this mixture of waves strikes an object that is not transparent, the object absorbs some of the light energy. Some of the light waves that are not absorbed are reflected. If the object reflects the red waves and absorbs all the others, the object appears red. Similarly, objects that look blue reflect only the blue waves. Some objects reflect all the colors in the visible spectrum. These objects appear white, while objects that absorb all visible light appear black. **Figure 15-8** shows gym shoes and socks as seen under white light and as seen when viewed through a red filter, which allows only red light to pass through.

The Primary Colors

How many colors are there? Often, the visible spectrum is said to be made up of red, orange, yellow, green, blue, indigo, and violet light. But, this is usually done for convenience. In reality, humans can distinguish thousands of colors, including many such as brown, pink, and purple that are not found in the spectrum.

Light of almost any color can be made by mixing different amounts of red light, green light, and blue light. Red, green, and blue are called the primary colors. Look at **Figure 15-9.** White light is produced where beams of red, green, and blue light overlap. Yellow light is produced where red and green light overlap. However, even though the light looks yellow, it still consists of light waves of two different wavelengths. You see the color yellow because of the way your brain interprets the combination of the red and green light striking your eye.

Figure 15-9 By mixing together light from the three primary colors—red, blue, and green—all the visible colors can be made.

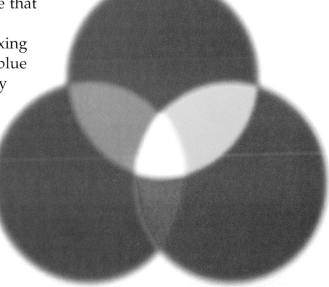

Color Pigments

If you have ever painted a picture, you may have mixed together paints of different colors to make a new color. Materials like paint that are used to change the color of other objects, like the walls of a room or an artist's canvas, are called *pigments*. If you've ever tried mixing red and green paint together, you've probably realized that mixing piments forms colors in a different way than mixing colored lights.

Like all colored materials, pigments absorb some colors and reflect others. When you mix pigments, the colors that reach your eye are the colors that are not absorbed by the mixture. The primary pigment colors are not red, blue, and green, but instead are yellow, magenta, and cyan. You can make any colored pigment by mixing different amounts of these primary pigment colors, as shown in **Figure 15-10.**

The primary pigment colors are related to the primary light colors. A yellow pigment absorbs blue light and reflects red and green. A magenta pigment absorbs green light and reflects red and blue. A cyan pigment absorbs red light and reflects blue and green. Thus each of the primary pigment colors is white light with one of the primary light colors removed.

Figure 15-10 The three primary color pigments—yellow, magenta, and cyan—can form all the visible colors when mixed together in various amounts.

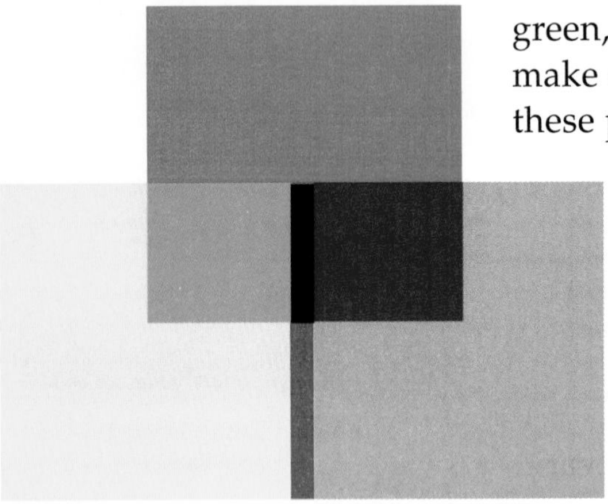

Section Assessment

1. Which has a higher frequency, red light or blue light?

2. What is the difference between an opaque object and a transparent object?

3. What colors are reflected by an object that appears black? Explain.

4. **Think Critically:** Why is it cooler to wear light-colored clothes on a hot day than dark clothes?

5. **Skill Builder**
   Observing and Inferring A white plastic bowl and a black plastic bowl have been sitting in sunlight. You observe that the black bowl feels warmer than the white bowl. From this information, infer which bowl absorbs and which bowl reflects more sunlight. If you need help, refer to Observing and Inferring in the **Skill Handbook** on page 532.

Science Journal
Read an article about the greenhouse effect and draw a diagram in your Science Journal explaining how the greenhouse effect works.

Reflection and Mirrors

The Law of Reflection

Have you ever noticed your image in a pool or lake? If the surface of the water is smooth, you can see your image clearly. If the surface is wavy, your image seems to be distorted. The image you see is the result of light reflecting from the surface and traveling to your eye.

When a light ray strikes a surface and is reflected, the reflected ray obeys the law of reflection. **Figure 15-11** shows a light ray striking a surface and being reflected. Imagine a line drawn perpendicular to the surface where the light ray strikes the surface. This line is called the normal to the surface. The incoming ray and the normal form an angle called the angle of incidence. The reflected light ray also forms an angle with the normal called the angle of reflection. The **law of reflection** states that the angle of incidence is equal to the angle of reflection. This is true for any surface, no matter what material it is made of.

Reflection from Surfaces

Why can you see your reflection in some surfaces such as mirrors, and not see any reflection from a surface such as a piece of paper? The answer is related to difference in smoothness of the two surfaces.

What You'll Learn

► How light is reflected from rough and smooth surfaces
► How a plane mirror forms an image
► How concave and convex mirrors form an image

Vocabulary
law of reflection
focal point
focal length

Why It's Important

► Mirrors can change the direction of light waves and enable you to see images, such as your own face, that normally would not be in view.

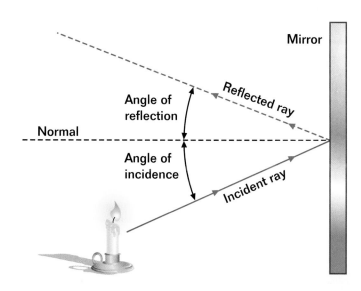

Figure 15-11 A light ray strikes a surface and is reflected. The angle of incidence is always equal to the angle of reflection. This is the law of reflection.

Figure 15-12 A highly magnified view of the surface of a paper towel shows that the surface is made of many cellulose wood fibers that make it rough and uneven.

Magnification: 35×

The surface of the paper is not as smooth as the surface of a mirror. Even though the paper may look smooth, **Figure 15-12** shows that under a microscope, its surface looks rough. The uneven surface of the paper causes light rays to be reflected in many directions as shown in **Figure 15-13.** The reflection of light waves from a rough surface is diffuse reflection. The mirrorlike reflection from a smooth surface that produces a sharp image of an object is called regular reflection. ☑

A piece of foil is smooth enough to act like a mirror and produce a regular reflection. If you crumple the foil, its surface no longer acts like one mirror. Now it acts like many tiny mirrors. Each of these tiny mirrors produces a regular reflection, but the reflections go in many different directions.

Reading Check ☑

Why does a rough surface cause a diffuse reflection?

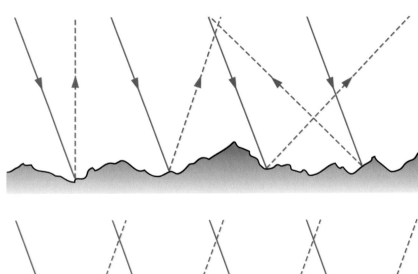

A

Figure 15-13 A rough surface (A) causes parallel light rays to be reflected in many different directions. A smooth surface (B) causes parallel light rays to be reflected in a single direction.

B

Reflection by Plane Mirrors

Did you glance in the mirror before leaving for school this morning? If you did, you probably saw your reflection in a plane mirror. A plane mirror is a mirror with a flat reflecting surface. The mirror produced an image of you that seemed to be coming from behind the mirror. The image in the mirror also had your left and right sides reversed. How was that image formed?

Figure 15-14A shows a person looking into a plane mirror. Light waves from the sun or a source of artificial light strike each part of the person. These light rays bounce off the person according to the law of reflection, and some of these rays strike the mirror. The rays that strike the mirror also are reflected according to the law of reflection. **Figure 15-14A** shows the path traveled by some of the rays that have bounced off the person and have been reflected by the mirror into the person's eye.

Why does the image seem to be behind the mirror? Your brain processes the light rays that enter your eyes and creates the sensation of seeing. Your brain interprets the light rays that have bounced off the mirror as having followed the path shown by the dashed lines in **Figure 15-14B**. The resulting image looks as though it is behind the mirror, even though there is nothing there. The image appears to be the same distance behind the mirror as the person is in front of the mirror.

Wave or Particle?
When a particle like a marble or a basketball bounces off a surface, it obeys the law of reflection. Because light also obeyed the law of reflection, people once thought that light must consist of streams of particles. Today, experiments have shown that light can behave as though it were both a wave and a stream of energy bundles called photons. Read an article about photons and write a description in your Science Journal.

Figure 15-14 A plane mirror forms an image by changing the direction of light rays.

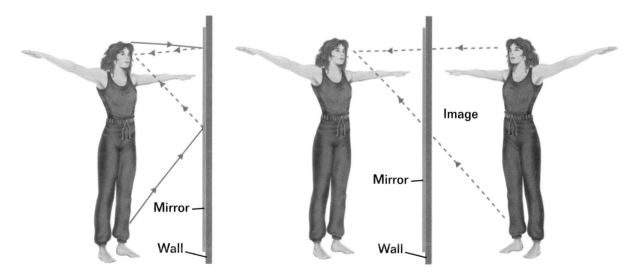

A Light rays that bounce off a person strike the mirror. Some of these light rays are reflected into the person's eye. As examples, the figure shows a light ray from the person's head and a ray from the leg.

B The light rays shown entering the person's eye in **Figure 15-14A** seem to be coming from a person behind the mirror.

Concave and Convex Mirrors

Some mirrors are not flat. A concave mirror has a surface that is curved inward, like the inside of a spoon. Unlike plane mirrors, concave mirrors cause light rays to come together, or converge. This difference causes the two types of mirrors to form different types of images.

A straight line drawn perpendicular to the center of a concave or convex mirror is called the optical axis. Look at **Figure 15-15A.** For a concave mirror, light rays that travel parallel to the optical axis and strike the mirror are reflected so that they pass through a single point on the optical axis called the **focal point.** The distance along the optical axis from the center of the mirror to the focal point is called the **focal length.**

VISUALIZING
Images Formed by Concave Mirrors

Figure 15-15 The image formed by a concave mirror depends on the location of the object.

A A concave mirror reflects all light rays traveling parallel to the optical axis so that they pass through the focal point.

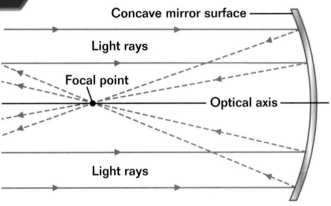

B If the object is farther from the mirror than the focal length, the mirror forms an image that is inverted.

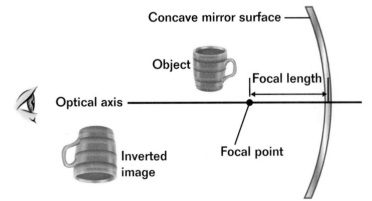

C This photograph shows the image formed by a concave mirror when the object is more than one focal length from the mirror.

The image formed by a concave mirror depends on the position of the object relative to the focal point of the mirror. **Figure 15-15B** shows how the image is formed if the object is farther from the mirror than the focal point, and **Figure 15-15C** is a photograph of such an image. The image is upside down, or inverted, and the size of the image decreases as the object is moved farther away from the mirror.

Light rays from an object placed at the focal point strike the mirror and are reflected so they travel parallel to the optical axis. If a light source is placed at the focal point, a beam of light will be produced. For example, in a flashlight the bulb is placed at the focal point of a concave reflector.

However, if the object is closer to the mirror than the focal point, **Figures 15-15D** and **15-15E** show that the image formed is upright. The image gets larger as the object moves closer to the mirror.

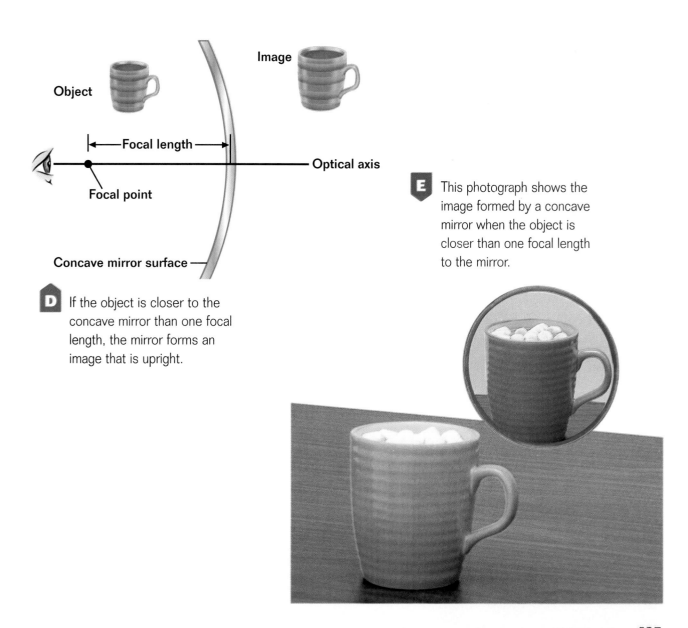

D If the object is closer to the concave mirror than one focal length, the mirror forms an image that is upright.

E This photograph shows the image formed by a concave mirror when the object is closer than one focal length to the mirror.

Figure 15-16 A convex mirror forms an image.

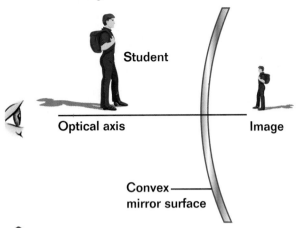

Student

Optical axis

Image

Convex mirror surface

A No matter how far the object is from a convex mirror, the image is always upright and smaller than the object.

B A convex mirror causes incoming light rays that are traveling parallel to the optical axis to spread apart after they are reflected.

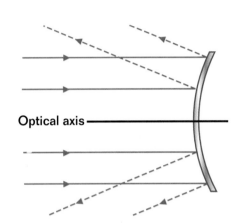

Optical axis

A convex mirror has surface that curves outward, like the outside of a spoon. **Figure 15-16A** shows how a convex mirror causes light rays to spread apart, or diverge. **Figure 15-16B** shows that the image formed by a convex mirror seems to be behind the mirror, like the image formed by a plane mirror. Like a plane mirror, the image formed by a convex mirror is always upright. But unlike a plane mirror, the image formed by a convex mirror is always smaller than the object.

Convex mirrors are used as security mirrors mounted above the aisles in stores and as outside rearview mirrors on cars and trucks. When used in this way on cars and trucks, objects seem smaller and farther away than they really are. As a result, these mirrors sometimes carry a warning that objects viwed in the mirror are closer than they seem.

Section Assessment

1. As you walk toward a large, vertical plane mirror, describe what happens to your image.

2. If the surface of a concave mirror is made more curved, what happens to its focal length?

3. **Think Critically:** The surface of a car is covered with dust and looks dull. After the car is washed and waxed, you can see your image reflected in the car's surface. Explain.

4. **Skill Builder**
   Forming a Hypothesis When you look at a window at night, you can sometimes see two images of yourself. Make a hypothesis to explain why two images are seen. If you need help, refer to Forming a Hypothesis in the **Skill Handbook** on page 534.

Using Computers

Spreadsheet Design a table using spreadsheet software to compare the images formed by plane, concave, and convex mirrors. Include in your table how the images depend on the distance of the object from the mirror. If you need help, refer to page 550.

Reflection from a Plane Mirror

Materials

- Flashlight
- Small plane mirror, at least 10 cm on a side
- Protractor
- Metric ruler
- Scissors
- Black construction paper
- Tape
- Modeling clay

A light ray strikes the surface of a plane mirror and is reflected. Is there a relationship between the direction of the incoming light ray and the direction of the reflected light ray?

What You'll Investigate

How does the angle of incidence compare with the angle of reflection for a plane mirror?

Goals

- **Measure** the angle of incidence and the angle of reflection for a light ray incident on a plane mirror.

Procedure

1. With the scissors, **cut** a slit in the construction paper and **tape** it over the flashlight lens. Make sure the slit is centered on the lens.

2. **Place** the mirror at one end of the unlined paper. Push the mirror into the lump of clay so it stands vertically, and tilt the mirror so it leans slightly toward the table.

3. **Measure** with the ruler to find the center of the bottom edge of the mirror and mark it. Then, use the protractor and the ruler to **draw** a line on the paper perpendicular to the mirror from the mark. Label this line P.

4. Using the protractor and the ruler, **draw** lines on the paper outward from the mark at the center of the mirror at angles of 30°, 45°, and 60° to line P.

5. Turn on the flashlight and place it so the beam is along the 60° line. This is the angle of incidence. **Locate** the reflected beam on the paper, and **measure** the angle the reflected beam makes with line P. **Record** this angle in your data table. This is the angle of reflection. If you cannot see the reflected beam, slightly increase the tilt of the mirror.

6. Repeat step 5 for the 30°, 45°, and P lines.

Conclude and Apply

1. What happened to the beam of light when it was shined along line P?

2. What can you **infer** about the relationship between the angle of incidence and the angle of reflection?

15·3 Refraction and Lenses

What You'll Learn

▶ Why light rays refract
▶ How convex and concave lenses form images

Vocabulary

refraction   convex lens
lens   concave lens

Why It's Important

▶ Many of the images you see every day in photographs, on TV, and in movies are made by using lenses.

Refraction

If you have ever looked at a glass of water that had a pencil in it, you may have noticed that the pencil appeared bent, as in **Figure 15-17.** You may have noticed in the Explore Activity that the penny under water seemed closer than the other penny. These images are due to the bending of light rays as they pass from one material to another. What causes light rays to change direction?

The Speeds of Light

The speed of light in empty space is about 300 million m/s. Light passing through a medium such as air, water, or glass travels slower than the speed of light in empty space. This is because the atoms that make up the medium interact with the light wave and slow it down. **Figure 15-18** shows how slowly light moves in some materials.

Figure 15-17 A pencil in a glass of water looks as if it has been broken at the water line.

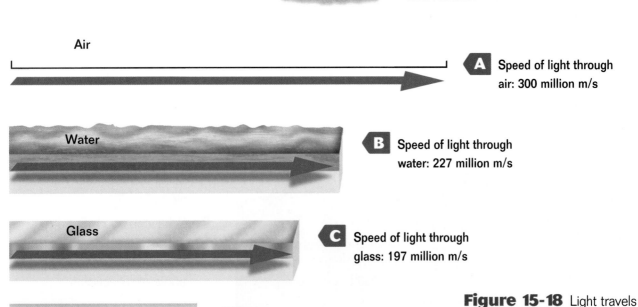

Air

A Speed of light through air: 300 million m/s

Water

B Speed of light through water: 227 million m/s

Glass

C Speed of light through glass: 197 million m/s

Diamond

D Speed of light through diamond: 125 million m/s

Figure 15-18 Light travels at different speeds in different materials.

Figure 15-19 A light ray is bent as it travels from air into glass. **In which medium does light travel more slowly?**

The Refraction of Light Waves

What happens when light waves travel from air into water where the speed of light is different? If the wave is traveling at an angle to the boundary between two materials, it changes direction. The bending of a light wave due to a change in speed when the wave moves from one medium to another is called **refraction. Figure 15-19** shows an example of refraction. The larger the change in speed, the more the light wave is refracted. ✔

Why does a change in speed cause the light wave to bend? Imagine a set of wheels on a car that travels from pavement to mud. The wheel that enters the mud first is slowed, while the other wheel continues at the original speed. This causes the wheel axle to turn as shown in **Figure 15-20,** and the wheels change direction.

Light behaves in a similar manner. Imagine again a light wave traveling from air into water. The first part of the wave to enter the water is slowed, just as the wheel that first hits the mud is slowed. Then, the rest of the wave is slowed down as it enters the water so the whole wave is turned, just like the axle.

Reading Check ✔

What causes light to bend?

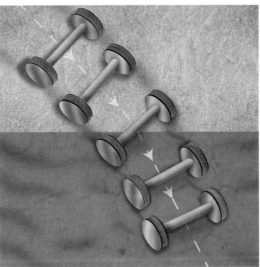

Figure 15-20 An axle turns as the wheels cross the boundary between pavement and mud. **How would the axle turn if the wheels were going from mud to pavement?**

Convex and Concave Lenses

Do you like snapping pictures of your friends and family with a camera? Have you ever watched a bird through binoculars or peered at something tiny through a magnifying glass? All of these involve the use of lenses. A **lens** is a transparent object with at least one curved side that causes light to bend. The amount of bending can be controlled by making the sides more or less curved. The more curved the sides, the more a ray of light entering the lens is bent.

Forming an Image with a Lens

Procedure 🤝 🥽 🖐️

1. Fill a glass test tube with water and seal it with a stopper.
2. Write your name on a 3 × 5 card. Lay the test tube on the card and observe the appearance of your name. Record your observations.
3. Hold the test tube about 1 cm above the card and observe the appearance of your name. Record your observations.
4. Now, observe what happens to your name as you slowly move the test tube away from the card. Record your observations.

Analyze

1. Is the water-filled test tube a concave lens or a convex lens?
2. Compare the image formed when the test tube was close to the card with the image formed when the test tube was far from the card.

Convex Lenses

A lens that is thicker in the center than at the edges is a **convex lens.** Convex lenses are also called converging lenses. Light rays traveling parallel to the optical axis are bent so they meet at the focal point, as shown in **Figure 15-21A.** If the surface is highly curved, the focal point is close to the lens and the focal length is short.

The image formed by a convex lens is similar to the image formed by a concave mirror. For both, the type of image depends on how far the object is from the focal point. Look at **Figure 15-21B.** If the object is farther than two focal lengths from the lens, the image is inverted and smaller than the object.

If the object is closer to the lens than one focal length, then the rays coming from points on the object diverge after passing through the lens, as shown in **Figure 15-21C.** The image formed is right-side up and larger than the object. Have you ever used

Figure 15-21 A convex lens forms an image that depends on the distance from the object to the lens.

 A Light rays parallel to the optical axis are bent so that they pass through the focal point.

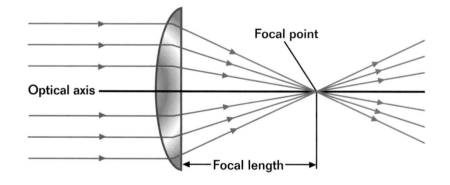

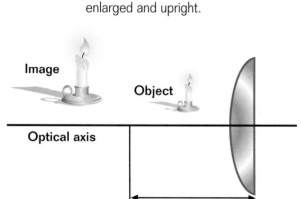

C If the object is closer to the lens than one focal length, the image formed is enlarged and upright.

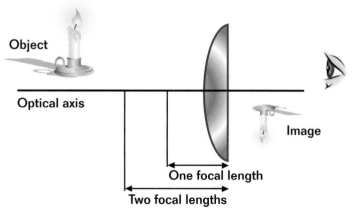

B If the object is far from the lens, the image formed is smaller than the object and inverted.

a magnifying glass? The image formed was right-side up and larger than the object. The image continues to get larger as the magnifying glass is brought closer to the object.

Concave Lens

A lens that is thicker at the edges than in the middle is a **concave lens.** A concave lens is also called a diverging lens. **Figure 15-22** shows how light rays traveling parallel to the optical axis are bent after passing through a concave lens.

A concave lens causes light rays to diverge, and the light rays are not brought to a focus. The type of image formed by a concave lens is similar to that formed by a convex mirror. The image is upright and smaller than the object. Concave lenses are used in eyeglasses to correct problems people sometimes have in seeing objects that are far away.

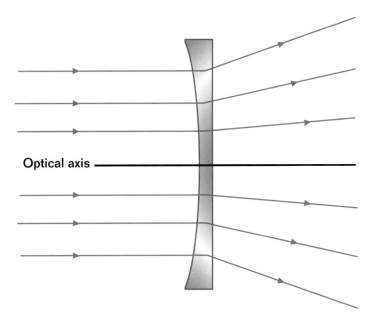

Figure 15-22 A concave lens causes light rays traveling parallel to the optical axis to diverge.

Section Assessment

1. How is the image formed by a concave lens similar to the image formed by a convex mirror?

2. To magnify an object, would you use a convex lens or a concave lens?

3. Describe two ways, using convex and concave lenses, to form an image that is smaller than the object.

4. **Think Critically:** A light wave is bent more as it travels from air to glass than in traveling from air to water. Is the speed of light greater in water or glass? Explain.

5. **Skill Builder**
   Predicting Air that is cool is more dense than air that is warm. Look at **Figure 15–18** and predict whether the speed of light is faster in warm air or cool air. If you need help, refer to Predicting in the **Skill Handbook** on page 542.

Using Math

Earth is about 150 000 000 km from the sun. Use the formula *distance = speed × time* to calculate how many seconds it takes a beam of light to travel from Earth to the sun. About how many minutes does it take?

Materials

- Convex lens
- Modeling clay
- Meterstick
- Flashlight
- Masking tape
- Cardboard with white surface, about 20-cm square

Image Formation by a Convex Lens

The type of image formed by a convex lens, also called a converging lens, is related to the distance of the object from the lens. This distance is called the object distance. The location of the image is also related to the distance of the object from the lens. The distance from the lens to the image is called the image distance. What happens to the position of the image as the object gets nearer or farther from the lens?

What You'll Investigate

How are the image distance and object distance related for a convex lens?

Goals

- **Measure** the image distance as the object distance changes.
- **Observe** the type of image formed as the object distance changes.

Safety Precautions

Procedure

1. **Design** a data table in which to record your data. You will need three columns in your table. One column will be for the object distance, another will be for the image distance, and the third will be for the type of image.

2. **Use** the modeling clay to make the lens stand vertically upright on the lab table.

3. **Form** the letter F on the glass surface of the flashlight with masking tape.

4. Turn on the flashlight and place it 1 m from the lens. **Position** the flashlight so the flashlight beam is shining through the lens.

5. **Record** the distance from the flashlight to the lens in the object distance column in your data table.

6. Hold the cardboard vertically upright on the other side of the lens, and move it back and forth

Convex Lens Data		
Object Distance	**Image Distance**	**Image Type**

until a sharp image of the letter F is obtained.

7. **Measure** the distance of the card from the lens using the meterstick, and **record** this distance in the image distance column in your data table.

8. **Record** in the third column of your data table whether the image is upright or inverted, and smaller or larger.

9. Repeat steps 6–9 for object distances of 50 cm and 25 cm.

Conclude and Apply

1. How did the image distance change as the object distance decreased?

2. How did the image change as the object distance decreased?

3. What would happen to the size of the image if the flashlight were much farther away than 1 m?

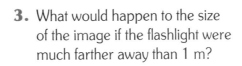

Microscopes, Telescopes, and Cameras

What You'll Learn

▶ How microscopes magnify objects
▶ How telescopes make distant objects visible
▶ How cameras work

Why It's Important

▶ Microscopes and telescopes are used to view parts of the universe that can't be seen with the eye alone. Cameras record images of the world around you.

Microscopes

Lenses have been used since the early 1600s to produce images of objects too small to be seen with the eye alone. Today, a compound microscope like the one in **Figure 15-23A** uses a combination of lenses to magnify objects by as much as 2500 times.

Figure 15-23B shows how a microscope forms an image. An object, such as a drop of water from a pond, is placed close to a convex lens called the objective lens. This lens produces an enlarged image inside the microscope tube. The light rays from that image then pass through a second convex lens called the eyepiece, or ocular, lens. This lens further magnifies the image formed by the objective lens. This results in a much larger image than a single lens can produce.

Figure 15-23 A compound microscope uses lenses to magnify objects.

A A compound microscope often has more than one objective lens, each giving a different magnification. A light underneath the objective lens makes the image bright enough to see clearly.

B The objective lens in a compound microscope forms an enlarged image, which is then magnified by the eyepiece lens. **How would the image be affected if the eyepiece lens were a concave lens?**

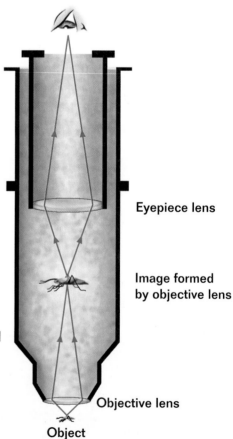

Eyepiece lens

Image formed by objective lens

Objective lens

Object

Telescopes

While microscopes are used to magnify very small objects, telescopes are used to examine objects that may be quite large but are far away. The first telescopes also were invented in the early 1600s, at about the same time as the first microscopes. Much of what we know about the distant universe has come from images and other information gathered by telescopes.

Refracting Telescopes

The simplest refracting telescopes use two convex lenses to form an image of a distant object. Just as in a compound microscope, light passes through an objective lens that forms an image. That image is then magnified by an eyepiece lens, as shown in **Figure 15-24.**

An important difference between a telescope and a microscope is the size of the objective lens. More light from a far-away object can enter a large objective lens than a small one. This makes images appear brighter and more detailed when they are magnified by the eyepiece. Increasing the size of the objective lens makes it possible to see stars and galaxies that are too far away to see with a telescope that has a small objective lens. Thus, the main purpose of a telescope is not to magnify the image, but to gather as much light as possible from distant objects. In **Figure 15-25**, the largest refracting telescope ever made is shown. ☑

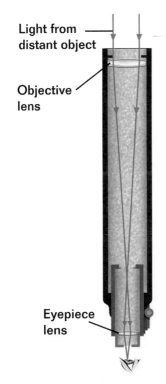

Figure 15-24 A refracting telescope is made from an objective lens and an eyepiece lens. The objective lens forms an image that is magnified by the eyepiece lens.

Reading Check ☑

How does a telescope objective lens enable distant objects to be seen?

Figure 15-25 The refracting telescope at the Yerkes Observatory in Wisconsin has the largest objective lens in the world. It has a diameter of 1 m.

Reflecting Telescopes

There are limits to how big a refracting telescope can be. One problem is that its objective lens can be supported only around its edges. If the lens is extremely large, it cannot be supported enough to keep it from sagging slightly under its own weight. This causes the image it forms to become distorted.

Reflecting telescopes can be made much larger than refracting telescopes. This is because they use a concave mirror instead of an objective lens to gather light from a distant object, as shown in **Figure 15-26B.** A small plane mirror called a secondary mirror is used to reflect the image toward the side of the telescope tube, where it is magnified by an eyepiece.

Because only the one reflecting surface on the mirror needs to be carefully made, telescope mirrors are less expensive to make than lenses of a similar size. Also, mirrors can be supported more rigidly on their back side so they can be made much larger without sagging under their own weight. The Keck Telescope in Hawaii is the largest reflecting telescope in the world with a mirror 10 m in diameter. **Figure 15-26A** shows another one of the largest telescopes in the world, the reflecting telescope at Mount Palomar in southern California.

Figure 15-26 Reflecting telescopes gather light by using a concave mirror.

A The Hale telescope at the Mount Palomar observatory in southern California has a concave mirror that is 5.1 m in diameter.

B Light entering the telescope tube is reflected by a concave mirror onto the secondary mirror. An eyepiece lens is used to magnify the image formed by the concave mirror. The secondary mirror in the largest telescopes usually reflects the rays through a hole in the concave mirror, instead of the side of the tube.

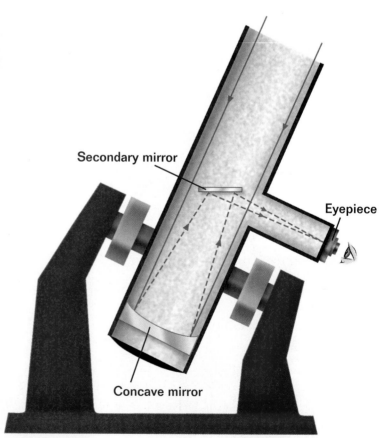

Secondary mirror

Eyepiece

Concave mirror

Cameras

You may have seen a number of photographs today in books, magazines, and newspapers. And, you may have used acamera yourself to take photographs. A typical camera hasa convex lens that forms an image on a section of film. Remember that a convex lens forms an image that is reduced and inverted if the object is more than two focal lengths away. A camera lens is a convex lens used in this way. Look at the camera shown in **Figure 15-27.** When the shutter is open, the convex lens forms an image on a piece of film that is sensitive to light. The film contains chemicals that undergo chemical reactions when struck by light. This causes light areas and dark areas in the image to be recorded. If the film is sensitive to color, the colors of the object also are recorded.

An image that is too bright may overexpose the film. If there is too little light that reaches the film, the image may be too dark. To control the amount of light reaching the film, a camera also contains a device called the diaphragm.

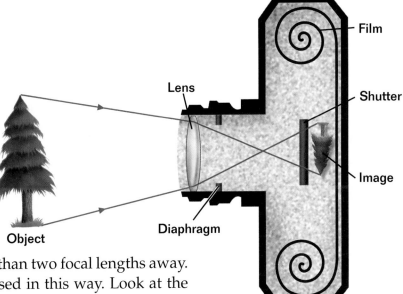

Figure 15-27 A camera uses a convex lens to form an image on a piece of light-sensitive film. The image formed by a camera lens is smaller than the object. The amount of light striking the film is controlled by the diaphragm.

Problem Solving

Radio Telescopes

On a clear night, you may be able to see the visible light from hundreds of stars. But, stars and galaxies emit radio waves, as well as visible light. Unlike light waves, radio waves from space are not affected by turbulence in Earth's atmosphere. These radio waves can be detected even on cloudy or stormy nights when no stars can be seen. By studying these radio waves, scientists can learn about the birth and death of stars and galaxies.

Just as reflecting and refracting telescopes collect light from distant stars and galaxies, radio telescopes collect radio waves. The photograph shows the radio telescope at Green Banks, West Virginia. The collector of a radio telescope is usually called the *dish*, and the device supported above the center of the dish is the *detector*. The detector contains electronic instruments that help to amplify and record the radio waves.

Solve the Problem

1. Examine the photograph carefully. Is a radio telescope a reflecting telescope or a refracting telescope? Explain.

2. How are the position of the detector and the focal point of the radio telescope related?

Think Critically: Do you think the information gathered by radio telescopes could be improved if a radio telescope were placed into orbit above Earth's atmosphere? Why or why not?

interNET
CONNECTION

Visit the Glencoe
Science Web Site at
**www.glencoe.com/
sec/science/ca** for
more information about
cameras.

The diaphragm is opened to let more light onto the film and closed to reduce the amount of light striking the film.

Camera Lenses

The image on the film depends on the camera lens used. Suppose you wished to photograph a friend. The size of your friend's image on the film depends on the focal length of the lens. The shorter the focal length, the smaller the image. To focus the image sharply, the lens must be moved closer to the film as the focal length is made smaller.

If you wanted the photograph to include your friend and the surrounding scenery, you would use a wide-angle lens. This lens has a short focal length and is positioned close to the film. If, instead, you wished to photograph only your friend's face, you might use a telephoto lens. This lens has a long focal length and must be positioned far from the film.

With a zoom lens, you can control the size of your friend's image in a photograph. The focal length of a zoom lens can be adjusted by moving the lens closer or farther from the film. A zoom lens is useful because it can be used as both a telephoto and a wide-angle lens.

Section Assessment

1. How is a compound microscope different from a magnifying glass?

2. Why are reflecting telescopes the biggest telescopes and not refracting telescopes?

3. Why is the objective lens of a refracting telescope bigger than the objective lens of a microscope?

4. **Think Critically:** If you could buy only one lens for your camera, what type of lens would you buy? Why?

5. **Skill Builder**
   Communicating Scientists need to clearly explain to others the results of their experiments, as well as their hypotheses and ideas. They do this by carefully writing research papers. Do the **Chapter 15 Skill Activity** on page 568 to learn how to write a research paper.

Using Math

The size of an image is related to the magnification of an optical instrument by the following formula:

Image size = magnification × object size

A blood cell has a diameter of about 0.001 cm. How large is the image formed by a microscope with a magnification of 1000?

Scientific Notation

A microscope allows us to see extremely small organisms. A cell that measures only 0.0007 cm in diameter can be seen clearly with a powerful microscope. A telescope can be used to see far-away objects, such as the galaxy, left. By using a telescope, we can see a galaxy as far as 2.2 million light-years away.

Scientists and mathematicians have devised a short way to write extremely small or large numbers. This is known as scientific notation. In scientific notation, a number is written as a number that is at least 1 but less than 10 multiplied by a power of 10.

How to Determine Scientific Notations

1. To write 2 200 000 in scientific notation, you first need a number that is at least 1 but less than 10. The number 2.2 is related to 2 200 000 and is at least 1 but less than 10. If you divide 2 200 000 by 2.2, you get 1 000 000. So, 2 200 000 = 2.2 × 1 000 000. Numbers such as 1 000 000 can be written as a power of ten.

$$10 = 10^1$$
$$100 = 10 \times 10 = 10^2$$
$$1000 = 10 \times 10 \times 10 = 10^3$$
$$10\ 000 = 10 \times 10 \times 10 \times 10 = 10^4$$
$$100\ 000 = 10 \times 10 \times 10 \times 10 \times 10 = 10^5$$
$$1\ 000\ 000 = 10 \times 10 \times 10 \times 10 \times 10 \times 10 = 10^6$$

$2.2 \times 1\ 000\ 000$ in scientific notation is 2.2×10^6.

2. To write 0.0007 in scientific notation, you first need a number that is at least 1 but less than 10. You can see that 7 is related to 0.0007 and is at least 1 but less than 10. If you divide 0.0007 by 7, you get 0.0001. So, 0.0007 = 7 × 0.0001. Numbers such as 0.0001 can be written as a power of ten using a negative number.

$$0.1 = \frac{1}{10} = 16–1$$

$$0.01 = \frac{1}{100} = 16–2$$

$$0.001 = \frac{1}{1000} = 16–3$$

7×0.0001 in scientific notation is $7 \times 16–4$.

Practice
PROBLEMS

1. One type of bacteria measures 0.000 015 cm in length. Write this number in scientific notation.
2. Pluto is 5.92 billion km from the sun. Write this number in scientific notation.
3. A light-year is the distance that light travels in one year. Light travels at about 300 million m/s. How many kilometers are in a light-year? Write your answer in scientific notation.

For a **preview** of this chapter, study this Reviewing Main Ideas before you read the chapter. After you have studied this chapter, you can use the Reviewing Main Ideas to **review** the chapter.

The Glencoe MindJogger, Audiocassettes, and CD-ROM provide additional opportunities for review.

Section

15-1 PROPERTIES OF LIGHT

Light is an **electromagnetic wave** and can travel in a vacuum. The energy carried by a light wave increases as the **frequency** gets larger. When a light wave strikes an object, some of the light wave's energy may be reflected, some may be absorbed, and some may be transmitted through the object. The color of a light wave depends on its wavelength. The color of an object depends on which wavelengths of light are reflected by the object. Light of almost any color can be made by mixing different amounts of red, green, and blue light. Mixing pigments such as paints makes colors by subtracting colors from the light that strikes the pigments. *How does the wavelength of a light wave change as its frequency increases?*

Section

15-2 REFLECTION OF LIGHT

Light reflected from the surface of an object obeys the **law of reflection:** the angle of incidence equals the angle of reflection. Diffuse reflection occurs when a surface is rough, while regular reflection occurs from very smooth surfaces and produces a clear, mirrorlike image. The image seen in a plane mirror seems to come from behind the mirror and is the same size as the object. The image formed by a concave mirror depends on the position of the object relative to the **focal point** of the mirror. Convex mirrors cause light waves to diverge and produce upright images smaller than the object. *Why doesn't diffuse reflection produce sharp, clear images?*

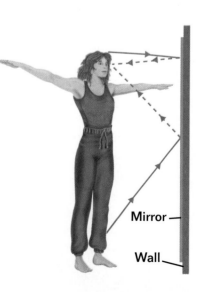

Mirror

Wall

Reading Check ✔

Describe **Figure 15-15** so that a student in the third or fourth grade could understand the ideas shown.

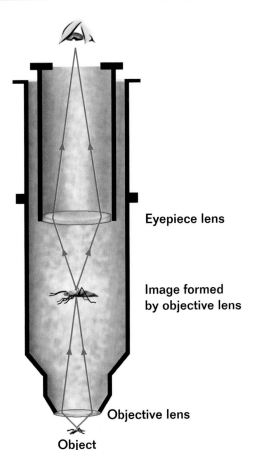

Eyepiece lens

Image formed by objective lens

Objective lens

Object

Section

15-3 REFRACTION OF LIGHT

Light waves tend to travel in straight lines, unless they change speed when they travel into another medium. Then, the waves change direction at the boundary between the two media. This change in direction is called **refraction.** A **convex lens** causes light waves to converge. The type of image formed by a convex lens depends on the location of the object relative to the focal point. A **concave lens** causes light waves to diverge. *How close must an object be to a convex lens to form an enlarged image?*

Section

15-4 MICROSCOPES, TELESCOPES, AND CAMERAS

A compound microscope is used to enlarge small objects. A convex objective lens forms an enlarged image that is further enlarged by an eyepiece lens. Most telescopes today are reflecting telescopes that use a concave mirror to form a real image that is enlarged by an eye-piece. The larger the mirror, the more light it can gather and the better the image formed by the telescope. Cameras use a lens to form an image on a light-sensitive piece of film. *Do the lenses used in microscopes, telescopes, and cameras cause light rays to converge or diverge?*

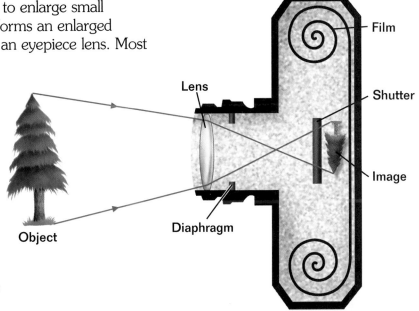

Film

Lens

Shutter

Image

Object

Diaphragm

Using Vocabulary

a. concave lens
b. convex lens
c. electromagnetic wave
d. focal length
e. focal point
f. frequency
g. law of reflection
h. lens
i. light ray
j. medium
k. reflection
l. refraction
m. wavelength

Match each phrase with the correct term from the list of Vocabulary words.

1. the bending of light when it changes speed in passing from one material to another
2. a part of a light wave traveling in a single direction
3. the number of wavelengths that pass a point in 1 s
4. the distance of the focal point from the center of the lens or mirror
5. the material in which a light wave travels

Checking Concepts

Choose the word or phrase that completes the sentence or answers the question.

6. What type of image does a plane mirror form?
   A) upright   C) magnified
   B) inverted   D) all of the above

7. How are light waves different than radio waves?
   A) Light waves have a higher frequency.
   B) Light waves have a longer wavelength.
   C) Light waves have a longer focal length.
   D) Radio waves are sound waves.

8. Which of the following types of electromagnetic waves is the most energetic?
   A) visible   C) infrared
   B) X rays   D) ultraviolet

9. The lowest-frequency visible light waves have what color?
   A) blue   C) infrared
   B) red   D) ultraviolet

10. Which of the following is true about an object that looks red?
    A) It absorbs only red light.
    B) It transmits only red light.
    C) It can be seen only in red light.
    D) None of the above.

11. In reflection, how is the angle of incidence related to the angle of reflection?
    A) It is always the same.
    B) It is always greater.
    C) It is twice as large.
    D) It depends on the change in the speed of light.

12. Why does a camera have a diaphragm?
    A) to control the amount of light striking the film
    B) to move the lens closer to the film
    C) to change the focal length of the lens
    D) to close the shutter

13. Which of the following can be used to magnify objects?
    A) a concave lens   C) a convex mirror
    B) a convex lens   D) all of the above

14. What is an object that reflects some light and transmits some light called?
    A) colored   C) opaque
    B) diffuse   D) translucent

15. How do the sides of a convex lens change as its focal length decreases?
    A) They become flatter.
    B) They become concave.
    C) They become more curved.
    D) They become regular reflectors.

Thinking Critically

16. Do all light rays that strike a convex lens pass through the focal point?

17. Does a plane mirror focus light rays? Why or why not?

18. Explain why a rough surface, such as a road, is a better reflector when it is wet.

19. If the speed of light were the same in all materials, could lenses be used to magnify objects? Why or why not?

20. A singer is wearing a blue outfit. What color spotlights would make the outfit appear black? Explain.

Developing Skills

If you need help, refer to the **Skill Handbook**.

21. **Using Graphs:** The graph below shows how the distance of an image from a convex lens is related to the distance of the object from the lens.

   A) How does the image move as the object gets closer to the lens?

   B) The magnification of the image is given by:
   $$magnification = \frac{image\ distance}{object\ distance}$$

   How does the magnification change as the object gets closer to the lens?

   C) What is the magnification when the object is 20 cm from the lens?

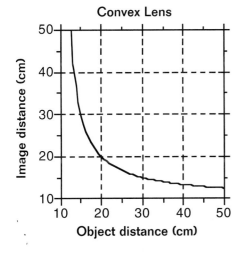

Convex Lens

THE PRINCETON REVIEW

Test-Taking Tip

Practice, Practice, Practice Practice to improve *your* performance. Don't compare yourself with anyone else.

Test Practice

Use these questions to test your Science Proficiency.

1. Two vases are identical except one is glass and the other is made of black plastic. If they are side by side in a well-lit room, which vase absorbs more light energy?
   A) The black vase absorbs more.
   B) The glass vase absorbs more.
   C) They absorb the same amount.
   D) They both absorb no light energy.

2. In glass, blue light travels slightly slower than red light. If a beam of white light passes through a glass convex lens, which statement describes what happens?
   A) The blue light is brought to a focus closer to the lens than the red light.
   B) The red light is focused closer to the lens than the blue light.
   C) All colors are focused at the same point, regardless of how slowly they move in the glass lens.
   D) Not enough information has been given.

CHAPTER
16

Electricity

Chapter Preview

Skills Preview

Skill Builders
- Observe and Infer
- Form a Hypothesis

Activities
- Make a Model
- Use Scientific Methods

MiniLabs
- Observe and Infer
- Form a Hypothesis

Reading Check ✔

As you read this chapter about electricity, write down the cause-effect relationships you identify.

Explore Activity

No computers, no CD players, no video games—can you even imagine life without electricity? You depend on it every day, and not just to make life more fun. Electricity also helps to heat and cool your homes and to provide light. Electric lighting even makes cities and towns visible from space, as shown in this satellite photo. Why is electricity so useful? Electricity provides energy that can be used to do work. This energy comes from the forces that electric charges exert on each other. What is the nature of these electric forces?

Observe Electric Forces

1. Inflate a rubber balloon.

2. Put some small bits of paper on your desktop and bring the balloon close to the bits of paper. Observe what happens.

3. Charge the balloon by holding it by the knot and rubbing the balloon on your hair or on a piece of wool.

4. Bring the balloon close to the bits of paper and observe what happens.

5. Charge two balloons using the procedure in step 3 and bring them close to each other. Observe what happens.

6. Repeat step 3, then touch the balloon with your hand. Now what happens when you bring the balloon close to the bits of paper?

Science Journal

In your Science Journal, record your observations of electric forces.

Electric Charge

You can't see, smell, or taste electricity, so maybe it seems mysterious. But, electricity is not so hard to understand when you start by thinking small—very small. All solids, liquids, and gases are made of tiny particles called atoms. Atoms themselves are made of even smaller particles called protons, neutrons, and electrons as shown in **Figure 16-1.** Protons and neutrons are held together tightly in the nucleus at the center of an atom, while electrons swarm around the nucleus in all directions. Protons and electrons possess electric charge, while neutrons have no electric charge.

Positive and Negative Charge

There are two types of electric charge. Protons carry a positive electric charge and electrons carry a negative charge. No one knows exactly what electric charge is, but it cannot be removed from a proton or an electron.

The amount of negative charge on an electron is exactly equal to the amount of positive charge on a proton. Atoms normally have equal numbers of protons and electrons. So, the amount of positive charge on all the protons in the nucleus of an atom is exactly balanced by the negative charge on all the electrons moving around the nucleus. Thus, atoms are electrically neutral, which means they behave as if they have no charge at all.

Sometimes, though, an atom will gain extra electrons and become negatively charged. If an atom loses electrons, it becomes positively charged.

What You'll Learn

► How objects can become electrically charged
► How electric charges affect other electric charges
► The difference between insulators and conductors
► How electric discharges such as lightning occur

Vocabulary
static charge
insulator
conductor
electric discharge

Why It's Important

► Lightning and other electric discharges can cause damage.

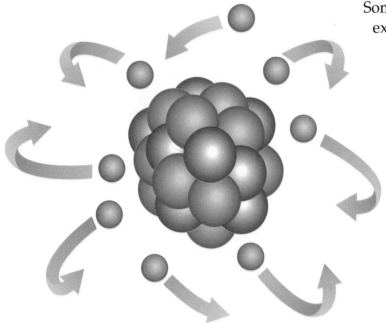

Figure 16-1 An atom is made of positively charged protons (purple), negatively charged electrons (red), and neutrons (green) with no electric charge. **Where are the protons and neutrons located?**

Electrons Move Between Objects

Electrons can move from atom to atom in a single object and also from the atoms in one object to the atoms in another object. Rubbing is one way that electrons can be transferred as shown in **Figure 16-2.** Suppose you rub a balloon on your hair as in the Explore Activity. The atoms on the balloon hold their electrons more tightly than the atoms in your hair hold their electrons. As a result, electrons are transferred from the atoms in your hair to the atoms on the surface of the balloon. Because your hair loses electrons, it becomes positively charged, while the balloon gains electrons and becomes negatively charged. The buildup of electric charges on an object is called a **static charge.** ☑

You may wonder whether objects can be charged by transferring protons from one object to another. After all, protons have a positive charge, so moving them from one object to another should change the charge on the two objects. But, protons cannot be moved from one object to another because they are held together tightly with neutrons in the nuclei of atoms. It is always electrons that are gained or lost when an object becomes charged, and never protons.

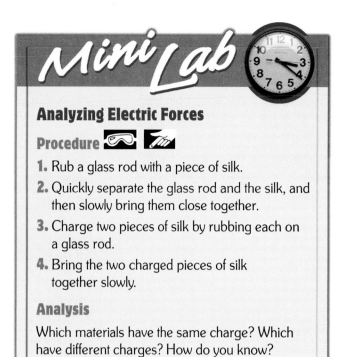

Analyzing Electric Forces

Procedure 🥽 🧤

1. Rub a glass rod with a piece of silk.
2. Quickly separate the glass rod and the silk, and then slowly bring them close together.
3. Charge two pieces of silk by rubbing each on a glass rod.
4. Bring the two charged pieces of silk together slowly.

Analysis

Which materials have the same charge? Which have different charges? How do you know?

Reading Check ☑

How does an object become electrically charged?

Figure 16-2 Electrons can be moved from one object to another by rubbing.

 Before being rubbed together, a glass rod and a piece of silk cloth both have equal numbers of positive and negative charges.

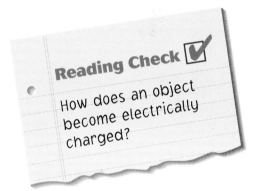 Rubbing causes electrons to be transferred from the atoms in the glass rod to atoms in the silk. **Which object has become positively charged and which has become negatively charged?**

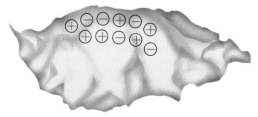

Glass rod

Silk cloth

Before rubbing

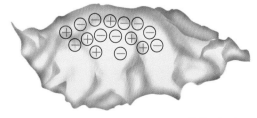

Glass rod

Silk cloth

After rubbing

Opposite charges attract

Like charges repel

Electric Forces

Charged objects exert an electric force on each other. The electric force between two charges can be attractive or repulsive as shown in **Figure 16-3**. Objects with the same type of charge repel one another, while objects with opposite charges attract one another. This rule is often stated as "like charges repel and unlike charges attract."

What keeps the nucleus of an atom from flying apart? Remember, the nucleus contains protons that have positive charges and neutrons that have no charge. You would expect the protons to repel each other. However, another force called the strong nuclear force is even stronger than the electric force. This strong nuclear force is the glue that holds protons and neutrons together in the nucleus.

Electric Fields

You may have noticed that two charged balloons repel each other even though they are not touching and that bits of paper and a charged balloon don't have to be touching for the paper to be attracted to the balloon. This behavior shows that charged objects don't have to be touching to exert an electric force on each other. The electric force acts on charged objects even though they may be some distance apart.

Electric charges exert a force on each other at a distance through an electric field, which exists around every electric charge. **Figure 16-4** shows the electric field around a positive and a negative charge. An electric field gets stronger as you get closer to a charge, just as the electric force between two charges becomes greater as the charges get closer together.

Figure 16-4 The arrows represent the electric field around electric charges. The direction of each arrow is the direction a positive charge would move if it were placed on the arrow.

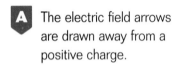 The electric field arrows are drawn away from a positive charge.

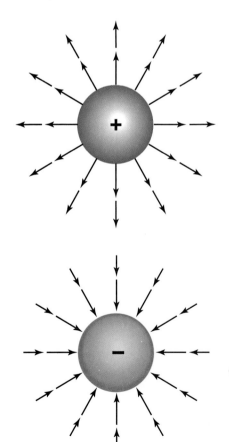

B The electric field arrows are drawn toward a negative charge. **Why are these arrows in the opposite direction of the arrows around the positive charge?**

Insulators

Rubbing a balloon on your hair transfers electrons from your hair to the balloon. But, only the part of the balloon that was rubbed on your hair becomes charged. This is because electrons cannot move easily through rubber. As a result, the electrons that were rubbed onto the balloon stayed in one place, as shown in **Figure 16-5A.** A material in which electrons cannot move easily from place to place is called an **insulator.** Examples of common materials that are insulators are plastic, wood, glass, and rubber.

Conductors

Materials that are **conductors** allow electrons to move through them more easily. Electrons placed on the surface of a conductor spread out over the entire surface, as shown in **Figure 16-5B.** The best conductors are metals such as copper, silver, and iron. An electrical wire is made from copper coated with an insulator such as plastic. Electrons move easily through the copper but do not move from the copper to the plastic insulation. This prevents electrons from escaping from the wire and causing an electric shock if someone touches the wire.

Do you think your body is an insulator or a conductor? Compared to common insulators, the human body is a conductor. You may have observed in the Explore Activity that if you touched the balloon after it had been charged, the balloon no longer attracted the bits of paper. Because electrons can move more easily along the surface of your skin than on the balloon, the excess electrons on the balloon were transferred to your hand when you touched the balloon.

Figure 16-5 Electric charges can move more easily through conductors than through insulators.

A Charges placed on an insulator repel each other but cannot move easily on the surface of the insulator. As a result, the charges remain in one place.

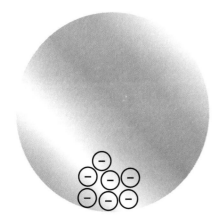

B Charges placed on a conductor repel each other but can move easily on the conductor's surface. Thus, they spread out as far apart as possible.

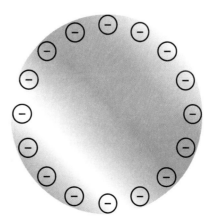

Induced Charge

Has this ever happened to you? You walk across a carpet, and as you reach for a metal doorknob, you feel an electric shock. Ouch! Maybe you even see a spark jump between your fingertip and the doorknob. To find out what happened, look at **Figure 16-6.**

As you walked, your shoes rubbed electrons off the rug, as shown in **Figure 16-6A.** The electrons then spread over the surface of your skin. As you brought your hand close to the doorknob, the electric field around the excess electrons on your hand repelled the electrons in the doorknob.

Because the doorknob was a good conductor, its electrons could move easily. The excess electrons on your hand repelled the electrons in the doorknob, as shown in **Figure 16-6B.** The part of the doorknob closest to your hand then became positively charged. This separation of positive and negative charges due to an electric field is called an induced charge.

If the electric field in the space between your hand and the knob is strong enough, electrons can be pulled across that space from your hand, as shown in **Figure 16-6C.** This rapid movement of excess electrons from one place to another is an **electric discharge.** See **Figure 16-7** for another familiar example of an electric discharge.

inter**NET** CONNECTION

Visit the Glencoe Science Web Site at **www.glencoe.com/ sec/science/ca** for more information about other types of lightning.

Figure 16-6 A spark that jumps between your fingers and a metal doorknob starts at your feet.

A As you walk across the floor, you rub electrons from the carpet onto the bottom of your shoes. These electrons then spread out all over your skin, including your hands.

B As you bring your hand close to the metal doorknob, electrons on the doorknob move as far away from your hand as possible. The part of the doorknob closest to your hand is left with a positive charge.

C The attractive electric force between the electrons on your hand and the induced positive charge on the doorknob may be strong enough to pull electrons from your hand to the doorknob. You may see this as a spark and feel a mild electric shock.

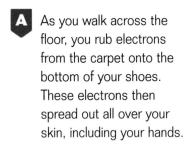

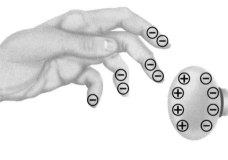

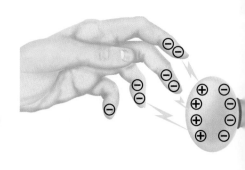

Figure 16-7

A The sun heats the air near the ground, causing it to rise. This rising air can sometimes cause a storm cloud to form. Air currents within the storm cloud carry electrons from the top of the cloud to its bottom.

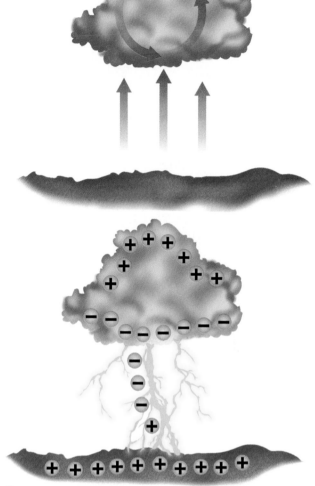

B As electrons build up on the bottom of the cloud, they repel electrons in the ground beneath the cloud. This causes the ground beneath the cloud to have an induced positive charge. At some point, electrons in the cloud bottom begin to move toward the ground in a zigzag pattern.

C When the electrons get close to the ground, they attract the positively charged atoms in the ground. These positive charges move upward, forming a discharge. A tremendous surge of positive charge flows from the ground up to the cloud. This is the discharge you see as a lightning flash.

Grounding

Electric discharges such as lightning can cause damage because they can release large amounts of electrical energy. Even electric discharges that release small amounts of energy can damage delicate circuitry in devices such as computers. One way to avoid the damage caused by electric discharges is to make the charges flow harmlessly into Earth's surface. Earth is a conductor, and because it is so large, it can absorb an enormous quantity of excess charge.

The process of providing a pathway to drain excess charge into Earth is called grounding. The pathway is usually a conductor such as a wire or a pipe. You may have noticed lightning rods at the top of buildings and towers, as shown in **Figure 16-8.** These rods are made of metal and connected to metal cables that conduct electric charge into the ground if the rod is struck by lightning. Objects that have lost electrons and are positively charged also can be grounded. In this case, electrons move from Earth to the object to make it electrically neutral.

Figure 16-8 A lightning rod can protect a building from being damaged by a lightning strike. **Should a lightning rod be an insulator or a conductor?**

Section Assessment

1. What is the difference between an object that is negatively charged and one that is positively charged?

2. Two electrically charged objects repel each other. What can you say about the type of charge on each object?

3. Suppose Earth's surface were an insulator instead of a conductor. Would lightning still strike Earth's surface? Why or why not?

4. **Think Critically:** Any excess charge placed on the surface of a conductor tends to spread out over the entire surface, while excess charge placed on an insulator tends to stay where it was placed originally. Explain.

5.  **Skill Builder**
   Recognizing Cause and Effect Clothes that are dried on a clothesline outdoors don't stick to each other when they are taken out of the laundry basket. Clothes that are dried in a clothes drier do tend to stick to each other. What is the reason for this difference? If you need help, refer to Recognizing Cause and Effect in the **Skill Handbook** on page 533.

Science Journal
You are sitting in a car. You slide out of the car seat, and as you start to touch the metal car door, a spark jumps from your hand to the door. In your Science Journal, describe how the spark was formed.

Electric Current

Voltage

An electric discharge such as a lightning stroke can release a huge amount of energy in an instant. However, electric lights, refrigerators, TVs, and stereos need a steady, constant source of electric energy. This source of electric energy comes from an **electric current,** which is the steady flow of electrons through a conductor. Electric current is measured in units of amperes (A).

Electrons flow continuously only if they are connected in an electric circuit. A **circuit** is a closed path through which an electric current can flow. Any device that uses electric current to operate has to be part of a circuit. Look at the diagram in **Figure 16-9.** A simple circuit consists of a source of electric energy such as a battery, and a conductor that provides the path for electrons to follow. A switch stops and starts the current flow by opening and closing the circuit.

Electric Energy in a Simple Circuit

How does an electric current provide electrical energy? In some ways, an electric current is a controlled electric discharge. However, instead of releasing a quick burst of energy, an electric current releases energy gradually in a continuous flow. In some ways, the electric current is similar to a continuous flow of water as shown in **Figure 16-10.** Just as a flow of water can be made to do work, an electric current also can do work.

What **You'll Learn**

► How voltage is related to the electric energy carried by an electric current
► How a battery produces an electric current
► Why materials have electric resistance

Vocabulary
electric current
circuit
voltage
resistance

Why **It's Important**

► The electric appliances you use every day need an electric current to operate.

Battery

Lightbulb

Switch

Figure 16-9 A simple circuit consists of a source of electric energy, such as a battery, a closed path for electrons to follow, and a switch that opens and closes the circuit.

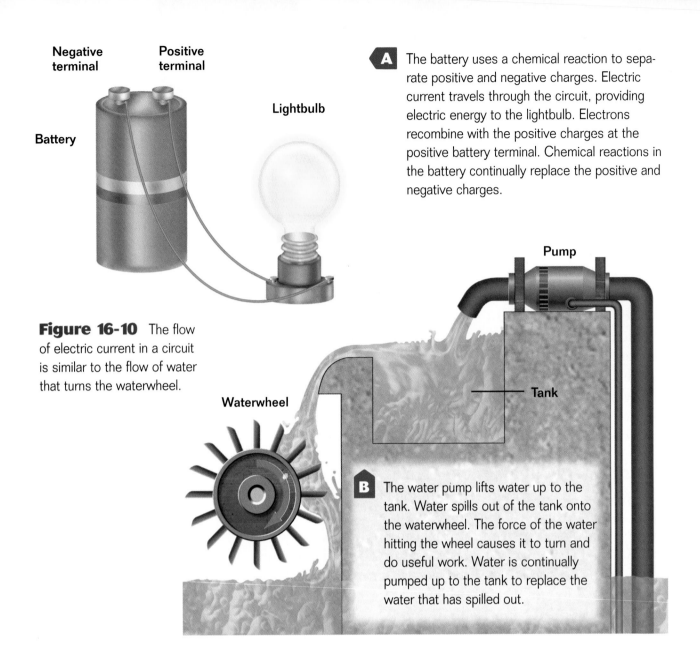

Negative terminal
Positive terminal
Battery
Lightbulb

A The battery uses a chemical reaction to separate positive and negative charges. Electric current travels through the circuit, providing electric energy to the lightbulb. Electrons recombine with the positive charges at the positive battery terminal. Chemical reactions in the battery continually replace the positive and negative charges.

Pump
Tank

Figure 16-10 The flow of electric current in a circuit is similar to the flow of water that turns the waterwheel.

Waterwheel

B The water pump lifts water up to the tank. Water spills out of the tank onto the waterwheel. The force of the water hitting the wheel causes it to turn and do useful work. Water is continually pumped up to the tank to replace the water that has spilled out.

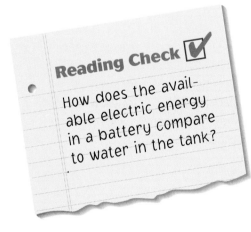

Reading Check

How does the available electric energy in a battery compare to water in the tank?

In a simple circuit, the battery is like the water pump shown in **Figure 16-10.** A chemical reaction in the battery separates electrons from atoms and piles them up at the negative battery terminal. The atoms that have lost electrons and are positively charged pile up at the positive terminal. The negatively charged electrons on the negative terminal can recombine with the positively charged atoms on the positive terminal only by traveling through a circuit connecting the two terminals.

Separating positive and negative charges enables electric energy to be stored. The electrons at the negative terminal of the battery are like the water in the tank in **Figure 16-10B.** This stored electric energy is released when the electrons flow from the negative terminal to the positive terminal of the battery. The water in the tank releases its stored energy when it falls from the tank and strikes the waterwheel.

The total stored electric energy in the battery is called the electric potential energy because it is energy that is potentially available to do work. The water in the tank also has potential energy because it can do work when it falls on the waterwheel.

In a battery, the electric potential energy is determined by the chemical reactions that occur inside the battery. By using different chemical reactions to separate the charges, different types of batteries have different electric potential energies. The **voltage** of the battery is a measure of the electric potential energy and is measured in units of volts (V).

The higher the voltage is, the more electric energy there is available to do work. The batteries in your portable boom box have a voltage of 1.5 V. By contrast, the voltage between the bottom of a thundercloud and the ground beneath can be 100 million volts.

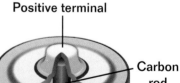

MiniLab

Lighting a Bulb with One Wire

Procedure

1. The filament in a lightbulb is a piece of wire. For the bulb to light, an electric current must flow through the filament in a complete circuit. Examine the base of the flashlight lightbulb carefully. Where are the ends of the filament connected to the base?

2. Connect a piece of wire, a battery, and a flashlight bulb to make the bulb light. (There are four possible ways to do this.)

Analysis

Draw and label a diagram showing the path followed by electrons in your circuit. Explain your diagram.

Batteries

You probably have replaced run-down batteries in a flashlight or portable radio. And, maybe you've looked under the hood of a car to see an automobile battery. How are these types of batteries different, and how does each type work? The batteries that are used to power flashlights, toys, portable radios, and CD players are examples of dry-cell batteries.

Dry Cells

Figure 16-11 shows a cutaway view of a dry cell. The dry cell consists of a carbon rod surrounded by a moist paste. The positive terminal of the battery is in contact with the carbon rod. The paste is surrounded by a container made of the metal zinc. When the two terminals of the battery are connected in a circuit, a chemical reaction occurs between several compounds in the paste and the zinc container. This chemical reaction causes positive charges to pile up on the carbon rod and electrons to pile up on the zinc. These electrons then flow through the circuit back to the carbon rod, where they recombine with the positive charges. The chemical reaction continues to produce electrons as long as the circuit remains closed.

Figure 16-11 In a dry-cell battery, a chemical reaction causes electrons to move to the zinc container. Atoms that have lost electrons move to the carbon rod. The container is the negative terminal and the carbon rod is the positive terminal.

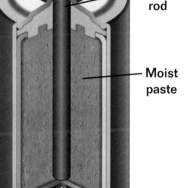

Positive terminal

Carbon rod

Moist paste

Zinc container

Negative terminal

Figure 16-12 A car battery has several wet cells connected together. This type of battery can be recharged.

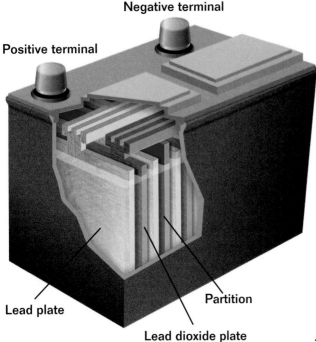

Negative terminal

Positive terminal

Lead plate

Partition

Lead dioxide plate

CHEMISTRY
INTEGRATION

Long-Lived Batteries
One of the chemicals in the moist paste of an ordinary dry cell is ammonium chloride. In an alkaline dry cell, this chemical is replaced by potassium hydroxide. The result is a battery with the same voltage but a longer life. Visit the Glencoe Science Web Site at **www.glencoe. com/sec/science/ca** for information about other types of long-lived batteries and their applications.

Wet Cells

A different type of battery, the wet-cell battery, is used in cars for starting engines. Unlike a dry-cell battery, a wet-cell battery is partially filled with a liquid. The automobile battery shown in **Figure 16-12** actually contains a series of six wet cells connected together. Each wet cell produces about 2 V and consists of two plates, one made of lead and the other made of lead dioxide bathed in a solution of sulfuric acid. A chemical reaction causes electrons to move from the lead dioxide plate to the lead plate. The lead plate becomes the negative terminal and the lead dioxide plate becomes the positive terminal. The six cells together give a total voltage of 12 V for the battery.

Battery Life

Batteries can't supply power forever. You know that's true if you've ever noticed taped music getting slower and slower after a portable tape player has been playing for several hours. Or, maybe you know someone whose car wouldn't start after the lights have been left on for a long time. Why do batteries run down? It's because the voltage they produce gradually decreases as some of the compounds that are involved in the chemical reactions are used up.

Batteries are not the only devices that separate positive and negative charges and create a continuous electrical current. Electric generators also work this way. Electric power plants use generators to supply electric current to the electric wall outlets in your home and school. In the United States, this current has a voltage of 120 V.

Resistance

Electrons can move much more easily through conductors than through insulators, but even conductors interfere with the flow of electrons. The measure of how difficult it is for electrons to flow through a material is called **resistance.** The unit of resistance is the ohm. Insulators generally have much higher resistance than conductors.

As electrons flow through a circuit, they collide with the atoms in the materials that make up the circuit. These collisions cause some of the electrons' electrical energy to be converted into thermal energy and light. The amount of electrical energy converted into heat and light depends on the resistance of the materials in the circuit. The amount of electrical energy lost as heat and light increases as the resistance increases.

For example, copper is one of the best electrical conductors and has a low resistance. Copper is used in household wiring because very little electrical energy is lost as current flows through copper wires. Also, not much heat is produced, which makes fires less likely. On the other hand, tungsten wire has a higher resistance and can be made to glow with a bright light as current passes through it. That makes tungsten wire a good choice for the filaments of lightbulbs.

The length and thickness of a conductor also affects its resistance. A short, thick wire has less resistance than a long, thin wire as shown in **Figure 16-13.** Think about walking down a hallway in your school to get to your next class. If the hallway is long and narrow, making your way through a crowd of other students like that shown in **Figure 16-14** will take you a long time. You'll be more likely to get to class on time if the hallway is short and wide. The shorter, wider hallway offers less resistance to you than a longer, narrower hallway.

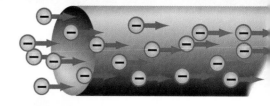

Figure 16-13 It is easier for electrons to flow through a thick wire than a thin wire.

Figure 16-14 Between classes, the hallway is filled with students. **How is a good electrical conductor similar to a hallway during classes?**

Section Assessment

1. How does increasing the voltage in a circuit affect the energy of the electrons flowing in the current?

2. What causes positive and negative charges to be separated in a battery?

3. **Think Critically:** Two identical 1.5-V batteries have the positive terminal of one battery connected to the negative terminal of the other. How does the voltage of the combination compare with the voltage of a single battery? Explain.

4. **Skill Builder**
   Observing and Inferring Observe the size of various batteries such as a camera battery, a flashlight battery, and an automobile battery. Infer whether the voltage produced by a battery is related to its physical size. If you need help, refer to Observing and Inferring in the **Skill Handbook** on page 532.

Using Computers

Spreadsheet A thundercloud and the ground beneath it are like a battery. The bottom of the cloud is like the negative terminal, and the ground beneath is like the positive terminal. Design a table using spreadsheet software to compare and contrast the thundercloud battery, dry-cell batteries, and wet-cell batteries. If you need help, refer to page 550.

Materials

- Plastic funnel
- Rubber or plastic tubing of different diameters (1 m each)
- Meterstick
- Ring stand with ring
- Stopwatch
  clock displaying seconds
- Hose clamp
  clothespin
- Beakers (500 mL) (2)
  Alternate Materials

A Model for Voltage and Current

The flow of electrons in an electric circuit is something like the flow of water. By raising or lowering the height of a water tank, you can increase or decrease the potential energy of the water. In this activity, you will use a water system to investigate how the flow of water in a tube depends on the height of the water and the diameter of the tube the water flows through.

What You'll Investigate

How is the flow of water through a tube affected by changing the height of a container of water and the diameter of the tube?

Goals

- **Make a model** for the flow of current in a simple circuit.

Safety Precautions

Procedure

1. **Design** a data table in which to record your data similar to the example below.
2. **Connect** the tubing to the bottom of the funnel and place the funnel in the ring of the ring stand.
3. **Measure** the diameter of the rubber tubing. **Record** your data.

Flow Rate Data				
Trial number	Height (cm)	Diameter of tubing (cm)	Time (s)	Rate of flow (mL/s)
1				
2				
3				
4				

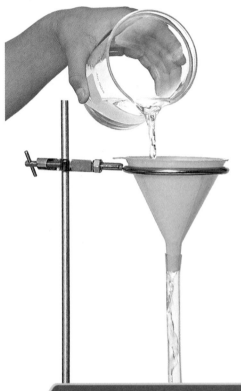

4. Place a 500-mL beaker at the bottom of the ring stand, and lower the ring so the open end of the tubing is in the beaker.

5. Use the meterstick to **measure** the height from the top of the funnel to the bottom of the ring stand. **Record** your data.

6. **Pour** water into the funnel fast enough to keep the funnel full but not overflowing. **Measure** the time needed for 100 mL of water to flow into the beaker. Use the hose clamp to start and stop the flow of water. **Record** your data.

7. **Connect** tubing with a different diameter to the funnel and repeat steps 2–6.

8. **Reconnect** the original piece of tubing and repeat steps 4–6 for several lower positions of the funnel, lowering the height by 10 cm each time.

9. **Calculate** the rate of flow for each trial by dividing 100 mL by the measured time.

Conclude and Apply

1. **Make a graph** to show how the rate of flow depends on the funnel height.

2. How does the rate of flow depend on the diameter of the tubing?

3. Which of the variables that you changed in your trials corresponds to the voltage in a circuit? Which variable corresponds to the resistance in a circuit? What part of a circuit would the hose clamp correspond to?

4. Based on your results, how would the current in a circuit depend on the voltage? How would the current depend on the resistance?

16·3 Electric Circuits

Voltage, Resistance, and Current (Ohm's law)

What You'll Learn

► How voltage, current, and resistance are related in an electrical circuit

► The difference between series and parallel circuits

► What determines the electrical power used in a circuit

► How to avoid dangerous electric shock

Vocabulary
Ohm's law
series circuit
parallel circuit
electrical power

Why It's Important

► Overloading electric circuits can create a fire hazard.

When you connect a conductor, such as a wire or a lightbulb, between the positive and negative terminals of a battery to form a circuit, an electrical current flows through the circuit. The amount of current is determined by the voltage supplied by the battery and the resistance of the conductor. To help understand this relationship, imagine a tank with a tube connected to a hole in the bottom, as shown in **Figure 16-15.** If the tank is raised higher, water will flow out of the tube faster and the water current will increase.

Think back to the waterwheel in **Figure 16-10B.** Remember that the water in the tank has potential, or stored, energy that is released when the water falls on the wheel. Raising the tank higher increases the potential energy of the water. Increasing the stored energy of the water is similar to increasing the voltage in a circuit. Just as the water current increases when the tank is raised higher, the electric current in a circuit should increase as voltage increases.

Now, imagine that the diameter of the tube in **Figure 16-15** is decreased. Then, there is more resistance to the flow of the water and the current decreases. In the same way, as the resistance in an electrical circuit increases, the current flowing in the circuit decreases.

Figure 16-15 Raising the tank higher increases the potential energy of the water in the tank. This causes the water to flow out of the tank faster.

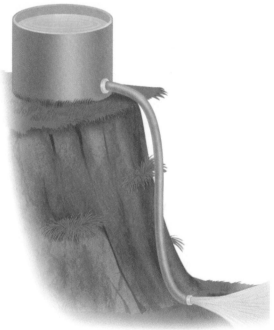

The relationship between voltage, current, and resistance is known as **Ohm's law.** The electrical current is usually represented by I, and if V represents the voltage and R the resistance, Ohm's law can be written in equation form as follows.

$$\text{Voltage} = \text{current} \times \text{resistance}$$

$$V = IR$$

Voltage is measured in volts (V), current is measured in amperes (A), and resistance is measured in V/A, or ohms.

Series and Parallel Circuits

Circuits control the movement of electric current by providing a path for electrons to follow. Have you ever been putting up holiday lights and had a string that wouldn't light because a single bulb was missing or had burned out? Or, maybe you've noticed that some strings of lights don't go out no matter how many bulbs burn out or are removed. These strings of holiday lights are examples of the two kinds of basic circuits.

Using Math

Calculating Resistance Using Ohm's Law

Example Problem
A hair dryer uses 12.5 A of current when it is plugged into a 120-V outlet. What is the electrical resistance of the hair dryer?

Problem-Solving Steps
1. What is known?
   voltage, $V = 120$ V; current, $I = 12.5$ A
2. What is unknown? resistance, R
3. Use Ohm's law $V = IR$.
4. Rearrange Ohm's law by dividing both sides by I to give $R = \dfrac{V}{I}$.
5. **Solution:** $R = \dfrac{V}{I}$

$$R = \frac{120\ V}{12.5\ A} = 9.6\ \text{ohms}$$

The electrical resistance of the hair dryer is 9.6 ohms.

Practice Problem
A lightbulb with a resistance of 10 ohms is plugged into a 120-V outlet. What is the current through the lightbulb?
Strategy Hint: In what units will your answer be given?

Figure 16-16 This circuit is an example of a series circuit. A series circuit has only one path for electric current to follow. **What happens to the current in this circuit if any of the connecting wires are removed?**

Series Circuits

A **series circuit** is a circuit that has only one path for the electric current to follow, as shown in **Figure 16-16.** If this path is broken, the current will no longer flow and all the devices in the circuit stop working. The string of lights that wouldn't work when only one bulb burned out was wired as a series circuit. When a bulb burns out, the filament in the bulb actually breaks and current stops flowing through the bulb.

In a series circuit, electrical devices are connected together on the same current path. As a result, the current is the same through every device. However, each new device that is added to the circuit decreases the current. This is because each device has electrical resistance, and in a series circuit, the total resistance to the flow of current is found by adding the resistance of all the devices. By Ohm's law, as the resistance increases, the current decreases. ✔

Parallel Circuits

What if you wanted to watch TV and had to turn on all the lights, hair dryers, and every other electrical appliance in the house? That's what it would be like if all the electrical appliances in your house were connected in a series circuit.

Instead, houses, schools, and other buildings are wired using parallel circuits. A **parallel circuit** is a circuit that has more than one path for the electric current to follow, as shown in **Figure 16-17.** The current leaving the battery or electrical outlet branches so that electrons flow through each of the paths. If one path is broken, current continues to flow through the other paths.

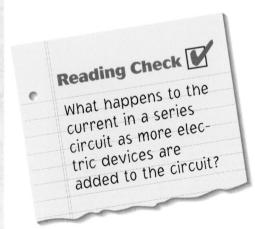

Reading Check ✔

What happens to the current in a series circuit as more electric devices are added to the circuit?

Figure 16-17 This circuit is an example of a parallel circuit. A parallel circuit has more than one path for electric current to follow. **What happens to the current in the circuit if either of the wires connecting the two light bulbs is removed?**

Unlike a series circuit, the current through each path in a parallel circuit is different and depends on the electrical resistance in each path. The lower the resistance in a path is, the more current that flows in that path. Adding or removing additional devices in a parallel circuit does not affect the other branches, so the devices on those branches continue to work normally.

Fuses

In a parallel circuit, the current that flows out of the battery or electrical outlet increases as more devices are added to the circuit. As the current flowing through the circuit increases, the wires heat up.

To keep the heat from building up enough to cause a fire, the circuits in houses and other buildings have fuses or circuit breakers, like those shown in **Figure 16-18,** that limit the amount of current in the wiring. When the current becomes larger than 15 A or 20 A, a piece of metal in the fuse melts or a switch in the circuit breaker opens, stopping the current. The cause of the overload can then be removed, and the circuit can be used again by replacing the fuse or resetting the circuit breaker.

Figure 16-18 You have fuses or circuit breakers in your home to prevent a fire.

A In some buildings, each circuit is connected to a fuse. The fuses are usually located in a fuse box.

Wire →

B A fuse contains a piece of wire that melts and breaks when the current flowing through the fuse becomes too large.

Electric Power

Electric energy is used in many ways to do useful work. Toasters and electric ovens convert electric energy to heat, stereos convert electric energy to sound, and a rotating fan blade converts electrical energy to mechanical energy. The rate at which an appliance converts electrical energy to another form of energy is the **electrical power** used by the appliance. The unit of electrical power is the watt (W). Sometimes, it is convenient to express electrical power in kilowatts (kW). One kilowatt equals 1000 watts.

An electric current releases electrical energy as it flows in a circuit. The rate at which energy is used in the circuit is related to the amount of energy carried by the electrons, which increases as the voltage increases. The energy used also is related to the number of electrons or current flowing in the circuit. The power being used in a circuit can be determined by multiplying the voltage by the current.

$$\text{Power} = \text{current} \times \text{voltage}$$

$$P = IV$$

One watt of power is used when a current of 1 A flows through a circuit with a voltage of 1 V. For household appliances such as televisions, refrigerators, and stereos that are

Using Math

A current of 6 A flows through a refrigerator plugged into a 120-V wall outlet. Calculate the electric power used by the refrigerator using the formula $P = IV$.

Problem Solving

The Cost of Using Electricity

Has someone ever told you to turn off an electric light because it was wasting electricity? Or, do you know someone who turns off all the unused lights in your house in order to save money? How much does it really cost to use a lightbulb? If the power used by an appliance is known, you can calculate the cost of total energy used by multiplying the power (P) the appliance uses in kilowatts by the number of hours (t) the appliance is used and the cost per kilowatt-hour.

The table shows the power consumed by some common household appliances and the amount of time they are typically used in a day. If the cost is $0.09 per kilowatt-hour, calculate the monthly cost of each remaining appliance.

Think Critically: Estimate the number of lightbulbs in your home. How much energy could be saved each month if these bulbs were used only four hours per day instead of six?

Power Consumption of Common Appliances			
Appliance	Power Usage (W)	Time Used (hours/day)	Monthly Cost
Hair dryer	1 000	0.25	$0.67
Microwave	700	0.5	
Stereo	110	2.5	
Refrigerator	700	10	
Television	200	4	
100-W lightbulb	100	6	

plugged into wall outlets, the voltage is always 120 V. If a current of 1 A flows through a household appliance, the power used is 1 A × 120 V = 120 W.

Cost of Electric Energy

Power is the rate at which energy is used, or the amount of energy used per second. When you use a hair dryer, the amount of electrical energy used depends on the power of the hair dryer and the amount of time you use it. If you used it for five minutes yesterday and ten minutes today, you used twice as much energy today as yesterday.

Using electrical energy costs money. The electricity in homes, schools, and businesses is supplied by electric companies, which generate electrical energy and sell it in units of kilowatt-hours. One kilowatt-hour (kWh) is an amount of electrical energy equal to using 1 kW of power continuously for one hour. This would be the amount of energy needed to light ten 100-W lightbulbs for one hour, or one 100-W lightbulb for ten hours.

An electric company usually charges its customers for the number of kilowatt-hours they use every month. The number of kilowatt-hours used in a building such as a house or a school is measured by an electric meter, which is usually attached to the outside of the building.

Electrical Safety

Have you ever had a mild electric shock? You probably felt only a mild tingling sensation, but electricity can have much more dangerous effects. In 1993, electric shocks killed an estimated 550 people in the United States.

You experience an electric shock when an electric current enters your body. In some ways, your body is like a piece of insulated wire. Inside your body, the electric resistance is low so the inside of your body is a good conductor. The electric resistance of dry skin is much higher, but not as high as insulators such as plastic and rubber. Still, skin insulates the body like the plastic insulation around an electric wire. But, in this case, the purpose of the insulation is to keep the electric current from getting inside.

For a current to enter your body, you must be part of an electric circuit. One way to do this is to touch a wire that is connected to a source of electric energy while you are in contact with the ground. Then, current will flow through you into the ground. Whether you receive a deadly shock depends on the amount of current that flows into your body.

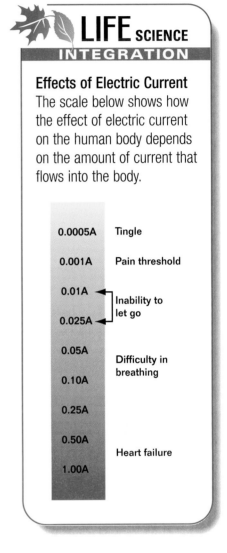

LIFE SCIENCE
INTEGRATION

Effects of Electric Current
The scale below shows how the effect of electric current on the human body depends on the amount of current that flows into the body.

0.0005A	Tingle
0.001A	Pain threshold
0.01A	Inability to let go
0.025A	
0.05A	Difficulty in breathing
0.10A	
0.25A	
0.50A	Heart failure
1.00A	

Even relatively small amounts of current can be dangerous. Even a current as small as 0.001 A can cause a tingling sensation. A current of only 0.01 A passing through the chest can cause the heart muscle to start twitching uncontrollably and stop pumping blood. This amount of electric current also can cause the muscles in the hand to contract violently, so a person who has grasped a current-carrying wire cannot let go.

Surprisingly, a large current can sometimes cause the heart to start beating after it has stopped. Hospitals and emergency medical teams often use a device called a defibrillator, like the one shown in **Figure 16-19,** to apply a brief pulse of current directly to a patient's chest.

Situations to Avoid

Never touch any exposed wire connected to a wall socket. Ordinary household current at a voltage of 120 V is particularly dangerous and can cause a shock that affects the heart and the ability to breathe.

Avoid using a metal ladder in the vicinity of power lines. A person touching the ladder will be electrocuted if the metal ladder touches the power line.

Avoid touching electric power lines under any circumstances. Even if a power line has been broken by a storm or a car accident, you will form a circuit into the ground if you touch it and you will be severely shocked. You may have noticed that birds can sit on a power line without receiving a shock. This is because birds are not in contact with the ground and touch only a single wire, as shown in **Figure 16-20.**

Do not use electric appliances while standing in water or on wet ground. Standing on wet ground or in water provides a good contact with Earth, so if you were to handle an appliance that was not properly insulated, your chances of

Figure 16-19 A defibrillator can sometimes restart a heart that has stopped beating or is beating irregularly. The condition in which the heart is beating irregularly is called fibrillation. The paddles are placed on the person's chest, and a brief current pulse is sent through the paddles. This current can be as high as 6 A.

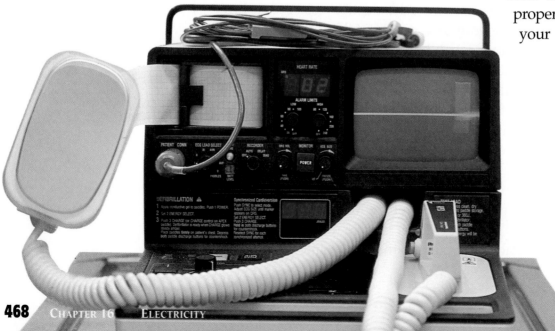

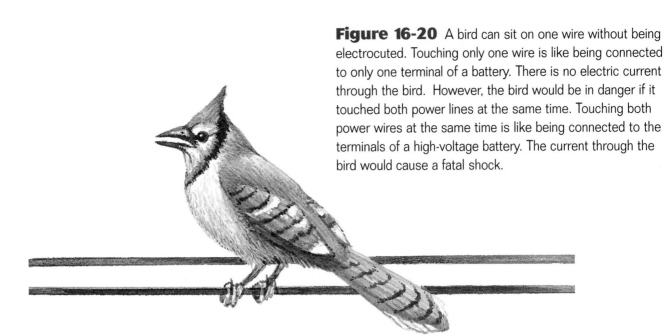

Figure 16-20 A bird can sit on one wire without being electrocuted. Touching only one wire is like being connected to only one terminal of a battery. There is no electric current through the bird. However, the bird would be in danger if it touched both power lines at the same time. Touching both power wires at the same time is like being connected to the terminals of a high-voltage battery. The current through the bird would cause a fatal shock.

receiving a dangerous shock would be increased. If the appliance such as a hair dryer or radio accidentally fell into the bathwater, you could be electrocuted.

Always respect signs warning of high voltage and dangerous electric shock, and keep a safe distance from these warning signs. The best rule is to avoid making contact with any electric current.

Section Assessment

1. As the resistance in a simple circuit increases, what happens to the current?

2. What is the difference between a series circuit and a parallel circuit?

3. Explain why you should avoid handling electrical appliances when standing on wet ground.

4. **Think Critically:** What determines whether a 100-W lightbulb costs more to use than a 1500-W hair dryer?

5. **Skill Builder**

   Sequencing A sequence is the order in which something is done or arranged. Putting your socks on before your shoes is a sequence. The alphabet is a sequence of letters. Do the **Chapter 16 Skill Activity** on page 569 to use a flow chart to help you arrange a sequence.

Using Math

A typical household uses 1000 kWh of electric energy every month. If a power company supplies electricity to 10 000 households, how much electric energy must it supply every year?

Materials

- Lightbulbs (1.5 V) (4)
- Batteries (1.5 V) (2)
- Pieces of insulated wire, each about 10 cm long (8)
- Battery holder (2)
- Minibulb sockets (4)

Current in a Parallel Circuit

In this activity, you will investigate how the current in a circuit changes when two or more lightbulbs are connected in parallel. Because the brightness of a lightbulb increases or decreases as more or less current flows through it, the brightness of the bulbs in the circuits can be used to determine which circuit has more current.

What You'll Investigate

How does connecting devices in parallel affect the electric current in a circuit?

Goals

- **Observe** how the current in a parallel circuit changes as more devices are added.

Procedure

1. **Connect** one lightbulb to the battery in a complete circuit. After you've made the bulb light, disconnect the bulb from the battery to keep the battery from running down. This circuit will be the brightness tester.

2. **Make** a parallel circuit by connecting two bulbs as shown in the diagram. **Reconnect** the bulb in the brightness tester and compare its brightness with the brightness of the two bulbs in the parallel circuit. **Record** your observations.

3. Add another bulb to the parallel circuit as shown in the figure. How does the brightness of the bulbs change? **Record** your observations.

4. **Disconnect** one bulb in the parallel circuit. What happens to the brightness of the remaining bulbs?

Conclude and Apply

1. Compared to the brightness tester, is the current in the parallel circuit more or less?

2. How does adding additional devices affect the current in a parallel circuit?

3. Are the electric circuits in your house wired in series or parallel? How do you know?

Energy Sources

Think of all the ways you used energy today. Much of this energy comes from burning fossil fuels such as coal to generate electricity. Other fossil fuels such as gasoline and natural gas power automobiles and heat homes.

However, fossil fuels are being used up at an ever-increasing rate. Fossil fuels are a nonrenewable energy resource, which means they can't be replaced once they are used up. Some scientists estimate that most of the world's fossil fuels such as oil (being drilled at left) will be nearly gone by the end of the twenty-first century.

Fuel Cells

As the world's population and the demand for energy grow, many scientists and engineers are trying to develop alternative energy sources for the future. A pioneer in this research is Dr. Meredith Gourdine, a prominent engineer and physicist, who was born in Newark, New Jersey, in 1929.

Dr. Gourdine has developed a method to improve the operation of fuel cells that produce an electric current. The chemicals most commonly used in fuel cells are hydrogen and oxygen gases, both of which can be obtained from ocean water. Unlike a battery, a fuel cell does not contain a limited amount of chemicals that gradually are used up. Instead, hydrogen and oxygen are injected into a reaction chamber in a fuel cell, and the fuel cell continues to produce electricity as long as the gases are added to the reaction chamber. Dr. Gourdine has designed a specially shaped reaction chamber that enables the gases to react with each other efficiently.

Ocean water is much more plentiful than fossil fuels and could provide a supply of oxygen and hydrogen for an extremely long time. Other renewable energy resources include solar energy, geothermal energy, and wind energy. The demand for skilled scientists and engineers to research alternative energy sources is expected to increase in the years to come.

Science
JOURNAL ▶

Conserving energy is an important step toward a positive future. In your Science Journal, list ways you can conserve energy every day.

For a **preview** of this chapter, study this Reviewing Main Ideas before you read the chapter. After you have studied this chapter, you can use the Reviewing Main Ideas to **review** the chapter.

 The Glencoe MindJogger, Audiocassettes, and CD-ROM provide additional opportunities for review.

Section 16-1 ELECTRIC CHARGE

There are two types of electric charge: positive and negative. An object becomes negatively charged if it gains electrons and positively charged if it loses electrons. Electrically charged objects have an electric field surrounding them and exert electric forces on one another. Objects with like charges repel one another, while objects with unlike charges attract one another. Electrons can move easily through **conductors,** but not so easily through **insulators.** *Why are atoms usually electrically neutral?*

Section 16-2 ELECTRIC CURRENT

Electrons can do useful work by flowing in a closed, unbroken path known as a **circuit.** The energy carried by electrons in a circuit increases as the **voltage** in the circuit increases. A battery provides a source of **electric current** by using chemical reactions to separate positive and negative charges. As electrons flow in a circuit, some of their electric energy is lost due to electric **resistance** in the circuit. *In a simple circuit, why do electrons stop flowing if the circuit is broken?*

Reading Check ✓

Someone says "Electricity is dangerous!" Is this a fact or an opinion? Explain your answer.

Section
16-3 ELECTRIC CIRCUITS

In an electric circuit, the voltage, current, and resistance are related by **Ohm's law,** $V = IR$. As a result, increasing the voltage in a circuit increases the current, while increasing the resistance decreases the current. There are two basic kinds of electric circuits: **parallel circuits** and **series circuits.** A series circuit has only one path for the current to follow, while a parallel circuit has more than one path. The rate at which electrical devices use electric energy is the **electric power** used by the device. Electric companies charge customers for using electric energy in units of kilowatt-hours. *Why are parallel circuits used for the wiring in homes and schools, rather than series circuits?*

ELECTRICAL SAFETY

Electricity can damage the human body by causing the heart to stop beating properly and by interfering with the ability to breathe, which can lead to suffocation. The amount of current flowing through the body determines how much damage occurs. The current from wall outlets can be dangerous. Operating electrical appliances while standing in water or on wet ground can lead to dangerous electric shocks. *Why are high-voltage lines dangerous?*

Chapter 16 Assessment

Using Vocabulary

a. circuit
b. conductor
c. electric current
d. electric discharge
e. electrical power
f. insulator
g. Ohm's law
h. parallel circuit
i. resistance
j. series circuit
k. static charge
l. voltage

Match each phrase with the correct term from the list of Vocabulary words.

1. the flow of electrons through a conductor
2. the relationship between voltage, current, and resistance in an electric circuit
3. a material through which electrons cannot move easily
4. an unbroken path for electrons to follow
5. a buildup of electric charge in one place

Checking Concepts

Choose the word or phrase that best answers the question.

6. Why is an object positively charged?
   A) It has more neutrons than protons.
   B) It has more protons than electrons.
   C) It has more electrons than protons.
   D) It has more electrons than neutrons.

7. What is the electric force between two electrons?
   A) unbalanced
   B) neutral
   C) attractive
   D) repulsive

8. What happens when the voltage in a circuit increases?
   A) The energy carried by the electric current increases.
   B) The chemicals in the battery are used up.
   C) The current decreases.
   D) The positive and negative battery terminals are connected.

9. What property of a wire increases when it is made thinner?
   A) resistance
   B) voltage
   C) current
   D) charge

10. What property does Earth have that causes grounding to drain away static charges?
    A) It is a planet.
    B) It has a high resistance.
    C) It is a conductor.
    D) It is like a battery.

11. Why is a severe electrical shock dangerous?
    A) It can stop the heart from beating.
    B) It can cause burns.
    C) It can interfere with breathing.
    D) All of the above are true.

12. Because an air conditioner uses more electrical power than a lightbulb, what also must be true?
    A) It must have a higher resistance.
    B) It must use more energy every second.
    C) It must have its own batteries.
    D) It must be wired in series.

13. What unit of electrical energy is sold by electric companies?
    A) ampere
    B) ohm
    C) volt
    D) kilowatt-hour

14. What surrounds electric charges that causes them to affect each other even though they are not touching?
    A) an induced charge
    B) a static discharge
    C) a conductor
    D) an electric field

15. As more devices are added to a series circuit, what happens to the current in the circuit?
    A) It decreases.
    B) It increases.
    C) It stays the same.
    D) It has a higher voltage.

Thinking Critically

16. Why do materials have electrical resistance?

17. Explain why a balloon that has a static charge will stick to a wall.

18. If you have two charged objects, how could you tell if the type of charge on them was the same or different?

19. Explain why the outside cases of electrical appliances are usually made of plastic.

20. Your hand has excess electrons on it, and you bring it close to a metal doorknob. Why do the electrons in the doorknob move and not the electrons on your hand?

Developing Skills

If you need help, refer to the Skill Handbook.

21. **Making and Using Graphs:** The following data show the current and voltage in a circuit containing a portable CD player and in a circuit containing a portable radio.
    A) Make a graph with the horizontal axis the current and vertical axis the voltage, and plot the data for the radio and the CD player.
    B) Which line is more horizontal: the plot of the radio data or the CD player data?
    C) Use Ohm's law to determine the electrical resistance of each device.
    D) For which device is the line more horizontal: the device with the higher or lower resistance?

Portable Radio		Portable CD Player	
Voltage (V)	Current (A)	Voltage (V)	Current (A)
2.0	1.0	2.0	0.5
4.0	2.0	4.0	1.0
6.0	3.0	6.0	1.5

THE PRINCETON REVIEW

Test-Taking Tip

Read the Label No matter how many times you've taken a particular type of test or practiced for an exam, it's always a good idea first to read the instructions provided at the beginning of each section. It only takes a moment.

Test Practice

Use these questions to test your Science Proficiency.

1. If you connect lightbulbs together so that the current flowing through each lightbulb is the same, you have made which type of circuit?
   A) a series circuit
   B) a parallel circuit
   C) a combination circuit
   D) none of these

2. Earth and the moon each contain an enormous number of both protons and electrons. Which of the following statements **BEST** describes the electric force between Earth and the moon?
   A) There is a repulsive electric force because they contain the same types of electric charges.
   B) There is an attractive electric force because Earth has a negative charge that induces a positive charge on the moon.
   C) There is no electric force because Earth and the moon contain nearly equal numbers of protons and electrons and so both are electrically neutral.
   D) The electric force depends on how far apart they are.

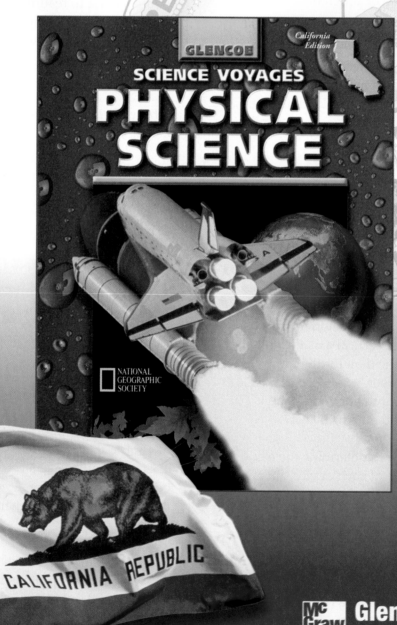

California
Science Standards
and Case Studies

GLENCOE

California Edition

SCIENCE VOYAGES
PHYSICAL
SCIENCE

NATIONAL
GEOGRAPHIC
SOCIETY

CALIFORNIA REPUBLIC

Glencoe
McGraw-Hill

Level Blue

California
The Golden State

State Tree:
The California
Red Wood

State Bird:
The California
Quail

State Flower:
The Golden Poppy

PHOTO AND ART CREDITS: 478 (t)Corbis Media, (b)Gerald L. French/Photo File; **481** David Matherly/Visuals Unlimited; **482** Dean Conger/Corbis Media; **483** Christian Michaels/FPG International; **484** Travelpix/FPG International; **485** Corbis Media; **486** Vic Cox/Peter Arnold Inc.; **487** Alison Wright/Photo Researchers; **488** file photo; **489** Raymond F. Newell Jr.; **490** D.C. Lowe/FPG International; **491** ©Jerry Lodriguss/Photo Researchers; **492** ©Jerry Schad/Photo Researchers; **493** Corbis Media; **494** Tony Freeman/PhotoEdit; **495** Richard Megna/Fundamental Photographs; **497** AC/GM/Peter Arnold Inc.; **498** Catherine Ursillo/Photo Researchers; **499** Kenneth Eward/BioGrafx-Science Source/Photo Researchers; **500** Manfred Kage/Peter Arnold Inc.; **501** Mark E. Gibson; **502** Lawrence Berkeley National Laboratory/Science Photo Library/Photo Researchers; **503** Tom McHugh/Photo Researchers; **504** James Blank/The Stock Market; **505** Matt Meadows; **506** Jim Corwin/Tony Stone Images; **507** John Lund/Tony Stone Images.

P/N G86731.11

Motion

**Content
Standard 1**
The velocity of
an object is the
rate of change
of its position.

1a. Position

Where are you right now? How do you
describe your position? For scientific purposes, the position of an object is compared
to a standard reference point and a set of
reference directions. So, the position of
Yosemite National Park can be described as
approximately 192 km southeast of Sacramento, California. In this case, Sacramento
is the chosen reference point and *192 km
southeast* is the set of reference directions.

1b. Average Speed

Average speed is the total distance traveled by an object divided by the total time
of the trip. Therefore, the average speed of
a train that travels 200 km in 3 hours is
67 km/h.

$$\text{average speed} = \frac{\text{distance traveled}}{\text{time}}$$

$$= \frac{200 \text{ km}}{3 \text{ h}}$$

$$= 67 \text{ km/h}$$

Of course, the speed of the object can
vary along the path traveled. For example,
a car that travels 40 km in 1 hour within San
Diego and an additional 200 km in 2 hours
on Interstate 15 has an overall average
speed of 80 km/h (240 km/3 h). However,
the car's average speed on city streets was
40 km/h, while the average speed on the
freeway was 100 km/h (200 km/2 h).

Figure CA1-1 To calculate a vehicle's speed,
you need to know how far it travelled in a specific
amount of time.

Investigation & Experimentation

Standards 9d, 9e, 9f

Table 1 shows the number of kilometers that a truck traveled from the starting point at different times during the day. What was the truck's average speed before stopping for lunch? What was the truck's average speed after lunch? What was the truck's average speed for the entire trip? What was the truck's highest average speed for any hour during the day? During what hour did the truck have its lowest average speed (excluding the lunch hour)?

Table 1

Delivery Truck Data	
Time	Distance from Warehouse (km)
9:00	0 (start)
10:00	40
11:00	100
12:00	150 (stopped for lunch from noon to 1:00)
1:00	150
2:00	205
3:00	250
4:00	280

1c. Problems Involving Distance, Time, and Average Speed

Now that you know that average speed equals the distance traveled divided by the time elapsed, you can figure out any of the three quantities (distance, time, and average speed) if you know the other two. For example, if a person travels at an average speed of 3 km/h for 2.5 hours, we can calculate the distance traveled as follows.

$$\text{average speed} = \frac{\text{distance traveled}}{\text{time}}$$

$$3 \text{ km/h} = \frac{\text{distance traveled}}{2.5 \text{ h}}$$

$$\text{distance traveled} = (3 \text{ km/h})(2.5 \text{ h})$$

$$= 7.5 \text{ km}$$

The person traveled a total of 7.5 km.

Investigation & Experimentation

Standard 9f

Suppose you are told that a ball rolled a distance of 10 m at an average speed of 2 m/s. What is the time elapsed for the ball to travel 10 m?

1d. Velocity

People sometimes use the words *speed* and *velocity* to mean the same thing. However, the scientific definition of velocity is different. The velocity of an object is described by both the speed and the direction that the object is traveling. Consider two motorcycles approaching each other from opposite directions. As they pass, they can have the same speed but different velocities because they are going in opposite directions.

Average velocity can be calculated from the following equation.

$$\text{Average velocity} = \frac{\text{displacement}}{\text{time}}$$

Displacement measures the change in position of an object.

Investigation & Experimentation

Standard 9f

Suppose a bicyclist travels 10 km east between 1:00 and 2:00, another 15 km east between 2:00 and 3:00 and then 15 km north between 3:00 and 4:30. What is the bicyclist's average velocity in the first hour? Between 1:00 and 3:00? Between 3:00 and 4:30?

479

1e. Changes in Velocity

Changes in the velocity of an object, called acceleration, can happen due to changes in its speed, its direction, or both. If a hiker in the Sierra Nevada is hiking at a constant pace of 4 km/h on a trail heading west and reaches a left bend in the trail and is now headed south, her velocity has changed even though her hiking speed has not.

1f. Interpreting Graphs

By looking at a graph of data for an object moving in a single direction, you can see more than you can easily determine from a table of numbers. If the graph shows the position of the object versus time, you can see how far the object has moved during each time interval. You also can determine the average speed of the object during each time interval. Change in speed can be determined from the slope of an average speed versus time graph.

Investigation & Experimentation

Standards 9d, 9e, 9g
Using the data from **Table 1**, construct a graph of the truck's position versus time and a graph of average speed versus time. Between which hours did the truck have an increase in average speed? Decrease in average speed?

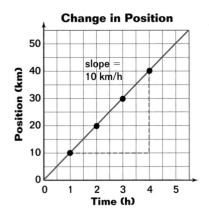

Change in Position

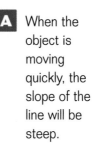

A When the object is moving quickly, the slope of the line will be steep.

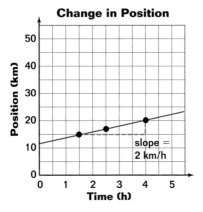

B Change in position will be small during each time interval when the object is moving slowly.

Change in Position

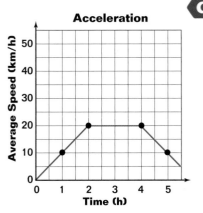

Acceleration

C When the graph's slope is up to the right, the object is speeding up. When the graph is horizontal, speed is constant. **What happens when the graph slopes down to the right?**

Figure CA1-2 A graph can tell you about an object's motion.

Going Further

To learn more about motion, see:

1a. Chapter 11, Section 1, What is motion?
1b. Chapter 11, Section 1, What is motion?
1c. Chapter 11, Section 1, What is motion?
   Chapter 12, Section 2, Newton's Second Law
   Chapter 12, Section 4, Describing Motion

1d. Chapter 11, Section 1, What is motion?
   Chapter 12, Section 1, Newton's First Law
1e. Chapter 11, Section 1, What is motion?
   Chapter 12, Section 1, Newton's First Law
   Chapter 12, Section 2, Newton's Second Law
1f. Chapter 11, Section 1, What is motion?

Global Positioning System

SCIENCE FOCUS

Read this case study to learn about how the movement of the ground along fault lines is determined from satellites in space.

Correlates
with Content
Standard 1

The Global Positioning System (GPS) includes a group of 24 satellites that orbit Earth. When receivers located on the ground have radio signal information from at least 4 of the 24 satellites, information is combined to determine the exact position—latitude, longitude and elevation—of the receivers at a specific time.

Measuring Fault Movement

In order to measure the movement along fault lines that occurs before, during, and after an earthquake, the U.S. Geological Survey (USGS) places several receiver sites near the fault. The receivers collect information from the same satellites at the same time. This allows the position of the receiver sites to be calculated precisely. Changes in the positions of the sites means that movement has taken place along the fault lines.

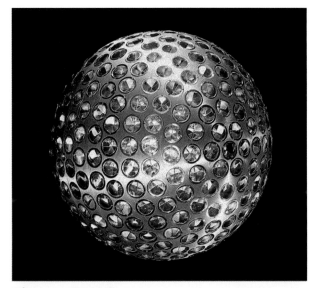

Figure CA1-3 Global positioning satellites orbit Earth for military, research, and commercial purposes.

Where are measurements made?

Measurements are made in many areas in California. Two measurement areas are in the San Francisco Bay Area and in southern California. The Bay Area Regional Deformation (BARD) network has about 25 continuously operating GPS receivers. The Southern California Integrated GPS Network (SCIGN) has about 40 continuously operating receivers in southern California. Other measurements are made near Parkfield and Mammoth Lakes, California; and in other states where earthquakes are common.

Using GPS makes it possible to accurately measure small movements. This is important because faults shift only about 4 cm per year. The information learned from studying movements near earthquake faults will help scientists understand what happens during earthquakes. This information will help speed up emergency response times and minimize the damage when an earthquake does occur.

Investigation & Experimentation

Standards 9b, 9c

When fault movements are measured using GPS, what factors are controlled by the researchers? What are the variables? How accurate do you think these data are compared to other methods for studying fault movement?

Content Standard 2
Unbalanced forces cause changes in velocity.

2a. & b. Forces

Look at the tugboat pushing the barge near the Golden Gate Bridge in San Francisco Bay above. The barge is not moving under its own power. The tugboat is exerting a force on the barge. A force can be anything that acts on an object and causes a change in the object's velocity. A force has direction as well as magnitude, which is a measure of how strong the force is. Another example of a force is Earth's gravity, which causes objects to fall toward Earth. The force of gravity on an object is called its weight.

As the barge is being pushed into the bay, the force from the tugboat is not the only force acting on the barge. The barge also may be pushed by wind, waves, or currents in the water. The motion of the barge will be affected by all of the forces acting on it at the time. For example, if the tugboat is pushing the barge east and strong winds and waves are pushing it north, the barge will tend to move in a northeasterly direction.

Investigation & Experimentation

Standards 9a, 9c

Tie a string to a weighty object such as a notebook. Pull gently on the string. What happens to the notebook? What happens if you pull harder? What happens when you stop pulling? Add a second string. While you pull one string toward you, have a friend pull the second string in a direction perpendicular to yours. In what direction does the notebook move? What happens if one of you pulls harder than the other?

2c. Balanced Forces

Now, suppose that the tugboat starts to push the barge into the bay at the same time that the tide is heading out. What happens if the magnitude of the force from the tugboat (going east) equals the magnitude of the force of the tide (going west)?

Assuming that there are no other forces acting on the barge, it will stay in one place. When the forces are balanced, the motion of the barge does not change.

Balanced forces also allow an object that is already in motion to continue traveling at constant velocity.

2d. Identifying Forces

The barge heading into San Francisco Bay is also being pulled toward Earth due to gravity and is being supported by the water in the bay. Gravity always acts on any object on Earth, so there must always be at least one other force keeping the object from falling.

Another important force is friction. Without friction, any object on a slope would tend to slide downward due to gravity. However, friction acts to keep objects in place on slopes. A car parked on a hill in San Francisco is a good example. The car has three main forces acting on it: gravity, the upward force of the road, and friction, which keeps the car from sliding.

Investigation & Experimentation

Standards 9a, 9c
Place a small book on top of your notebook. Identify the forces acting on the book. Now lift one end of the notebook up slightly so that it makes a slope. What forces are acting on the book now? Can you think of ways to test the idea that there is a frictional force acting on the book? What ways can you think of to reduce the frictional force?

2e. Unbalanced Forces

Push a toy car and the car starts to roll across the floor. Your push is an unbalanced force that causes the car to increase its speed. Then, after you stop pushing, the car will begin to slow down and will

eventually stop. The slowing is a result of friction, which is an unbalanced force in the direction opposite to the car's motion. If the car bumps into a piece of furniture or a wall before it slows down enough to stop, it will change its direction and head back toward you.

Investigation & Experimentation

Standards 9b, 9c
In which of the activities involving the notebook and a string were there unbalanced forces? How did those unbalanced forces affect the notebook's motion? What other ways are there (rather than pulling the string) to apply a force to the notebook to make it move in similar ways? What would you have to change to exert a different force? What would be the same no matter what force you exerted?

Figure CA2-1 Engineers who built the Oakland Bay Bridge had to consider all of the forces that would be acting upon the bridge.

2f. Force, Mass, and Motion

To push a barge, a tugboat must exert a large force because the barge is a large object with a lot of mass. Suppose that instead of pushing a barge, the tugboat was pushing a small rowboat. Would the tugboat have to exert the same force to cause the rowboat to move? No. The greater the mass of an object is, the larger is the force needed to achieve the same change in motion.

2g. Gravity and the Solar System

Gravity plays an important role in forming planets and stars. Every object has a gravitational force that attracts other objects toward it. However, the size of the force is related to the mass of the object, and the gravitational force exerted by most objects is so small that it is not noticed. Planets and stars form when pieces of matter or gas in space attract each other. When they get close, they combine into a larger object. This object then has a larger gravitational force that attracts other objects.

Gravity also maintains the solar system. In our solar system, nine planets orbit the sun. It is the gravitational attraction of the sun that keeps the planets in orbit.

Figure CA2-2 The force of gravity causes cars to roll down the hill. **Which would roll faster down the hill if the brakes were released, a car or a truck?**

Investigation & Experimentation

Standard 9a
Think about what would happen to the solar system if the sun did not have a gravitational force. Would the planets still travel around the sun? How might you test the idea that objects will only travel in a circular orbit if there is a force acting to pull them toward a center? (Hint: You might consider using a piece of string.) What happens if the force toward the center disappears?

Going Further

Rockets and Satellites

SCIENCE FOCUS

Read this case study to learn about forces on rockets as they are launched into space and on satellites that orbit Earth.

California **CASE STUDY**

Correlates with Content Standard 2

At Vandenberg Air Force Base (AFB) in California, rockets are used to launch satellites into space several times each year. The launches serve military and civilian purposes. Some satellites are used to provide information and support research about weather or atmospheric conditions. Others are used for communications, including satellites for a network that will provide handheld, wireless telephone service worldwide.

Forces on Rockets

Of course, it takes a huge force to lift a rocket off the ground and propel it out of the atmosphere and into space. How is this force created? In order to lift off or change velocity once it is moving, a rocket ejects burned fuel in the direction opposite to the planned direction of the rocket. On takeoff, the rocket ejects its exhaust downward and the exhaust exerts a force back on the rocket that causes the rocket to go upward. Once the rocket is in motion, exhaust can be ejected in various directions to allow the rocket to change its course in the direction opposite to the exhaust. For example, if the rocket needs to turn to the left, it ejects exhaust to the right.

Forces on Satellites

In space, there is no gravity, right? Wrong! Although it is true that the gravitational force is weaker when you are farther away from an object, such as Earth, the gravitational force still exists.

Figure CA2-3 Some loads are lifted into space from Vandenberg Air Force Base by the Atlas-E rocket.

485

In fact, if there were no gravitational force in space, no satellites, not even the moon, could orbit Earth. Similarly, without the sun's gravitational pull, planets in the solar system could not orbit the sun.

What forces are acting on a satellite orbiting Earth? Assuming that the satellite is in orbit, there is only one force acting on it—gravity. If there were no gravitational force acting on it, the satellite would head away from Earth in approximately a straight line. Instead, the satellite is basically falling toward Earth at all times, but because of its forward motion while it is being pulled downward by gravity it continues to orbit. This constant falling is why astronauts in orbit are said to be in freefall.

Launches from Airplanes

Not all rockets launched from Vandenberg AFB start off on the ground at rest. An area of safe airspace over the Pacific Ocean near the base, called the Western Range, is used to launch rockets from airplanes. The rocket starts its launch with forward motion because it is attached to a plane that

Figure CA2-4 This 747 transport plane moves the space shuttle *Discovery* from Vandenberg Air Force Base to Cape Canaveral for another launch.

is moving forward. After being dropped, the rocket must eject exhaust in order to propel itself higher than the plane and to achieve its orbit.

Changing Times

In 1998, for the first time, more of the rocket launches from Vandenberg AFB were for commercial projects than for military ones. Although satellites are still useful for obtaining military information, they are now being used for civilian activities. These activities include com-munications, weather forecasting, monitoring areas prone to earthquakes or volcanic eruptions, gathering environmental data, and research projects.

Investigation & Experimentation

Standard 9a
Sit on a chair with wheels. Throw a small ball to a friend in front of you. In which direction do you and your chair move? Now, throw something heavier, like a basketball or a soccer ball. What happens to you and the chair now? How is this demonstration similar to the motion of a rocket?

Structure of Matter

Content Standard 3
Elements have distinct properties and atomic structure. All matter is comprised of one or more of over 100 elements.

3a. Structure of the Atom

All matter is made up of atoms—the chair you are sitting on, the trees outside, even people! But, what is an atom made up of? Atoms contain protons, neutrons, and electrons. The protons and neutrons are in the nucleus, which is at the center of the atom. The electrons move in a cloudlike area around the nucleus.

What is different between atoms of different elements? The differences lie in the numbers of protons, neutrons, and electrons. In any element, the number of protons equals the number of electrons. Hydrogen is the lightest element; it has only one proton. The next lightest is helium, which has two protons.

3b. Compounds

Most things are not made up of single elements. They are made up of elements in combination with one another. Water is made up of a combination of hydrogen and oxygen. When two or more different elements combine, they form compounds.

Do compounds act like the elements that are included in them? Not necessarily. When elements combine into compounds, these new substances have different properties. Water does not act somewhat like hydrogen and somewhat like oxygen. It acts like a new substance you know as water.

Investigation & Experimentation

Standard 9a

Take small amounts of two different colors of paint and combine them. Once these paints are combined, can you separate them again into their original colors? Can you separate chemical compounds into their separate elements without special equipment or procedures?

3c. Solids

Can you feel separate atoms if you touch your desk? Of course not. From what you can see and feel, the top of your desk feels like one solid item, not like it is made up of many smaller particles. Solids are formed by the build up of a three-dimensional, repeating pattern such as a crystal structure. The sodium and chlorine in table salt alternate to form a cube-shaped solid.

Rather than being crystals, some solids such as rubber, silk, and plastics are long chains called polymers. This creates a long line of molecules that is flexible, unlike a crystal.

3d. & 3e. States of Matter

What do water, ice, and water vapor (steam) have in common? They are all composed of the same molecules. But, water is a liquid, ice is a solid, and water vapor is a gas. How can the same molecule take three different forms? The state of matter—solid, liquid, or gas—is determined by the motion of its atoms or molecules.

Figure CA3-1 A geode is a hollow body of rock with crystals growing inward from the walls.

In a solid, the particles are closely locked in position and only can vibrate. In a liquid, the atoms or molecules are more loosely connected. They collide with and move past one another. In a gas, the atoms or molecules are free to move independently. They move around constantly and collide frequently.

Investigation & Experimentation

Standard 9c
Think about what, in addition to the state of matter, is different about water, ice, and water vapor. What do you have to do to get ice or water vapor from water? What does this teach you about how molecules move?

3f. The Periodic Table

In all, there are 112 known elements. To make it easier to keep track of some of the important properties of those elements, they are arranged in a table, called the periodic table of the elements. You can see the periodic table on the inside back cover of this book. Details of the history of the table and how elements are arranged will be found in Chapter 4.

Going Further

To learn more about the structure of matter, see:

3a. Chapter 5, Section 1, The Story of the Atom
Chapter 5, Section 2, The Nucleus
Chapter 7, Section 1, Why do atoms combine?

3b. Chapter 7, Chemical Bonds
Chapter 8, Section 1, Describing a Chemical Reaction

3c. Chapter 4, Section 1, Solids

3d. & 3e. Chapter 4, Section 1, Solids
Chapter 4, Section 2, Liquids and Gases
Chapter 4, Section 3, Behavior of Liquids and Gases

3f. Chapter 6, Section 1, Introduction to the Periodic Table
Chapter 6, Section 2, Representative Elements
Chapter 6, Section 3, Transition Elements
Chapter 7, Section 1, Why do atoms combine?

Making New Elements

SCIENCE FOCUS
Read this case study to learn about elements that were made at the Lawrence Berkeley National Laboratory in Berkeley, California.

California CASE STUDY

Some of the 112 known elements on the periodic table are easy to find all around you. Oxygen and nitrogen make up most of the air you breathe. Sodium and chlorine combine to make table salt. You may have jewelry with some gold or silver in it. Other elements are much less common in the world around you. In fact, some of the elements that have been discovered are not present naturally on Earth at all! Those elements have only been made in a laboratory and are called synthetic elements.

One of the laboratories where researchers made several elements is the Lawrence Berkeley National Laboratory (LBNL), at the University of California in Berkeley. In all, ten elements on the periodic table were made there: plutonium, americium, curium, berkelium, californium, einsteinium, fermium, mendelevium, nobelium and seaborgium. What do you recognize about some of the names?

Making Plutonium

The first element that was made at LBNL was plutonium, in 1941. It was created by taking uranium, which has 92 protons in its nucleus and is the heaviest element that is found naturally on Earth, and bombarding it with a special form of hydrogen. This was done by using a circular tunnel called a cyclotron. The hydrogen particles were accelerated to a high speed inside the tunnel and allowed to collide with the uranium.

Figure CA3-2 Elements are formed in stars such as our sun. Some of those elements are not found on Earth.

Correlates with Content Standard 3

Plutonium has 94 protons in its nucleus. So, we know that the particles combined with the uranium and added two protons into its nucleus. The other nine elements made at LBNL were made in similar ways.

Investigation & Experimentation

Standard 9a
Create a track with sides. Place a small lump of modeling clay near the end of the track. Send several small ball bearings traveling along the track. Did all of the ball bearings collide with the clay, or did some of them travel past? Did any of the ball bearings leave dents on or get stuck to the soft clay? How is this demonstration similar to a cyclotron? How is it different?

Content
Standard 4
The structure
and composi-
tion of the uni-
verse can be
learned from
the study of
stars and galax-
ies and their
evolution.

California CONTENT STANDARD 4

Earth in the Solar System

4a. & b. Stars and Galaxies

Each day, the sun rises over the Sierra Nevada mountain range shown above and provides energy for plants and wildlife. But, is the sun really unique? Actually, no. The sun is an average star.

Our sun is a yellow, medium-sized star. The color of a star depends upon its temperature. The larger a star is, the cooler it tends to be. The giant star Betelgeuse is red. Very hot stars that give off a blue-white color may be small, about the size of Earth.

The sun is one of about 200 billion stars in the Milky Way Galaxy. A galaxy is a large group of stars, gas, and dust held together by the force of gravity. There may be more than 100 billion galaxies in the universe.

There are three major classes of galaxies: spiral, elliptical, and irregular. Spiral galaxies have arms that wind outward from a center packed with stars. Elliptical galaxies often are football shaped, but some are almost spheres. Most of the known galaxies have irregular shapes. We see the Milky Way Galaxy as a band of light across the night sky. We cannot see its spiral shape because our solar system is located within one of its spiral arms.

4c. Units of Distance

Scientists use the light-year to describe the distance between Earth and stars other than the sun. A light-year is the distance traveled by light in one year—about 9.5 trillion km. The moon is only one light-second away, which means that the distance between Earth and the moon is the distance that light travels in one second.

When scientists talk about distances from the sun, they use the astronomical unit (AU). One AU is the distance between Earth and the sun. The distances between the sun and the other planets can then be described in relation to the distance between Earth and the sun. For example, Mars is about 1.5 times as far from the sun as Earth is or 1.5 AU, and Neptune is 30 times as far from the sun as Earth is or 30 AU.

4d. Sources of Light

The sun shines on us during the day, and the moon shines at night. However, where their light comes from is different.

Stars such as our sun produce their own light through a process called fusion. The pressure and temperature inside a star are so great that atoms fuse to form larger atoms, and release large amounts of energy. The moon and planets shine by reflecting the light of the sun.

4e. The Solar System

The sun is the central and largest body in our solar system. There are nine planets. Some of these planets have satellites, called moons, in orbit around them. There also are smaller objects—asteroids and comets—in the solar system.

There are two types of planets—terrestrial planets and gas giants. The terrestrial planets—Mercury, Venus, Earth, and Mars—are made up of rock. They have few, if any, moons. They are the planets closest to the sun. The gas giants—Jupiter, Saturn, Uranus, and Neptune—are made mostly of gases. They are much larger than the terrestrial planets and are farther away from the sun. These planets also have multiple moons and rings. The composition of Pluto is still being debated.

Asteroids are chunks of rock that are smaller than planets. The pieces of rock are made of minerals similar to those that formed the planets. Most of the asteroids in the solar system appear in a belt between Mars and Jupiter.

Did you see comet Hale-Bopp when it was visible in the spring of 1997? Comets

Figure CA4-1 Halley's comet is visible from Earth approximately every 75 years.

are relatively small objects made up of dust and ice. They are generally found on the outer edge of the solar system far away from the sun. Sometimes the path of a comet is affected by the gravitational force of the sun and it ends up traveling closer to the sun. In some of those cases, comets are visible from Earth.

Planets orbit the sun, but why do they stay in orbit? Because of the gravitational attraction between the sun and the planets. The sun has much more mass than any of the planets in the solar system, so it has the greatest gravitational force.

Investigation & Experimentation

Standards 9e, 9g
Find out how long it takes for each of the nine planets to go around the sun, called the planet's period, and how far each is from the sun. Make a graph of period versus distance.

Going Further

To learn more about Earth as a part of the solar system, see:

Searching for Unknown Planets

SCIENCE FOCUS

Read this case study to learn about how researchers at San Francisco State University and the University of California, Berkeley are finding planets orbiting stars other than the sun.

The ninth planet of our solar system, Pluto, was identified in 1930. Until 1995, no planets had been discovered orbiting any other stars. Since then, extrasolar planets—meaning planets outside of our solar system—have been discovered.

Which other stars might have new planets?

How are extrasolar planets discovered? First, remember that there is gravitational attraction between any two objects, such as stars and planets. Although it seems like the sun is motionless at the center of the solar system while the planets travel around it, that is not the case. The sun moves a small amount because of the gravitational forces of the nine planets. Jupiter has the greatest effect because it is the most massive planet.

Scientists can look for planets around other stars by seeing if a star wobbles. If there is a regular wobble in the star's position and speed, they can conclude that there is a planet in orbit whose gravitational force is causing the star to shift slightly. These wobbles are very small changes in position and speed, so they are difficult to detect.

How to Detect a Wobble

If stars that wobble have at least one planet in orbit, then how can scientists detect the wobble? The change in position of the stars is much too small to see. Instead, scientists use telescopes at observatories, such as the Lick Observatory in San Jose, California, to look at the light emitted from stars. If the star is moving, the color of the light that reaches the telescope varies. By looking at how the color of the light changes over time, scientists can tell

Figure CA4-2 The constellations Canis Major, Orion, and Taurus can be seen over Mudstone Cliff in the Anzaborrego Desert State Park, California.

Figure CA4-3 University of California Observatories operates the Lick Observatory in Hamilton, California, for public programs and research.

whether there is a repeating pattern. If so, there could be a planet whose gravitational force is causing the star to move. The pattern repeats each time the planet completes an orbit. So for example, if the pattern repeats in 150 days, it means that the planet travels once around its star in 150 days. Scientists can also estimate the mass of the planet and its distance from the star by the size of the wobble.

Extrasolar Planets

Several of the extrasolar planets discovered so far have been found by researchers at San Francisco State University and the University of California in Berkeley. Their first observations were done at the Lick Observatory. Those were followed by observations with a stronger telescope at the Keck Observatory in Hawaii.

All of the planets found so far have been similar in size or larger than Jupiter, which is the largest planet in our solar system. A larger planet has a larger gravitational force, which causes a wobble large enough to detect. The telescopes available now are not powerful enough to search for planets that are much smaller.

Are the planets that scientists have found what they expected? Actually, no—there have been surprises. Several extrasolar planets have had orbits close to their stars and they travel around them quickly. Scientists also have been surprised to find planets around stars that are much smaller than the sun. They expected to find planets around stars similar to the sun, but apparently many other stars, even much smaller ones, have planets. Finally, some of the newly discovered planets have orbits that are shaped more like large ovals rather than having orbits that are nearly circular, like the planets in our solar system.

The Search Continues

Currently, researchers are studying several hundred stars for wobbles, indicating the presence of planets. If the planets take a long time to travel around their stars, the repeating pattern of the wobble will take a while to detect. So, continuously watching the stars over long periods of time is necessary.

Investigation & Experimentation

Standard 9b

Research one of the newly discovered planets. Who first discovered the planet? How big do scientists think it is? How does it compare in size to Jupiter? How fast does it travel around its star? How far is it from its star? What is the shape of its orbit? What else can you find out about the planet or its star? Compare your information to what other students in your class have found.

Reactions

5a. Chemical Reactions

Fireworks light up the sky over Irvine, California, in the photo above. Whenever you see a fireworks display, you observe a chemical reaction.

A chemical reaction happens when substances, called reactants, undergo a chemical change to form products. The chemical properties of the products are different from those of the reactants. When a chemical reaction occurs, there are usually differences you can observe. Signs of chemical change include a change in color or odor; formation of heat, light, or a solid from solution; or the release of a gas. For example, the solid substances in the fireworks combine with oxygen gas in the air to make solids, gases, heat, light, and sound.

5b. Conservation of Matter

When chemicals react, do they produce more matter? Or, do they use up matter in the process of reacting? Actually, the total amount of mass stays the same. This is called the law of conservation of mass.

Why is matter conserved? To understand this idea, remember that all matter is made up of atoms. In chemical reactions, the atoms are rearranged, but there are the same number of atoms in the products of the reaction as there were in the original chemicals. So, the total mass stays the same. All of the atoms involved in chemical reactions are present before and after the reaction. But, the way in which the atoms are combined into compounds changes.

Investigation & Experimentation

Standards 9a, 9c

Think about how you might create water from hydrogen and oxygen. Remember that a water molecule, H_2O, has two hydrogen atoms and one oxygen atom. How would you test for conservation of matter? If you started out with equal numbers of hydrogen and oxygen atoms, what would be left after the reaction? If you started out with twice as many hydrogen as oxygen atoms, what would be left?

5c. Heat of Reaction

Many different compounds will react with each other under the right conditions. When you mix baking soda and vinegar, the mixture immediately foams and fizzes. In some cases, compounds only react when they are exposed to heat. For example, when baking soda is mixed in some kinds of cookie dough and placed into a hot oven, the baking soda breaks down into carbon dioxide and water gases, and sodium carbonate. The gases cause the cookies to puff up.

In other cases, heat is released by the chemical reaction. One example is the reaction of the metal magnesium with oxygen gas. The two combine to form magnesium oxide, a white powder. When this happens, the reaction releases heat and light. This reaction has been used in photographic flashbulbs.

Investigation & Experimentation

Standard 9a
There are chemicals on the tip of a match that react when they are exposed to friction. What happens when someone strikes a match on the side of its box? Does it absorb or release heat?

5d. Physical Change

Is every change involving a substance a reaction? No, materials can go through physical changes, such as freezing and boiling, that do not involve reactions or recombining atoms. In a physical change, the substance changes its form, or state of matter, but the particles in the substance are still the same. For example, water, ice and water vapor (steam) are all made up of the same atoms—a combination of two hydrogen atoms and one oxygen atom, H_2O—but, one is a liquid, one is a solid, and one is a gas. No chemical reaction has occurred because the chemical properties of the water have not changed.

Investigation & Experimentation

Standards 9b, 9c
Think about water, ice and water vapor. What changes occur to make the H_2O molecule take the three different forms? If you make similar changes to another molecule, will that also change the state of matter? Nitrogen is usually a gas. But, you may have heard of liquid nitrogen. How could you make nitrogen into a liquid?

Figure CA5-1 Magnesium reacts with oxygen when burned and gives off a bright light.

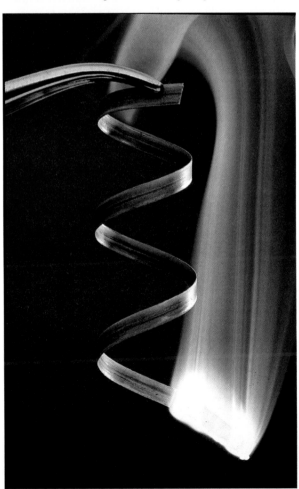

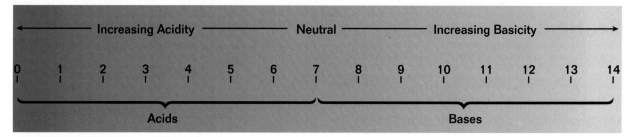

Figure CA5-2 The pH scale is used to measure whether a solution is an acid, a base, or neutral.

5e. Acids and Bases

You have probably heard of acids and bases. Vinegar is an acid and like other acids it has a sharp, sour taste. Bases taste bitter and are slippery to the touch. Most soaps are bases. Although acids and bases do taste different, you should never taste a substance to test whether it is an acid or a base because some can be very dangerous!

Acids and bases differ when dissolved in water. An acid produces hydronium ions when dissolved in water. The acid releases hydrogen ions, H^+, that combine with water molecules to form hydronium ions, H_3O^+. A base is a substance that produces hydroxide ions, OH^-, when dissolved in water. If you mix an acid and a base into the same container of water, they react to form more water molecules.

$$H_3O^+ + OH^- \rightarrow 2H_2O$$

This is a process called neutralization.

You may have heard about people measuring the pH of a solution, such as the water in a swimming pool. Measuring pH is a way of finding out whether a solution is an acid, a base, or neither. The pH of a solution depends upon the number of hydronium ions or hydroxide ions present. If there are more hydronium ions, then the solution is acidic and has a low pH. The solution is basic if there are more hydroxide ions—it will have a high pH. A solution that contains an equal number of hydronium ions and hydroxide ions is neutral.

A small strip of paper with a substance that changes color depending on pH is dipped into the solution. The color of the strip can then be compared with a chart that shows whether the solution is an acid, a base, or neutral. Often, acids turn the strip red and bases turn it blue, but the color can vary depending on the type of strip used.

Investigation & Experimentation

Standard 9a

Using strips of pH paper, try to find some common acids and bases. Try things such as dish soap, lemon juice, orange juice, vinegar, soft drinks, bath soap, etc. Which are acids? Which are bases? Which are neutral?

Going Further

To learn more about chemical reactions, acids, and bases, see:

5a. Chapter 8, Section 1, Describing a Chemical Reaction
Chapter 8, Section 2, Rates of Chemical Reactions
5b. Chapter 8, Section 1, Describing a Chemical Reaction

5c. Chapter 8, Section 1, Describing a Chemical Reaction
Chapter 8, Section 2, Rates of Chemical Reactions
5d. Chapter 8, Section 1, Describing a Chemical Reaction
5e. Chapter 9, Section 3, Acids and Bases

Catalytic Converters

SCIENCE FOCUS

Read this case study to learn about how catalytic converters in cars help reduce air pollution, including the smog in the Los Angeles area.

California CASE STUDY

Correlates with Content Standard 5

All recently built cars include a catalytic converter. What is a catalytic converter? It is an additional device located in the exhaust system of a car. All emissions from the car pass through the catalytic converter before being released from the car's tailpipe.

Why is it called a catalytic converter? It converts harmful chemicals into less harmful ones by providing a catalyst. A catalyst inside the catalytic converter helps speed up chemical reactions in the car's exhaust. But, the catalyst does not change into something else or get used up. This way, the same catalytic converter can be used over and over to make the car's emissions safer. Having a catalyst to speed reactions is important. Without one, these reactions would take thousands of years!

How do the emissions come into contact with the catalyst? The substance used as a catalyst is in the form of solid pellets. They are located on surfaces inside the converter that look like a honeycomb. The emissions can flow through many different passages. So, it is very likely that the emissions will contact the catalyst.

What are the reactions?

There are two main types of reactions that occur in a catalytic converter. Both types need to absorb heat. This means that a catalytic converter works better after it gets hot.

One type of reaction that happens in a catalytic converter is called oxidation. For example, one of the emissions from a car is carbon monoxide, CO, a colorless, odorless

Figure CA5-3
Car emissions pass through the catalytic converter before leaving the tailpipe.

gas that can be fatal to people who breathe it. In the oxidation process, carbon monoxide is changed into carbon dioxide, CO_2, which people exhale when they breathe, and water.

The second type of reaction that occurs in a catalytic converter is called reduction. In this case, harmful chemicals are broken down into less harmful elements. For example, nitrogen oxide (NO) is reduced to nitrogen and oxygen gases. If nitrogen oxide is released into the air, it can produce chemicals that would irritate people's eyes.

Using catalytic converters in cars is one way chemical reactions are used every day to help keep people safe.

Investigation & Experimentation

Standard 9c

Is the presence of a catalyst in a chemical reaction something controlled by the researchers? Or, is it a variable in the reaction? Think about the speed of the reaction with or without a catalyst. Is the reaction speed a variable?

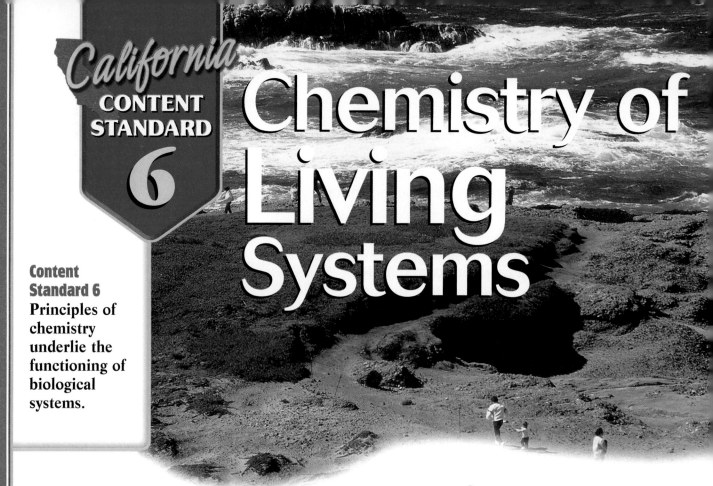

California

CONTENT
STANDARD

6

Chemistry of
Living
Systems

Content
Standard 6
Principles of
chemistry
underlie the
functioning of
biological
systems.

6a. Carbon

What elements are you made up of? One of the most common elements found in living things—including plants, animals, and people—is carbon. Carbon is found in many compounds that are necessary for life. Why is carbon so common? Carbon is able to combine in many ways with itself and with other elements. Therefore, this one element is part of many different compounds. Some of those compounds are simple, such as carbon monoxide, CO, which has one carbon atom and one oxygen atom, and others are complex. Cholesterol, $C_{27}H_{46}O$, is made up of many carbon and hydrogen atoms, and an oxygen atom.

Carbon atoms are particularly likely to combine with other carbon atoms or with hydrogen atoms. For example, the gases methane, ethane, propane, and butane are all made up of carbon and hydrogen atoms, but the numbers of atoms of carbon and hydrogen vary.

Investigation & Experimentation

Standards 9d, 9e, 9g

Find out how many carbon atoms and how many hydrogen atoms are in methane, ethane, propane, and butane. Make a graph showing the number of hydrogen atoms versus the number of carbon atoms. Is the graph linear? What does the slope indicate? Octane is an eight-carbon compound. Use your graph to predict how many hydrogen atoms are in octane.

6b. & c. Molecules in Living Things

Not all molecules in living things are made up of carbon and hydrogen only. Other elements include nitrogen, oxygen, phosphorus and sulfur. For example, phosphorus is present in compounds in bones and teeth. Oxygen is present in large amounts in the body in water molecules.

498

The human body is about 66 percent water. An apple is about 80 percent water, and many meats are as much as 90 percent water. The proteins in your body are made up of carbon, hydrogen, oxygen, and nitrogen.

Investigation & Experimentation

Standard 9f
Calculate the mass of water in your body. To do this, you will need to know your weight in pounds. Divide by 2.2 to convert your weight in pounds to your mass in kilograms. Then multiply 70 percent.

Most of your body mass is water. Water molecules are fairly small, being made up of only three atoms—two hydrogen and one oxygen. The human body also contains the salt sodium chloride, which is another small molecule. Table salt has one sodium atom and one chlorine atom.

Are humans made up of small molecules? No, other molecules in living things are much larger and more complex. Examples of larger molecules include fats, proteins that are made up of smaller amino acids, and DNA, which has a complex structure called a double helix.

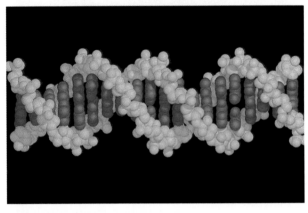

Figure CA6-1 DNA is a molecule that resembles a ladder twisted into a spiral. This spiral structure is known as a double helix.

Investigation & Experimentation

Standard 9f
The carbohydrates in the peanut butter and jelly sandwich that gives your body energy are chains of simple sugars. The number of hydrogen and oxygen atoms in a simple sugar can be calculated by the formula, $C_nH_{2n}O_n$, where n equals the number of carbons in the molecule. For example, ribose has five carbon atoms. It has ten hydrogen atoms and five oxygen atoms. Glucose has six carbons. What is the formula for glucose?

Going Further

To learn more about the chemistry of living systems, see:

Nitric Oxide in the Body

SCIENCE FOCUS
Read this case study to learn about how nitric oxide (NO) signals cells in the body to act in certain ways.

A researcher from the University of California at Los Angeles (UCLA) School of Medicine was one of three Americans awarded the 1998 Noble Prize in Medicine for research on nitric oxide. Nitric oxide, NO, has one nitrogen atom and one oxygen atom. It is a gas that comes from car emissions and causes air pollution. As a result of this award-winning research, scientists now know that cells also produce nitric oxide.

Nitric oxide can cause blood vessels to expand, which affects a person's blood pressure. Nitric oxide produced by nerve cells affects how people move, as well as how food and nutrients are processed in the body. In addition, nitric oxide helps the immune system fight disease in the body.

Research and Applications

Now that researchers have learned much about what nitric oxide does in the body, how can this information be used to help people? One possibility is that more effective drugs can be developed to help people with disease. For example, because only healthy blood vessels produce nitric oxide, people with damaged vessels can be given drugs that provide the nitric oxide they need.

For people with cancer, research is testing whether nitric oxide may be able to slow or stop the growth of tumors.

In some cases, nitric oxide gas can be given to patients with extremely high blood pressure to cause the blood vessels to expand and the blood pressure to fall. Research on nitric oxide is still being done to understand it better.

Investigation & Experimentation

Standard 9c
Nitric oxide is not the only chemical that is necessary in small quantities, but dangerous in larger quantities. Lots of vitamins, minerals, and other compounds are like that. For example, we need iron and vitamin D to live, but each can cause health problems in larger quantities. Would the amount of iron that would be dangerous be the same for a 100-kg man, a 60-kg woman and a 20-kg child?

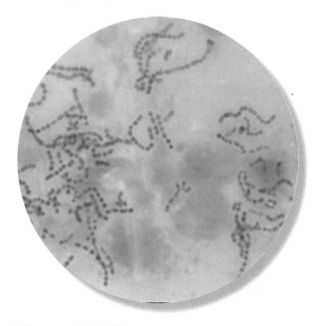

Figure CA6-2 These *Streptococcus pyogenes* bacteria were obtained from a tonsil.

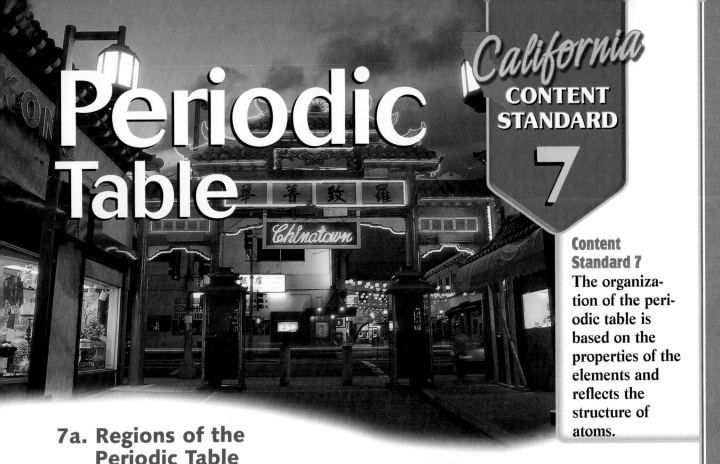

Periodic Table

California
CONTENT
STANDARD
7

Content Standard 7
The organization of the periodic table is based on the properties of the elements and reflects the structure of atoms.

7a. Regions of the Periodic Table

Neon lights up the signs in the photo above. It is a member of Group 18 on the periodic table, the noble gases. The noble gases share a chemical property—they do not readily react with other elements. The noble gases are part of a larger region on the periodic table called nonmetals. Nonmetals share chemical and physical properties. They are poor conductors of heat and electricity. Many are gases at room temperature. Solid nonmetals are brittle or soft, lack shine, and melt at low temperatures. Look at the periodic table inside the cover of this book. Nonmetals are located in the yellow region of the table.

Notice the large blue region on the periodic table. These elements are metals. Metals are shiny, conduct heat and electricity, and usually bend without breaking.

There is a small group of elements in green on the periodic table. Does their location have anything to do with their properties? Yes, metalloids have some chemical and physical properties of metals and nonmetals.

7b. Isotopes

The periodic table organizes the elements into large regions based on physical and chemical properties. Elements are ordered by the number of protons in the nucleus. The first element, hydrogen, has one proton. The second element, helium, has two protons. The number of protons in the nucleus of an atom is called its atomic number. This number defines which element an atom is. Any atom with one proton in the nucleus is hydrogen. Any atom with six protons in the nucleus is carbon.

Although the number of protons in the nucleus of any element doesn't change, the number of neutrons in the nucleus can change. Atoms of the same element with different numbers of neutrons are called isotopes. Isotopes of an element have the same chemical properties. They just differ in mass. Isotopes of uranium or plutonium are used to fuel nuclear power plants. Other isotopes are used to date fossils and ancient artifacts. Isotopes also are useful in medical diagnosis and treatment and in industry.

7c. Properties of Substances

Any property of an element or a compound that you can observe without changing its identity is a physical property. For example, you can observe that all substances exist as a gas, a liquid, a solid, or plasma. Most elements are solids, some are gases and a few, such as mercury, are liquids at room temperature. How can you tell the physical state of an element when you look at the periodic table?

The melting temperature of a substance is a physical property. For example, what happens if you accidentally leave a plastic spoon next to a hot stove? The plastic starts to melt and loses its shape. Some substances melt at fairly low temperatures. Others only melt if they get very hot.

The hardness of a substance is another property. If you rub your fingers across a flat piece of metal, how does it feel? Can you make a dent in it with your finger? Now, what if you rub a piece of chalk on a chalkboard? Can you dent the chalk? Can you scrape off small pieces of chalk? Metals are usually hard substances, so you cannot easily dent them, scrape off small bits, or break them. Chalk is not as hard so it is easier to dent, break, and scrape off small pieces.

How well a substance conducts heat and electricity are two other physical properties. Suppose you place the tip of a metal rod in a fire. Could you continue holding the other end of the rod for a long period of time? Metal conducts heat, which means that even though the end of the rod in your

Figure CA7-1
Californian Dr. Glenn T. Seaborg discovered ten elements on the periodic table. He died in 1999 at the age of 86.

hand is not in the fire, it will soon begin to feel warm and then will get hot enough to burn your hand. The fact that the heat travels from the tip of the rod to the end that you are holding means that the rod conducts heat. Similarly, some substances conduct electricity.

Investigation & Experimentation

Standards 9e, 9g

Research the melting point of elements. Make a graph of the melting points versus the atomic number of the elements. What does your graph look like? Is there a linear relationship between atomic number and the melting point? If not, is there some other typical pattern, or is it random?

Going Further

To learn more about the periodic table, see:

Carbon-14 Dating

SCIENCE FOCUS
Read this case study to learn about how scientists use the isotope carbon-14 to figure out the age of fossils found at the La Brea Tar Pits.

California
CASE STUDY

Correlates with Content Standard 7

Fossils for a variety of animals from the Ice Age—saber-toothed tigers, mammoths, wolves, birds, insects, and lizards—as well as seeds, pollen, and plants have been discovered at the Rancho La Brea Tar Pits in Los Angeles. Tar is a substance that preserves bones, so many complete fossils have been found, as shown in **Figure CA7-2.** The fossils found at Rancho La Brea are between 10 000 and 40 000 years old. How do scientists know how old fossils are? One common method for testing the age of fossils is called carbon-14 dating.

Figure CA7-2 Fossils from at least 59 mammal species have been recovered from Rancho La Brea Tar Pits.

Dating Fossils

Carbon is an element found in all living things. Carbon-14 is an isotope of carbon that has six protons and eight neutrons in its nucleus. The nucleus of carbon-14 is unstable and will break down, or decay, into carbon-12. Carbon-14 has a half-life of about 5730 years. This means that after 5730 years, half of the carbon-14 in a sample will have turned to carbon-12.

As long as plants and animals are alive, they take in both isotopes of carbon. The ratio of carbon-12 to carbon-14 in a living thing is the same as the ratio in the atmosphere in which it lives. When a plant or animal dies, it no longer takes in carbon. As the carbon-14 decays, the amount of carbon-12 in the remains increases. So, scientists can use carbon-14 to date fossils if they know how much carbon-14 was in the plant or animal when it died, how fast carbon-14 decays, and how much carbon-14 is left. This process can only be used to date fossils that are up to about 60 000 years old. For much older objects such as dinosaur bones and rocks other isotopes must be used.

Investigation & Experimentation

Standards 9b, 9c
When scientists use carbon-14 dating to find out how old a fossil is, what are the variables? What are constants? If several researchers try to find out how old the same fossil is, will they come up with the same age?

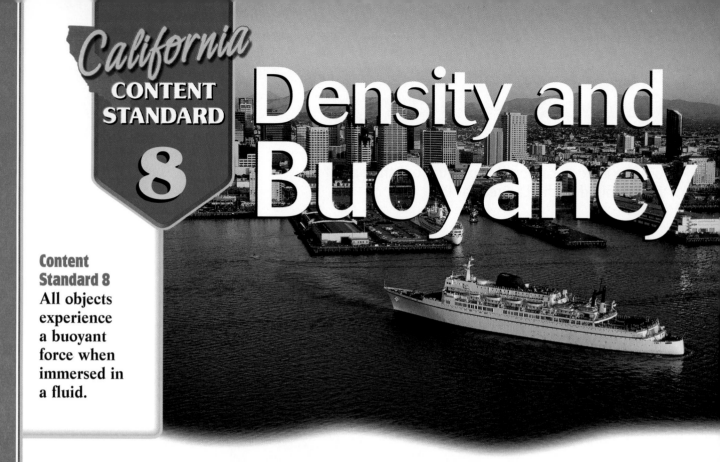

Content Standard 8
All objects experience a buoyant force when immersed in a fluid.

8a. & b. Calculating Density

The density of a substance is the amount of mass in an object of a particular size (volume). Suppose you have a block of plastic foam, a block of wood, and a block of metal, each the same size. Will all of the blocks feel equally heavy? No. Even though the blocks are the same size, the density of the substances, that is, the amount of mass contained in the block, is different. The metal block is denser than the plastic foam block. It has more mass, so it will feel heavier.

If you know the measurements of mass and volume for any substance, you can calculate the density.

$$\text{density} = \frac{\text{mass}}{\text{volume}}$$

This is true for any substance—a block, a rock, a fluid, and so on. Some objects have irregular shapes that are difficult to measure with a meterstick or ruler. How can you measure the volume? An understanding of buoyancy can help you solve this problem.

8c. & d. Buoyant Force

How does a ship float? What is the force that acts in an upward direction to keep the ship from sinking due to the force of gravity? The force is called a buoyant force. The buoyant force is also what makes things seem lighter in water than in air. Air and water are fluids.

Suppose you have a cup of water filled to the rim. If you drop a marble into the cup, some of the water will spill out because the marble takes up space equal to its volume. If you collected the water that spilled out and measured the weight of that water, you would know the magnitude of the buoyant force on the marble. The buoyant force equals the weight of the displaced fluid.

So, how might you know whether an object will sink or float? If the buoyant force upwards on an object that is fully underwater is greater than the pull of gravity downward, the object floats. If the gravitational force is greater than the buoyant force, the object will sink. So, if the weight of the water displaced by the entire object is greater than the weight of the object itself, the object will float.

Investigation & Experimentation

Standard 9f
Suppose you have an object with a mass of 1000 kg and a volume of 2 m³. If the object was completely underwater in the ocean, how much seawater would it displace? The density of seawater is 1025 kg/m³. Calculate the mass of the seawater that is displaced? Compare the masses of the object and the seawater. Which is greater? Will the object float or sink?

8e. Calculating Densities

Suppose you measure the weight of an object on a spring scale in air and it is 7.92 N. Then, you submerge the object in water and measure its weight again. This time the weight is only 7.03 N. The difference in the two weight measurements (0.89 N) is equal to the buoyant force of the water. The force of gravity acting on the object is the same whether the object is in air or water. So, the only difference in the weight of the object in air and in water is the buoyant force pushing up on the object. Density in a fluid is related to buoyant force by the following relationship.

$$\frac{\text{Weight of the object in air}}{\text{buoyant force}} = \frac{\text{density of the object}}{\text{density of the fluid}}$$

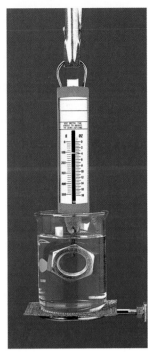

Figure CA8-1 The buoyant force reduces the effect of the force of gravity on an object. The mass does not change, but the weight of the object in water is less than in air.

To determine the density of the object, substitute the given values. The density of water is 1000 kg/m³.

$$\frac{7.92 \text{ N}}{0.89 \text{ N}} = \frac{\text{density of the object}}{1000 \text{ kg/m}^3}$$

$$\text{density of the object} = \frac{(7.92 \text{ N})(1000 \text{ kg/m}^3)}{0.89 \text{ N}}$$

$$= 8899 \text{ kg/m}^3$$

This method for calculating the density of materials can be used for solids and liquids, even if the volume of the material is unknown. All you need to know is the weight in air and in a fluid of known density, such as water.

Going Further

To learn more about density and buoyancy, see:

8a. Chapter 4, Section 3, Behavior of Liquids and Gases

8b. Chapter 4, Section 3, Behavior of Liquids and Gases

8c. Chapter 4, Section 3, Behavior of Liquids and Gases

Problems with Ballast Waters

SCIENCE FOCUS

Read this case study to learn about how ballast waters, which help ships operate safely, bring nonnative animal species that affect the ecosystem of San Francisco Bay.

Huge ships carry cargo to California ports from all over the world. In order for ships to operate safely, they must have a certain amount of their hulls underwater. This increases stability and allows more control over speed and direction.

The cargo and the containers that hold it add ballast, or weight, to the ships. However, when the ships are empty of cargo, they need to use something else for ballast.

Historically, ships used solid objects such as sand or rocks for ballast. But, since the 1880s, seawater has been the main form of ballast. Ships take on ballast waters from the seas near the port they sail from and release those waters near the port they sail into.

Organisms in Ballast Waters

When ships take in ballast water, they also take in many species of microscopic plants and animals. These plants and animals live in the ballast tanks during the ship's journey. Then, when the ship nears its destination, the ballast waters are released, along with all of the plants and animals. In many cases, the species in the ballast waters are not native to the areas where the ballast water is being emptied. Then, some of these nonnative species become established in the new locations. Up to 3000 different species of plants and animals may be carried in various ships all over the world in ballast waters at any one time.

Figure CA8-2 Ships full of cargo need less water in their ballast tanks.

Nonnative Species in San Francisco Bay

In some cases, when nonnative species become established in new locations, they harm the ecosystem of the new home. New species may eat much of the available food, leaving little for the animals that were there originally. This can lead to the extinction of some of the native species. Also, new species may or may not be an appropriate

Figure CA8-3 Much of a ship's hull will be visible when the ship holds little ballast.

food source for animals higher on the food chain. Therefore, the introduction of these new species may affect the entire ecosystem.

San Francisco Bay is one of the areas in the world that has been most affected by the introduction of new plant and animal species in ballast waters. At least 50 non-native species have become established in the bay since 1970.

One species that was new to the bay in 1986 was the Asian clam. This species has eaten large amounts of the plankton, which is a major food source for the bay's marine life. As a result, there has been a large drop in the number of shrimp in the bay. Animals higher up on the food chain, such as fish and ducks, have also been affected. Since the introduction of Asian clams, the number of striped bass in the bay has decreased significantly.

What can be done?

Although the problem of transporting species in ballast water has not been solved, there are some ideas about how to help. One possibility is for ships to change their ballast water during their trip so that they do not bring species from the starting port to the destination port. However, because ballast water is used for stability, this transfer could be tricky. Researchers also are testing two other possibilities. One is to filter ballast water as it is taken onto the ship. The second is to kill organisms in the ballast water using radiation or heat while the water is in the ship's tank.

Investigation & Experimentation

Standard 9a

Take a plastic foam cup and tape a piece of paper over the opening. Place the cup in a tub or sink of water. Then, place a rock on top of the paper covering the cup. How stable is the cup? Does it tip over? Now add some ballast—water, sand, or coins—to the cup and retape the paper on top. Place the rock on top again. Is the cup any more stable?

Appendices

Safety in the Science Classroom

1. Always obtain your teacher's permission to begin an investigation.

2. Study the procedure. If you have questions, ask your teacher. Be sure you understand any safety symbols shown on the page.

3. Use the safety equipment provided for you. Goggles and a safety apron should be worn during an investigation.

4. Always slant test tubes away from yourself and others when heating them.

5. Never eat or drink in the lab, and never use lab glassware as food or drink containers. Never inhale chemicals. Do not taste any substances or draw any material into a tube with your mouth.

6. If you spill any chemical, wash it off immediately with water. Report the spill immediately to your teacher.

7. Know the location and proper use of the fire extinguisher, safety shower, fire blanket, first aid kit, and fire alarm.

8. Keep all materials away from open flames. Tie back long hair and loose clothing.

9. If a fire should break out in the classroom, or if your clothing should catch fire, smother it with the fire blanket or a coat, or get under a safety shower. NEVER RUN.

10. Report any accident or injury, no matter how small, to your teacher.

Follow these procedures as you clean up your work area.

1. Turn off the water and gas. Disconnect electrical devices.

2. Return all materials to their proper places.

3. Dispose of chemicals and other materials as directed by your teacher. Place broken glass and solid substances in the proper containers. Never discard materials in the sink.

4. Clean your work area.

5. Wash your hands thoroughly after working in the laboratory.

Table A-1

First Aid	
Injury	**Safe Response**
Burns	Apply cold water. Call your teacher immediately.
Cuts and bruises	Stop any bleeding by applying direct pressure. Cover cuts with a clean dressing. Apply cold compresses to bruises. Call your teacher immediately.
Fainting	Leave the person lying down. Loosen any tight clothing and keep crowds away. Call your teacher immediately.
Foreign matter in eye	Flush with plenty of water. Use eyewash bottle or fountain.
Poisoning	Note the suspected poisoning agent and call your teacher immediately.
Any spills on skin	Flush with large amounts of water or use safety shower. Call your teacher immediately.

Appendix
B

SI/Metric to English Conversions

	When you want to convert:	To:	Multiply by:
Length	inches	centimeters	2.54
	centimeters	inches	0.39
	feet	meters	0.30
	meters	feet	3.28
	yards	meters	0.91
	meters	yards	1.09
	miles	kilometers	1.61
	kilometers	miles	0.62
Mass and Weight*	ounces	grams	28.35
	grams	ounces	0.04
	pounds	kilograms	0.45
	kilograms	pounds	2.2
	tons (short)	tonnes (metric tons)	0.91
	tonnes (metric tons)	tons (short)	1.10
	pounds	newtons	4.45
	newtons	pounds	0.23
Volume	cubic inches	cubic centimeters	16.39
	cubic centimeters	cubic inches	0.06
	cubic feet	cubic meters	0.03
	cubic meters	cubic feet	35.30
	liters	quarts	1.06
	liters	gallons	0.26
	gallons	liters	3.78
Area	square inches	square centimeters	6.45
	square centimeters	square inches	0.16
	square feet	square meters	0.09
	square meters	square feet	10.76
	square miles	square kilometers	2.59
	square kilometers	square miles	0.39
	hectares	acres	2.47
	acres	hectares	0.40
Temperature	Fahrenheit	$5/9\,(°F - 32)$ =	Celsius
	Celsius	$9/5\,(°C) + 32$ =	Fahrenheit

*Weight as measured in standard Earth gravity

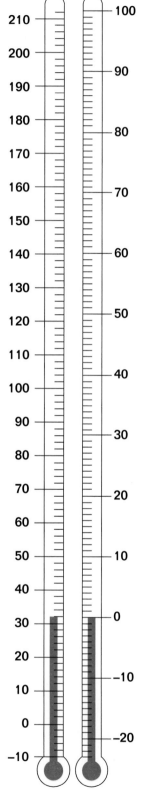

Appendix C

SI Units of Measurement

Table C-1

SI Base Units					
Measurement	**Unit**	**Symbol**	**Measurement**	**Unit**	**Symbol**
length	meter	m	temperature	kelvin	K
mass	kilogram	kg	amount of substance	mole	mol
time	second	s			

Table C-2

Units Derived from SI Base Units		
Measurement	**Unit**	**Symbol**
energy	joule	J
force	newton	N
frequency	hertz	Hz
potential difference	volt	V
power	watt	W
pressure	pascal	Pa

Table C-3

Common SI Prefixes					
Prefix	**Symbol**	**Multiplier**	**Prefix**	**Symbol**	**Multiplier**
Greater than 1			Less than 1		
mega-	M	1 000 000	*deci-*	d	0.1
kilo-	k	1 000	*centi-*	c	0.01
hecto-	h	100	*milli-*	m	0.001
deca-	da	10	*micro-*	μ	0.000 001

Care and Use of a Microscope

Eyepiece Contains a magnifying lens you look through

Arm Supports the body tube

Low-power objective Contains the lens with low-power magnification

Stage clips Hold the microscope slide in place

Coarse adjustment Focuses the image under low power

Fine adjustment Sharpens the image under high and low magnification

Body tube Connects the eyepiece to the revolving nosepiece

Revolving nosepiece Holds and turns the objectives into viewing position

High-power objective Contains the lens with the highest magnification

Stage Supports the microscope slide

Light source Allows light to reflect upward through the diaphragm, the specimen, and the lenses

Base Provides support for the microscope

Care of a Microscope

1. Always carry the microscope holding the arm with one hand and supporting the base with the other hand.

2. Don't touch the lenses with your fingers.

3. Never lower the coarse adjustment knob when looking through the eyepiece lens.

4. Always focus first with the low-power objective.

5. Don't use the coarse adjustment knob when the high-power objective is in place.

6. Store the microscope covered.

Using a Microscope

1. Place the microscope on a flat surface that is clear of objects. The arm should be toward you.

2. Look through the eyepiece. Adjust the diaphragm so that light comes through the opening in the stage.

3. Place a slide on the stage so that the specimen is in the field of view. Hold it firmly in place by using the stage clips.

4. Always focus first with the coarse adjustment and the low-power objective lens. Once the object is in focus on low power, turn the nosepiece until the high-power objective is in place. Use ONLY the fine adjustment to focus with the high-power objective lens.

Making a Wet-Mount Slide

1. Carefully place the item you want to look at in the center of a clean, glass slide. Make sure the sample is thin enough for light to pass through.

2. Use a dropper to place one or two drops of water on the sample.

3. Hold a clean coverslip by the edges and place it at one edge of the drop of water. Slowly lower the coverslip onto the drop of water until it lies flat.

4. If you have too much water or a lot of air bubbles, touch the edge of a paper towel to the edge of the coverslip to draw off extra water and force out air.

Diversity of Life: Classification of Living Organisms

Scientists use a six-kingdom system of classification of organisms. In this system, there are two kingdoms of organisms, Kingdoms Archaebacteria and Eubacteria, which contain organisms that do not have a nucleus and lack membrane-bound structures in the cytoplasm of their cells. The members of the other four kingdoms have cells which contain a nucleus and structures in the cytoplasm that are surrounded by membranes. These kingdoms are Kingdom Protista, Kingdom Fungi, the Kingdom Plantae, and the Kingdom Animalia.

Kingdom Archaebacteria

One-celled prokaryotes; absorb food from surroundings or make their own food by chemosynthesis; found in extremely harsh environments including salt ponds, hot springs, swamps, and deep-sea hydrothermal vents.

Kingdom Eubacteria

Cyanobacteria one-celled prokaryotes; make their own food; contain chlorophyll; some species form colonies; most are blue-green

Bacteria one-celled prokaryotes; most absorb food from their surroundings; some are photosynthetic; many are parasites; round, spiral, or rod-shaped

Kingdom Protista

Phylum Euglenophyta one-celled; can photosynthesize or take in food; most have one flagellum; euglenoids

Phylum Bacillariophyta one-celled; make their own food through photosynthesis; have unique double shells made of silica; diatoms

Phylum Dinoflagellata one-celled; make their own food through photosynthesis; contain red pigments; have two flagella; dinoflagellates

Phylum Chlorophyta one-celled, many-celled, or colonies; contain chlorophyll; make their own food; live on land, in fresh water, or salt water; green algae

Phylum Rhodophyta most are many-celled; photosynthetic; contain red pigments; most live in deep saltwater environments; red algae

Phylum Phaeophyta most are many-celled; photosynthetic; contain brown pigments; most live in saltwater environments; brown algae

Phylum Foraminifera many-celled; take in food; primarily marine; shells constructed of calcium carbonate, or made from grains of sand; forams

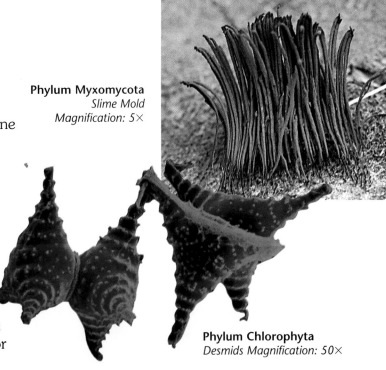

Phylum Myxomycota
Slime Mold
Magnification: 5×

Phylum Chlorophyta
Desmids Magnification: 50×

Phylum Rhizopoda one-celled; take in food; move by means of pseudopods; free-living or parasitic; amoebas

Phylum Zoomastigina one-celled; take in food; have one or more flagella; free-living or parasitic; zoomastigotes

Phylum Ciliophora one-celled; take in food; have large numbers of cilia; ciliates

Phylum Sporozoa one-celled; take in food; no means of movement; parasites in animals; sporozoans

Phylum Myxomycota and Acrasiomycota: one- or many-celled; absorb food; change form during life cycle; cellular and plasmodial slime molds

Phylum Oomycota many-celled; live in fresh or salt water; are either parasites or decomposers; water molds, rusts and downy mildews

Kingdom Fungi

Phylum Zygomycota many-celled; absorb food; spores are produced in sporangia; zygote fungi; bread mold

Phylum Ascomycota one- and many-celled; absorb food; spores produced in asci; sac fungi; yeast

Phylum Basidiomycota many-celled; absorb food; spores produced in basidia; club fungi; mushrooms

Phylum Deuteromycota: members with unknown reproductive structures; imperfect fungi; penicillin

Lichens organisms formed by symbiotic relationship between an ascomycote or a basidiomycote and green alga or cyanobacterium

Kingdom Plantae

Non-seed Plants

Division Bryophyta nonvascular plants; reproduce by spores produced in capsules; many-celled; green; grow in moist land environments; mosses and liverworts

Division Lycophyta many-celled vascular plants; spores produced in conelike structures; live on land; are photosynthetic; club mosses

Division Sphenophyta vascular plants; ribbed and jointed stems; scalelike leaves; spores produced in conelike structures; horsetails

Division Pterophyta vascular plants; leaves called fronds; spores produced in clusters of sporangia called sori; live on land or in water; ferns

Division Bryophyta
Liverwort

Lichens
British soldier lichen × 3

Appendix E

Seed Plants

Division Ginkgophyta: deciduous gymnosperms; only one living species; fan-shaped leaves with branching veins; reproduces with seeds; ginkgos

Division Cycadophyta: palmlike gymnosperms; large featherlike leaves; produce seeds in cones; cycads

Division Coniferophyta: deciduous or evergreen gymnosperms; trees or shrubs; needlelike or scalelike leaves; seeds produced in cones; conifers

Division Gnetophyta: shrubs or woody vines; seeds produced in cones; division contains only three genera; gnetum

Division Anthophyta: dominant group of plants; ovules protected in an ovary; sperm carried to ovules by pollen tube; produce flowers and seeds in fruits; flowering plants

Kingdom Animalia

Phylum Porifera: aquatic organisms that lack true tissues and organs; they are asymmetrical and sessile; sponges

Phylum Cnidaria: radially symmetrical organisms; have a digestive cavity with one opening; most have tentacles armed with stinging cells; live in aquatic environments singly or in colonies; includes jellyfish, corals, hydra, and sea anemones

Phylum Platyhelminthes: bilaterally symmetrical worms; have flattened bodies; digestive system has one opening; parasitic and free-living species; flatworms

Phylum Cnidaria
Jellyfish

Phylum Arthopoda
Orb Weaver Spider

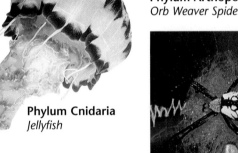

Phylum Arthropoda
Hermit Crab

Division Coniferophyta
Pine cone

Division Anthophyta
Strawberry Blossoms

Phylum Mollusca
Florida Fighting Conch

Phylum Annelida
Sabellid Worms Feather Duster

Division Anthophyta
Strawberries

Phylum Nematoda: round, bilaterally symmetrical body; digestive system with two openings; many parasitic forms but mostly free-living; roundworms

Phylum Mollusca: soft-bodied animals, many with a hard shell; a mantle covers the soft body; aquatic and terrestrial species; includes clams, snails, squid, and octopuses

Phylum Annelida: bilaterally symmetrical worms; have round, segmented bodies; terrestrial and aquatic species; includes earthworms, leeches, and marine polychaetes

Phylum Arthropoda: largest phylum of organisms; have segmented bodies; pairs of jointed appendages; have hard exoskeletons; terrestrial and aquatic species; includes insects, crustaceans, spiders, and horseshoe crabs

Phylum Echinodermata: marine organisms; have spiny or leathery skin; water-vascular system with tube feet; radial symmetry; includes sea stars, sand dollars, and sea urchins

Phylum Chordata: organisms with internal skeletons; specialized body systems; paired appendages; all at some time have a notochord, dorsal nerve cord, gill slits, and a tail; include fish, amphibians, reptiles, birds, and mammals

Phylum Arthropoda
Giant Swallowtail Butterfly

Phylum Echinodermata
Blood Sea Star and Red Sea Urchin

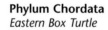

Phylum Chordata
Eastern Box Turtle

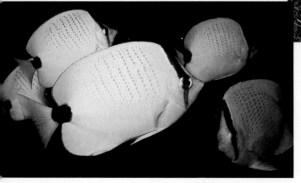

Phylum Chordata
Lemon Butterfly fish

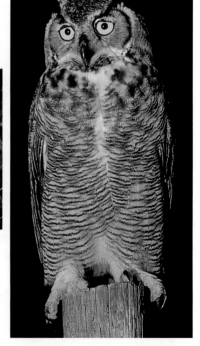

Phylum Chordata
Great Horned Owl

Appendix
F

Minerals

Mineral (formula)	Color	Streak	Hardness	Breakage pattern	Uses and other properties
graphite (C)	black to gray	black to gray	1–1.5	basal cleavage (scales)	pencil lead, lubricants for locks, rods to control some small nuclear reactions, battery poles
galena (PbS)	gray	gray to black	2.5	cubic cleavage perfect	source of lead, used in pipes, shields for X rays, fishing equipment sinkers
hematite (Fe_2O_3)	black or reddish brown	reddish brown	5.7–6.5	irregular fracture	source of iron; converted to "pig" iron, made into steel
magnetite (Fe_3O_4)	black	black	6	conchoidal fracture	source of iron, naturally magnetic, called lodestone
pyrite (FeS_2)	light, brassy, yellow	greenish black	8–6.5	uneven fracture	source of iron, "fool's gold"
talc ($Mg_3Si_4O_{10}(OH)_2$)	white greenish	white	1	cleavage in one direction	used for talcum powder, sculptures, paper, and tabletops
gypsum ($CaSO_4 \cdot 2H_2O$)	colorless, gray, white brown	white	2	basal cleavage	used in plaster of paris and dry wall for building construction
sphalerite (ZnS)	brown, reddish brown, greenish	light to dark brown	3.7–4	cleavage in six directions	main ore of zinc; used in paints, dyes and medicine
muscovite ($KAl_3Si_3O_{10}(OH)_2$)	white, light gray, yellow, rose, green	colorless	4–2.5	basal cleavage	occurs in large flexible plates; used as an insulator in electrical equipment, lubricant
biotite ($K(Mg, Fe)_3(AlSi_3O_{10})(OH)_2$)	black to dark brown	colorless	2.7–3	basal cleavage	occurs in large flexible plates
halite (NaCl)	colorless, red, white, blue	colorless	2.5	cubic cleavage	salt; soluble in water; a preservative

Appendix
F

Minerals

Mineral (formula)	Color	Streak	Hardness	Breakage pattern	Uses and other properties
calcite ($CaCO_3$)	colorless, white, pale blue	colorless, white	3	cleavage in three directions	fizzes when HCl is added; used in cements and other building materials
dolomite ($CaMg$ $(CO_3)_2$)	colorless, white, pink green, gray black	white	3.7–4	cleavage in three directions	concrete and cement; used as an ornamental building stone
fluorite (CaF_2)	colorless, white, blue green, red yellow, purple	colorless	4	cleavage in four directions	used in the manufacture of optical equipment; glows under ultraviolet light
hornblende ($(CaNa)_{4\text{-}3}(Mg,$ $Al,Fe)_5(Al,Si)_2$ $Si_6O_{22}(OH)_2$	green to black	gray to white	7–6	cleavage in two directions	will transmit light on thin edges; 6-sided cross section
feldspar ($KAlSi_3O_8$) ($NaAlSi_3O_8$) ($CaAl_2Si_2O_8$)	colorless, white to gray, green	colorless	6	two cleavage planes meet at ~ 90° angle	used in the manufacture of ceramics
augite ((Ca, Na) (Mg, Fe, Al) $(Al, Si)_2O_6$)	black	colorless	6	cleavage in two directions	square or 8-sided cross section
olivine ($(Mg, Fe)_2$ SiO_4)	olive, green	none	6.7–7	conchoidal fracture	gemstones, refractory sand
quartz (SiO_2)	colorless, various colors	none	7	conchoidal fracture	used in glass manufacture, electronic equipment, radios, computers, watches, gemstones

Appendix
G

Rocks

Rock Type	Rock Name	Characteristics
Igneous (intrusive)	Granite	Large mineral grains of quartz, feldspar, hornblende, and mica. Usually light in color.
	Diorite	Large mineral grains of feldspar, hornblende, mica. Less quartz than granite. Intermediate in color.
	Gabbro	Large mineral grains of feldspar, hornblende, augite, olivine, and mica. No quartz. Dark in color.
Igneous (extrusive)	Rhyolite	Small mineral grains of quartz, feldspar, hornblende, and mica or no visible grains. Light in color.
	Andesite	Small mineral grains of feldspar, hornblende, mica or no visible grains. Less quartz than rhyolite. Intermediate in color.
	Basalt	Small mineral grains of feldspar, hornblende, augite, olivine, mica or no visible grains. No quartz. Dark in color.
	Obsidian	Glassy texture. No visible grains. Volcanic glass. Fracture looks like broken glass.
	Pumice	Frothy texture. Floats. Usually light in color.
Sedimentary (detrital)	Conglomerate	Coarse-grained. Gravel or pebble-sized grains.
	Sandstone	Sand-sized grains 1/16 to 2 mm in size.
	Siltstone	Grains are smaller than sand but larger than clay.
	Shale	Smallest grains. Usually dark in color.
Sedimentary (chemical or biochemical)	Limestone	Major mineral is calcite. Usually forms in oceans, lakes, rivers, and caves. Often contains fossils.
	Coal	Occurs in swampy. low-lying areas. Compacted layers of organic material, mainly plant remains.
Sedimentary (chemical)	Rock Salt	Commonly forms by the evaporation of seawater.
Metamorphic (foliated)	Gneiss	Well-developed banding because of alternating layers of different minerals, usually of different colors. Common parent rock is granite.
	Schist	Well-defined parallel arrangement of flat, sheet-like minerals, mainly micas. Common parent rocks are shale, phyllite.
	Phyllite	Shiny or silky appearance. May look wrinkled. Common parent rocks are shale, slate.
	Slate	Harder, denser, and shinier than shale. Common parent rock is shale.
Metamorphic (non-foliated)	Marble	Interlocking calcite or dolomite crystals. Common parent rock is limestone.
	Soapstone	Composed mainly of the mineral talc. Soft with a greasy feel.
	Quartzite	Hard and well cemented with interlocking quartz crystals. Common parent rock is sandstone.

Topographic Map Symbols

Primary highway, hard surface	
Secondary highway, hard surface	
Light-duty road, hard or Improved surface	
Unimproved road	
Railroad: single track and multiple track	
Railroads in juxtaposition	
Buildings	
Schools, church, and cemetery	cem
Buildings (barn, warehouse, etc)	
Wells other than water (labeled as to type)	o oil o gas water
Tanks: oil, water, etc. (labeled only if water)	
Located or landmark object; windmill	
Open pit, mine, or quarry; prospect	

Marsh (swamp)	
Wooded marsh	
Woods or brushwood	
Vineyard	
Land subject to controlled inundation	
Submerged marsh	
Mangrove	
Orchard	
Scrub	
Urban area	

Spot elevation	×7369
Water elevation	670

Index contour	
Supplementary contour	
Intermediate contour	
Depression contours	
Boundaries: National	
State	
County, parish, municipal	
Civil township, precinct, town, barrio	
Incorporated city, village, town, hamlet	
Reservation, National or State	
Small park, cemetery, airport, etc.	
Land grant	
Township or range line, United States land survey	
Township or range line, approximate location	

Perennial streams	
Elevated aqueduct	
Water well and spring	o ⌒
Small rapids	
Large rapids	
Intermittent lake	
Intermittent streams	
Aqueduct tunnel	
Glacier	
Small falls	
Large falls	
Dry lake bed	

Appendix

I

Weather Map Symbols

Sample Plotted Report at Each Station

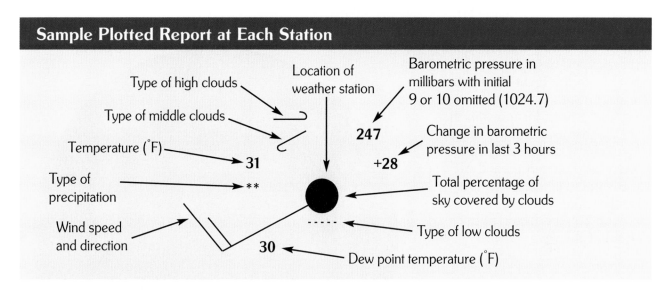

- Type of high clouds
- Type of middle clouds
- Temperature (°F) — **31**
- Type of precipitation — ******
- Wind speed and direction
- Location of weather station
- Barometric pressure in millibars with initial 9 or 10 omitted (1024.7) — **247**
- Change in barometric pressure in last 3 hours — **+28**
- Total percentage of sky covered by clouds
- Type of low clouds
- **30** — Dew point temperature (°F)

Sample Plotted Report at Each Station

Precipitation	Wind Speed and direction		Sky coverage		Some types of high clouds	
☰ Fog	○	0 knots; calm	○	No cover	⌐⊃	Scattered cirrus
★ Snow	/	1-2 knots	◒	1/10 or less		
● Rain	⌐	5-7 knots	◔	2/10 to 3/10	⊐⊃	Dense cirrus in patches
⊼ Thunderstorm	⌐	10-12 knots	◑	4/10		
	⌐	13-17 knots	◐	1/2	⌐ʗ	Veil of cirrus covering entire sky
	⌐	18-22 knots	◒	6/10		
' Drizzle	⌐	23-27 knots	◕	7/10	_ʗ	Cirrus not covering entire sky
▽ Showers	⌐	48-52 knots	◉	Overcast with openings		
	1 knot = 1.852 km/h		●	Complete overcast		

Some types of middle clouds		Some types of low clouds		Fronts and pressure systems	
∠	Thin altostratus layer	⌒	Cumulus of fair weather	(H) or High	Center of high-or
∥	Thick altostratus layer	⌄	Stratocumulus	(L) or Low	low-pressure system
⌒	Thin altostratus in patches	-----	Fractocumulus of bad weather	▲▲▲▲	Cold front
⌒	Thin altostratus in bands	—	Stratus of fair weather	●●●●	Warm Front
				▲▲▲	Occluded front
				▲●▲●	Stationary front

Appendix

J

Star Charts

Shown here are star charts for viewing stars in the northern hemisphere during the four different seasons. These charts are drawn from the night sky at about 35° north latitude, but they can be used for most locations in the northern hemisphere. The lines on the charts outline major constellations. The dense band of stars is the Milky Way. To use, hold the chart vertically, with the direction you are facing at the bottom of the map.

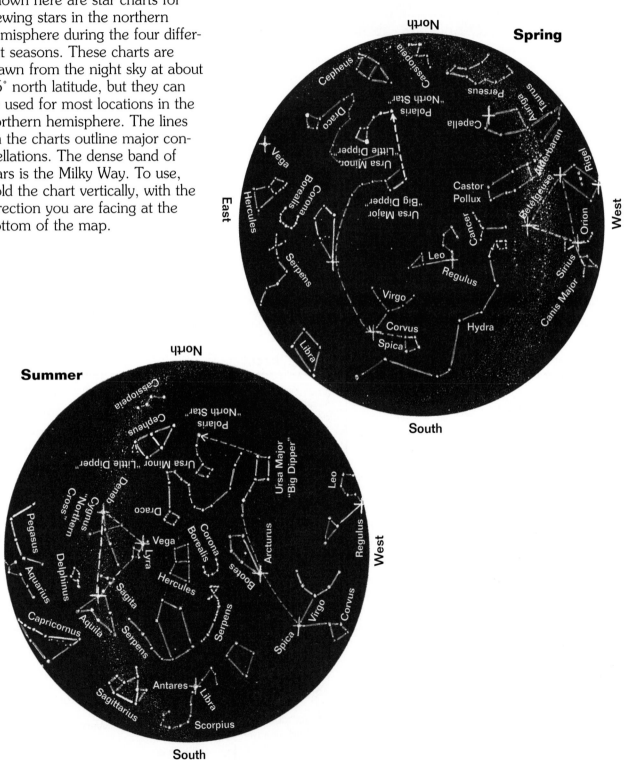

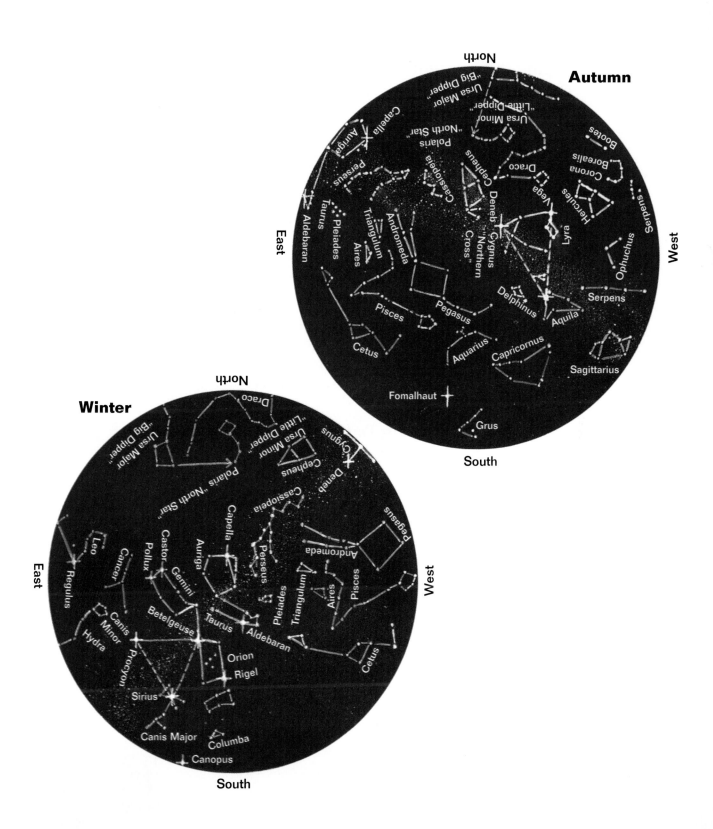

Skill Handbook

Table of Contents

Science Skill Handbook

Organizing Information

Communicating

The communication of ideas is an important part of our everyday lives. Whether reading a book, writing a letter, or watching a television program, people everywhere are expressing opinions and sharing information with one another. Writing in your Science Journal allows you to express your opinions and demonstrate your knowledge of the information presented on a subject. When writing, keep in mind the purpose of the assignment and the audience with which you are communicating.

Examples Science Journal assignments vary greatly. They may ask you to take a viewpoint other than your own; perhaps you will be a scientist, a TV reporter, or a committee member of a local environmental group. Maybe you will be expressing your opinions to a member of Congress, a doctor, or to the editor of your local newspaper, as shown in **Figure 1**. Sometimes, Science Journal writing may allow you to summarize information in the form of an outline, a letter, or in a paragraph.

Figure 1 A Science Journal entry

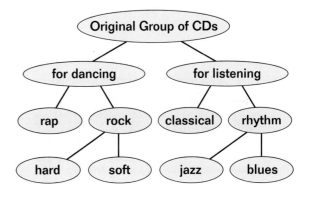

Figure 2 Classifying CDs

Classifying

You may not realize it, but you make things orderly in the world around you. If you hang your shirts together in the closet or if your favorite CDs are stacked together, you have used the skill of classifying.

Classifying is the process of sorting objects or events into groups based on common features. When classifying, first observe the objects or events to be classified. Then, select one feature that is shared by some members in the group, but not by all. Place those members that share that feature into a subgroup. You can classify members into smaller and smaller subgroups based on characteristics.

Remember, when you classify, you are grouping objects or events for a purpose. Keep your purpose in mind as you select the features to form groups and subgroups.

Example How would you classify a collection of CDs? As shown in **Figure 2**, you might classify those you like to dance to in one subgroup and CDs you like to listen to in the next subgroup. The CDs you like to dance to could be subdivided into a rap subgroup and a rock subgroup. Note that for each feature selected, each CD fits into only one subgroup. You would keep selecting features until all the CDs are classified. **Figure 2** shows one possible classification.

Figure 3 A recipe for bread contains sequenced instructions

Sequencing

A sequence is an arrangement of things or events in a particular order. When you are asked to sequence objects or events within a group, figure out what comes first, then think about what should come second. Continue to choose objects or events until all of the objects you started out with are in order. Then, go back over the sequence to make sure each thing or event in your sequence logically leads to the next.

Example A sequence with which you are most familiar is the use of alphabetical order. Another example of sequence would be the steps in a recipe, as shown in **Figure 3.** Think about baking bread. Steps in the recipe have to be followed in order for the bread to turn out right.

Concept Mapping

If you were taking an automobile trip, you would probably take along a road map. The road map shows your location, your destination, and other places along the way. By looking at the map and finding where you are, you can begin to understand where you are in relation to other locations on the map.

A concept map is similar to a road map. But, a concept map shows relationships among ideas (or concepts) rather than places. A concept map is a diagram that visually shows how concepts are related. Because the concept map shows relationships among ideas, it can make the meanings of ideas and terms clear, and help you understand better what you are studying.

There is usually not one correct way to create a concept map. As you construct one type of map, you may discover other ways to construct the map that show the

Figure 4 Network tree describing U.S. currency

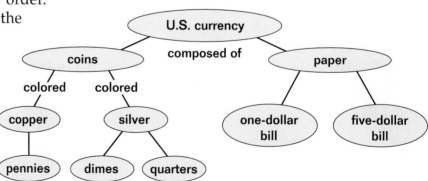

relationships between concepts in a better way. If you do discover what you think is a better way to create a concept map, go ahead and use the new one. Overall, concept maps are useful for breaking a big concept down into smaller parts, making learning easier.

Examples

Network Tree Look at the concept map about U.S. currency in **Figure 4.** This is called a network tree. Notice how some words are in ovals while others are written across connecting lines. The words inside the ovals are science concepts. The lines in the map show related concepts. The words written on the lines describe the relationships between concepts.

When you are asked to construct a network tree, write down the topic and list the major concepts related to that topic on a piece of paper. Then look at your list and begin to put them in order from general to specific. Branch the related concepts from the major concept and describe the relationships on the lines. Continue to write the more specific concepts. Write the relationships between the concepts on the lines until all concepts are mapped. Examine the concept map for relationships that cross branches, and add them to the concept map.

Events Chain An events chain is another type of concept map. An events chain map, such as the one describing a typical morning routine in **Figure 5,** is used to describe ideas in order. In science, an events chain can be used to describe a sequence of events, the steps in a procedure, or the stages of a process.

When making an events chain, first find the one event that starts the chain. This

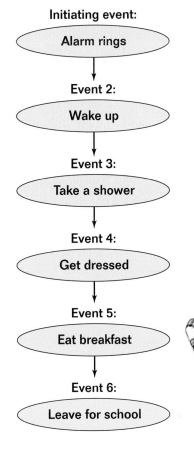

Figure 5 Events chain of a typical morning routine

event is called the initiating event. Then, find the next event in the chain and continue until you reach an outcome. Suppose you are asked to describe what happens when your alarm rings. An events chain map describing the steps might look like **Figure 5.** Notice that connecting words are not necessary in an events chain.

Science Skill Handbook

Cycle Map A cycle concept map is a special type of events chain map. In a cycle concept map, the series of events does not produce a final outcome. Instead, the last event in the chain relates back to the initiating event.

As in the events chain map, you first decide on an initiating event and then list each event in order. Because there is no outcome and the last event relates back to the initiating event, the cycle repeats itself. Look at the cycle map describing the relationship between day and night in **Figure 6.**

Figure 6 Cycle map of day and night.

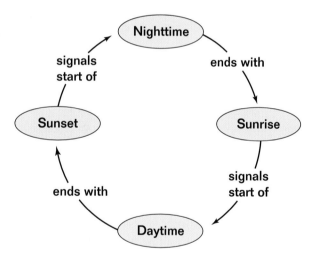

Spider Map A fourth type of concept map is the spider map. This is a map that you can use for brainstorming. Once you have a central idea, you may find you have a jumble of ideas that relate to it, but are not necessarily clearly related to each other. As illustrated by the homework spider map in **Figure 7,** by writing these ideas outside the main concept, you may begin to separate and group unrelated terms so that they become more useful.

Figure 7 Spider map about homework.

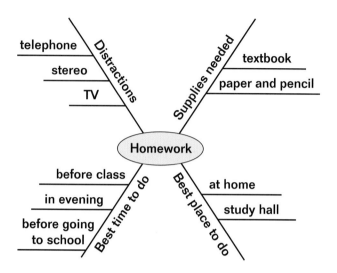

Making and Using Tables

Browse through your textbook and you will notice tables in the text and in the activities. In a table, data or information is arranged in a way that makes it easier for you to understand. Activity tables help organize the data you collect during an activity so that results can be interpreted.

Examples Most tables have a title. At a glance, the title tells you what the table is about. A table is divided into columns and rows. The first column lists items to be compared. In **Figure 8,** the collection of recyclable materials is being compared in a table. The row across the top lists the specific characteristics being compared. Within the grid of the table, the collected data are recorded.

What is the title of the table in **Figure 8?** The title is "Recycled Materials." What is being compared? The different materials being recycled and on which days they are recycled.

Making Tables To make a table, list the items to be compared down in columns and the characteristics to be compared across in rows. The table in

Science Skill Handbook

Figure 8 Table of recycled materials

Recycled Materials			
Day of Week	Paper (kg)	Aluminum (kg)	Plastic (kg)
Mon.	4.0	2.0	0.5
Wed.	3.5	1.5	0.5
Fri.	3.0	1.0	1.5

Figure 8 compares the mass of recycled materials collected by a class. On Monday, students turned in 4.0 kg of paper, 2.0 kg of aluminum, and 0.5 kg of plastic. On Wednesday, they turned in 3.5 kg of paper, 1.5 kg of aluminum, and 0.5 kg of plastic. On Friday, the totals were 3.0 kg of paper, 1.0 kg of aluminum, and 1.5 kg of plastic.

Using Tables How much plastic, in kilograms, is being recycled on Wednesday? Locate the column labeled "Plastic (kg)" and the row "Wed." The data in the box where the column and row intersect is the answer. Did you answer "0.5"? How much aluminum, in kilograms, is being recycled on Friday? If you answered "1.0," you understand how to use the parts of the table.

Making and Using Graphs

After scientists organize data in tables, they may display the data in a graph. A graph is a diagram that shows the relationship of one variable to another. A graph makes interpretation and analysis of data easier. There are three basic types of graphs used in science—the line graph, the bar graph, and the circle graph.

Examples

Line Graphs A line graph is used to show the relationship between two variables. The variables being compared go on two axes of the graph. The independent variable always goes on the horizontal axis, called the *x*-axis. The dependent variable always goes on the vertical axis, called the *y*-axis.

Suppose your class started to record the amount of materials they collected in one week for their school to recycle. The collected information is shown in **Figure 9.**

You could make a graph of the materials collected over the three days of the school week. The three weekdays are the independent variables and are placed on the *x*-axis of your graph. The amount of materials collected is the dependent variable and would go on the *y*-axis.

After drawing your axes, label each with a scale. The *x*-axis lists the three weekdays. To make a scale of the amount of materials collected on the *y*-axis, look at the data values. Because the lowest amount collected was 1.0 and the highest was 5.0, you will have to start numbering at least at 1.0 and go through 5.0. You decide to start numbering at 0 and number by ones through 6.0, as shown in **Figure 10.**

Next, plot the data points for collected paper. The first pair of data you want to plot is Monday and 5.0 kg of paper.

Figure 9 Amount of recyclable materials collected during one week

Materials Collected During Week		
Day of Week	Paper (kg)	Aluminum (kg)
Mon.	5.0	4.0
Wed.	4.0	1.0
Fri.	2.5	2.0

Science Skill Handbook

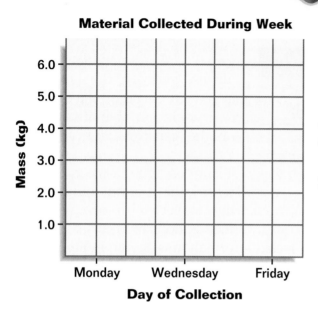

Material Collected During Week

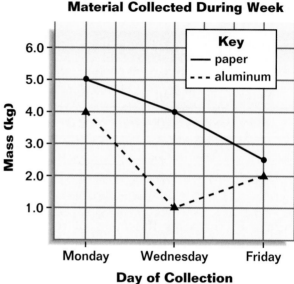

Material Collected During Week

Key
— paper
- - - aluminum

Figure 10 Graph outline for material collected during week

Figure 11 Line graph of materials collected during week

Locate "Monday" on the *x*-axis and locate "5.0" on the *y*-axis. Where an imaginary vertical line from the *x*-axis and an imaginary horizontal line from the *y*-axis would meet, place the first data point. Place the other data points the same way. After all the points are plotted, connect them with the best smooth curve. Repeat this procedure for the data points for aluminum. Use continuous and dashed lines to distinguish the two line graphs. The resulting graph should look like **Figure 11.**

Bar Graphs   Bar graphs are similar to line graphs. They compare data that do not continuously change. In a bar graph, vertical bars show the relationships among data.

To make a bar graph, set up the *x*-axis and *y*-axis as you did for the line graph. The data is plotted by drawing vertical bars from the *x*-axis up to a point where the *y*-axis would meet the bar if it were extended.

Look at the bar graph in **Figure 12** comparing the mass of aluminum collected

over three weekdays. The *x*-axis is the days on which the aluminum was collected. The *y*-axis is the mass of aluminum collected, in kilograms.

Circle Graphs   A circle graph uses a circle divided into sections to display data. Each section represents part of the whole. All the sections together equal 100 percent.

Suppose you wanted to make a circle graph to show the number of seeds that germinated in a package. You would count the total number of seeds. You find that there are 143 seeds in the package. This represents 100 percent, the whole circle.

You plant the seeds, and 129 seeds germinate. The seeds that germinated will make up one section of the circle graph, and the seeds that did not germinate will make up the remaining section.

To find out how much of the circle each section should take, divide the number of seeds in each section by the total number of seeds. Then, multiply your answer by 360, the number of degrees in a circle, and round to the nearest whole number. The

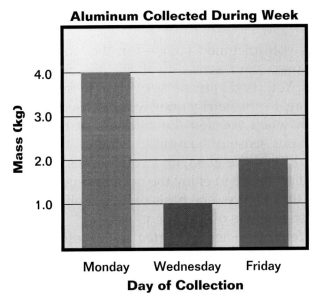

Aluminum Collected During Week

Mass (kg): 4.0, 3.0, 2.0, 1.0

Monday   Wednesday   Friday

Day of Collection

Figure 12 Bar graph of aluminum collected during week

section of the circle graph in degrees that represents the seeds germinated is figured below.

$$\frac{129}{143} \times 360 = 324.75 \text{ or } 325 \text{ degrees (or } 325°)$$

Plot this group on the circle graph using a compass and a protractor. Use the compass to draw a circle. It will be easier to

measure the part of the circle representing the non-germinating seeds, so subtract 325° from 360° to get 35°. Draw a straight line from the center to the edge of the circle. Place your protractor on this line and use it to mark a point at 325°. Use this point to draw a straight line from the center of the circle to the edge. This is the section for the group of seeds that did not germinate. The other section represents the group of 129 seeds that did germinate. Label the sections of your graph and title the graph as shown in **Figure 13.**

Figure 13 Circle graph of germinated seeds

Seeds Germinated

Not germinating (35°)

Germinating (325°)

Science Skill Handbook

Thinking Critically

Observing and Inferring

Observing Scientists try to make careful and accurate observations. When possible, they use instruments such as microscopes, thermometers, and balances to make observations. Measurements with a balance or thermometer provide numerical data that can be checked and repeated.

When you make observations in science, you'll find it helpful to examine the entire object or situation first. Then, look carefully for details. Write down everything you observe.

Example Imagine that you have just finished a volleyball game. At home, you open the refrigerator and see a jug of orange juice on the back of the top shelf. The jug, shown in **Figure 14,** feels cold as you grasp it. Then, you drink the juice, smell the oranges, and enjoy the tart taste in your mouth.

Figure 14 Why is this jug of orange juice cold?

As you imagined yourself in the story, you used your senses to make observations. You used your sense of sight to find the jug in the refrigerator, your sense of touch when you felt the coldness of the jug, your sense of hearing to listen as the liquid filled the glass, and your senses of smell and taste to enjoy the odor and tartness of the juice. The basis of all scientific investigation is observation.

Inferring Scientists often make inferences based on their observations. An inference is an attempt to explain or interpret observations or to say what caused what you observed.

When making an inference, be certain to use accurate data and observations. Analyze all of the data that you've collected. Then, based on everything you know, explain or interpret what you've observed.

Example When you drank a glass of orange juice after the volleyball game, you observed that the orange juice was cold as well as refreshing. You might infer that the juice was cold because it had been made much earlier in the day and had been kept in the refrigerator, or you might infer that it had just been made, using both cold water and ice. The only way to be sure which inference is correct is to investigate further.

Comparing and Contrasting

Observations can be analyzed by noting the similarities and differences between two or more objects or events that you observe. When you look at objects or events to see how they are similar, you are comparing them. Contrasting is looking for differences in similar objects or events.

Science Skill Handbook

Figure 15 Table comparing the nutritional value of *Cereal A* and *Cereal B*

Nutritional Value		
	Cereal A	**Cereal B**
Serving size	103 g	105 g
Calories	220	160
Total Fat	10 g	10 g
Protein	2.5 g	2.6 g
Total Carbohydrate	30 g	15 g

Example Suppose you were asked to compare and contrast the nutritional value of two kinds of cereal, *Cereal A* and *Cereal B*. You would start by looking at what is known about these cereals. Arrange this information in a table, like the one in **Figure 15**.

Similarities you might point out are that both cereals have similar serving sizes, amounts of total fat, and protein. Differences include *Cereal A* having a higher calorie value and containing more total carbohydrates than *Cereal B*.

Recognizing Cause and Effect

Have you ever watched something happen and then made suggestions about why it happened? If so, you have observed an effect and inferred a cause. The event is an effect, and the reason for the event is the cause.

Example Suppose that every time your teacher fed the fish in a classroom aquarium, she or he tapped the food container on the edge of the aquarium. Then, one day your teacher just happened to tap the edge of the aquarium with a pencil while making a point. You observed the fish swim to the surface of the aquarium to feed, as shown in **Figure 16**. What is the effect, and what would you infer to be the cause? The effect is the fish swimming to the surface of the aquarium. You might infer the cause to be the teacher tapping on the edge of the aquarium. In determining cause and effect, you have made a logical inference based on your observations.

Perhaps the fish swam to the surface because they reacted to the teacher's waving hand or for some other reason. When scientists are unsure of the cause of a certain event, they design controlled experiments to determine what causes the event. Although you have made a logical conclusion about the behavior of the fish, you would have to perform an experiment to be certain that it was the tapping that caused the effect you observed.

Figure 16 What cause-and-effect situations are occurring in this aquarium?

Science Skill Handbook

Practicing Scientific Processes

You might say that the work of a scientist is to solve problems. But when you decide how to dress on a particular day, you are doing problem solving, too. You may observe what the weather looks like through a window. You may go outside and see whether what you are wearing is heavy or light enough.

Scientists use an orderly approach to learn new information and to solve problems. The methods scientists may use include observing to form a hypothesis, designing an experiment to test a hypothesis, separating and controlling variables, and interpreting data.

Forming Operational Definitions

Operational definitions define an object by showing how it functions, works, or behaves. Such definitions are written in terms of how an object works or how it can be used; that is, what is its job or purpose?

Figure 17 What observations can be made about this dog?

Example Some operational definitions explain how an object can be used.
- A ruler is a tool that measures the size of an object.
- An automobile can move things from one place to another.

Or such a definition may explain how an object works.
- A ruler contains a series of marks that can be used as a standard when measuring.
- An automobile is a vehicle that can move from place to place.

Forming a Hypothesis

Observations You observe all the time. Scientists try to observe as much as possible about the things and events they study so they know that what they say about their observations is reliable.

Some observations describe something using only words. These observations are called qualitative observations. Other observations describe how much of something there is. These are quantitative observations and use numbers, as well as words, in the description. Tools or equipment are used to measure the characteristic being described.

Example If you were making qualitative observations of the dog in **Figure 17,** you might use words such as *furry, yellow,* and *short-haired.* Quantitative observations of this dog might include a mass of 14 kg, a height of 46 cm, ear length of 10 cm, and an age of 150 days.

Hypotheses Hypotheses are tested to help explain observations that have been made. They are often stated as *if* and *then* statements.

Examples Suppose you want to make a perfect score on a spelling test. Begin by thinking of several ways to accomplish this. Base these possibilities on past observations. If you put each of these possibilities into sentence form, using the words *if* and *then,* you can form a hypothesis. All of the following are hypotheses you might consider to explain how you could score 100 percent on your test:

If the test is easy, then I will get a perfect score.

If I am intelligent, then I will get a perfect score.

If I study hard, then I will get a perfect score.

Perhaps a scientist has observed that plants that receive fertilizer grow taller than plants that do not. A scientist may form a hypothesis that says: If plants are fertilized, then their growth will increase.

Designing an Experiment to Test a Hypothesis

In order to test a hypothesis, it's best to write out a procedure. A procedure is the plan that you follow in your experiment. A procedure tells you what materials to use and how to use them. After following the procedure, data are generated. From this generated data, you can then draw a conclusion and make a statement about your results.

If the conclusion you draw from the data supports your hypothesis, then you can say that your hypothesis is reliable. *Reliable* means that you can trust your conclusion. If it did not support your hypothesis, then you would have to make new observations and state a new hypothesis—just make sure that it is one that you can test.

Example Super premium gasoline costs more than regular gasoline. Does super premium gasoline increase the efficiency or fuel mileage of your family car? Let's figure out how to conduct an experiment to test the hypothesis, *"if* premium gas is more efficient, *then* it should increase the fuel mileage of our family car."* Then a procedure similar to **Figure 18** must be written to generate data presented in **Figure 19** on the next page.

These data show that premium gasoline is less efficient than regular gasoline. It took more gasoline to travel one mile (0.064) using premium gasoline than it does to travel one mile using regular gasoline (0.059). This conclusion does not support the original hypothesis made.

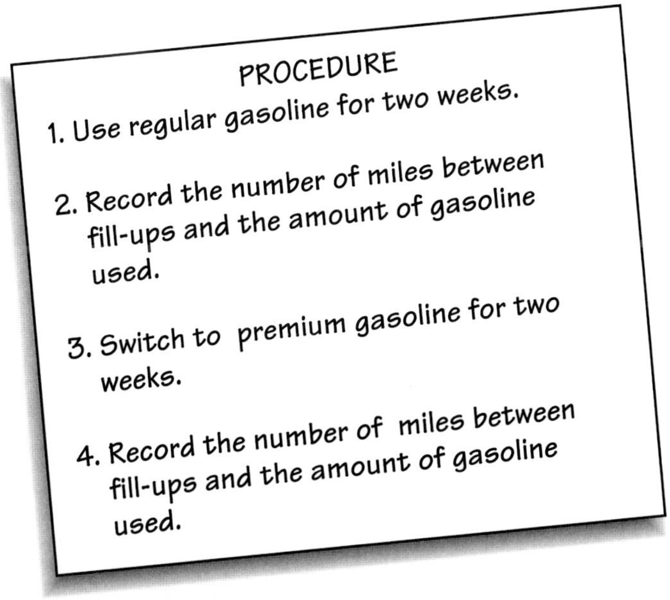

PROCEDURE

1. Use regular gasoline for two weeks.

2. Record the number of miles between fill-ups and the amount of gasoline used.

3. Switch to premium gasoline for two weeks.

4. Record the number of miles between fill-ups and the amount of gasoline used.

Figure 18 Possible procedural steps

Figure 19 Data generated from procedure steps

Gasoline Data			
	Miles traveled	Gallons used	Gallons per mile
Regular gasoline	762	45.34	0.059
Premium gasoline	661	42.30	0.064

Separating and Controlling Variables

In any experiment, it is important to keep everything the same except for the item you are testing. The one factor that you change is called the *independent variable.* The factor that changes as a result of the independent variable is called the *dependent variable.* Always make sure that there is only one independent variable. If you allow more than one, you will not know what causes the changes you observe in the independent variable. Many experiments have *controls*—a treatment or an experiment that you can compare with the results of your test groups.

Example In the experiment with the gasoline, you made everything the same except the type of gasoline being used. The driver, the type of automobile, and the weather conditions should remain the same throughout. The gasoline should also be purchased from the same service station. By doing so, you made sure that at the end of the experiment, any differences were the result of the type of fuel being used—regular or premium. The type of gasoline was the *independent factor* and the gas mileage achieved was the *dependent factor.* The use of regular gasoline was the *control.*

Interpreting Data

The word *interpret* means "to explain the meaning of something." Look at the problem originally being explored in the gasoline experiment and find out what the data show. Identify the control group and the test group so you can see whether or not the variable has had an effect. Then, you need to check differences between the control and test groups.

Figure 20 Which gasoline type is most efficient?

These differences may be qualitative or quantitative. A qualitative difference would be a difference that you could observe and describe, while a quantitative difference would be a difference you can measure using numbers. If there are differences, the variable being tested may have had an effect. If there is no difference between the control and the test groups, the variable being tested apparently has had no effect.

Example Perhaps you are looking at a table from an experiment designed to test the hypothesis: If premium gas is more efficient, then it should increase the fuel mileage of our family car. Look back at **Figure 19** showing the results of this experiment. In this example, the use of regular gasoline in the family car was the control, while the car being fueled by premium gasoline was the test group.

Data showed a quantitative difference in efficiency for gasoline consumption. It took 0.059 gallons of regular gasoline to travel one mile, while it took 0.064 gallons of the premium gasoline to travel the same distance. The regular gasoline was more efficient; it increased the fuel mileage of the family car.

What are data? In the experiment described on these pages, measurements were taken so that at the end of the experiment, you had something concrete to interpret. You had numbers to work with. Not every experiment that you do will give you data in the form of numbers. Sometimes, data will be in the form of a description. At the end of a chemistry experiment, you might have noted that

Figure 21

one solution turned yellow when treated with a particular chemical, and another remained colorless, as water, when treated with the same chemical. Data, therefore, are stated in different forms for different types of scientific experiments.

Are all experiments alike? Keep in mind as you perform experiments in science that not every experiment makes use of all of the parts that have been described on these pages. For some, it may be difficult to design an experiment that will always have a control. Other experiments are complex enough that it may be hard to have only one dependent variable. Real scientists encounter many variations in the methods that they use when they perform experiments. The skills in this handbook are here for you to use and practice. In real situations, their uses will vary.

Representing and Applying Data

Interpreting Scientific Illustrations

As you read a science textbook, you will see many drawings, diagrams, and photographs. Illustrations help you to understand what you read. Some illustrations are included to help you understand an idea that you can't see easily by yourself. For instance, we can't see atoms, but we can look at a diagram of an atom and that helps us to understand some things about atoms. Seeing something often helps you remember more easily. Illustrations also provide examples that clarify difficult concepts or give additional information about the topic you are studying. Maps, for example, help you to locate places that may be described in the text.

Examples

Captions and Labels Most illustrations have captions. A caption is a comment that identifies or explains the illustration. Diagrams, such as **Figure 22,** often have

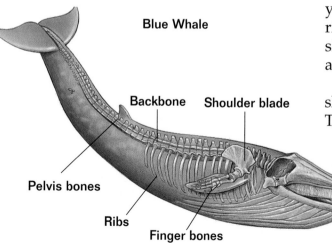

Figure 22 A labeled diagram of a blue whale

Blue Whale

Backbone Shoulder blade

Pelvis bones

Ribs

Finger bones

Figure 23 The orientation of a dog is shown here.

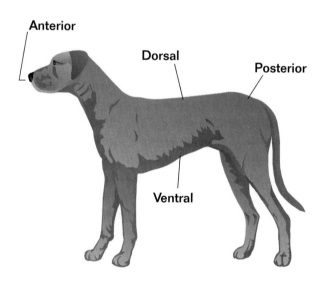

Anterior

Dorsal

Posterior

Ventral

labels that identify parts of the organism or the order of steps in a process.

Learning with Illustrations An illustration of an organism shows that organism from a particular view or orientation. In order to understand the illustration, you may need to identify the front (anterior) end, tail (posterior) end, the underside (ventral), and the back (dorsal) side, as shown in **Figure 23.**

You might also check for symmetry. A shark in **Figure 24** has bilateral symmetry. This means that drawing an imaginary line through the center of the animal from the anterior to posterior end forms two mirror images.

Radial symmetry is the arrangement of similar parts around a central point. An object or organism, such as a hydra, can be divided anywhere through the center into similar parts.

Some organisms and objects cannot be divided into two similar parts. If an

Science Skill Handbook

Figure 24 A shark (A) illustrating bilateral symmetry and a pear (B) illustrating a longitudinal section and a cross section

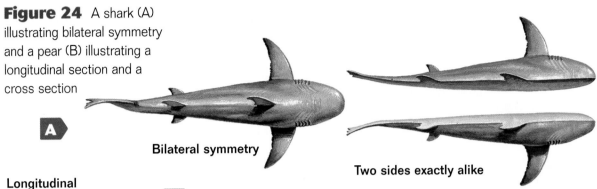

Bilateral symmetry

Two sides exactly alike

Longitudinal section

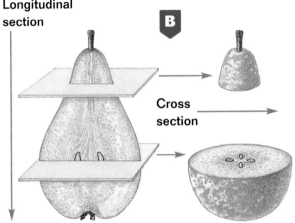

Cross section

organism or object cannot be divided, it is asymmetrical. Regardless of how you try to divide a natural sponge, you cannot divide it into two parts that look alike.

Some illustrations enable you to see the inside of an organism or object. These illustrations are called sections. **Figure 24** also illustrates some common sections.

Look at all illustrations carefully. Read captions and labels so that you understand exactly what the illustration is showing you.

Making Models

Have you ever worked on a model car, plane, or rocket? These models look, and sometimes work, much like the real thing, but they are often on a different scale than the real thing. In science, models are used to help simplify large or small processes or structures that otherwise would be dif-

ficult to see and understand. Your understanding of a structure or process is enhanced when you work with materials to make a model that shows the basic features of the structure or process.

Example In order to make a model, you first have to get a basic idea about the structure or process involved. You decide to make a model to show the differences in size of arteries, veins, and capillaries. First, read about these structures. All three are hollow tubes. Arteries are round and thick. Veins are flat and have thinner walls than arteries. Capillaries are small.

Now, decide what you can use for your model. Common materials are often most useful and cheapest to work with when making models. As illustrated in **Figure 25** on the next page, different kinds and sizes of pasta might work for these models. Different sizes of rubber tubing might do just as well. Cut and glue the different noodles or tubing onto thick paper so the openings can be seen. Then label each. Now you have a simple, easy-to-understand model showing the differences in size of arteries, veins, and capillaries.

What other scientific ideas might a model help you to understand? A model of a molecule can be made from balls of modeling clay (using different colors for the different elements present) and toothpicks (to show different chemical bonds).

Figure 25 Different types of pasta may be used to model blood vessels

A working model of a volcano can be made from clay, a small amount of baking soda, vinegar, and a bottle cap. Other models can be devised on a computer. Some models are mathematical and are represented by equations.

Measuring in SI

The metric system is a system of measurement developed by a group of scientists in 1795. It helps scientists avoid problems by providing standard measurements that all scientists around the world can understand. A modern form of the metric system, called the International System, or SI, was adopted for worldwide use in 1960.

The metric system is convenient because unit sizes vary by multiples of 10. When changing from smaller units to larger units, divide by 10. When changing

from larger units to smaller, multiply by 10. For example, to convert millimeters to centimeters, divide the millimeters by 10. To convert 30 millimeters to centimeters, divide 30 by 10 (30 millimeters equal 3 centimeters).

Prefixes are used to name units. Look at **Figure 26** for some common metric prefixes and their meanings. Do you see how the prefix *kilo-* attached to the unit *gram* is *kilogram,* or 1000 grams? The prefix *deci-* attached to the unit *meter* is *decimeter,* or one-tenth (0.1) of a meter.

Examples

Length You have probably measured lengths or distances many times. The meter is the SI unit used to measure length. A baseball bat is about one meter long. When measuring smaller lengths, the meter is divided into smaller units called centimeters and millimeters. A centimeter is one-hundredth (0.01) of a meter, which is about the size of the width of the fingernail on your ring finger. A millimeter is one-thousandth of a meter (0.001), about the thickness of a dime.

Most metric rulers have lines indicating centimeters and millimeters, as shown in

Figure 26 Common metric prefixes

Metric Prefixes			
Prefix	Symbol	Meaning	
kilo-	k	1000	thousand
hecto-	h	100	hundred
deca-	da	10	ten
deci-	d	0.1	tenth
centi-	c	0.01	hundredth
milli-	m	0.001	thousandth

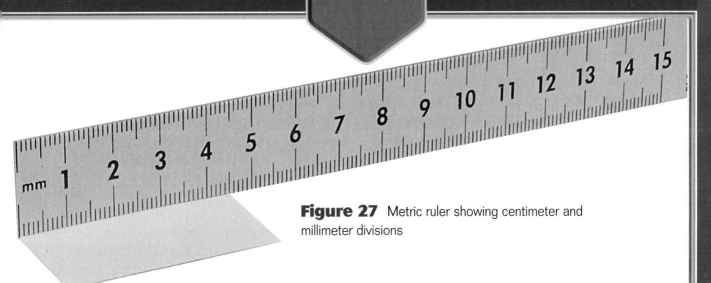

Figure 27 Metric ruler showing centimeter and millimeter divisions

Figure 27. The centimeter lines are the longer, numbered lines; the shorter lines are millimeter lines. When using a metric ruler, line up the 0-centimeter mark with the end of the object being measured, and read the number of the unit where the object ends, in this instance 4.5 cm.

Surface Area Units of length are also used to measure surface area. The standard unit of area is the square meter (m^2). A square that's one meter long on each side has a surface area of one square meter. Similarly, a square centimeter, (cm^2), shown in **Figure 28,** is one centimeter long on each side. The surface area of an object is determined by multiplying the length times the width.

Volume The volume of a rectangular solid is also calculated using units of length. The cubic meter (m^3) is the standard SI unit of volume. A cubic meter is a cube one meter on each side. You can determine the volume of rectangular solids by multiplying length times width times height.

Liquid Volume During science activities, you will measure liquids using beakers and graduated cylinders marked in milliliters, as illustrated in **Figure 29.** A graduated cylinder is a cylindrical container marked with lines from bottom to top.

Liquid volume is measured using a unit called a liter. A liter has the volume of 1000 cubic centimeters. Because the prefix *milli-* means thousandth (0.001), a milliliter equals one cubic centimeter. One milliliter of liquid would completely fill a cube measuring one centimeter on each side.

Figure 29 A volume of 79 mL is measured by reading at the lowest point of the curve.

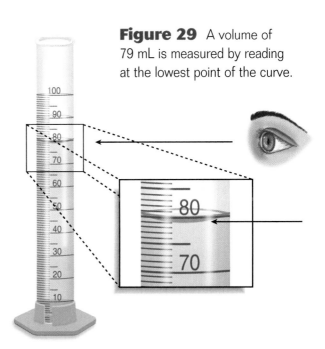

Figure 28 A square centimeter

1 cm

1 cm

Mass Scientists use balances to find the mass of objects in grams. You might use a beam balance similar to **Figure 30.** Notice that on one side of the balance is a pan and on the other side is a set of beams. Each beam has an object of a known mass called a *rider* that slides on the beam.

Before you find the mass of an object, set the balance to zero by sliding all the riders back to the zero point. Check the pointer on the right to make sure it swings an equal distance above and below the zero point on the scale. If the swing is unequal, find and turn the adjusting screw until you have an equal swing.

Place an object on the pan. Slide the rider with the largest mass along its beam until the pointer drops below zero. Then move it back one notch. Repeat the process on each beam until the pointer swings an equal distance above and below the zero point. Add the masses on each beam to find the mass of the object.

You should never place a hot object or pour chemicals directly onto the pan. Instead, find the mass of a clean beaker or a glass jar. Place the dry or liquid chemicals in the container. Then find the combined mass of the container and the chemicals. Calculate the mass of the chemicals by subtracting the mass of the empty container from the combined mass.

Predicting

When you apply a hypothesis, or general explanation, to a specific situation, you predict something about that situation. First, you must identify which hypothesis fits the situation you are considering.

Examples People use prediction to make everyday decisions. Based on previous observations and experiences, you may form a hypothesis that if it is wintertime, then temperatures will be lower. From past experience in your area, temperatures are lowest in February. You may then use this hypothesis to predict specific temperatures and weather for the month of February in advance. Someone could use these predictions to plan to set aside more money for heating bills during that month.

Figure 30 A beam balance is used to measure mass.

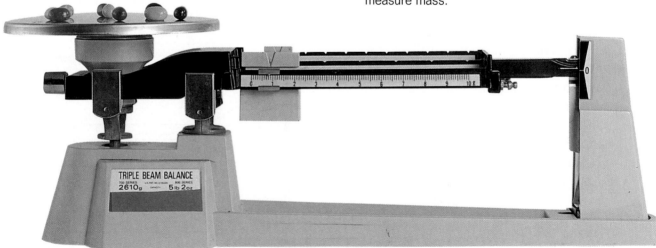

Using Numbers

When working with large populations of organisms, scientists usually cannot observe or study every organism in the population. Instead, they use a sample or a portion of the population. To sample is to take a small representative portion of organisms of a population for research. By making careful observations or manipulating variables within a portion of a group, information is discovered and conclusions are drawn that might then be applied to the whole population.

Scientific work also involves estimating. To estimate is to make a judgment about the size of something or the number of something without actually measuring or counting every member of a population.

Examples Suppose you are trying to determine the effect of a specific nutrient on the growth of black-eyed Susans. It would be impossible to test the entire population of black-eyed Susans, so you would select part of the population for your experiment. Through careful experimentation and observation on a sample of the population, you could generalize the effect of the chemical on the entire population.

Here is a more familiar example. Have you ever tried to guess how many beans were in a sealed jar? If you

did, you were estimating. What if you knew the jar of beans held one liter (1000 mL)? If you knew that 30 beans would fit in a 100-milliliter jar, how many beans would you estimate to be in the one-liter jar? If you said about 300 beans, your estimate would be close to the actual number of beans. Can you estimate how many jelly beans are on the cookie sheet in **Figure 31?**

Scientists use a similar process to estimate populations of organisms from bacteria to buffalo. Scientists count the actual number of organisms in a small sample and then estimate the number of organisms in a larger area. For example, if a scientist wanted to count the number of bacterial colonies in a petri dish, a microscope could be used to count the number of organisms in a one-square-centimeter sample. To determine the total population of the culture, the number of organisms in the square-centimeter sample is multiplied by the total number of square centimeters in the culture.

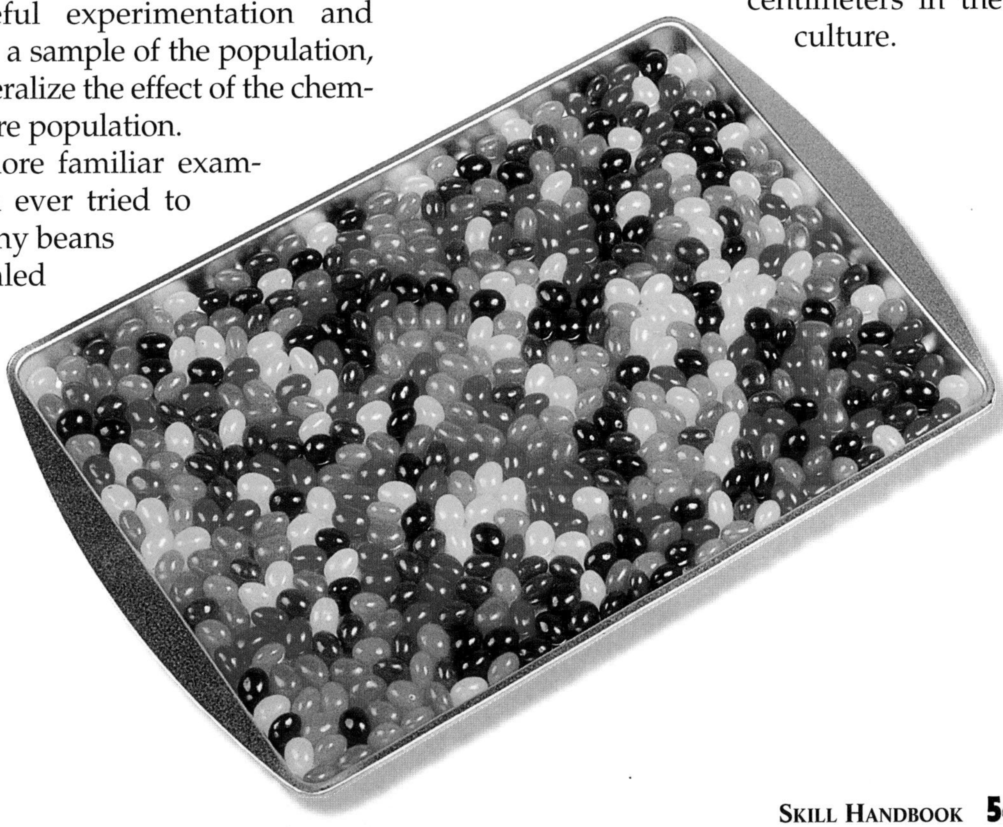

Figure 31
Sampling a group of jelly beans allows for an estimation of the total number of jelly beans in the group.

Using a Word Processor

Suppose your teacher has assigned you to write a report. After you've done your research and decided how you want to write the information, you need to put all that information on paper. The easiest way to do this is with a word processor.

A word processor is a computer program in which you can write your information, change it as many times as you need to, and then print it out so that it looks neat and clean. You can also use a word processor to create tables and columns, add bullets or cartoon art, include page numbers, and even check your spelling.

Example Last week in Science class, your teacher assigned a report on the history of the atom. It has to be double spaced and include at least one table. You've collected all the facts, and you're ready to write your report. Sitting down at your computer, you decide you want to begin by explaining early scientific ideas about the atom and then talk about what scientists think about the atom now.

After you've written the two parts of your report, you decide to put a heading or subtitle above each part and add a title to the paper. To make each of these look different from the rest of your report, you can use a word processor to make the words bigger and bolder. The word processor also can double space your entire report, so that you don't have to add an extra space between each line.

You decide to include a table that lists each scientist that contributed to the theory of the atom along with his or her contribution. Using your word processor, you can create a table with as many rows and columns as you need. And, if you forget to include a scientist in the middle, you can go back and insert a row in the middle of your table without redoing the entire table.

When you've finished with your report, you can tell the word processor to check your spelling. If it finds misspelled words, it often will suggest a word you can use to replace the misspelled word. But, remember that the word processor may not know how to spell all the words in your report. Scan your report and double check your spelling with a dictionary if you're not sure if a word is spelled correctly.

After you've made sure that your report looks just the way you want it on the screen, the word processor will print your report on a printer. With a word processor, your report can look like it was written by a real scientist.

Helpful Hints

- If you aren't sure how to do something using your word processor, look under the help menu. You can look up how to do something, and the word processor will tell you how to do it. Just follow the instructions that the word processor puts on your screen.

- Just because you've spelled checked your report doesn't mean that the spelling is perfect. The spell check can't catch misspelled words that look like other words. So, if you've accidentally typed *mind* instead of *mine,* the spell checker won't know the difference. Always reread your report to make sure you didn't miss any mistakes.

Technology Skill Handbook

Using a Database

Imagine you're in the middle of research project. You are busily gathering facts and information. But, soon you realize that its becoming harder and harder to organize and keep track of all the information. The tool to solve "information overload" is a database. A database is exactly what it sounds like—a base on which to organize data. Similar to how a file cabinet organizes records, a database also organizes records. However, a database is more powerful than a simple file cabinet because at the click of a mouse, the entire contents can be reshuffled and reorganized. At computer-quick speeds, databases can sort information by any characteristic and filter data into multiple categories. Once you use a database, you will be amazed at how quickly all those facts and bits of information become manageable.

Example For the past few weeks, you have been gathering information on living and extinct primates. A database would be ideal to organize your information. An entry for gorillas might contain fields (categories) for fossil locations, brain size, average height, earliest fossil, and so on. Later on, if you wanted to know which primates have been found in Asia, you could quickly filter all entries using Asia in the field that listed locations. The database will scan all the entries and select the entries containing Asia. If you wanted to rank all the primates by arm length, you would sort all the entries by arm length. By using different combinations of sorting and filtering, you can discover relationships between the data that otherwise might remain hidden.

Helpful Hints

- Before setting up your own database, it's easier to learn the features of your database software by practicing with an established database.
- Entering the data into a database can be time consuming. Learn shortcuts such as tabbing between entry fields and automatic formatting of data that your software may provide.
- Get in the habit of periodically saving your database as you are entering data. That way, if something happens and your computer locks up or the power goes out, you won't lose all of your work. Most databases have specific words you can use to narrow your search.
- AND: If you place an AND between two words in your search, the database will look for any entries that have both the words. For example, "blood AND cell" would give you information about both blood and cells.
- OR: If you place an OR between two words, the database will show entries that have at least one of the words. For example, "bird OR fish" would show you information on either birds or fish.
- NOT: If you place a NOT between two words, the database will look for entries that have the first word but do not have the second word. For example, "reproduction NOT plant" would show you information about reproduction but not about plant reproduction.

Technology Skill Handbook

Using Graphics Software

Having trouble finding that exact piece of art you're looking for? Do you have a picture in your mind of what you want but can't seem to find the right graphic to represent your ideas? To solve these problems, you can use graphics software. Graphics software allows you to change and create images and diagrams in almost unlimited ways. Typical uses for graphics software include arranging clip-art, changing scanned images, and constructing pictures from scratch. Most graphics-software applications work in similar ways. They use the same basic tools and functions. Once you master one graphics application, you can use any other graphics application relatively easily.

Example For your report on bird adaptations, you want to make a poster displaying a variety of beak and foot types. You have acquired many photos of birds, scanned from magazines and downloaded off the Internet. Using graphics software, you separate the beaks and feet from the birds and enlarge them. Then, you use arrows and text to diagram the particular features that you want to highlight. You also highlight the key features in color, keeping the rest of the graphic in black and white. With graphics software, the possibilities are endless. For the final layout, you place the picture of the bird next to enlarged graphics of the feet and beak. Graphics software allows you to integrate text into your diagrams, which makes your bird poster look clean and professional.

Helpful Hints

- As with any method of drawing, the more you practice using the graphic software, the better your results.

- Start by using the software to manipulate existing drawings. Once you master this, making your own illustrations will be easier.
- Clip art is available on CD-ROMs, and on the Internet. With these resources, finding a piece of clip art to suit your purposes is simple.
- As you work on a drawing, save it often.
- Often you can learn a lot from studying other people's art. Look at other computer illustrations and try to figure out how the artist created it.

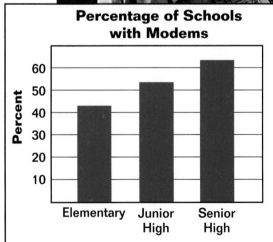

Percentage of Schools with Modems

Using a Computerized Card Catalog

When you have a report or paper to research, you go to the library. To find the information, skill is needed in using a computerized card catalog. You use the computerized card catalog by typing in a subject, the title of a book, or an author's name. The computer will list on the screen all the holdings the library has on the subject, title, or author requested.

A library's holdings include books, magazines, databases, videos, and audio materials. When you have chosen something from this list, the computer will show whether an item is available and where in the library to find it.

Example You have a report due on dinosaurs, and you need to find three books on the subject. In the library, follow the instructions on the computer screen to select the "Subject" heading. You could start by typing in the word *dinosaurs.* This will give you a list of books on that subject. Now you need to narrow your search to the kind of dinosaur you are interested in, for example, *Tyrannosaurus rex.* You can type in *Tyrannosaurus rex* or just look through the list to find titles that you think would have information you need. Once you have selected a short list of books, click on each selection to find out if the library has the books. Then, check on where they are located in the library.

Helpful Hints

- Remember that you can use the computer to search by subject, author, or title. If you know a book's author, but not the title, you can search for all the books the library has by that author.

- When searching by subject, it's often most helpful to narrow your search by using specific search terms. If you don't find enough, you can then broaden your search.

- Pay attention to the type of materials found in your search. If you need a book, you can eliminate any videos or other resources that come up in your search.

- Knowing how your library is arranged can save a lot of time. The librarian will show you where certain types of material are kept and how to find something.

Developing Multimedia Presentations

It's your turn—you have to present your science report to the entire class. How do you do it? You can use many different sources of information to get the class excited about your presentation. Posters, videos, photographs, sound, computers, and the Internet can help show our ideas. First, decide the most important points you want your presentation to make. Then, sketch out what materials and types of media would be best to illustrate those points. Maybe you could start with an outline on an overhead projector, then show a video, followed by something from the Internet or a slide show accompanied by music or recorded voices. Make sure you don't make the presentation too complicated, or you will confuse yourself and the class. Practice your presentation a few times for your parents or brothers and sisters before you present it to the class.

Example Your assignment is to give a presentation on bird-watching. You could have a poster that shows what features you use to identify birds, with a sketch of your favorite bird. A tape of the calls of your favorite bird or a video of birds in your area would work well with the poster. If possible, include an Internet site with illustrations of birds that the class can look at.

Helpful Hints

- Carefully consider what media will best communicate the point you are trying to make.
- Keep your topic and your presentation simple.
- Make sure you learn how to use any equipment you will be using in your presentation.
- Practice the presentation several times.
- If possible, set up all of the equipment ahead of time. Make sure everything is working correctly.

Technology Skill Handbook

Using E-Mail

It's science fair time and you want to ask a scientist a question about your project, but he or she lives far away. You could write a letter or make a phone call. But you can also use the computer to communicate. You can do this using electronic mail (E-mail). You will need a computer that is connected to an E-mail network. The computer is usually hooked up to the network by a device called a *modem*. A modem works through the telephone lines. Finally, you need an address for the person you want to talk with. The E-mail address works just like a street address to send mail to that person.

Example There are just a few steps needed to send a message to a friend on an E-mail network. First, select Message from the E-mail software menu. Then, enter the E-mail address of your friend. Next, type your message. Make sure you

check it for spelling and other errors. Finally, click the Send button to mail your message and off it goes! You will get a reply back in your electronic mailbox. To read your reply, just click on the message and the reply will appear on the screen.

Helpful Hints

- Make sure that you have entered the correct address of the person you're sending the message to.
- Reread your message to make sure it says what you want to say, and check for spelling and grammar.
- If you receive an E-mail message, respond to it as soon as possible.
- If you receive frequent email messages, keep them organized by either deleting them, or saving them in folders according to the subject or sender.

Technology Skill Handbook

Using an Electronic Spreadsheet

Your science fair experiment has produced lots of numbers. How do you keep track of all the data, and how can you easily work out all the calculations needed? You can use a computer program called a *spreadsheet* to keep track of data that involve numbers. A spreadsheet is an electronic worksheet. Type in your data in rows and columns, just as in a data table on a sheet of paper. A spreadsheet uses some simple math to do calculations on the data. For example, you could add, subtract, divide, or multiply any of the values in the spreadsheet by another number. Or you can set up a series of math steps you want to apply to the data. If you want to add 12 to all the numbers and then multiply all the numbers by 10, the computer does all the calculations for you in the spreadsheet. Below is an example of a spreadsheet that is a schedule.

Example Let's say that to complete your project, you need to calculate the speed of the model cars in your experiment. Enter the distance traveled by each car in the rows of the spreadsheet. Then enter the time you recorded for each car to travel the measured distance in the column across from each car. To make the formula, just type in the equation you want the computer to calculate; in this case, *speed = distance ÷ time*. You must make sure the computer knows what data are in the rows and what data are in the

columns so the calculation will be correct. Once all the distance and time data and the formula have been entered into the spreadsheet program, the computer will calculate the speed for all the trials you ran. You can even make graphs of the results.

Helpful Hints
- Before you set up the spreadsheet, sketch out how you want to organize the data. Include any formulas you will need to use.
- Make sure you have entered the correct data into the correct rows and columns.
- As you experiment with your particular spreadsheet program you will learn more of its features.
- You can also display your results in a graph. Pick the style of graph that best represents the data you are working with.

Test Run Data

	A	B	C	D
1	Test Runs	Time	Distance	Speed
2	Car 1	5 mins.	5 miles	60 mph
3	Car 2	10 mins.	4 miles	24 mph
4	Car 3	6 mins.	3 miles	30 mph
5				
6				
7				
8				
9				
10				
11				
12				
13				
14				

Technology Skill Handbook

Using a CD-ROM

What's your favorite music? You probably listen to your favorite music on compact discs (CDs). But, there is another use for compact discs, called CD-ROM. CD-ROM means Compact Disc-Read Only Memory. CD-ROMs hold information. Whole encyclopedias and dictionaries can be stored on CD-ROM discs. This kind of CD-ROM and others are used to research information for reports and papers. The information is accessed by putting the disc in your computer's CD-ROM drive and following the computer's installation instructions. The CD-ROM will have words, pictures, photographs, and maybe even sound and video on a range of topics.

Example Load the CD-ROM into the computer. Find the topic you are interested in by clicking on the Search button. If there is no Search button, try the Help button. Most CD-ROMs are easy to use, but refer to the Help instructions if you have problems. Use the arrow keys to move down through the list of titles on your topic. When you double-click on a title, the article will appear on the screen. You can print the article by clicking on the Print button. Each CD-ROM is different. Click the Help menu to see how to find what you want.

Helpful Hints

- Always open and close the CD-ROM drive on your computer by pushing the button next to the drive. Pushing on the tray to close it will stress the opening mechanism over time.
- Place the disc in the tray so the side with no printing is facing down.
- Read through the installation instructions that come with the CD-ROM.
- Remember to remove the CD-ROM before you shut your computer down.

Using Probeware

Data collecting in an experiment sometimes requires that you take the same measurement over and over again. With probeware, you can hook a probe directly to a computer and have the computer collect the data about temperature, pressure, motion, or pH. Probeware is a combination sensor and software that makes the process of collecting data easier. With probes hooked to computers, you can make many measurements quickly, and you can collect data over a long period of time without needing to be present. Not only will the software record the data, most software will graph the data.

Example Suppose you want to monitor the health of an enclosed ecosystem. You might use an oxygen and a carbon dioxide sensor to monitor the gas concentrations or humidity or temperature. If the gas concentrations remain stable, you could predict that the ecosystem is healthy. After all the data is collected, you can use the software to graph the data and analyze it. With probeware, experimenting is made efficient and precise.

Helpful Hints

- Find out how to properly use each probe before using it.
- Make sure all cables are solidly connected. A loose cable can interrupt the data collection and give you inaccurate results.
- Because probeware makes data collection so easy, do as many trials as possible to strengthen your data.

Technology Skill Handbook

Using a Graphing Calculator

Science can be thought of as a means to predict the future and explain the past. In other language, if *x* happens, can we predict *y*? Can we explain the reason *y* happened? Simply, is there a relationship between *x* and *y*? In nature, a relationship between two events or two quantities, *x* and *y*, often occurs. However, the relationship is often complicated and can only be readily seen by making a graph. To analyze a graph, there is no quicker tool than a graphing calculator. The graphing calculator shows the mathematical relationship between two quantities.

Example If you have collected data on the position and time for a migrating whale, you can use the calculator to graph the data. Using the linear regression function on the calculator, you can determine the average migration speed of the whale. The more you use the graphing calculator to solve problems, the more you will discover its power and efficiency.

Graphing calculators have some keys that other calculators do not have. The keys on the bottom half of the calculator are those found on all scientific calculators. The keys located just below the screen are the graphing keys. You will also notice the up, down, left, and right arrow keys. These allow you to move the cursor around on the screen, to "trace" graphs that have been plotted, and to choose items from the menus. The other keys located on the top of the calculator access the special features such as statistical computations and programming features.

A few of the keystrokes that can save you time when using the graphing calculator are listed below.

- The commands above the calculator keys are accessed with the [2nd] or [ALPHA] key. The [2nd] key and its commands are yellow and the [ALPHA] and its commands are green.
- [2nd] [ENTRY] copies the previous calculation so you can edit and use it again.
- Pressing [ON] while the calculator is graphing stops the calculator from completing the graph.
- [2nd] [QUIT] will return you to the home (or text) screen.
- [2nd] [A-LOCK] locks the [ALPHA] key, which is like pressing "shift lock" or "caps lock" on a typewriter or computer. The result is that all letters will be typed and you do not have to repeatedly press the [ALPHA] key. (This is handy for programming.) Stop typing letters by pressing [ALPHA] again.
- [2nd] [OFF] turns the calculator off.

Helpful Hints
- Mastering the graphing calculator takes practice. Don't expect to learn it all in an afternoon.
- Programming a graphing calculator takes a plan. Write out all of the steps before entering them.
- It's easiest to learn how to program the calculator by first using programs that have already been written. As you enter them, figure out what each step is telling the calculator to do.

Skill Activities

Table of Contents

Sequencing

Background

A complex project, such as a crewed mission to Mars, requires a great deal of planning over many years. The sequence of the plan is important because many of the steps cannot be done until a previous item is completed. The people responsible for the project have an overall planning sequence required for a crewed mission to Mars.

One of the recent ideas for a Mars mission involves building a spacecraft at a space station orbiting Earth. A space shuttle would ferry materials and people between Earth's surface and the space station. Then, the astronauts would travel in the spacecraft to Mars and return again to the space station.

Procedure

1. Read through the steps, which are out of order, listed in the table for a crewed mission to Mars.

2. Decide in what order the steps need to be completed.

3. On a separate sheet of paper, list the letters of the steps in what you consider to be the most logical sequence.

Steps for a Mission to Mars	
a. Plan second Mars mission	**k.** Estimate cost of mission
b. Spacecraft leaves Mars orbit for Earth	**l.** Spacecraft leaves Earth orbit for Mars
c. Study Mars data and samples	**m.** Astronauts explore Mars
d. Space shuttle meets returning spacecraft	**n.** Construct spacecraft
e. Mars Rover returns to spacecraft	**o.** Design spacecraft
f. Spacecraft enters orbit around Earth	**p.** Select astronauts
g. Make any necessary course adjustments	**q.** Astronauts receive hero's welcome
h. Select a company to build spacecraft	**r.** Space shuttle carries astronauts to Earth
i. Astronauts send television viewers greetings from Mars	**s.** Space shuttle carries astronauts to space station
j. Study future positions of Earth and Mars and select launch date	**t.** Space shuttle carries building materials into orbit

Practicing the SKILL

1. This mission plan is very brief and some details are left out. A real plan for a Mars mission would be many, many pages long. Read over your plan sequence. Add at least three more details to your plan and indicate where they should be placed in the sequence.

2. Think about how you would go about planting a vegetable or flower garden. Write down in the most logical sequence the steps you would take to plant a garden.

For more skill practice, do the Chapter 1 Interactive Exploration on the **Science Voyages Level Blue CD-ROM.**

GLENCOE TECHNOLOGY

Observing and Inferring

Background

Suppose you smell a cinnamon-like scent. You might suspect someone nearby is baking cinnamon rolls. However, you might be wrong. The scent might be from candy or a kind of air freshener. You cannot be sure unless you actually see the source of the scent. Whenever you use your senses, you are making *observations* about the world around you. When you make a conclusion based on what you observe, you are making an *inference.* When you smell a scent and conclude that the scent is from a cinnamon roll, you are *inferring.*

Scientists use their senses to make observations. Based on what they observe, they make inferences. The inferences help them solve problems and predict future events. You can make observations and inferences about almost anything. Try improving your observing skills by looking carefully at an object. A visual observation should be made in an orderly way. First, look at the entire object. Then, look at its parts.

Procedure

1. Observe **Figure A** carefully. Write down your observations on a separate paper.

2. Did you notice (1) the color of the candle, (2) the blackened wick, (3) the melted wax on the candle and in the holder, and (4) the color of the holder?

3. Now, try making inferences based on what you observed in **Figure A.** You can base your observations on your own experience with candles. You might infer (1) how long the candle was lit (based on the amount of melted wax), (2) how much of the candle has melted, or

(3) why the candle is not burning now. Inferences are based on incomplete information. Therefore, they may be incorrect. The flame may have been lit for only a short time, for example.

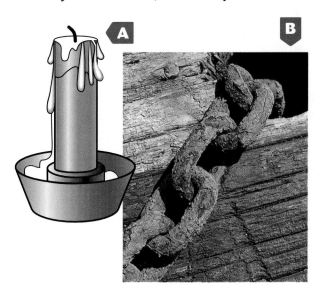

Practicing the SKILL

1. Look carefully at **Figure B.** On a separate sheet of paper, write down (1) what you observe and (2) what you can infer from the figure.

2. Identify any changes you see as physical or chemical. Are your identifications of chemical or physical changes observations or inferences? Explain.

For more skill practice, do the Chapter 2 Interactive Exploration on the **Science Voyages Level Red CD-ROM.**

GLENCOE TECHNOLOGY

Using Numbers

Background

Consumers who are energy conscious and who live in sunny climates look to solar-energy technicians to help them utilize energy from the sun.

One type of solar-energy system that a solar-heating technician can suggest collects the sun's energy, transforms that energy into thermal energy, stores thermal energy in bins of rocks, and then distributes heated air to various parts of the house by means of duct work.

The diagram below shows the solar-collector component of a solar-energy system on the roof of a house.

A solar-heating technician calculates the area of a home and the area of the solar collectors in square feet (ft^2), instead of using a metric unit, such as the square meter (m^2). In the United States, the use of English units, such as feet and yards, is still a common practice in many industries. For example, fabric stores sell material by the yard, and gas companies calculate how much natural gas homes use by the cubic foot (ft^3).

The technician can use the fact that a home owner will need 1 ft^2 of solar-collector area for every 2.5 to 4 ft^2 of living space.

Suppose you are a home owner who wants to heat 1200 ft^2 of living space by using a

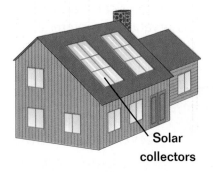

Solar collectors

solar-heating system. You contact a solar-heating technician and ask to have 400 ft^2 of solar collector installed. Is your request reasonable?

Procedure

1 You can test your request by using the following proportion.

$$\frac{\text{collector area}}{\text{living space}}$$

2 Solve the proportion.

$$\frac{\text{collector area}}{\text{living space}} = \frac{400 \text{ ft}^2}{1200 \text{ ft}^2} = \frac{1}{3}$$

3 Compare the calculated proportion you requested against the technician's given guidelines about area of solar collector per area of living space. Because 1 ft^2 of solar collector per 3 ft^2 of living space is between 1 ft^2 of collector per 2.5 ft^2 and 1 ft^2 of collector per 4 ft^2 of living space, the request is reasonable.

Practicing the SKILL

Determine whether each estimate of collector space is reasonable. Explain each answer.

1 300 ft^2 of collector per 1200 ft^2 of living space

2 300 ft^2 of collector per 1500 ft^2 of living space

For more skill practice, do the Chapter 3 Interactive Exploration on the **Science Voyages Level Red CD-ROM.**

GLENCOE TECHNOLOGY

Comparing and Contrasting

Background

Scientists often have more than one object or event to look at. For example, they often carry out experiments that have many similarities and a single difference. When scientists look at objects or events to see how they are similar, they are comparing them. Contrasting involves looking for differences in similar objects or events. In this activity, you will compare and contrast the results from the experiment you will perform.

Procedure

PART 1

1. Take a tissue and loosely wad it up.

2. Tape it inside the bottom of a 12-ounce paper or foam cup.

3. Fill a bowl or sink with water.

4. Push the cup straight down into the water with the open end downward.

5. Pull the cup straight up from the water and examine the tissue.

PART 2

6. Punch a small hole in the bottom of the cup.

7. Push the cup straight down into the water with the open end downward, nearly—but not quite—immersing the bottom of the cup.

8. Pull the cup straight up from the water and examine the tissue.

Practicing the SKILL

1. Compare and contrast the results from parts 1 and 2 of your experiment.

2. What conclusions can you draw from performing your experiment?

For more skill practice, do the Chapter 4 Interactive Exploration on the **Science Voyages Level Blue CD-ROM.**

Making Models

Background

You can use a model to help you better understand the structure of an atom. A model can be a drawing or something you build, like a model car. A model isn't exactly like the real object. It is often a simplified picture of a more complex object. For example, a diagram of an atom shows only a two-dimensional representation of a three-dimensional object. However, it gives you a simple picture of how the particles in an atom are arranged, and it helps you understand how matter behaves.

Procedure

1. Copy the Subatomic Particles table in your Science Journal.

2. Use the periodic table to find the number of protons, neutrons, and electrons in a lithium-7 atom. The number 7 in lithium-7 means that this is the isotope of lithium with mass number 7. In a neutral atom, the number of protons is the atomic number. The number of neutrons is the mass number minus the atomic number. The number of electrons is the same as the number of protons.

3. In the table, list the number of each particle in lithium-7.

4. Draw a circle about 2 cm in diameter. See the example in the figure at the right.

5. Write the number of protons in the circle next to a p^+ symbol.

6. Write the number of neutrons in the circle next to an n symbol.

7. Draw another circle around the circle you already drew. On this circle, write next to an e^- symbol the number of electrons that are in the atom's electron cloud.

Subatomic Particles			
Atoms	Protons	Neutrons	Electrons
Lithium-7			
Boron-10			
Boron-11			
Carbon-12			
Carbon-14			

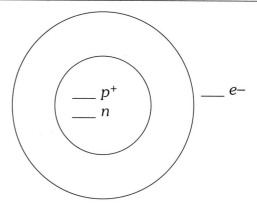

Practicing the SKILL

1. Refer to the periodic table and list the numbers of protons, neutrons, and electrons in the isotopes of boron and carbon listed in the Subatomic Particles table.

2. Using the steps given in the procedure, make models for the boron and carbon isotopes.

For more skill practice, do the Chapter 5 Interactive Exploration on the **Science Voyages Level Blue CD-ROM.**

GLENCOE TECHNOLOGY

Classifying

Background

You classify objects every day. You may put all your socks in one drawer and your sweaters in another. You store soaps, detergents, and other cleaners separately from food. You may store canned vegetables and soups on one shelf and spices on another. Putting similar objects together is classification.

By classifying objects into groups, scientists can organize information. Classifying helps them compare and contrast properties of different groups. For example, scientists classify some substances as metals, nonmetals, or metalloids. Once classified, these substances can be more easily studied.

Procedure

Use the periodic table and what you have learned to classify the following elements into categories. Label each category. Write your answers on a separate sheet of paper.

F	Li	B	Cl	Si	Na
Br	Po	Cs	Al	He	Ni

Practicing the SKILL

(1) Classify the following elements into two categories. Label each category.

hydrogen	aluminum
silver	gold
iron	oxygen
fluorine	copper
zinc	bromine
mercury	helium
radon	tungsten
bismuth	actinium

(2) In what other ways can these elements be classified?

For more skill practice, do the Chapter 6 Interactive Exploration on the **Science Voyages Level Blue CD-ROM.**

GLENCOE TECHNOLOGY

H																	He
Li	Be											B	C	N	O	F	Ne
Na	Mg											Al	Si	P	S	Cl	Ar
K	Ca	Sc	Ti	V	Cr	Mn	Fe	Co	Ni	Cu	Zn	Ga	Ge	As	Se	Br	Kr
Rb	Sr	Y	Zr	Nb	Mo	Tc	Ru	Rh	Pd	Ag	Cd	In	Sn	Sb	Te	I	Xe
Cs	Ba	La	Hf	Ta	W	Re	Os	Ir	Pt	Au	Hg	Tl	Pb	Bi	Po	At	Rn
Fr	Ra	Ac	Rf	Db	Sg	Bh	Hs	Mt	Uun	Uuu	Uub						

Metal
Metalloid
Nonmetal

Predicting

Background

Any time you apply a hypothesis to a specific situation, you are making a prediction. Predictions can be made using tables, graphs, and other tools that give information. They also can be made based upon previous experience.

Electrons are more strongly attracted to some atoms. You can think of the sharing of electrons in a bond as a tug-of-war between two atoms. Electronegativity is a measure of the ability of an atom in a bond to attract electrons. When there is little difference in the electronegativities of two atoms, the bond is covalent. The bond has a small percentage of ionic character. As the difference between their electronegativities gets larger, the electrons are more attracted to one of the atoms. The bond has a greater percent ionic character. If the difference is large enough, one atom will lose an electron and the other atom will gain one. An ionic bond forms.

Chemists often use graphs to predict whether two atoms will form an ionic or covalent bond. The difference in the electronegativities of potassium and chlorine is 2.2. Use the graph to predict the type of bond that they will form.

Procedure

1. Notice that the difference in electronegativity is plotted on the x-axis.

2. When reading the y-axis, the larger the percent ionic character, the more certain you can be that the bond will be ionic.

3. Locate 2.2 on the x-axis. Go straight up from 2.2 to the curve.

4. Go straight from the point on the curve to the y-axis. Read that the percent ionic character is 69 percent.

5. The bond between potassium and chlorine will be ionic.

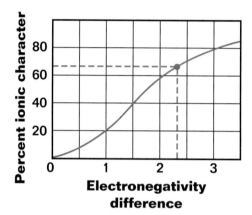

Practicing the SKILL

1. Predict the type of bond that will form between carbon and nitrogen. The difference in electronegativity is 0.5.

2. Predict the type of bond that will form between lithium and fluorine. The difference in electronegativity is 3.0.

3. What is the difference in electronegativity for a bond with 40 percent ionic character?

For more skill practice, do the Chapter 7 Interactive Exploration on the **Science Voyages Level Blue CD-ROM.**

Observing

Background

Many prescription drugs come with detailed instructions on how to take them. If you don't follow the instructions carefully, the drug may not work well. It could also make you seriously ill. Over-the-counter medications have instructions, too. You can buy medication for heartburn, indigestion, upset stomach, and a cold from almost any grocery or drug store.

How do scientists determine the best way to take a drug so that it gives the patient the relief he or she needs? Before any drug is given to a patient, it is tested many times. Scientists have to observe how the chemicals in a drug react with the chemicals in the body. In some cases, scientists recommend that the drug be taken in a certain way. The label on the bottle or box may say to take the medication with food, water, on an empty stomach, or with milk. It is always important to follow the directions so the medication can work properly. In this activity, you will observe how water temperature affects the reaction time of an effervescent tablet.

Procedure 🥽 🧤 🚫

1. Copy the data table.

2. Use masking tape to label three beakers A, B, and C.

3. Write a hypothesis stating the effect of temperature on the decomposition of an effervescent tablet.

4. Pour exactly 150 mL of ice water into beaker A. Measure the temperature of the water. Record the temperature in the data table.

5. Carefully drop one effervescent tablet into the beaker. Measure and record the number of seconds needed for the tablet to completely dissolve.

6. Pour 150 mL of water at room temperature into beaker B. Measure and record the temperature of the water.

7. Repeat step 5 using the room-temperature water.

8. Pour 150 mL of warm water into beaker C. Measure and record the temperature of the water.

9. Repeat step 5 using the warm water.

Dissolving an Effervescent Tablet		
Beaker	Temperature of Water	Time to Dissolve
A		
B		
C		

Practicing the SKILL

1. In which beaker did the reaction occur most rapidly?

2. In which beaker was the reaction slowest?

3. What effect did temperature have on the reaction time of an effervescent tablet?

For more skill practice, do the Chapter 8 Interactive Exploration on the **Science Voyages Level Blue CD-ROM.**

GLENCOE TECHNOLOGY

Variables and Controls

Background

Suppose you disagree with a friend about which sports drink contains the most flavoring, sweetener, and other dissolved materials. You cannot accurately find out by tasting each sports drink because every individual's sense of taste is slightly different. To settle the matter, you try to find some method of testing the sports drinks that is fair, or unbiased. You don't want any personal preferences to influence the test results. You devise a test involving three brands of sports drink.

You label and weigh three identical, heat-resistant jars. You measure 100 mL of each drink into the appropriate jar. You set the jars on a hot plate and heat the drinks. Being careful to avoid burning the dry material that remains, you remove each jar when all the liquid has boiled away. You let the jars cool to room temperature, then weigh each jar. To find the mass of dry material from each drink, you subtract the mass of the empty jar from the total mass.

Scientists design experiments in much the same way. They take great care to make sure only one factor in the experiment, the independent variable, is changed. The independent variable in your experiment is the brand of sports drink. The factor that changes as a result of the independent variable is called the dependent variable. The dependent variable in your experiment is the mass of dry material. Controls are factors that are kept the same, providing a basis for comparison. Controls in your experiment are the identical jars, amounts of drink, and the temperature of the hot plate. See if you can identify the controls and variables in the following Skill Activity.

Procedure

1. Pour the same amount of water into two beakers.

2. Take the temperature of the water in each beaker to make sure the temperatures are the same.

3. Add salt to one beaker and stir the water in both beakers until all the salt has dissolved.

4. Take the temperature of the water and of the salt solution.

5. How did dissolving salt in one beaker affect the water temperature?

6. What were the controls? Variables?

Practicing the SKILL

1. Ten grams of sugar dissolves more quickly in a liter of pure, hot, tap water than it does in a liter of pure, cold, tap water. List the controls, the independent variable, and the dependent variable.

2. Identify the dependent variable from testing the following hypothesis: If premium gasoline is more efficient, then it should increase the fuel mileage of our family car.

For more skill practice, do the Chapter 9 Interactive Exploration on the **Science Voyages Level Blue CD-ROM.**

GLENCOE TECHNOLOGY

Making Models

Background

Many molecules are isomers. Isomers are molecules that have the same chemical formula but different structures. Many organic compounds have isomers. Some large hydrocarbons have thousands of isomers. The different arrangements of the atoms in the isomers give them different properties. To understand the properties of a molecule, it is necessary to know the structure of the molecule. In this Skill Activity, you will make a model to show that isomers differ from one another.

Procedure

1. Use large foam balls to represent carbon atoms and small foam balls to represent hydrogen atoms. Pipe cleaners can be used to represent the bonds and attach the balls together.

2. Use four large balls and ten small balls to make a model of butane, C_4H_{10}, with the four carbon atoms in a straight chain. Place the bonds evenly around each carbon atom.

3. Draw a diagram of your model and describe it in your own words.

4. Remove the end carbon with its three hydrogen atoms.

5. You now have a three-carbon chain. Remove one hydrogen atom from the middle carbon and place it in the position from which you removed the carbon atom and its three hydrogens.

6. Attach the carbon and its three hydrogen atoms to the center carbon where the hydrogen atom was.

7. Draw a diagram of your model and describe it in your own words. The models in steps 3 and 7 are two isomers of butane.

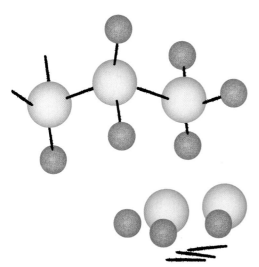

Practicing the SKILL

1. Use five large balls, ten small balls, and 16 pieces of pipe cleaner to make a model of pentane, C_5H_{12}.

2. Rearrange the same set of materials to form an isomer of pentane.

For more skill practice, do the Chapter 10 Interactive Exploration on the **Science Voyages Level Blue CD-ROM.**

GLENCOE TECHNOLOGY

Using Numbers

Background

Scientists often use formulas to solve problems. Suppose you are asked: How does the average velocity of a ball change during flight? You could use the formula that says the average velocity equals displacement over time. It is written below.

$$v = \frac{d}{t}$$

Procedure

1. The figure shows a ball in motion. The time interval between each position of the ball is 1/30 of a second.

2. Place a piece of paper on top of the drawing.

3. Mark each position of the ball with a dot.

4. Remove the paper. Draw a straight line connecting the four positions of the ball (three intervals). The time between three intervals of the ball is 0.1 s. Why?

5. Measure and record the length of the straight line. The length of the line can be used to show the distance traveled during the first 0.1 s of flight.

6. Repeat steps 4 and 5 for the next four positions of the ball, and so on. The length of each line shows the distance traveled during each 0.1 s of flight.

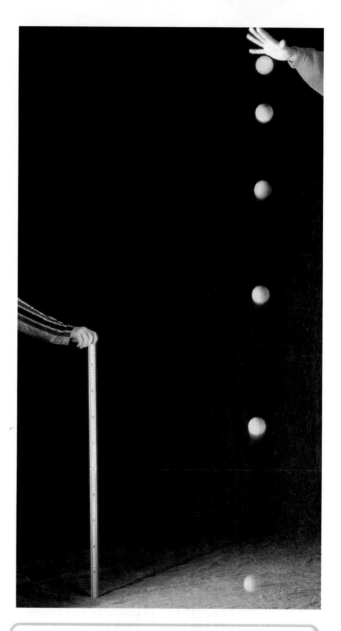

Practicing the SKILL

At what interval is the average velocity smallest? Largest?

For more skill practice, do the Chapter 11 Interactive Exploration on the **Science Voyages Level Blue CD-ROM.**

Making and Using Tables

Background

Scientists collect and interpret data as a part of their investigations. they often organize the data into a data table. Data tables help the scientists to arrange information so it is easier for them to understand. Scientists interpret the data by looking for patterns that may lead to general conclusions.

Suppose the class decides to see how far a ball will travel over a period of time.

Procedure

1. Look at the Rolling Distance table.

2. Notice that the time, per second, that the ball rolled is listed in the first column.

3. The distance, per meter, that the ball traveled in that amount of time is listed in the second column.

4. Now, see if there is a pattern between the time allowed for the ball to roll and the distance it traveled.

5. By looking at the table, you can see that the longer the ball rolled, the further it traveled.

6. You can also see that the distance traveled was double the time allowed each time.

7. Look at the Planetary Weight Factors table.

8. To figure out what you would weigh on different planets, multiply your weight on Earth by the factor listed next to each planet in the Planetary Weight Factors table.

Rolling Distance

Time (s)	Distance (m)
0.0	0.0
1.0	2.0
2.0	4.0
3.0	6.0

Planetary Weight Factors

Planet	Factor	Your Weight on Earth	Your Weight on Planet
Venus	0.91		
Mars	0.36		
Jupiter	2.3		
Saturn	0.88		
Neptune	1.3		

Practicing the SKILL

Use the Planetary Weight Factors table to answer the following questions.

1. On which planet(s) do you weigh more than you do on Earth? Less than Earth?

2. On which planet(s) would you weigh nearly the same as you do on Earth?

For more skill practice, do the Chapter 12 Interactive Exploration on the **Science Voyages Level Blue CD-Rom.**

Comparing and Contrasting

Background

Are you an educated consumer? You are when you learn about a product before you buy it. Suppose you want to buy a compact disc player. How do you choose which one to buy? You read all the available information on the various models. Then, you find properties that each CD player has in common. That is, you compare the models. However, you also consider the options available. Each model has its own options. They make each model different. When you consider differences between the CD players, you are contrasting.

Comparing and contrasting are important tools for scientists also. For example, in determining the possible health benefits, a researcher might compare and contrast the nutritional value of foods that contain artificial sweeteners with foods that do not contain artificial sweeteners. How would you go about comparing and contrasting a lever and wheel and axle shown at the right?

Procedure

1. Look at the physical characteristics of each simple machine. How do they increase force? Are they used for the same or different types of jobs?

2. Prepare a table to organize your observations.

3. Fill in your table by writing as many similarities you can think of when comparing a lever to a wheel and axle.

4. Complete your table by listing the differences between a lever and a wheel and axle.

Practicing the SKILL

Compare and contrast the following:

1. a single pulley and a pulley system having four pulleys

2. an inclined plane and a screw

For more skill practice, do the Chapter 13 Interactive Exploration on the **Science Voyages Level Green CD-ROM.**

GLENCOE TECHNOLOGY

Interpreting Scientific Illustrations

Background

You may have heard the saying "A picture is worth a thousand words." A good scientific diagram often can explain an idea better than several paragraphs of words. In order to get the most from diagrams, do the following.

- Study the entire diagram. Review the part of the text that the diagram illustrates.

- If there is a caption, read it carefully.

- Read all the labels and identify the parts.

- Visualize the dimensions. Arrows often indicate distances and direction. Distances often are indicated between arrows. The heads of the arrows show where the measurements start and end.

Use these guidelines to interpret the diagram at right.

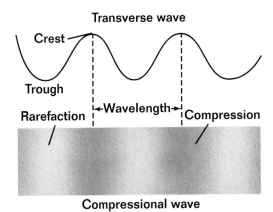

Transverse wave

Compressional wave

Procedure

1. What is the purpose of this diagram?

2. Identify the text in Chapter 5 to which the diagram relates. Locate the discussions about types of waves.

3. What does the crest of a transverse wave correspond to on a compressional wave?

4. What does the trough of a transverse wave correspond to on a compressional wave?

5. What is another way you can diagram the wavelength of a transverse wave?

Practicing the SKILL

1. What do the darker areas of the compressional wave represent?

2. What are the white areas?

3. How would you measure one wavelength of a compressional wave?

For more skill practice, do the Chapter 14 Interactive Exploration on the **Science Voyages Level Blue CD-ROM.**

Communicating

Background

Have you ever wanted to learn more about a topic? Writing a report is one way you can explore new topics. You can learn about anything from the galaxy Andromeda to the element zirconium.

Scientists also write reports. Their reports give them the chance to communicate their work to other scientists in their field and to exchange ideas.

Procedure

1. Select a topic for your paper that interests you.

2. Once you have chosen a topic, go to the library to find information. Start with *The Reader's Guide to Periodical Literature.* It lists magazine articles by subject. To find books on your topic, look in the card catalog. Using technology also can help you find good sources of information.

3. Write down the author and title of each reference. For books, record the publisher and date of publication. For magazine articles, include the name and date of the magazine, the volume, and the issue number. Also indicate the page numbers where the reference is located.

4. As you read your references, decide what is important. In your own words, write down the information and where you found it. Keep your notes brief.

5. After you have read all your material, pick out the main ideas and the subtopics. Use them to make a detailed outline. Once this is done, you are ready to write. At the end of the paper, list the references you used.

Practicing the SKILL

1. Research the Hubble Space Telescope.

2. Comunicate the information you find by writing a report.

For more skill practice, do the Chapter 15 Interactive Exploration on the **Science Voyages Level Blue CD-ROM.**

GLENCOE TECHNOLOGY

Sequencing

Background

Every day you do things in a certain order. For example, you may have a schedule that tells the order of your classes. Language arts may be taught first, followed by science, math, and so on. When you go to your classes in a certain order, you follow a sequence. A sequence is a series of things or events arranged in a specific order.

For scientists, knowing the sequence of a set of events can be very important. Sequencing helps scientists better understand a process that is under study or predict what may happen next.

To help themselves outline a particular sequence, many scientists make a *flow chart,* which is a detailed description of the operations and decisions needed to solve a problem. A flow chart breaks a process down into its most basic steps.

Procedure

To understand flow charts, think about when you make a telephone call. What steps do you take?

Figure A shows the sequence of steps taken for the above activity in the form of a flow chart. Each step is written in a special kind of box. A circle (○) begins and ends a chart. A diamond (◇) shows that a question is being asked. A square (□) indicates something you do. A parallelogram (▱) represents a result. Whenever you ask a question, you must provide two paths. One path shows what to do if the answer is yes. The other path shows what to do if the answer is no.

A

look up phone number — know the phone number? — N / start → lift up receiver — Y — wait for dial tone — N — dial tone? — Y — dial number — phone rings — your friend answers — speak with your friend — finished speaking? — N — Y — hang up — end

B

Practicing the SKILL

Make a flow chart to show the path electric current in **Figure B** might take in going through a circuit.

For more skill practice, do the Chapter 16 Interactive Exploration on the **Science Voyages Level Blue CD-ROM.**

GLENCOE TECHNOLOGY

English Glossary

This glossary defines each key term that appears in bold type in the text. It also shows the chapter and page number where you can find the word used.

Pronunciation Key

a...back (bak)	oh...go (goh)	sh...shelf (shelf)
ay...day (day)	aw...soft (sawft)	ch...nature (nay chur)
ah...father (fahth ur)	or...orbit (or but)	g...gift (gihft)
ow...flower (flow ur)	oy...coin (coyn)	j...gem (jem)
ar...car (car)	oo...foot (foot)	ing...sing (sing)
e...less (les)	ew...food (fewd)	zh...vision (vihzh un)
ee...leaf (leef)	yoo...pure (pyoor)	k...cake (kayk)
ih...trip (trihp)	yew...few (fyew)	s...seed, cent (seed, sent)
i (i + con + e)...idea	uh...comma (cahm uh)	z...zone, raise (zohn, rayz)
(i dee uh), life (life)	u (+ con)...flower (flo ur)	

A

acceleration: rate of change of velocity; can act in the direction of motion, at an angle, or opposite to the direction of motion. (ch. 11, p. 304)

alloy (AL oy): mixture made of two or more elements, one of which is a metal. (ch. 6, p. 162)

amino acid: building block of proteins; contains both an amino group and a carboxyl group substituted on the same carbon atom. (ch. 10, p. 278)

amino (uh ME no) **group:** consists of a nitrogen atom joined by covalent bonds to two hydrogen atoms; formula is $-NH_2$; when substituted for hydrogen in a hydrocarbon, forms an amine. (ch. 10, p. 279)

amplitude: measure of the energy a wave carries; one-half the distance between a crest and a trough of a transverse wave. (ch. 14, p. 395)

aqueous (AH kwee us): solution in which water is the solvent. (ch. 9, p. 243)

Archimedes' principle: states that when a object is placed in a fluid, the object weighs less by an amount equal to the weight of the displaced fluid. (ch. 4, p. 115)

atom: small particle that makes up most types of matter and is made up of smaller parts called protons, neutrons, and electrons. (ch. 2, p. 37)

atomic mass: number that tells how heavy an element's atoms are compared with atoms of other elements. (ch. 2, p. 46)

atomic number: number of protons in the nucleus of an atom of a specific element. (ch. 3, p. 75); whole number that tells how many protons are in the nucleus of each atom of an element. (ch. 5, p. 135)

balanced forces: two or more forces acting on an object that cancel each other out and do not cause a change in the object's motion. (ch. 12, p. 329)

boiling point: temperature at which added heat energy causes the molecules of a liquid to move faster and the liquid's particles to enter the gaseous state in large numbers. (ch. 1, p. 105)

buoyancy: decrease in weight of an object in a fluid due to the net upward force caused by the displaced fluid. (ch. 4, p. 115)

carbohydrates: energy-supplying organic compounds that are broken down into simple sugars in the body; contain only carbon, hydrogen, and oxygen. (ch. 10, p. 284)

carboxyl (car BOX ul) **group:** consists of one carbon atom, two oxygen atoms, and one hydrogen atom; formula is –COOH; when substituted for hydrogen in a hydrocarbon, forms a carboxylic acid. (ch. 10, p. 278)

catalyst (KAT uh lihst): substance, such as an enzyme, that speeds up a chemical reaction but is not used up or permanently changed. (ch. 8, p. 226)

chemical energy: energy stored within chemical bonds. (ch. 3, p. 85)

chemical reaction: energy-requiring process in which chemical changes occur; results in the formation of new substances that have different properties than the original substances. (ch. 8, p. 212)

circuit: closed, unbroken path through which an electric current can flow. (ch. 16, p. 455)

compound: pure substance that contains two or more elements. (ch. 7, p. 197); pure substance produced when elements combine and whose properties are different from those of the elements from which it is formed. (ch. 2, p. 51)

compound machine: combination of two or more simple machines. (ch. 13, p. 366)

compressional wave: wave in which matter in the medium moves forward and backward in the same direction the wave travels. (ch. 14, p. 393)

concave lens: lens whose edges are thicker than its middle; causes light waves to diverge. (ch. 15, p. 433)

concentrated: solution that contains a large amount of solute per given amount of solvent. (ch. 9, p. 247)

concentration: measure of the amount of solute in a solution compared to the amount of solvent. (ch. 9, p. 247)

condensation: process where particles in a cooling gas slow down and come together to form droplets of liquid. (ch. 4, p. 107)

conduction: transfer of thermal energy from particle to particle through a material when there is a temperature difference (ch. 4, p. 104); transfer of energy that occurs when molecules bump into each other. (ch. 3, p. 78)

conductor: material, such as copper, silver, and iron, through which electrons can move easily. (ch. 16, p. 451)

constant: variable that stays the same in an experiment. (ch. 1, p. 14)

control: standard used for comparison in an experiment. (ch. 1, p. 13)

convection: transfer of thermal energy that happens when particles move from one place to another where there is a temperature difference (ch. 3, p. 80)

convex lens: lens whose center is thicker than its edges; causes light waves to converge. (ch. 15, p. 432)

covalent (koh VAY luhnt) **bond:** chemical bond that forms between atoms when they share one or more electrons. (ch. 7, p. 199)

D

density: mass of an object divided by its volume. (ch. 4, p. 114)

dependent variable: factor being measured or observed in a controlled experiment. (ch. 1, p. 13)

diffraction: bending of waves around a barrier. (ch. 14, p. 402)

diffusion: mixing of particles in a gas or a liquid. (ch. 4, p. 109)

dilute: solution that contains a small amount of solute per given amount of solvent. (ch. 9, p. 247)

displacement: measures the change in position of an object, using the starting point and ending point and noting the direction. (ch. 11, p. 301)

E

efficiency: ability of a machine to convert work input to work output; always less than 100 percent in real machines due to some loss to friction or heat. (ch. 13, p. 374)

effort force (F_e): force applied to a machine. (ch. 13, p. 366)

electric current: continuous flow of electrons through a conductor; measured in units of amperes (A). (ch. 16, p. 455)

electric discharge: rapid movement of excess electrons from one place to another. (ch. 16, p. 452)

electrical power: rate at which an appliance converts electrical energy to another form of energy; unit is the watt (W). (ch. 16, p. 466)

electromagnetic wave: type of wave, such as a light wave or a radio wave, that can travel in a vacuum as well as in various materials. (ch. 15, p. 416)

electromagnetic waves: waves that do not need matter to carry energy; can travel through air, through solid walls, and through space and have wavelengths and frequencies that vary greatly. (ch. 14, p. 392)

electromagnetic wave: type of wave, such as a light wave or a radio wave, that can travel in a vacuum as well as in various materials. (ch. 15, p. 466)

electron: negatively charged particle found in a cloudlike formation surrounding an atom's nucleus. (ch. 2, p. 40); tiny, negatively charged particle that is present in all atoms and that has almost no mass. (ch. 5, p. 127)

electron cloud: region surrounding the nucleus of an atom, where electrons are more likely to be found. (ch. 5, p. 133)

electron dot diagram: shows the chemical symbol for an element surrounded by as many dots as there are electrons in its outer energy level. (ch. 7, p. 192)

element: substance that cannot be broken down into simpler substances and whose atoms are exactly alike. (ch. 5, p. 125); naturally occurring or synthetic material that cannot be broken down to simpler materials by ordinary means, has a unique set of properties, and that is generally classified as a metal, a metalloid, or a nonmetal. (ch. 2, p. 44)

endothermic (en duh THUR mihk) **reaction:** chemical reaction in which energy is absorbed, such as the reaction that breaks water down into hydrogen and oxygen. (ch. 8, p. 217)

energy: ability to cause change; can affect the temperature, speed, shape, or direction of an object. (ch. 3, p. 64); ability to cause change; cannot be destroyed or created, only transferred from one form to another. (ch. 11, p. 317)

evaporation: process by which the fastest-moving molecules of a liquid escape from the surface and form a gas. (ch. 4, p. 106)

exothermic (ek soh THUR mihk) **reaction:** chemical reaction that releases energy, such as occurs when propane is burned in a gas grill. (ch. 8, p. 218)

F

focal length: distance of the focal point from the center of the mirror or lens. (ch. 15, p. 426)

focal point: single point on the optical axis of a mirror or lens. (ch. 15, p. 426)

force: push or a pull exerted on an object. (ch. 12, p. 328)

formula: combination of chemical symbols that tells what elements are in molecules and how many atoms of each element are present. (ch. 7, p. 203)

freezing point: temperature at which attractive forces trap particles in a cooling liquid and form crystals. (ch. 4, p. 101)

frequency: number of waves that pass a given point in one second; measured in waves per second, or hertz (Hz). (ch. 14, p. 397); number of wavelengths that pass a point in one second. (ch. 15, p. 419)

friction: rubbing force that acts against motion between two touching surfaces. (ch. 12, p. 331)

fulcrum: point about which a lever pivots. (ch. 13, p. 370)

G

graph: diagram that shows the relationship of one variable to another variable and that makes it easier to interpret and analyze data. (ch. 1, p. 18)

gravitational potential energy: energy an object could potentially gain if it falls, depending on its mass and the height it can fall. (ch. 11, p. 319)

group: family of elements with similar physical or chemical properties that occupies the same column in the periodic table. (ch. 6, p. 156)

H

half-life: time needed for one-half the mass of a sample of a radioactive isotope to decay; can vary from fractions of a second to billions of years. (ch. 5, p. 138)

heat: energy transfer that causes a change in temperature. (ch. 3, p. 75)

heat of fusion: heat required to melt one kilogram of a solid at its melting point. (ch. 4, p. 100)

heat of vaporization: amount of energy required to change one kilogram of a liquid to a gas. (ch 4, p. 105)

hydrocarbon: compound that contains only carbon and hydrogen atoms—for example, methane, CH_4, and ethane, C_2H_6. (ch. 10, p. 271)

hydroxyl (hi DROX ul) **group:** consists of one oxygen atom and one hydrogen atom joined by a covalent bond; formula is –OH; when substituted for hydrogen in a hydrocarbon, forms an alcohol. (ch. 10, p. 277)

hypothesis: prediction about a problem that can be tested; may be based on observations, new information, and personal experience, and is often written as an if-and-then statement. (ch. 1, p. 12)

inclined plane: simple machine that is a sloped surface, or ramp; allows heavy loads to be lifted by using less force over a greater distance. (ch. 13, p. 368)

independent variable: factor that is changed in a controlled experiment. (ch. 1, p. 13)

indicator: compound that reacts with acidic and basic solutions and changes color at different pH values. (ch. 9, p. 254)

inertia: measures an object's tendency to remain at rest or to stay in constant motion. (ch. 11, p. 310)

inference: attempt at an explanation based on observation. (ch. 1, p. 25)

inhibitor: substance, such as butyl hydroxy toluene (BHT), that doesn't totally stop a chemical reaction but slows it down. (ch. 8, p. 226)

insulator: material, such as rubber or glass, through which electrons cannot move easily. (ch. 16, p. 451)

interference: ability of two or more waves to combine and form a new wave when they overlap; can be constructive, forming a larger wave, or destructive, forming a smaller wave. (ch. 14, p. 404)

ion (I ahn): atom that is no longer neutral because it has gained or lost an electron. (ch. 7, p. 196)

ionic bond: chemical bond that is created when one atom loses one or more electrons and another atom gains one or more electrons. (ch. 7, p. 197)

isomers (I suh murz): compounds with the same chemical formulas but different structures and different chemical and physical properties. (ch. 10, p. 274)

isotopes (I suh tohps): atoms of the same element that have different numbers of neutrons in their nuclei. (ch. 5, p. 135); two or more atoms of the same element that have different numbers of neutrons. (ch. 2, p. 46)

kinetic (kuh NET ihk) **energy:** energy an object has due to its motion; depends on the object's mass and velocity. (ch. 11, p. 317); energy of motion; is influenced by an object's mass and speed and can be transferred from one object to another when objects collide. (ch. 3, p. 66)

kinetic theory of matter: states that the particles of all matter are in constant, random motion. (ch. 4, p. 97)

law: well-tested description of how something in nature works. (ch. 1, p. 12)

law of conservation of energy: states that energy cannot be destroyed or created, but it is only transformed from one form to another. (ch. 3, p. 70); (ch. 11, p. 317)

law of conservation of matter: states that matter is neither created nor destroyed, only changed in form. (ch. 2, p. 38)

law of conservation of momentum: states that if no outside forces act on a group of objects, the momentum of the group will not change. (ch. 11, p. 313)

law of definite proportions: states that a given compound is always made of the same elements in the same proportion by mass. (ch. 2, p. 52)

law of reflection: states that the angle of incidence is equal to the angle of reflection. (ch. 15, p. 423)

lens: transparent object that has at least one curved side that causes light to bend. (ch. 15, p. 431)

lever: simple machine made from a rod or plank that pivots about a point. (ch. 13, p. 370)

light ray: narrow beam of light traveling in a straight line. (ch. 15, p. 416)

lipids: energy-supplying and energy-storing organic compounds composed of three long-chain carboxylic acids bonded to glycerol; commonly called fats and oils and can be saturated or unsaturated. (ch. 10, p. 287)

M

mass: quantity of matter in an object and a measure of the object's inertia; unit is the kilogram (kg). (ch. 11, p.310)

mass number: number of neutrons plus the number of protons in the nucleus of an atom. (ch. 5, p. 135); (ch. 2, p. 46)

matter: anything that has mass and takes up space and whose particles are in constant motion. (ch. 2, p. 36); (ch. 4, p. 96)

mechanical advantage (*M.A.*): comparison of the effort force to the resistance force for a machine. (ch. 13, p. 368)

mechanical waves: waves that can travel only through matter; can be either transverse or compressional waves. (ch. 14, p. 391)

medium: material in which a light wave travels. (ch. 15, p. 416)

melting point: temperature at which a solid becomes a liquid. (ch. 4, p. 100)

metal: element that is a good conductor of electricity and heat, is usually a solid at room temperature and usually is shiny, ductile, and malleable. (ch. 6, p. 157)

metalloid: element that shares some properties with metals and some with nonmetals. (ch. 6, p. 158)

metalloids: elements that have characteristics of both metals and nonmetals, generally are brittle and dull, and are poor conductors of heat and electricity. (ch. 2, p. 48)

metals: elements that are malleable, ductile, generally have a shiny or metallic luster, and are not as good conductors of heat and electricity. (ch. 2, p. 47)

mixture: combination of substances that can be separated by physical means and can be either the same throughout (homogeneous) or have different parts with different compositions (heterogeneous). (ch. 9, p. 236)

mixtures: combinations of two or more substances that have not combined to form new, pure substances; can be uniform, where the individual parts cannot be seen, or nonuniform, where you can see individual parts. (ch. 2, p. 53)

molecule (MAH luh kyewl): neutral particle that is formed when atoms share electrons. (ch. 7, p. 199)

momentum: product of mass and velocity; quantity of motion for an object. (ch. 11, p. 311)

N

net force: sum of the forces acting on an object. (ch. 12, p. 328)

neutralization (new truh luh ZAY shun): the interaction between acids and bases in which the properties of each are canceled out by the other and a neutral solution is produced. (ch. 9, p. 255)

neutron (NEW trahn): electrically neutral particle that is present in the nucleus of all atoms; has the same mass as a proton. (ch. 2, p. 42)(ch. 5, p. 132)

Newton's first law of motion: states that an object at rest or moving at a constant speed in a straight path continues to do so until a net force acts on it. (ch. 12, p. 330)

Newton's second law of motion: states that an object acted upon by a net force will accelerate in the direction of this force according to the following equation: $a = F_{net}/m$, where a is the acceleration, F_{net} is the net force, and m is the mass. (ch. 12, p. 336)

Newton's third law of motion: states that forces always act in equal but opposite pairs. (ch. 12, p. 344)

nonmetal: element that is a poor conductor of heat and electricity and may be a gas or a brittle solid at room temperature. (ch. 6, p. 158)

nonmetals: elements that are usually dull and are poor conductors of heat and electricity. (ch. 2, p. 48)

normal force: outward force a surface supplies to support an object. (ch. 12, p. 337)

nucleus (NEW klee us): positively charged, central part of an atom. (ch. 2, p. 42)

Ohm's law: relationship between voltage, current, and resistance in an electric circuit; $V = IR$, where V represents the voltage, I represents the electrical current, and R the resistance. (ch. 16, p. 463)

organic compound: compound that contains carbon. (ch. 10, p. 270)

parallel circuit: circuit that has more than one path for the electric current to follow. (ch. 16, p. 464)

Pascal's principle: states that the pressure exerted on any point of a confined fluid is transmitted unchanged throughout the fluid. (ch. 4, p. 111)

period: horizontal row of elements in the periodic table whose properties change gradually and predictably. (ch. 6, p. 153)

pH: measure of how acidic or basic a solution is, related to its concentration of hydronium ions and hydroxide ions; solutions with a pH below 7 are acidic; solutions with a pH above 7 are basic; solutions with a pH of 7 are neutral. (ch. 9, p. 253)

polymer: large natural or synthetic molecule made of many small organic molecules that link together to form a long chain. (ch. 10, p. 282)

potential (puh TEN chul) **energy:** energy that is stored and that comes from an object's position or condition. (ch. 3, p. 68)

power: measures the rate at which work is done in a certain period of time; unit is the watt (W). (ch. 13, p. 363)

pressure: amount of force applied per unit of area; the SI unit is the pascal (Pa). (ch. 4, p. 110)

product: substance that is formed by a chemical reaction; in a chemical equation, the product is placed on the right side of the arrow. (ch. 8, p. 214)

protein: polymer made of individual amino acids linked together in a chain; catalyzes many cell reactions and provides the structural material for many parts of the body. (ch. 10, p. 283)

proton: positively charged, heavy particle contained in the nucleus of all atoms. (ch. 5, p. 128); particle in the nucleus of an atom that carries a positive charge. (ch. 2, p. 42)

pulley: surface, such as a wheel, that redirects force using a rope; a simple machine that allows you to pull down to lift a weight. (ch. 13, p. 373)

radiation: energy that travels by waves in all directions from its source (ch. 3, p. 77)

radioactive decay: release of nuclear particles and energy from unstable atomic nuclei. (ch. 5, p. 136)

rate of reaction: measure of how quickly a chemical reaction occurs, which can be influenced by temperature, particle size, the concentration of the reactants, and the amount of activation energy that starts the reaction. (ch. 8, p. 223)

reactant (ree AK tunt): substance that exists before a chemical reaction begins; in a chemical equation, the reactant is listed on the left side of the arrow. (ch. 8, p. 214)

reflection: occurs when a wave strikes an object or surface and bounces off. (ch. 14, p. 400); process of light striking an object and bouncing off. (ch. 15, p. 417)

refraction: bending of a wave as it moves from one medium into another. (ch. 15, p. 431); bending of a light wave when it changes speed in moving from one material to another. (ch. 14, p. 401)

resistance: measure of how difficult it is for electrons to flow through a material; unit is the ohm. (ch. 16, p. 458)

resistance force (F_r): force a machine must overcome. (ch. 13, p. 366)

saturated: solution that contains the total amount of solute that it can hold under specific conditions. (ch. 9, p. 246)

saturated hydrocarbon: hydrocarbon with only single bonds—for example,

propane, C_3H_8, and butane, C_4H_{10}. (ch. 10, p. 272)

science: process used to investigate the world and provide some possible answers to scientific questions. (ch. 1, p. 8)

scientific methods: approaches taken to try and solve a problem; can include recognizing the problem, forming a hypothesis, testing the hypothesis, analyzing the data, and drawing conclusions. (ch. 1, p. 10)

screw: inclined plane wrapped around a shaft. (ch. 13, p. 369)

semiconductor: element that doesn't conduct electricity as well as a metal but does conduct electricity better than a nonmetal. (ch. 6, p. 164)

sequence: arrangement of things or events in a certain order. (ch. 1, p. 25)

series circuit: circuit that has only one path for the electric current to follow. (ch. 16, p. 464)

simple machine: machine that works with only one motion—an inclined plane, lever, wheel and axle, and pulley. (ch. 13, p. 366)

solubility: maximum amount of a solute that can be dissolved in a given amount of solvent; can be affected by temperature and pressure. (ch. 9, p. 244)

solute: in a solution, the substance that dissolves into another substance. (ch. 9, p. 238)

solution: homogeneous mixture made up of two or more materials where one material seems to disappear into the other; can be unsaturated, saturated, or supersaturated and can be classified as gaseous, liquid, or solid. (ch. 9, p. 238)

solvent: in a solution, the substance that dissolves the solute. (ch. 9, p. 238)

speed: rate of change of an object's position. (ch. 11, p. 300)

state of matter: physical state of a material, whether a solid, a liquid, or a gas, which depends mostly on how the material's atoms and molecules are arranged and how they move. (ch. 4, p. 96)

static charge: buildup of electric charges in one place. (ch. 15, p. 449)

substance: sample of matter that has the same composition and properties throughout. (ch. 2, p. 51)

technology: application of what has been learned through science. (ch. 1, p. 22)

temperature: measure of the average kinetic energy of the particles in any object; the greater the average kinetic energy, the higher an object's temperature. (ch. 3, p. 74)

theory: explanation backed by results received from repeated tests or experiments. (ch. 1, p. 12)

thermal energy: total amount of kinetic energy of the particles in a material. (ch. 3, p. 75)

transverse wave: wave in which matter moves back and forth at right angles to the direction the wave travels. (ch. 14, p. 392)

unbalanced forces: two or more unequal forces acting on an object that cause the object to accelerate. (ch. 12, p. 329)

unsaturated hydrocarbon: hydrocarbon that has one or more double or triple bonds—for example, ethylene, C_2H_4, and propylene, C_3H_6. (ch. 10, p. 273)

velocity (vel AH seh TEE): rate of change of displacement; includes both speed and direction. (ch. 11, p. 302)

voltage: measure of electric potential energy; measured in units of volts (V). (ch. 16, p. 457)

wavelength: distance between a point on one wave and an identical point on the next wave, measured from crest to crest or trough to trough; in compressional waves, is measured from one compression or rarefaction to the next. (ch. 14, p. 396); distance between the tops of two adjacent ripples. (ch. 15, p. 419)

waves: regular disturbances that carry energy through matter or space without carrying matter; can have different amplitudes, frequencies, wavelengths, and speeds (ch. 14, p. 390)

wedge: moving inclined plane with one or two sloping sides. (ch. 13, p. 369)

wheel and axle: simple machine made from two rigidly attached wheels that rotate together. (ch. 13, p. 372)

work: occurs when a force produces movement parallel to the direction in which the force is applied; unit is the joule (J). (ch. 13, p. 360)

Glossary/Glosario

Este glossario define cada término clave que aparece en **negrillas** en el texto. También muestra el número de página donde se usa dicho término.

A

acceleration / aceleración: Razón de cambio de la velocidad. El acelerar, el decelerar y el voltear son formas de aceleración. (Cap. 11, pág. 304)

acids / ácidos: Sustancias que contienen hidrógeno y que producen iones hidronio positivos cuando se disuelven en agua, formando soluciones ácidas. (Cap. 9, pág. 250)

alloy / aleación: Mezcla de dos o más elementos, uno de los cuales es un metal. (Cap. 6, pág. 162)

amino acid / aminoácido: Unidad básica de la cual están compuestas las proteínas, las cuales son una clase importante de moléculas biológicas necesarias para las células vivas. (Cap. 10, pág. 279)

amino group / grupo amino: Grupo formado por un átomo de nitrógeno unido por enlaces covalentes a dos átomos de hidrógeno. (Cap. 10, pág. 278)

amplitude / amplitud: La mitad de la distancia entre una cresta y un valle de una onda transversal; una medida de la energía que transporta una onda. (Cap. 14, pág. 395)

aqueous / acuosa: Describe una solución en la cual el agua es el disolvente. Por ejemplo: el agua salada, los jugos de frutas y las soluciones que forman las estalactitas y las estalagmitas. (Cap. 9, pág. 243)

Archimedes' principle / principio de Arquímedes: Principio que enuncia que cuando un objeto se sumerge en un fluido, el objeto pesa menos de acuerdo con una cantidad igual al peso del fluido desplazado. (Cap. 24, pág. 115)

atom / átomo: La partícula más pequeña que compone la mayoría de los tipos de materia. (Cap. 2, pág. 37)

atomic mass / masa atómica: Indica el peso de los átomos de un elemento en comparación con los átomos de otros elementos. (Cap. 2, pág. 46)

atomic number / número atómico: Indica el número de protones en el núcleo de cada átomo de un elemento. (Cap. 2, pág. 46); (Cap. 5, pág. 135)

B

balanced forces / fuerzas equilibradas: Dos o más fuerzas cuyos efectos se cancelan entre sí y no causan un cambio en el movimiento del objeto. (Cap. 12, pág. 329)

boiling point / punto de ebullición: Temperatura a la cual se forman burbujas de vapor en el fondo de un líquido y se elevan hasta la superficie, haciendo que el líquido entre en estado gaseoso. La ebullición también se llama vaporización. (Cap. 4, pág. 105)

buoyancy / flotabilidad: Disminución del peso de un objeto en un fluido debido a la fuerza ascendente neta causada por el fluido desplazado. (Cap. 4, pág. 115)

carbohydrates / carbohidratos: Compuestos orgánicos que solo contienen carbono, hidrógeno y oxígeno, en una proporción de dos átomos de hidrógeno por átomo de oxígeno y de carbono. (Cap. 10, pág. 284)

carboxyl group / grupo carboxilo: Grupo formado por un átomo de carbono, dos átomos de oxígeno y un átomo de hidrógeno. (Cap. 10, pág. 278)

catalyst / catalizador: Sustancia que acelera una reacción química, pero que no aparece en la ecuación química porque dicha sustancia no sufre cambio permanente ni se agota. (Cap. 8, pág. 226)

chemical bond / enlace químico: Fuerza que mantiene unidos dos átomos. (Cap. 7, pág. 197)

chemical energy / energía química: Energía almacenada (potencial) en los enlaces químicos de las partículas de una sustancia. (Cap. 3, pág. 85)

chemical reaction / reacción química: Proceso en que ocurren cambios químicos. El óxido sobre la carrocería de un auto de acero, un huevo que se fríe y las hojas que se tornan rojas en el otoño, son ejemplos de reacciones químicas. (Cap. 8, pág. 212)

circuit/circuito: Trayectoria cerrada ininterrumpida a través de la cual puede fluir una corriente eléctrica. (Cap. 16, pág. 455)

compound / compuesto: Sustancia pura cuya unidad constitutiva está compuesta por átomos de más de un elemento. (Cap. 2, pág. 51); (Cap 7, pág. 197)

compound machine/máquina compuesta: Combinación de máquinas simples. (Cap. 13, pág. 366)

compressional wave / onda de compresión: Onda en la cual la materia en el medio se mueve de un lado a otro en la misma dirección en que viaja la onda. (Cap. 14, pág. 393)

concave lens/lente cóncava: Lente que es más gruesa en las orillas que en el centro y que desvía las ondas luminosas. (Cap. 15, pág. 433)

concentrated / concentrada: Solución que contiene una gran cantidad de soluto por cantidad dada de disolvente. (Cap. 9, pág. 247)

concentration / concentración: Indica la cantidad de soluto que contiene una solución, comparada con la cantidad de disolvente. (Cap. 9, pág. 247)

condensation / condensación: Proceso de enfriamiento en que las partículas de un gas se vuelven más lentas y la atracción entre ellas aumenta, haciendo que se formen gotas de líquido. (Cap. 4, pág. 107)

conductor/conductor: Material como el cobre, la plata y el hierro a través del cual los electrones se mueven con facilidad. (Cap. 16, pág. 451)

constant / constante: Variable que permanece inalterada en un experimento. (Cap. 1, pág. 14)

control / control: Un estándar de comparación. (Cap. 1, pág. 13)

convex lens/lente convexa: Lente que es más gruesa en el centro que en las orillas; hace que las ondas luminosas converjan. (Cap. 15, pág. 432)

covalent bond / enlace covalente: Enlace químico que se forma entre átomos que comparten electrones. (Cap. 7, pág. 199)

density / densidad: Masa dividida entre volumen. (Cap. 4, pág. 114)

dependent variable / variable dependiente: Factor que se mide, o se observa, en un experimento. (Cap. 1, pág. 13)

diffraction / difracción: Doblamiento de una onda alrededor de una barrera. (Cap. 14, pág. 402)

diffusion / difusión: Libre propagación de las partículas de un gas. (Cap. 4, pág. 109)

dilute / diluida: Solución que contiene una cantidad pequeña de soluto por cantidad dada de disolvente. (Cap. 9, pág. 247)

displacement / desplazamiento: Mide el cambio en la posición de un objeto, el cual incluye dirección. (Cap. 11, pág. 301)

E

efficiency/eficiencia: Capacidad de una máquina para convertir el trabajo de entrada en trabajo de salida; siempre es menos de 100 por ciento en máquinas reales debido a la pérdida por fricción o calor. (Cap. 13, pág. 374)

effort force (F_e)/fuerza de esfuerzo (F_e): La fuerza que se le aplica a una máquina. (Cap. 13, pág. 366)

electric current/corriente eléctrica: Flujo continuo de electrones a través de un conductor; se mide en amperios (A). (Cap. 16, pág. 455)

electric discharge/descarga eléctrica: Movimiento rápido del exceso de electrones de un lugar a otro. (Cap. 16, pág. 452)

electrical power/potencia eléctrica: La razón a la cual un artefacto convierte energía eléctrica en otra forma de energía; se mide en vatios. (Cap. 16, pág. 466)

electromagnetic wave/onda electromagnética: Tipo de onda, como las ondas luminosas o radiales, que puede viajar en el vacío y también en otros materiales. (Cap. 15, pág. 416); (Cap. 14, pág. 392)

electron / electrón: Partícula de materia con carga negativa. (Cap. 5, pág. 127); (Cap. 2, pág. 40)

electron cloud / nube de electrones: Región que rodea el núcleo del átomo y en donde, posiblemente, se encuentran los electrones. (Cap. 5, pág. 133)

electron dot diagram / diagrama de puntos electrónicos: Símbolo químico de un elemento rodeado por puntos que representan los electrones en el nivel energético externo. (Cap. 7, pág. 192)

element / elemento: Material que no se puede descomponer en materiales más simples por medios comunes. (Cap. 2, pág. 44); Sustancia que no puede ser dividida en sustancias más sencillas; por ejemplo, el carbono. (Cap. 5, pág. 125)

endothermic reaction / reacción endotérmica: Reacción en la cual se absorbe energía. (Cap. 8, pág. 217)

energy / energía: Capacidad de causar cambio. (Cap. 3, pág. 64); (Cap. 11, pág. 317)

evaporation / evaporación: Proceso mediante el cual las partículas individuales de un líquido se escapan de la superficie y forman un gas. (Cap. 4, pág. 106)

exothermic reaction / reacción exotérmica: Reacción en la cual se libera energía. (Cap. 8, pág. 218)

F

focal length/longitud focal: Distancia desde el centro del espejo o lente hasta el punto focal. (Cap. 15, pág. 426)

focal point/punto focal: Punto único del eje óptico de un espejo o lente. (Cap. 15, pág. 426)

force / fuerza: Empuje o fuerza de atracción sobre un objeto. (Cap. 12, pág. 328)

formula / fórmula: Combinación de símbolos químicos de elementos, la cual indica los elementos que posee una molécula y cuántos átomos de cada elemento hay. (Cap. 7, pág. 203)

freezing point / punto de congelación: Temperatura a la cual una sustancia pasa de líquido a sólido. Es la misma temperatura que el punto de fusión de un sólido. (Cap. 4, pág. 101)

frequency/frecuencia: Número de longitudes de onda que pasan por un punto en un segundo. (Cap. 15, pág. 419); Se mide en ondas por segundo o hertz (Hz). (Cap. 14, pág. 397)

friction / fricción: Fuerza desequilibrada que hace que casi todos los objetos se detengan y que causa una fuerza de roce que se opone al movimiento entre dos superficies que están en contacto una con otra. (Cap. 12, pág. 331)

fulcrum/fulcro: El punto sobre el cual gira una palanca. (Cap. 13, pág. 370)

graph / gráfica: Diagrama que muestra la relación entre variables y el cual facilita la interpretación y el análisis de los datos. (Cap. 1, pág. 18)

group / grupo: Familia de elementos que contiene elementos con propiedades físicas o químicas parecidas. (Cap. 6, pág. 156)

half-life / media vida: Tiempo requerido para que se desintegre la mitad de una muestra de un elemento radiactivo. (Cap. 5, pág. 138)

heat / calor: Transferencia de energía que ocasiona un cambio de temperatura. (Cap. 3, pág. 75)

heat of fusion / calor de fusión: Cantidad de calor necesario para derretir un kilogramo de un sólido hasta su punto de fusión. (Cap. 4, pág. 100)

heat of vaporization / calor de vaporización: Cantidad de energía necesaria para cambiar un kilogramo de un líquido en un gas. (Cap. 4, pág. 105)

hydrocarbon / hidrocarburo: Compuesto que solo contiene carbono e hidrógeno. (Cap. 10, pág. 271)

hydroxyl group / grupo hidroxilo: Grupo formado por un átomo de oxígeno y un átomo de hidrógeno unidos por un enlace covalente. (Cap. 10, pág. 277)

hypothesis / hipótesis: Predicción acerca de un problema que puede probarse. (Cap. 1, pág. 12)

inclined plane/plano inclinado: Máquina simple formada por una superficie en declive o rampa; permite levantar cargas pesadas usando menos fuerza, a lo largo de una mayor distancia. (Cap. 13, pág. 368)

independent variable / variable independiente: Variable que se cambia en un experimento. (Cap. 1, pág. 13)

indicator / indicador: Compuesto que reacciona con soluciones ácidas o básicas para producir ciertos colores. Sirve para averiguar el grado de acidez o basicidad de una solución. (Cap. 9, pág. 254)

inertia / inercia: Mide la tendencia de un objeto a permanecer en reposo o de continuar en movimiento constante. Una medida de la inercia de un objeto es su masa. (Cap. 11, pág. 310)

inference / inferencia: Intento de explicar algo, con base en la observación. (Cap. 1, pág. 25)

inhibitor / inhibidor: Sustancia que decelera una reacción química. (Cap. 8, pág. 226)

insulator/aislador: Material como el plástico, la madera, el vidrio y el caucho, a través del cual los electrones no pueden moverse con facilidad. (Cap. 16, pág. 451)

interference / interferencia: La capacidad de dos o más ondas de combinarse y formar una nueva onda cuando se sobreponen una sobre la otra. (Cap. 14, pág. 404)

ion / ion: Átomo que ya no es neutro porque ha ganado o perdido un electrón. (Cap. 7, pág. 196)

ionic bond / enlace iónico: Fuerza de atracción que mantiene unidos los iones de carga opuesta. (Cap. 7, pág. 197)

isomers / isómeros: Compuestos que tienen fórmulas químicas idénticas, pero diferentes estructuras y diferentes propiedades químicas y físicas. (Cap. 10, pág. 274)

isotopes / isótopos: Átomos del mismo elemento que poseen diferentes números de neutrones. (Cap. 5, pág. 135); (Cap. 2, pág. 46)

K

kinetic energy / energía cinética: La energía de la materia en movimiento. (Cap. 3, pág. 66)

kinetic theory of matter / teoría cinética de la materia: Idea que dice que las partículas de materia se encuentran en movimiento constante y aleatorio. (Cap. 4, pág. 97)

L

law / ley: Descripción probada repetidamente de cómo funciona algo en la naturaleza. Por lo general predice o describe una situación dada, pero no explica por qué se da dicha situación. (Cap. 1, pág. 12)

law of conservation of energy / ley de conservación de la energía: Ley que enuncia que la energía no puede ser creada ni destruida, solo puede ser transformada de una forma a otra. (Cap. 3, pág. 70)

law of conservation of matter / ley de conservación de la materia: Enuncia que la materia no puede ser creada ni destruida, pero que solo cambia de forma. (Cap. 2, pág. 38)

law of conservation of momentum / ley de conservación del momento: Ley que dice que si no existe una fuerza externa que actúe sobre un grupo de objetos, el momento del grupo entero nunca cambia. (Cap. 11, pág. 313)

law of definite proportions / ley de proporciones definidas: Ley que enuncia que un compuesto dado siempre está formado por los mismos elementos en la misma proporción por masa. (Cap. 2, pág. 52)

law of reflection/ley de reflexión: Enuncia que el ángulo de incidencia es igual al ángulo de reflexión. (Cap. 15, pág. 423)

lens/lente: Objeto transparente con, por lo menos, un lado encorvado que hace que la luz se doble. (Cap. 15, pág. 431)

lever/palanca: Máquina simple que consiste en una barra o tablón que gira alrededor de un punto. (Cap. 13, pág. 370)

light ray/rayo de luz: Trayectoria muy estrecha de luz que viaja en línea recta. (Cap. 15, pág. 416)

lipids / lípidos: Compuestos orgánicos que contienen los mismos elementos que los carbohidratos: carbono, hidrógeno y oxígeno, pero en diferentes proporciones. (Cap. 10, pág. 287)

M

mass / masa: Medida de la cantidad de materia. (Cap. 11, pág. 310)

mass number / número de masa: Número de protones y neutrones en el núcleo de un átomo. (Cap. 5, pág. 135);(Cap. 2, pág. 46)

matter / materia: Cualquier cosa que ocupa espacio y posee masa; es decir, cualquier cosa que puedes ver, tocar, oler o saborear. (Cap. 4, pág. 96);(Cap. 2, pág. 36)

mechanical advantage (M.A.)/ventaja mecánica (V.M.): Compara la fuerza de esfuerzo que se le aplica a una máquina con la fuerza de resistencia que debe superar la máquina. (Cap. 13, pág. 368)

mechanical waves / ondas mecánicas: Ondas que solo pueden viajar a través de un medio: la materia. (Cap. 14, pág. 391)

medium/medio: Cualquier material por el cual viaja una onda. (Cap. 15, pág. 416)

melting point / punto de fusión: Temperatura a la cual una sustancia pasa de sólido a líquido. (Cap. 4, pág. 100)

metal / metal: Elemento que tiene lustre, es buen conductor de calor y electricidad y por lo general es sólido a temperatura ambiente. (Cap. 6, pág. 157);(Cap. 2, pág. 47)

metalloids / metaloides: Elementos que poseen características tanto de los metales como de los no metales y que son por lo general quebradizos y opacos; no son buenos conductores de calor y de electricidad como los metales. (Cap. 2, pág. 48)

mixture / mezcla: Combinación de sustancias que puede ser separada por medios físicos. Por ejemplo, puedes usar un imán para separar una mezcla de limaduras de hierro y arena. (Cap. 9, pág. 236);(Cap. 2, pág. 53)

molecule / molécula: Partícula neutra que se forma cuando los átomos comparten electrones. (Cap. 7, pág. 199)

momentum / momento: El producto de la masa y la velocidad, incluyendo dirección. (Cap. 11, pág. 311)

net force / fuerza neta: Fuerza total que siente un objeto, la cual siempre hace que el objeto acelere en la dirección de la fuerza neta. (Cap. 12, pág. 328)

neutralization / neutralización: Interacción entre ácidos y bases, en que las propiedades de cada uno de estos se cancelan mutuamente. (Cap. 9, pág. 255)

neutron / neutrón: Partícula neutra con la misma masa que un protón. (Cap. 5, pág. 132);(Cap. 2, pág. 42)

Newton's first law of motion / primera ley de movimiento de Newton: Esta ley enuncia que un objeto en reposo o que se mueve a una rapidez constante en una trayectoria recta continúa en dicha posición o movimiento hasta que una fuerza neta actúe sobre él. (Cap. 12, pág. 330)

Newton's second law of motion / segunda ley de movimiento de Newton: Ley que dice que una fuerza neta que actúa sobre un objeto hace que el objeto acelere en la dirección de la fuerza, de acuerdo con la siguiente ecuación: a = Fnet\m, en que a es la aceleración, Fnet es la fuerza neta y m es la masa. (Cap. 12, pág. 336)

Newton's third law of motion / tercera ley de movimiento de Newton: Enuncia que las fuerzas siempre actúan en pares iguales pero opuestos. Es decir, que por cada acción existe una reacción igual y opuesta. (Cap. 12, pág. 344)

nonmetal / no metal: Por lo general, un gas o sólido quebradizo a temperatura ambiente, el cual no es buen conductor de calor y electricidad. (Cap. 6, pág. 158); (Cap. 2, pág. 48)

normal force / fuerza normal: La fuerza exterior que ejerce una superficie, la cual es provista por la potencia de la superficie. Por ejemplo, si colocas un objeto pesado sobre una silla desvencijada, podría suceder que la silla no provea suficiente fuerza normal para equilibrar el peso y se rompa bajo el peso. (Cap. 12, pág. 337)

nucleus / núcleo: Centro con carga positiva del átomo. (Cap. 2, pág. 42)

O

Ohm's law/ley de Ohm: Relación entre el voltaje, la corriente y la resistencia en un circuito eléctrico; $V = IR$, donde V representa el voltaje, I representa la corriente y R representa la resistencia. (Cap. 16, pág. 463)

organic compound / compuesto orgánico: Compuesto que contiene carbono. (Cap. 10, pág. 270)

P

parallel circuit/circuito en paralelo: El que posee más de una ruta para que fluya la corriente. Si una de las rutas se interrumpe, la corriente continúa fluyendo a lo largo de las otras rutas. (Cap. 16, pág. 464)

Pascal's principle / principio de Pascal: Principio que dice que la presión que se le aplica a un fluido confinado, en cualquiera de los puntos, es transmitida sin cambio a través del fluido. (Cap. 4, pág. 111)

period / período: Hilera de elementos en la tabla periódica cuyas propiedades cambian paulatina y previsiblemente. (Cap. 6, pág. 153)

pH / pH: Medida del grado de acidez o basicidad de una solución, en relación con su concentración de iones hidronio y iones hidroxilo; las soluciones con un pH menor que 7 son ácidas, las soluciones con un pH mayor que 7 son básicas y las soluciones con un pH de 7 son neutras.

(Cap. 9, pág. 253)

polymer / polímero: Molécula compuesta de muchas moléculas orgánicas pequeñas que se enlazan una a la otra formando una cadena larga. (Cap. 10, pág. 282)

potential energy / energía potencial: Energía almacenada que no proviene del movimiento, sino de la posición o condición de un objeto. (Cap. 3, pág. 68)

power/potencia: Describe la razón a la cual se realiza trabajo y mide cuánto trabajo se realiza en cierto período de tiempo: un segundo, por lo general. (Cap. 13, pág. 363)

pressure / presión: Cantidad de fuerza ejercida por unidad de área. (Cap. 4, pág. 110)

product / producto: Sustancia que se forma al ocurrir una reacción química. (Cap. 8, pág. 214)

protein / proteína: Polímero que consiste en una cadena de aminoácidos individuales unidos entre sí. Las proteínas son necesarias para el funcionamiento adecuado del cuerpo humano. (Cap. 10, pág. 283)

proton / protón: Partícula con carga positiva que se encuentra en todos los átomos. (Cap. 5, pág. 128);(Cap. 2, pág. 42)

pulley/polea: Superficie, como por ejemplo una rueda, que usa una cuerda para reaplicar la fuerza y que permite levantar un peso tirando de la cuerda, sin necesidad de alzarlo manualmente. (Cap. 13, pág. 373)

R

radioactive decay / desintegración radiactiva: Liberación de partículas nucleares y energía del núcleo de un átomo, lo cual hace que el número atómico del núcleo cambie y se forme un nuevo elemento. (Cap. 5, pág. 223)

rate of reaction / tasa de reacción: Es una medida de la rapidez con que ocurre una reacción. (Cap. 8, pág. 214)

reactant / reactivo: Sustancia que existe antes de que comience una reacción química y la cual reacciona durante la reacción química. (Cap. 8, pág. 214)

reflection / reflexión: Ocurre cuando una onda choca contra un objeto o superficie y luego rebota. (Cap. 14, pág. 400); Proceso que ocurre cuando la luz choca contra un objeto y rebota del mismo. (Cap. 15, pág. 417)

refraction / refracción: Doblamiento de una onda a medida que se mueve de un medio a otro. (Cap. 15, pág. 431); Cualquier artículo que se puede procesar y volver a usar, para así conservar los recursos naturales y disminuir los desechos sólidos. (Cap. 14, pág. 401)

resistance/resistencia: Medida del grado de dificultad que tienen los electrones para fluir a través de un material. La unidad de resistencia es el ohmio. (Cap. 16, pág. 458)

resistance force (F_r)/fuerza de resistencia (F_r): La fuerza que debe superar una máquina. (Cap. 13, pág. 366)

S

saturated / saturada: Solución que contiene todo el soluto que es capaz de retener bajo ciertas condiciones dadas. (Cap. 9, pág. 246)

saturated hydrocarbon / hidrocarburo saturado: Hidrocarburo cuyos átomos solo contienen enlaces sencillos. (Cap. 10, pág. 272)

science / ciencia: Proceso que se usa para investigar el mundo a tu alrededor y el cual te provee algunas posibles respuestas. (Cap. 1, pág. 8)

scientific methods / métodos científicos: Procedimientos que se usan para tratar de resolver un problema; pueden incluir: reconocer el problema, analizar los datos y sacar conclusiones. (Cap. 1, pág. 10)

screw/tornillo: Plano inclinado enrollado alrededor de un eje. (Cap. 13, pág. 369)

semiconductor / semiconductor: Elemento que no conduce electricidad tan bien como un metal, pero que sí la conduce mejor que un no metal. (Cap. 6, pág. 164)

sequence / sucesión: Arreglo de cosas o eventos en cierto orden. (Cap. 1, pág. 25)

series circuit/circuito en serie: El que posee solo una ruta para que fluya la corriente. Si dicha ruta se interrumpe, la corriente cesa de fluir y todos los artefactos en el circuito dejan de funcionar. (Cap. 16, pág. 464)

simple machine/máquina simple: Máquina con un solo movimiento. (Cap. 13, pág. 366)

solubility / solubilidad: Término que se usa para describir la cantidad de soluto que se disuelve en una cantidad dada de disolvente. (Cap. 9, pág. 244)

solute / soluto: Sustancia que parece desaparecer o que se disuelve en el disolvente. (Cap. 9, pág. 238)

solution / solución: Otro nombre para una mezcla homogénea. (Cap. 9, pág. 238)

solvent / disolvente: Sustancia que disuelve el soluto. (Cap. 9, pág. 238)

speed / rapidez: Razón del cambio en posición. (Cap. 11, pág. 300)

state of matter / estado de la materia: Estado físico de un material, ya sea sólido, líquido o gas, lo cual depende en el arreglo de los átomos y las moléculas del material y la manera como se mueven. (Cap. 4, pág. 96)

static charge/carga estática: Acumulación de cargas eléctricas en un lugar. (Cap. 16, pág. 449)

substance / sustancia: Muestra de materia que tiene la misma composición y propiedades en toda su extensión. (Cap. 2, pág. 51)

T

technology / tecnología: La aplicación del conocimiento aprendido a través de la ciencia. (Cap. 1, pág. 22)

temperature / temperatura: Es una medida de la energía cinética promedio de las partículas de cualquier objeto. Entre más alta sea la energía cinética promedio de un objeto, mayor será su temperatura. (Cap. 3, pág. 74)

theory / teoría: Explicación basada en los resultados obtenidos al hacer pruebas o experimentos repetidamente. (Cap. 1, pág. 12)

thermal energy / energía térmica: Es la energía cinética total de las partículas de un material. (Cap. 3, pág. 75)

transverse wave / onda transversal: Tipo de onda mecánica en la cual la materia se mueve de un lado a otro formando ángulos rectos con la dirección en que viaja la onda. (Cap. 14, pág. 392)

U

unbalanced forces / fuerzas desequilibradas: Fuerzas cuya fuerza neta es cero y que provocan la aceleración de un objeto. (Cap. 12, pág. 329)

unsaturated hydrocarbon / hidrocarburo no saturado: Hidrocarburo cuyos átomos de carbono forman enlaces dobles o triples; por ejemplo, el etileno: C_2H_4 y el propileno: C_3H_6. (Cap. 10, pág. 273)

V

velocity / velocidad: Razón de cambio del desplazamiento, la cual incluye tanto rapidez como dirección. (Cap. 11, pág. 302)

voltage/voltaje: Medida del potencial de energía eléctrica. Se mide en unidades de voltios (V). (Cap. 16, pág. 457)

W

wavelength / longitud de onda: Distancia entre un punto de una onda y otro punto idéntico en la siguiente onda, como por ejemplo, de una cresta a la siguiente o de un valle al siguiente. (Cap. 14, pág. 396); (Cap. 15, pág. 419)

wedge/cuña: Plano inclinado en movimiento y que puede tener uno o dos lados inclinados. (Cap. 13, pág. 369)

wheel and axle/rueda y eje: Máquina simple compuesta de dos ruedas unidas rígidamente y que giran juntas. (Cap. 13, pág. 372)

work/trabajo: En sentido científico, se realiza trabajo cuando una fuerza produce movimiento en dirección paralela a la dirección de la fuerza. (Cap. 13, pág. 360)

Index

The index for *Science Voyages* will help you locate major topics in the book quickly and easily. Each entry in the index is followed by the numbers of the pages on which the entry is discussed. A page number given in **boldface type** indicates the page on which that entry is defined. A page number given in *italic type* indicates a page on which the entry is used in an illustration or photograph. The abbreviation *act.* indicates a page on which the entry is used in an activity.

A

Absolute zero, 98
Acceleration, **304**–306, *305*, 307, 322
  calculating, 344
  distance and, 304–306
  force and, 335–336, *335*, 338, *338*, 340
Acetic acid, 214, 215, *215*, 241, *278*
Acetylene (ethyne), 274, *274*
Acid(s), **250**–252, *250*, 265
  amino, 278–**279**, *279*, 283–284, *284*
  carboxylic, 278, *278*, 293
  neutralization of, 255–256, *256*, 265, *265*
  strengths of, 254–255
  uses of, 251–252
Acid rain, 251, *251*, 255
Acidic solutions, 250–251, *250*, 265
Actinide series, 156, 175, 176, 181
Action-reaction forces, 344–346, *344*, *345*, *346*
Activation energy, 222–223, *223*, 231
Agriculture. *See* Farming
Air, fractionation of, 240, *240*
Air pollution
  acid rain, 251, *251*
Air resistance, 333–334, *334*,

338, *338*
Alanine, 279, *279*, *284*
Alchemist, *202*, 207
Alcohols, 277, *277*, *act.* 280, 293
Alkali metals, 160, *160*, *161*, 180
Alkaline earth metals, 162, *162*, 180
Alloys, **162**, *162*, *act.* 171, *175*, 241–242, *241*
Alpha particles, 41, 137, *137*, 146, 147
Alternative energy resources
  geothermal energy, 89, *89*
  hydroelectric power, 66, *66*
  nuclear energy, 65
Aluminum, 158, 162, *162*, 163, *163*, 181, *181*
Aluminum oxide, *242*
Americium, 137, *137*, 176
Amethyst, *242*
Amines, 278, *278*
Amino acids, 278–**279**, *279*, 283–284, *284*
Amino group, **278**, 293
Ammonia, 165, *165*, 181, 229, 252
  molecule of, *203*, 207
Amperes, **455**
Amplitude, **395**–396, *395*, 407, *407*, 410
Angle of incidence, **423**
Angle of reflection, **423**

Anode, 40, 126, *126*
Aqueous solutions, **243**–248, *243*, *244*, *245*, *246*, *247*, 264
Archimedes, 113, 114, 115
Archimedes' Principle, **115**, 119
Argon, 169, 170
Arsenic, 165, 166, *166*, 167
Ascorbic acid, 251
Astronauts, 352, 353, *353*
Atherosclerosis, 289, *289*
Atmosphere
  of Earth, 107, 239
  of planets, 107, 239, 240
Atmospheric pressure, 112–113, *113*
Atom(s), **37**, 58, 122–149, 448
  model of, 38–43, *41*, *42*, *43*, 58, *58*, 125–133, *125*, *128*, *131*, *132*, 146, 193, *act.* 194–195
  nuclear, 130–131, *131*, *132*, 146
  nucleus of, 41–42, *42*, *131*, 132–133, *132*, 135–140, *135*, 146–147
  radioactive decay of, 136–140, 147
  size of, 39, *39*
  states of matter and, 96–97
  structure of, 38, *41*, *42*, 47, *act.* 123, 188–193, *188*, *189*, *190*, *191*, *192*, *193*,

Definite proportions, law of, **52**
Democritus, 37
Density, **114**
  comparing, *act.* 28
  formula for, 28
  inferring, 25
Dependent variable, 13
Desalination, 53, *53*
Destructive interference, 404, 405–406, *405, 406, 407*
Dewey Decimal System, *45*
Diaphragm, 439
Diffraction, **402**–403, *403, 411*
Diffuse reflection, 424, 442
Diffusion, **109,** *109*
Dilute solution, **247,** *247*
Diseases, natural medicines and, 281, *281*
Displacement, *act.* 5, **301,** *301*
Dissolution, 238–239, 244, *244,* 245–246, *246,* 247, 264
Distance
  acceleration and, 304–306
  formula for, 305
Distillation, 53
Döbereiner, Johann, 50
Doping, 164
Double bond, 200, *200*
Dry cell batteries, 457, *457*
Ductility, 47, *47,* 217, 218

E

Earth, atmosphere of, 107, 239
Earthquake(s), tsunamis caused by, 396
Earthquake faults. See Fault(s), earthquake
Efficiency, **374,** 383
Effort force, **366,** 383
Electric charge, 448, 472

Electric circuits, 462–470, 473
Electric current, **455**–461, 472
  conduction of, 197
Electric discharge, **452**
Electric energy, 455–456
  cost of, 467
Electric fields, 450
Electric forces, 329, 447, 450
Electric potential energy, 456
Electric power, **466,** 473
Electrical safety, 467–469, 473
Electrically neutral, 448
Electricity
  hydroelectric power, 66, *66*
  wind power, 66
Electrodes, 125–126, *126*
Electromagnetic energy, 317
Electromagnetic spectrum, 396, *396,* 419–420
Electromagnetic waves, **392,** *392, 396, 396,* 410, **416,** 442
Electron cloud, 43, *43,* **133,** *133,* 188, *188,* 206
Electron dot diagram, **192**–193, *192, 207*
Electrons, **40,** 41, 58, **127**–128, *128,* 133, 146, 448, *448*
  arrangement of, 188–193, *189, 190, 191, 192,* 206, *206*
  energy of, *act.* 187, 188–190, *189*
  moving between objects, 449
  sharing, 199–200, *199, 200*
Element keys, 158, *158*
Elements, **44,** 49 59, **125,** 236
  chemical symbols for, 159
  classification of, 47, *47, 48*
  in dental materials, 177, *177*

groups of, 156, *156,* 160–176, 180, *180,* 181, 190–191, *190, 191,* 192
isotopes of, 46–47, *46,* 48, 59
organizing, 44–48, *46*
periodic table of, 45–48, *46, act.* 49, 50, *50. See also* Periodic table
representative, 160–170
synthetic, 159, 176, 181
tracer, 140–142, *141, 142*
transition, 156, 172–176, *172, 173, 174, 175,* 180, 181
transmutation of, 136–138, *137, 138,* 140–142, 147
Endothermic reaction, 86, *86,* 91, **217,** *218, act.* 220–221, 230, 287
Energy, 62–93, *64,* **317**–320, *317, 318, 320,* 323
  activation, 222–223, *223, 231*
  amplitude and, 395, *395*
  chemical, 65, 84–88, *84, 85, 85, 86, 87, 88,* 91, 317
  in chemical reactions, 85–88, *85, 86, 87, 88,* 91, 217–219, *217, 218, 219, act.* 220–221
  classifying types of, 70
  comparing energy content, 80
  conduction of, 78–79, *78, 91*
  conservation of, 70–71, *71,* 90, **317**–318, 321, 323
  convection of, 80–81, *80, 81,* 91
  electromagnetic, 317
  of electrons, *act.* 187, 188–190, *189*
  geothermal, 89, *89*
  gravitational potential, **319,** *320,* 323

Glacier, *94*

Glass, 100, *100*, 101, 164, 176

Global Positioning System (GPS), 397

Glucose, 285, *285*

Glycerol, 287

Glycine, 279, *279*, *284*

Glycogen, 286

Gold, 114, 132–133, 159, 172, *173*, 175, 177

Gold foil experiment (Rutherford), 41

GPS (Global Positioning System), 397

Granite, 242

Graph(s), **18**, *18*
 bar, 71
 line, *18*
 making and using, 25, 28, 101, 108, 121, 145, 149,183, 267, *267*, 275, 295, 325, 404
 of motion, 306–307, *307*
 of wave interference, 404, *404*, 407, *408*

Graphite, 164, 236, *236*

Gravitational potential energy, **319**, *320*, 323

Gravity, center of, 25

Grounding, 454

Groundwater, 239

Groups, in periodic table, **156**, *156*, 160–176, 180, *180*, 181, 190–191, *190*, *191*, 192

H

Half–life, **138**–139, *138*, *act.* 144–145, 147

Halley's comet, 167, *167*

Halogens, 168, *168*, 181, 190

Health, heavy metals and, *act.* 178–179

Heat, 75, 91
 energy and, 317
 of fusion, **100**

from solar energy, 556
 states of matter and, 97–98, *97*
 See also Temperature
 thermal energy and, 75–76, *77*
 of vaporization, **105**, *105*, 119

Heavy metals, *act.* 178–179

Helium
 atomic structure of, 96, 190
 in periodic table, 169

Hemoglobin, 172, 283

Hertz (Hz), 397

Heterogeneous mixtures, 237

Hexane, 273, 275, *275*

Homogeneous mixtures, 237–238, *237*

Hot-vent inhabitants, 89, *89*

Hurricanes, 395, *395*

Hydrocarbons, **271**–280, *271*, 292, 293
 alcohols, 277, *277*, *act.* 280, 293
 isomers of, 274–275, *274*, 292
 in rings, 275, *275*
 saturated, **272**, *272*, 273, 275, 292
 substituted, 276–279, *276*, *277*, *278*, *279*, 293
 unsaturated, **273**–274, *273*, *274*, 292

Hydrochloric acid, 252, 255

Hydroelectric power, 66, *66*

Hydrogen
 in ammonia, 165, *165*
 atomic structure of, 190
 chemical symbol for, 159
 isotopes of, 138, *138*
 liquid, 51
 molecule of, 202–203, *202*
 reaction with oxygen, 85
 in water, 51, *52*
 in water molecule, 201,

201

Hydrogen chloride, *199*

Hydrogen peroxide, 51–52, *52*

Hydroxyl group, **277**, *277*, *act.* 280, 293

Hypothesis, **12**, 30
 forming, 12, 20
 testing, 13–14, *14*, 21

Hypothesizing, 12

I

Image, 425

Inclined plane, **368**–369, 383

Independent variable, 13

Indicators, **254**–255, *act.* 258–259

Induced charge, 452

Inertia, **310**, 314, 322

Inference, **25**

Inferring, 21, 25

Infrared waves, 420

Inhibitors, **226**, 231

Inner transition elements, 156, 175–176, *175*

Insoluble substance, 238

Insulator(s), 79, *79*, **451**, 472

Interference, **404**–406, *404*, *405*, *406*, 407, *407*, 411

International System of Units (SI), 307, 510, 511

Interpreting scientific illustrations, 567

Iodine, *48*

Iodine isotopes, 138, *138*, 141, *141*

Ion(s), **196**
 hydronium ions, 250, 253–254, *253*, 256, 265
 hydroxide ions, 252, 253–254, *253*, 256, 265
 positive and negative, 196–197

Ionic bonds, 196–198, *196*, **197**, *197*, *198*, *act.* 204,

N

R

frequency of, 397, *397*, 410

interference and, 404–406, *404, 405, 406,* 407, *407,* 411

light, 396, *396,* 397–398, 400, *400,* 401–402, *401,* 403, *403,* 404

mechanical, 390–**391,** *391,* 410

properties of, 395–398, *395, 396, 397,* 410

reflection of, 400, *400,* 404, 411

refraction of, 401–402, *401, 402,* 411

sound, 390–391, *391,* 393–394, *393, 394,* 395, 397–398, 402, 403, *403,* 404

speed of, 397–398, 401–402, 410

transverse, **392,** *392,* 396, *act.* 399, 410

trough of, 392, *392, 395,* 407

water, 391

Wavelength, 396, *396,* 397, 410, **419,** 442

Weather, *act.* 108

  hurricanes, 395, *395*

  thunderstorms, 397

Weather balloon, *169*

Wedge, **369**

Wheel and axle, **372,** 383

Wind power, 66

Word equations, 214–215

Word processing, 27, 115, 142, 279

Work, **360,** 360–363, 382

  measuring, 362–363, 370

  and pyramid building, *act.* 365

Worms, 89, *89*

X ray, *88,* 162, 392, 396

Xenon, 169, 170

Ytterbium, 175

Zero, absolute, 98

Art Credits

Photo Credits

Photo Credits

Frerck/Odyssey Productions.
Chapter 10 - 268-9 KS Studio; **269** Matt Meadows; **270** (l)Mark Burnett, (r)KS Studio; **272** Mark Burnett; **273** (l,c)Mark Burnett, (r)Will & Deni McIntyre/Photo Researchers; **274** Ted Horowitz/The Stock Market; **276** (l)KS Studio, (c)Michael Kevin Daly/The Stock Market, (r)KS Studio; **278** (t)Roger K. Burnard, (b)John Sims/Tony Stone Images; **280** KS Studio; **281** (l)Ron Spomer/Visuals Unlimited, (r)Jean-Loup Charmet/Science Photo Library/Photo Researchers; **283 284** KS Studio; **285** Mark Burnett; **286** (t)Mark Burnett, (b)KS Studio; **287** Hans Pfletschinger/Peter Arnold, Inc.; **288** (t)Victor Scocozza/FPG International, (b)Tony Craddock/Tony Stone Images; **289** Biophoto Associates/Science Source/Photo Researchers; **290** KS Studio; **292** (t)Mark Burnett, (b)Ted Horowitz/The Stock Market; **293** (t)Roger K. Burnard, (b)KS Studio.

UNIT 3

Opener - 296-7 ©Dan McCoy/Rainbow; **297** ©The Harold E. Edgerton 1992 Trust, courtesy of Palm Press, Inc.
Chapter 11 - 298-9 Tom & DeeAnn McCarthy/The Stock Market; **299** Aaron Haupt; **300** Frans Lanting/Minden Pictures; **302** JPL-NASA/Phototake; **305** Tom Stack/Tom Stack & Associates; **308** Tom Stack/Tom Stack & Associates; **310** (l)Chuck Savage/The Stock Market, (r)Aaron Haupt; **311** (l)Tui De Roy/Minden Pictures, (r)NASA/Science Source/Photo Researchers; **312** (l)Alan Schein/The Stock Market, (r)John Shaw/Tom Stack & Associates; **316** Aaron Haupt; **317** David Stoecklein/The Stock Market; **318** Tom Brakefield/The Stock Market; **320** Ron Levy/Liaison International; **321** (l)Science Photo Library/Photo Researchers, (r)C. Powell, P. Fowler & D. Perkins/Science Photo Library/Photo Researchers; **322** Chuck Savage/The Stock Market; **323** Tom Brakefield/The Stock Market.
Chapter 12 - 326-7 VCG/FPG International; **327** KS Studio; **328** (tr)Matt Meadows, (l)file photo, (br)KS Studio; **329** (l,r)KS Studio, (b)Bruce Curtis/Peter Arnold, Inc.; **331** (l)KS Studio, (r)Jim Cummins/FPG International; **332 333** KS Studio; **334** (l)KS Studio, (r)Jon Eisberg/FPG International; **335** KS Studio; **336** Mike Powell/AllSport; **337** file photo; **338** (t)Telegraph Colour Library/FPG International, (b)Brian Bahr/AllSport; **339** KS Studio; **340** AllSport; **341** National Geographic photographer Jodi Cobb; **342** Aaron Haupt; **344** Steven Sutton/Duomo; **346** KS Studio; **347** (l)Gunter Ziesler/Peter Arnold, Inc, (r)Ron Chapple/FPG International; **348** KS Studio; **349** Jim Cummins/FPG International; **352** (t)Telegraph Colour Library/FPG International; (b)NASA/Science Source/Photo Researchers; **353** VCG/FPG International; **354** (tr)file photo, (rc)Matt Meadows, (b)KS Studio; **355** (t)Steven Sutton/Duomo, (c)Gunter Ziesler/Peter Arnold, Inc., (b)Jim Cummins/FPG International.
Chapter 13 - 358-9 Telegraph Colour Library/FPG; **359** Doug Martin; **360** (l)Alan Schein/The Stock Market, (r)Doug Lee/Peter Arnold, Inc.; **361** KS Studio; **362** (t)Aaron Haupt, (b)Doug Martin; **365 366** Doug Martin; **367** KS Studio; **369** (t)Doug Martin, (b)PhotoDisc; **371** (t)Doug Martin, (c)Paul Avis/Liaison International, (b)Allan Kaye/DRK Photo; **372** Warren Stone/Visuals Unlimited; **375** (l)Mugshots/Tony Stone Images, (r)National Geographic Society; **376** Aaron Haupt; **378** (l)Stephen Swinburne/Stock Boston, (r)Don Mason/The Stock Market; **378-81** (bkgd)Lester Lefkowitz/The Stock Market; **379** (tl)SuperStock, (tc)Stuart L. Craig/Bruce Coleman Inc., (tr)Richard Pasley/Stock Boston, (cl)Mark E. Gibson, (cr)Aaron Haupt, (bl)Science VU/Visuals Unlimited, (br)SuperStock; **380** (t)Pablo Corral V/Corbis, (cl)SuperStock, (c)Myrleen Ferguson/PhotoEdit, (cr)Rick Gayle/The Stock Market, (bl)Aaron Haupt, (br)Nancy P. Alexander/Lightwave; **381** (t)StudiOhio, (c,b)RUBE GOLDBERG and © Rube Goldberg Inc. Distributed by United Media; **382** (t)KS Studio, (b)Aaron Haupt; **383** David Allen.

UNIT 4

Opener - 386-7 George Steinmetz; **387** Dan McCoy/Rainbow/PNI.
Chapter 14 - 388-9 Richard B. Sanchez/The Stock Market; **389** Matt Meadows; **390** (l)Steve Lissau, (r)Doug Martin; **393** Andy Sacks/Tony Stone Images; **395** Buck Campbell/FPG; **400** (l)Danny Lehman/Corbis Los Angeles, (r)Aaron Haupt; **404** William D. Popejoy; **406** (l)Mark Richards/PhotoEdit, (r)Alan Kearney/FPG; **408** Matt Meadows; **410** Steve Lissau; **411** (t)Aaron Haupt, (b)Mark Richards/PhotoEdit.
Chapter 15 - 414-5 Chris Rogers/The Stock Market; **415** Matt Meadows; **416** Richard Shock/Liaison International; **417** Matt Meadows; **418** (l)Bob Wooward/The Stock Market, (c)P.W. Grace/Photo Researchers, (r)Janis Burger/Bruce Coleman Inc.; **420** H.R. Bramaz/Peter Arnold, Inc.; **421** Mark Thayer; **424** Dr. Dennis Kunkel/Phototake NYC; **426 427 430** Geoff Butler; **431** E.R. Degginger/Color-Pic; **434** Geoff Butler; **435** Geoff Butler; **436** Matt Meadows; **437 438** Roger Ressmeyer/Corbis; **439** Bill Beatty/Visuals Unlimited; **441** NOAO/TSADO/Tom Stack & Assoc.; **442** Richard Shock/Liaison International.
Chapter 16 - 446-7 WT Sullivan III/Science Photo Library/Photo Researchers; **447** Geoff Butler; **453** Rouxaime/Jacana/Photo Researchers; **454** J. Tinning/Photo Researchers; **459** Tony Stone Images; **460 461 465** Geoff Butler; **468** Andrew McClenaghan/Science Photo Library; **470** Geoff Butler; **471** Steven Starr/Stock Boston/PNI; **472** J. Tinning/Photo Researchers; **473** Geoff Butler.

PERIODIC TABLE OF THE ELEMENTS

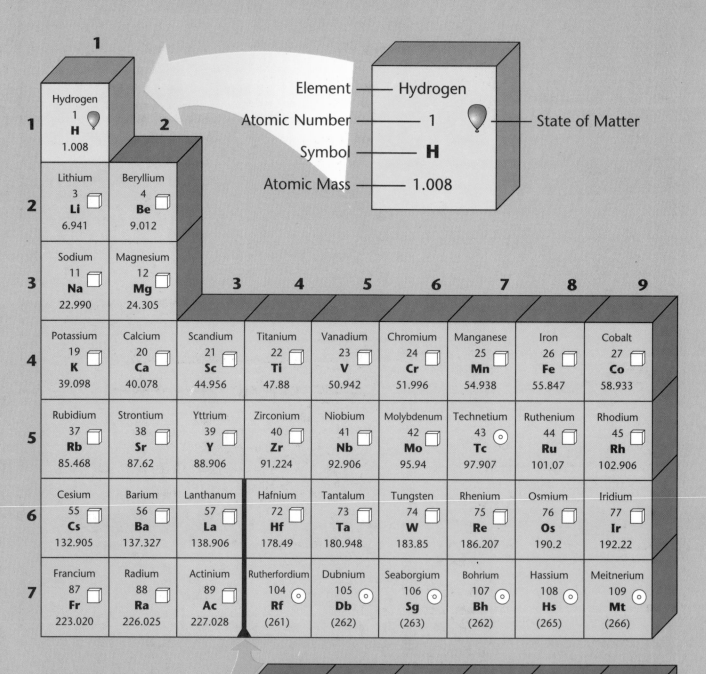

Element	Hydrogen
Atomic Number	1
Symbol	H
Atomic Mass	1.008

State of Matter

Lanthanide Series

Actinide Series